HEAT TRANSFER

HEAT TRANSFER

BENJAMIN GEBHART

Associate Professor of Mechanical Engineering
Cornell University

McGRAW-HILL BOOK COMPANY, INC.

New York   Toronto   London   1961

HEAT TRANSFER

Preface

This book is a description of the more important physical processes, theories, and methods of analysis loosely grouped in the field referred to as "heat transfer." The book is cast in the form of a text, but it is hoped that the content and method of presentation will serve the general reader and the practicing engineer as well.

The basic theories and fundamental formulations of the three modes, conduction, radiation, and convection (including convection of mass) are presented. Phase-change processes, combined-mode analysis, exchanger design, and analogues are considered. The physical nature of heat-transfer processes and the significance of defined quantities are emphasized initially to provide a clear conceptual basis for subsequent developments. For processes which are susceptible to mathematical analysis the role of the mathematical statement of a problem is repeatedly emphasized. The intent is to demonstrate the diverse and special considerations whereby general theoretical formulations, such as differential equations, are adapted to particular applications. This is one of the principal components of an effective engineering approach to a problem.

No attempt has been made to include a description of the latest findings in every field related to those treated. A number of topics have been brought up to date in order to indicate the nature of current technical preoccupations among heat-transfer engineers. Several quite specialized topics are given considerable space (e.g., combined forced- and natural-convection effects and noncontinuum processes) in anticipation of their greater importance in the immediate future.

Many types of conduction problems are solved. Separation of variables is used for partial differential equation solution. Since the method of Laplace transforms is not yet generally required knowledge, it is not used. The effects of extended surface are demonstrated for plate fins on a flat surface. However, the customary one-dimensional analyses for various cases are not given, in view of the oft-demonstrated inadequacies of the underlying assumptions.

Numerical methods are introduced for finite-difference estimation of "exact" solutions. Numerical techniques are applied to steady and to unsteady state, first for temperature boundary conditions, then for general boundary conditions.

Analogues are discussed in detail in order to emphasize similarities between various physical phenomena and to develop an intuitive understanding of the meaning of a "solution" to a problem. A number of direct and indirect geometric and network analogues are considered.

The treatment of thermal radiation includes the reflection method and the relations for simple radiative arrangements. In addition, a method of computation is presented which permits solutions for arrangements of arbitrary complexity.

The treatment of convection begins with the equations which govern density, velocity, temperature, and concentration distributions. The transport equations which relate the various heat-transfer and flow parameters are first approached from the general and boundary-layer equations. In convection, an attempt is made to help the reader develop a sense for the present boundary between the regimes of successful theoretical analysis and appeal to experiment. The technique sometimes called "differential similarity" is used, instead of dimensional analysis.

The developments and arguments in the book assume that the reader has a knowledge of calculus and some training in ordinary differential equations. The disadvantage of a limited background in fluid mechanics may be overcome by careful study of Chapter 6. Many readers may skip most (or all) of Chapter 6. Since it will not be possible to cover the complete book in the time customarily allotted to a first course in heat transfer, it is suggested that omissions be made in the following material: Sections 2-4, 3-4, 4-7, 6-7, 6-8, 6-9, 7-5, 7-9, 8-2, 8-4, 8-6, 9-4, 9-5, 10-4, 10-6, 11-5, 11-6, 12-4, 12-5, 12-6, and Chapter 13.

A table of notation is included at the end of each chapter. The notation reflects the eclectic nature of the field of heat transfer. That is, information is brought in from many other fields of study. An attempt has been made to remain consistent with the notation customarily used in these other fields in order to help prepare the student for reference to other works. As a result, however, there are a number of cases wherein a single symbol denotes several different quantities, even in the same chapter. This is not thought to be undesirable, from the pedagogical point of view.

References are listed alphabetically at the end of each chapter and are referred to in the text by the author's name followed by the year of publication in parentheses. The Appendix contains physical-property information adequate to the needs of the book and includes a table of standard pipe and tube dimensions.

The author wishes to thank the many whose efforts have made this book possible. Helpful technical advice was given by many colleagues, including Profs. C. O. Mackey and D. G. Shepherd. Valuable guidance was obtained from reviews of the manuscript by Profs. R. M. Drake, Jr., R. J. Nickerson, and J. Edward Sutherland. The careful proofreading by Mr. R. E. Mates has done much to reduce errors. The author is grateful for the long labor of Leora Decker, who typed a major portion of the manuscript.

Benjamin Gebhart

To Lillian Oettinger Gebhart

Contents

CHAPTER 1

Introduction

1-1. HEAT-TRANSFER PROCESSES

Heat-transfer considerations are often of crucial importance in modern engineering design. Equipment size in power production and chemical processing may be determined primarily by the attainable heat-transfer rates. A considerable fraction of the cost of many devices—for example, air-conditioning and refrigeration systems—is due to heat exchangers. In many types of equipment a successful design is possible only if provision is made to maintain reasonable temperatures by adequate heat transfer. Among such modern devices are rocket nozzles, compact electronic components, high-speed aircraft, and atmosphere-reentry vehicles.

These many and diverse demands upon the store of knowledge concerning heat-transfer characteristics have led to a long period of sustained study of such processes. From the pioneer work of Fourier to the present, many kinds of processes have been studied both experimentally and analytically by scientists and by engineers. Many of the broad divisions of the field have been established, and satisfactory and productive theories have been presented for many types of heat transfer. There are, however, many processes of both theoretical and practical importance which are not adequately understood. In addition, new technologies give importance to types of processes not previously studied. As a result, work continues at an ever-accelerating pace to the present day.

The study of heat transfer includes the physical processes whereby thermal energy is transferred as a result of a difference, or gradient, of temperature. The information generally desired is the way in which the rate of heat transfer depends upon the various features of the process.

There are two basically different processes whereby thermal energy is transported: conduction and radiation. Energy is conducted through a material in which a temperature gradient exists by the thermal motion of various of the microscopic particles of which the material is composed;

1

energy is diffused through the material by these thermal motions.   Radiation is an energy transport from material into the surrounding space by
electromagnetic waves.   Radiant emission is also due to the thermal motion
of microscopic particles, but the energy is transmitted electromagneti-
cally.   If conduction occurs in a fluid in motion, the diffusion of thermal energy will be affected by the relative motion within the fluid.   Conduction
processes affected by relative motion are called convection processes.

Since the field of heat transfer includes processes involving thermal diffusion, electromagnetic radiation, and fluid motion, the study includes
theories from many branches of science and employs many different types
of analytic techniques.   Therefore, the study of heat transfer requires the
mastery of many concepts and methods of analysis.   The succeeding sections of this chapter introduce various definitions and concepts associated
with the three modes of heat transfer: conduction, radiation, and convection.   The remainder of the book is devoted to a consideration of numerous
theoretical and experimental studies of heat-transfer behavior, to a discussion of several special calculation techniques, and to a discussion of the
design of heat-transfer equipment.

1-2. HEAT CONDUCTION AND THERMAL CONDUCTIVITY

The rate of heat conduction through a solid material (or fluid without
relative motion) is proportional to the temperature difference across the
material and to the area perpendicular to heat flow and inversely proportional to the length of the path of heat flow between the two temperature
levels.   This dependence was established by Fourier and is analogous to the
relation for the conduction of electricity, called Ohm's law.   The constant
of proportionality in Fourier's law, denoted by k, is called the thermal conductivity and is a property of the conducting material and of its state.
With the notation indicated in Fig. 1-1, Fourier's law is

$$q = \frac{kA}{L}(t_1 - t_2) \qquad (1\text{-}1)$$

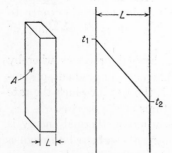

FIG. 1-1.   One-dimensional
steady-state heat conduction.

where kA/L is called the conductance of the
plate.

The thermal conductivity k, which is analogous to electrical conductivity, is a property
of the material.   It is equivalent to the rate
of heat transfer between opposite faces of a
unit cube of the material which are maintained at temperatures differing by one degree.   In engineering units in the English

system, k is expressed in

$$\frac{\text{Btu}}{\text{hr ft}^2 \text{ °F/ft}} = \text{Btu/hr ft °F}$$

In metric units, k may be expressed as

$$\text{cal/sec cm °C} \quad \text{or} \quad \text{watts/cm °C}$$

The conduction equation (1-1) may also be written as the heat-transfer rate per unit area normal to the direction of heat flow:

$$\frac{q}{A} = q'' = \frac{k}{L}(t_1 - t_2) \tag{1-2}$$

The quantity q'' is very useful and is hereafter called the heat flux.

The transport property, thermal conductivity, varies over a wide range for the various substances commonly encountered. For example, for air at 14.7 psia and 60°F it is 0.015 and for silver it is 240, in English units. This is a ratio of 1:16,000. Gases generally have the lowest thermal conductivities, followed by good insulators, nonmetallic liquids, nonmetallic solids, liquid metals, metal alloys, and, finally, the best conductors, pure metals. A selection of thermal-conductivity data is given in Tables A-2 to A-9, in the Appendix.

Thermal conductivity for a given material depends upon its state and may vary with temperature, pressure, etc. For moderate pressure levels the effect of pressure is small. However, for many substances the effect of temperature upon k is not negligible. Therefore, the thermal conductivity in Eq. (1-1) is meant to be some average value if k is a function of temperature. This ambiguity concerning thermal conductivity may be avoided if the relationship between heat flux and temperature difference is written for a very thin conduction region. Another and equivalent procedure is to write the local heat flux in terms of the local value of k and the local temperature gradient in the direction of heat flow:

$$q'' = -k_n \frac{\partial t}{\partial n} \tag{1-3}$$

This is the heat-transfer rate per unit area in terms of the local temperature gradient in the direction of heat flow. The coordinate in the direction of heat flow is denoted by n. The thermal conductivity k_n applies for heat conduction in the direction of n. Many materials have different conduction characteristics in different directions. For example, wood and other fibrous materials have higher thermal conductivities parallel to the grain than perpendicular to it. In multidimensional temperature fields there may be temperature gradients in each coordinate direction. Equation (1-3), with the proper value of k, is expected to apply in any direction.

The minus sign appears in Eq. (1-3) because it is customary to denote heat flow in the direction of increasing n, that is, in the positive direction, as positive. However, positive heat flow results if t decreases with n, that is, if $\partial t / \partial n$ is negative. Therefore, a minus sign is required.

Equation (1-3) is called Fourier's law of conduction, and indeed it is a law if k is taken as dependent only upon the local state of the material and upon the direction in which n is measured. To a good approximation, the thermal conductivity is a function only of the local state for most circumstances common in engineering practice. That is, k is essentially independent of the local temperature gradient. Therefore, the analysis of heat conduction is based upon Eq. (1-3), wherein k is considered to be a property.

Theoretical predictions have been made of the value of thermal conductivity for several types of substances. In gases, heat is conducted (i.e., thermal energy is diffused) by the random motion of molecules. Higher-velocity molecules from higher-temperature regions move about randomly, and some reach regions of lower temperature. By a similar random process lower-velocity molecules reach higher-temperature regions. Thereby net energy is exchanged between the two regions. The thermal conductivity depends upon the space density of molecules, upon their mean free path, and upon the magnitude of the molecular velocities. The net result of these effects for gases having very simple molecules is a dependence of k upon $\sqrt{T}$, where T is the absolute temperature. This is a result of the kinetic theory of gases.

A similar temperature dependence is found for the viscosity of gases. The viscosity μ is a measure of the diffusion of momentum. It may be shown that there is a simple relation between k and μ involving the specific heat c_v and a factor i, where the value of i depends upon the way in which energy is stored in the gas molecules:

$$k = i c_v \mu \tag{1-4}$$

where c_v is the specific heat at constant volume. Using Eq. (1-4), thermal conductivities may be calculated from measured viscosities. The value of i for monatomic gases was shown by Chapman, in 1912, to be 2.5. Eucken, in 1913, considered polyatomic gases and determined, for example, that for diatomic gases without appreciable vibration the value of i is 1.9.

Equation (1-4), in effect, assigns a value to the Prandtl number, which is defined below and which is a very important parameter in heat transfer:

$$N_{\text{Pr}} = \frac{c_p \mu}{k} = \left(\frac{c_p}{c_v} \right) \left(\frac{c_v \mu}{k} \right) = \frac{\gamma}{i} \tag{1-5}$$

where c_p is the specific heat at constant pressure and γ is the specific-heat ratio. The Prandtl number is the ratio of the momentum and thermal-diffusion rates due to molecular motion and is dimensionless. For mon-atomic and diatomic gases (without appreciable vibration) the values of γ are 1.67 and 1.4, respectively. The resulting values of the Prandtl number, 0.67 and 0.74, are in close agreement with measured values. In practice, measured values are used when available.

For liquids, Bridgman, in 1923, developed a theory which predicts thermal conductivity with fair accuracy from a knowledge of the molecular spacing and the sonic velocity in the liquid. Consider the cubical array of molecules depicted in Fig. 1-2. Because of a temperature gradient $\partial t / \partial x$ in the x direction, adjacent molecules will, on the average, have a difference in energy of

$$c \left(- \frac{\partial t}{\partial x} \right) \lambda$$

where c is the specific heat per molecule. The specific heat is taken as $3\overline{R}/A_o$, where $\overline{R}$ is the universal gas constant and A_o is Avogadro's number. This difference in energy is passed from one molecule to another in the direc-tion of decreasing temperature at approximately the sonic velocity v_s. Therefore, the number of transfers between adjacent molecules per unit time will be v_s/λ. The rate of thermal energy transport between adjacent molecules is, therefore,

$$\left(\frac{v_s}{\lambda} \right) \left(\frac{3\overline{R}}{A_o} \right) \left(- \frac{\partial t}{\partial x} \right) \lambda$$

The rate of conduction of thermal energy may also be written from Fourier's law as the flux q'' times the area associated with each molecule, λ^2:

$$q'' \lambda^2 = -k \frac{\partial t}{\partial x} \lambda^2$$

Equating the two quantities, we have

$$k = \frac{3\overline{R}}{A_o} \frac{v_s}{\lambda^2} \qquad (1\text{-}6)$$

This prediction is in good agreement with experimentally determined thermal conduc-tivities for many types of liquids and may be used when more precise information is not available.

Fourier's law of conduction, Eq. (1-3), is applied to the analysis of conduction processes

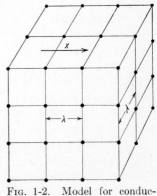

FIG. 1-2. Model for conduc-tion in a liquid.

without regard to the way in which the thermal conductivity will be determined for various substances. Equation (1-3) is employed in writing an energy balance for a small element of material in a conduction region. This energy balance equates the rate of gain of energy by conduction to the rate of change of stored energy in the element. The resulting relation is a partial differential equation which must be satisfied by the temperature distribution in the conduction region. This differential equation is derived in Sec. 2-2. The remainder of Chap. 2 is devoted to the analysis of steady-state conduction, that is, processes for which the temperature distribution is independent of time. Unsteady-state conduction processes are considered in Chap. 3.

1-3. THERMAL RADIATION

Thermal radiation is energy emitted by matter in the form of electro-magnetic waves. The energy emission arises because of changes in the thermal energy states of the microscopic particles of which the material is composed. The rate of emission and its character, that is, its distribution in wavelengths, depend entirely upon the nature of the emitting material and upon its state. The net rate of heat transfer among a group of radiating objects depends upon the intervening medium, upon each material and its temperature, and upon the geometric relation of the objects to one another. However, the rate of emission from any object depends only upon the material and its state.

The radiation characteristics of surfaces vary widely and, even for a given material, depend upon the specific condition of the surface. For all surfaces the emission rate increases sharply with temperature. However, for one type of surface condition, the emission rate is independent of material and depends only upon temperature level. If a surface is "black," that is, if it absorbs all incident radiation and therefore appears black, the emission rate per unit area is given by the Stefan-Boltzmann law:

$$W_b = \sigma T^4 = 0.1713 \times 10^{-8} T^4 \tag{1-7}$$

where T is the absolute temperature and σ is a universal constant. The value of σ given in Eq. (1-7) applies for T in degrees Rankine and W_b in Btu/hr ft^2. The emission rate W_b is called the total hemispherical emissive power of a black surface.

The radiant energy arising at a surface is emitted to the hemispherical space above it. The intensity varies over this hemispherical space, being a maximum directly above the surface and decreasing to zero away from the normal direction. At any given angular position the intensity is inversely proportional to the square of the distance from the emitting surface.

Most actual surfaces emit at a lower rate than does a black surface at the same temperature.   The hemispherical emissive power is, therefore,

$$W = \epsilon W_b = \epsilon \sigma T^4 \qquad (1\text{-}8)$$

where ϵ is the fraction of the black-surface emissive power and is called the hemispherical emissivity of the actual surface.   The value of ϵ depends upon the material, its state, and upon the condition of the surface.   Emissivities of various materials are listed in Table A-10.

The emission characteristics of actual surfaces differ in many ways from those of a black surface at the same temperature.   Observed radiation phenomena are considered in Chap. 4.   Thermal-radiation heat transfer is analyzed in Chap. 5.

1-4. CONVECTION

Energy is conducted through fluids, as through solids, and Eq. (1-3) relates the heat flux, the temperature gradient, and the thermal conductivity for a conduction process.   However, for Eq. (1-1) to be valid for a layer of fluid, it is necessary that there be no relative fluid motion in the layer.   All portions of the fluid must be at rest with respect to one another.   This requirement arises because relative motion gives rise to thermal energy transport by convection.   That is, relative motion distorts the temperature distribution which would result from simple conduction, thereby changing the heat flux.

The effect of fluid motion upon the heat-transfer rate may be shown by an example.   Consider the loss of heat through a building wall, whose inside surface is at t_i, to cold outside air, at t_a.   For convenience it is assumed that the wall is made of a single solid material.   Therefore, heat is transferred through the wall by simple conduction.   We note from Tables A-3 and A-4 that the thermal conductivities of typical building materials are of the order of thirty times that of air.   Therefore, if the heat is also transferred by simple conduction in the air adjacent to the outside surface of the wall, the total resistance to heat transfer would be essentially equal to the resistance of the layers of outside air.   High temperatures would be found far out from the outside surface, and the temperature of the outside surface of the wall would be relatively high.   The resulting temperature distribution is sketched as curve a in Fig. 1-3, assuming that the conduction layer in the air is of finite thickness.

However, the heat-transfer process in the air is not simple conduction. Even in the absence of wind a flow process results.   The buoyant effects in the heated layers of air near the surface cause them to rise and move away from the surface.   These layers are replaced by cooler air from below and from farther out from the surface. This effect results in temperature distribution b. The resulting heat-transfer process in the outside air is called natural convection. Convection processes in which the fluid motion is induced by heat transfer are called natural convection.

A wind velocity would further modify the temperature distribution by aiding in the displacement of the heated air layers by cooler air. Resulting distributions are shown in Fig. 1-3. The effect of a wind velocity, which is imposed upon the natural-convection heat-transfer process, is called forced convection. For sufficiently high wind velocities, buoyancy effects would be negligible, and the process would be pure forced convection.

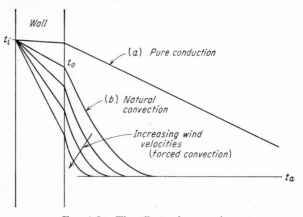

FIG. 1-3.   The effects of convection.

It is evident from the preceding example of heat transfer that both types of convection result in cool fluid being brought near the surface. The resulting modifications of the temperature distribution, from that for pure conduction, result in higher temperature gradients (see Fig. 1-3). Therefore, heat-transfer rates are higher.

Although the effects of relative fluid motion invalidate equations such as (1-1) for convection processes, it is still convenient to relate the heat-transfer rate to the temperature difference causing the heat flow. For a surface of area A, a convection conductance (or convection coefficient) h is defined as follows:

$$q = hA \ \Delta t$$

where Δt is the temperature difference for the convection process. In Fig. 1-3 this temperature difference is $(t_o - t_a)$. In English units the convection coefficient is usually expressed in terms of Btu/hr ft^2 °F. The convection coefficient defined above is also often called the surface or film co-efficient, in certain rather special convection circumstances. However, the coefficient is always defined as shown above.

For surfaces in general, the convection coefficient (and perhaps even the temperature difference) may vary over the surface. Therefore, a local convection coefficient is defined in terms of the local heat flux and local temperature difference:

$$q'' = h_x \, \Delta t_x \qquad\qquad (1\text{-}9)$$

where x denotes the location on the surface. For a circumstance in which h_x and Δt_x vary, it is often convenient to write the total convection heat-transfer rate for a heat-exchange surface of extent A_T in terms of mean values of h and Δt as follows:

$$q = h A_T \, \Delta t_m \qquad\qquad (1\text{-}10)$$

The mean convection coefficient and temperature difference are determined from the nature of the process. The procedure shown below is for a particular case.

Consider a fluid at temperature t_1 flowing into a pipe whose inside surface (of area A_T) is maintained at t_w (see Fig. 1-4). As the fluid flows through the pipe, its local average temperature will approach t_w. Therefore, the temperature difference causing convection heat transfer decreases. The convection coefficient may also vary in practice but is assumed constant in this example. For the complete convection process, Eq. (1-10) applies, and we shall determine the proper value for the mean temperature difference for this circumstance.

The fluid mass-flow rate, specific heat, and exit temperature are denoted by m, c_p, and t_2, respectively. Consider a small element of heat-transfer surface dA. The heat-transfer rate across dA is written in terms of the convection coefficient and the local temperature difference as

$$dq = q'' \, dA = h \, dA \, (t_w - t)$$

where t is the average temperature of the fluid at this location. This heat-transfer rate must equal the time rate of change of the energy content of the fluid stream while passing over dA:

$$dq = m c_p \, dt$$

where dt is the change in average fluid temperature across dA. Equating these two results, a differential equation is obtained which is integrated from the inlet (where $A = 0$) to the outlet (where $A = A_T$):

$$dq = h \, dA \, (t_w - t) = mc_p \, dt$$

$$\frac{h \, dA}{mc_p} = \frac{dt}{t_w - t} = - \frac{d(t_w - t)}{t_w - t}$$

$$\int_0^{A_T} \frac{h \, dA}{mc_p} = - \int_{t_w - t_1}^{t_w - t_2} d \ln (t_w - t)$$

$$\frac{hA_T}{mc_p} = - \ln \frac{t_w - t_2}{t_w - t_1} = \ln \frac{t_w - t_1}{t_w - t_2} \qquad (1\text{-}11)$$

The total heat-transfer rate, given by Eq. (1-10), is equal to the rate of energy reception by the flowing fluid:

$$q = hA_T \, \Delta t_m = mc_p(t_2 - t_1)$$

From this result hA_T/mc_p is found and substituted into Eq. (1-11) to yield

$$\Delta t_m = \frac{t_2 - t_1}{\ln \left[(t_w - t_1)/(t_w - t_2) \right]} = \frac{(t_w - t_1) - (t_w - t_2)}{\ln \left[(t_w - t_1)/(t_w - t_2) \right]} \qquad (1\text{-}12)$$

The temperature difference given in Eq. (1-12) is called the logarithmic mean temperature difference and is the proper one to use in Eq. (1-10) for

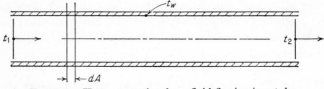

FIG. 1-4.   Heat convection for a fluid flowing in a tube.

this circumstance.   In general, it is not equal to the average of $(t_w - t_1)$ and $(t_w - t_2)$ but approaches this average value if $(t_2 - t_1)$ is small compared with $(t_1 - t_w)$.

The foregoing definition of h and the determination of the logarithmic mean temperature difference provide a means of calculating h from experimental information.   However, they give no indication of how h may be calculated from a consideration of the physical process.   Such a calculation must be based upon the details of the convection process.

In general, the magnitude of the convection coefficient is dependent not merely upon the properties of the convective fluid but also upon the flow process.   For example, for convection heat loss from the outside surface of a building wall, discussed earlier in this section, the convection coefficient h would be a minimum for pure natural convection and would increase as the outside wind velocity increases. The increase for a wind velocity of 20 mph would be by a factor of the order of 10. Typically, the convection coefficient depends strongly upon the magnitude of the imposed velocity, upon the orientation of the surface, and upon the detailed nature of the resulting fluid flow process. As a result, the classifications of convection processes and the calculations of surface coefficients are based primarily upon flow considerations.

Convection processes are considered in Chaps. 6, 7, and 8. Fluid flow processes are discussed in Chap. 6, and various analyses that are particularly pertinent to heat-transfer calculation and design are given. Chapter 7 is devoted to forced convection; the various types of processes are delineated, experimentally determined behavior is considered, and a number of analytic treatments are presented. Natural and combined forced and natural convection are considered in Chap. 8.

NOTATION

A_o	Avogadro's number
c	specific heat
c_p	specific heat at constant pressure, per unit mass
c_v	specific heat at constant volume, per unit mass
h	convection coefficient
i	arrangement factor
k	thermal conductivity
m	rate of mass flow
N_{Pr}	Prandtl number
q	heat-transfer rate
q''	heat-transfer rate per unit area (i.e., heat flux)
$\bar{R}$	universal gas constant (i.e., per mole)
t	temperature, °F or °C
T	absolute temperature
v_s	sonic velocity in a liquid
W_b	total hemispherical emissive power of a "black" surface
γ	specific-heat ratio
ϵ	hemispherical emissivity
λ	molecular spacing in a liquid
μ	absolute (or dynamic) viscosity
σ	universal constant for black-body radiation

PROBLEMS

1. A 20- by 16-ft floor consists of a 4-ft-thick slab of gravel aggregate concrete. If the upper and lower temperatures are 70 and 55°F, find the heat flux and the heat-transfer rate through the floor.

2. Derive the conversion factors for converting the thermal conductivity from units of Btu/hr ft^2 °F/ft to Btu/hr ft^2 °F/in., cal/sec cm °C, and watts/cm °C.

3. Plot the logarithm of thermal conductivity vs. temperature (as possible) in the range 0 to 500°F for the following substances:

air	liquid sodium	brass
low-pressure steam	concrete	steel
carbon dioxide gas	building brick	tin
water	glass	copper
mercury	ice	silver

Put all curves on a single plot of scale 2 in. per logarithmic cycle and 1 in. per 100°F. The thermal conductivities are to be in Btu/hr ft °F and are to be taken from the Appendix.

4. Prove, for steady-state conduction in a slab whose surfaces are maintained at t_1 and t_2, that the temperature distribution is a straight line if k is uniform throughout the slab. Indicate the shape of the temperature distribution if k increases with t, if $t_2 > t_1$.

5. For the gases CO_2 and O_2 at atmospheric pressure and steam at zero pressure, calculate the Prandtl number at 200°F. Compare the value for O_2 with that computed from Eq. (1-5).

6. For water at 60°F the molecular spacing and sonic velocity are 1.2×10^{-8} in. and 5000 fps. From these values, compute the thermal conductivity and compare the result with the value tabulated in the Appendix. $\bar{R} = 1.986$ Btu/lb mole °R.

7. An oxidized 1- by 2-ft metal surface is at 1000°F. Find the radiant flux and total emission rate if the surface is assumed black and if the surface has an emissivity of 0.90.

8. Compare the emissive power of heavily oxidized aluminum and lampblack surfaces at a given temperature and find the temperature necessary for a heavily oxidized aluminum surface to have an emissive power equal to that of lampblack at 150°F.

9. A plate 2 ft high and 1 ft wide, having a surface temperature of 90°F, is in contact with air at 60°F. If the observed convection heat-transfer rate is 2.5 Btu/min for each side, compute the average convection coefficient.

10. In an experimental study of forced convection, air, initially at 60°F and 20 psia, flows at 80 fps through a 30-ft-long, 1-in.-ID pipe. The inside surface of the pipe is maintained at 120°F. The outlet air temperature is 110°F. Find the logarithmic mean and average temperature differences and the convection coefficient, assuming that the convection coefficient is constant over the heat-transfer surface.

CHAPTER 2

The General Conduction Equations and Steady-state Conduction

2-1. CONDUCTION PROCESSES

The general conduction equations are developed in Sec. 2-2, and in the remaining sections of this chapter they are applied to steady-state conduction. Chapter 3 treats unsteady-state conduction. Various types of steady- and unsteady-state problems are considered, and the numerous methods of solution presented are due to many contributions, from the treatise of Fourier in 1822 to the present.

Since the analytical techniques which are to be used for a particular problem depend primarily upon the detailed nature of the conduction process, a classification system is used. Steady state means that the conditions (i.e., temperature, density, etc.) at all points of the conduction region are independent of time. Unsteady state implies a change with time, usually only of the temperature. There are two distinct types of unsteady state: periodic, wherein the temperature variation with time at all points in the region is periodic; and transient, wherein the temperature changes are not periodic. An example of periodic conduction may be the conduction of energy in a thick concrete roof slab due to solar effects. The immersion of a hot piece of metal in a quenching bath is an example of transient conduction.

Another important aspect of classification is the minimum number of space coordinates (or dimensions) necessary to describe the temperature field. Three coordinates suffice in all cases, but many problems are simpler because of the geometry of the conduction region or because of the symmetries of the temperature distribution. One- and two-dimensional cases often arise.

Many problems involve the additional feature of heat generation internal to the conduction region, which is due, for example, to chemical reaction

13

or to a dissipation process. The source of energy may be concentrated, as in a small-diameter current-carrying electrical conductor inside thick insulation. Or the source may be distributed, as in the elements or shield of a nuclear reactor, where the generation of energy is due to the deceleration and absorption of high-energy particles and radiation throughout the solid material.

The classification of a problem according to the distinctions enumerated above indicates the particular approach to be used for its solution and suggests the amount of difficulty that will be encountered in obtaining the solution. Often a complete analytic solution is not possible, and only approximate information may be obtained by numerical techniques.

The "solution" of a conduction problem almost invariably involves the functional dependence of temperature upon location in the conduction region and upon time in unsteady-state circumstances. That is, obtaining a solution means finding a temperature distribution which is consistent with the conditions on the boundaries and also consistent with any specified conditions internal to the region.

The temperature distribution, that is, the solution to the problem, must also be consistent with the relation among heat flux, thermal conductivity, and temperature gradient embodied in Fourier's law of conduction, Eq. (1-3). That is, the temperature distribution must satisfy any specified conditions and Fourier's law simultaneously. However, the law of conduction is not applied in the form of Eq. (1-3). Instead, a differential equation is derived from this relation which specifies the form of the temperature distribution by specifying a relation between derivatives of this distribution. The general differential equation for conduction in a material of invariant density is developed in the next section.

2-2. THE GENERAL CONDUCTION EQUATION

Consider a differential element of volume $(dx\,dy\,dz)$ of a material subject to a conduction process (see Fig. 2-1). The differential equation of conduction is derived by writing an energy balance for this element. The net rate of energy gain across the six faces by conduction is added to the rate of energy generation in the element. This sum is set equal to the time rate of change of energy stored in the mass inside the volume element, as indicated by its temperature level. The conduction rates are related to the relevant thermal conductivities and temperature gradients by Fourier's law of conduction, Eq. (1-3). The time rate of change of stored energy is equal to the thermal capacity of the mass times the time rate of change of temperature.

The midpoint of the differential element is denoted as x, y, z, and at time

τ the temperature and specific heat at this point are t and c. The density ρ is considered independent of time. The energy generation is assumed due to a source distributed throughout the material, and its strength, q''', is the rate of energy generation at x, y, z at time τ per unit volume.

In the general analysis the thermal conductivity at x, y, z will be considered to depend upon the orientation of the surface for which Fourier's law of conduction is written. Such a variation in conductive characteristics is accounted for by assigning a distinctive thermal conductivity for each

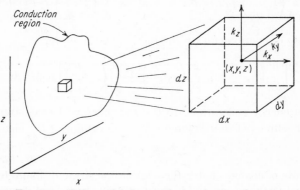

Fig. 2-1.   Differential element for conduction analysis.

of the three surface orientations perpendicular to a coordinate axis. Thus k_x, k_y, and k_z specify the directional characteristics of the material. If the three values are equal, the material is called isotropic; if unequal, anisotropic. For example, wood is anisotropic; if the x axis is taken perpendicular to the grain, then k_y and k_z will be greater than k_x. In general, the thermal conductivities may also be a function of location and temperature. The symbols k_x, k_y, k_z denote the values at x, y, z at time τ.

The rate of conduction per unit area at x, y, z across a surface perpendicular to the x axis is

$$q''_x = -k_x \frac{\partial t}{\partial x}$$

If differentials of higher order than the first are neglected, the difference in the rate of conduction per unit area across the two surfaces of the element (in Fig. 2-1) perpendicular to the x axis is

$$-\frac{\partial}{\partial x}(q''_x)\,dx = -\frac{\partial}{\partial x}\left(-k_x \frac{\partial t}{\partial x}\right)dx = \frac{\partial}{\partial x}\left(k_x \frac{\partial t}{\partial x}\right)dx$$

The minus sign is introduced to yield a minus quantity if the conduction rate out of the right face is greater than the conduction rate into the left face. The net rate of gain in the element $(dx\ dy\ dz)$ due to conduction in the x direction is the net rate times the area $(dy\ dz)$:

$$\frac{\partial}{\partial x}\left(k_x \frac{\partial t}{\partial x}\right) dx\ (dy\ dz)$$

Similar relations are written for the y and z directions:

$$\frac{\partial}{\partial y}\left(k_y \frac{\partial t}{\partial y}\right) dy\ (dx\ dz) \qquad \text{and} \qquad \frac{\partial}{\partial z}\left(k_z \frac{\partial t}{\partial z}\right) dz\ (dx\ dy)$$

The net rate of energy gain by conduction is, therefore,

$$\left[\frac{\partial}{\partial x}\left(k_x \frac{\partial t}{\partial x}\right) + \frac{\partial}{\partial y}\left(k_y \frac{\partial t}{\partial y}\right) + \frac{\partial}{\partial z}\left(k_z \frac{\partial t}{\partial z}\right)\right] dx\ dy\ dz$$

The rate of energy generation in $(dx\ dy\ dz)$ is equal to the strength of the distributed source per unit volume times the volume of the element:

$$q'''(dx\ dy\ dz)$$

The time rate of change of stored energy in the element due to temperature level is equal to the product of its mass, specific heat, and the time rate of change of temperature:

$$(\rho\ dx\ dy\ dz)c\ \frac{\partial t}{\partial \tau}$$

The general conduction equation is obtained by equating the sum of the net rates of energy gain by conduction and generation to the time rate of increase of stored energy. The result is

$$\frac{\partial}{\partial x}\left(k_x \frac{\partial t}{\partial x}\right) + \frac{\partial}{\partial y}\left(k_y \frac{\partial t}{\partial y}\right) + \frac{\partial}{\partial z}\left(k_z \frac{\partial t}{\partial z}\right) + q''' = \rho c\ \frac{\partial t}{\partial \tau} \qquad (2\text{-}1)$$

The general conduction equation is applied to specific problems by reducing it to the simplest form consistent with the conditions established by the problem. Several of the more important of these simpler forms have been given specific names and are presented below.

For an isotropic material, $k_x = k_y = k_z$, and the subscripts x, y, z may be suppressed in Eq. (2-1). However, the thermal conductivity k may not be factored out of the three conduction terms unless it is independent of x, y, and z, that is, unless k is uniform over the conduction region. This results for a conduction region consisting of a homogeneous material whose thermal conductivity is independent of temperature. For such a uniform thermal conductivity (or homogeneous region) the differential equation becomes

$$\frac{\partial^2 t}{\partial x^2} + \frac{\partial^2 t}{\partial y^2} + \frac{\partial^2 t}{\partial z^2} + \frac{q'''}{k} = \frac{\rho c}{k}\frac{\partial t}{\partial \tau} = \frac{1}{\alpha}\frac{\partial t}{\partial \tau} \qquad (2\text{-}2)$$

where the quantity $k/\rho c$, the thermal conductivity divided by the thermal capacity, is denoted by α and is called the thermal diffusivity.

If, in addition to the conditions necessary for Eq. (2-2), there is no distributed source, that is, if $q''' = 0$, the Fourier equation results:

$$\frac{\partial^2 t}{\partial x^2} + \frac{\partial^2 t}{\partial y^2} + \frac{\partial^2 t}{\partial z^2} = \frac{1}{\alpha}\frac{\partial t}{\partial \tau} \qquad (2\text{-}3)$$

This equation then applies to three-dimensional unsteady-state conduction in an isotropic region of uniform thermal conductivity.

If the conditions for Eq. (2-3) are met and the conduction circumstance occurs in steady state, the time derivative is zero. The resulting relation is called the Laplace equation:

$$\frac{\partial^2 t}{\partial x^2} + \frac{\partial^2 t}{\partial y^2} + \frac{\partial^2 t}{\partial z^2} = 0 \qquad (2\text{-}4)$$

Another common circumstance is steady-state conduction in an isotropic region of uniform thermal conductivity which is subject to a distributed source of energy. The strength of the generation process, q''', may vary over the region. The resulting equation is called Poisson's equation:

$$\frac{\partial^2 t}{\partial x^2} + \frac{\partial^2 t}{\partial y^2} + \frac{\partial^2 t}{\partial z^2} + \frac{q'''}{k} = 0 \qquad (2\text{-}5)$$

The similarity between Eqs. (2-3) to (2-5) and those which characterize various other physical phenomena is an interesting and important fact. It means, for example, that the solution of a heat-transfer problem may also be the solution of an interesting problem involving completely different phenomena. This similarity of equations is also the basis of analogues, as discussed in detail in Chap. 13.

The equations developed above are in terms of a cartesian coordinate system. For many problems the cylindrical or spherical system is more convenient. The equations may be converted to the cylindrical or spherical forms by the relations between coordinates in these different systems. The Fourier equation in cylindrical coordinates (r,θ,z) is

$$\frac{\partial^2 t}{\partial r^2} + \frac{1}{r}\frac{\partial t}{\partial r} + \frac{1}{r^2}\frac{\partial^2 t}{\partial \theta^2} + \frac{\partial^2 t}{\partial z^2} = \frac{1}{\alpha}\frac{\partial t}{\partial \tau} \qquad (2\text{-}6)$$

In spherical coordinates (r,θ,ϕ) it becomes

$$\frac{\partial^2 t}{\partial r^2} + \frac{2}{r}\frac{\partial t}{\partial r} + \frac{1}{r^2 \sin\theta}\frac{\partial}{\partial\theta}\left(\sin\theta\,\frac{\partial t}{\partial\theta}\right) + \frac{1}{r^2\sin^2\theta}\frac{\partial^2 t}{\partial\phi^2} = \frac{1}{\alpha}\frac{\partial t}{\partial\tau} \qquad (2\text{-}7)$$

The subsequent sections of this chapter are devoted to the solution of various steady-state conduction problems through the use of the relevant form of the conduction differential equation. The boundary conditions specify the conditions that the temperature distribution must satisfy at boundaries. The differential equation specifies the nature of the temperature-distribution function by requiring that a certain relationship between its derivatives be satisfied at every point in the conduction region. The boundary conditions and differential equation are called the mathematical statement of the problem. The solution of the problem is the resulting temperature distribution, and heat-flow rates are obtained by computing derivatives of this distribution.

The last section of this chapter presents the approximate numerical methods which are often employed to solve steady-state problems for which analytic solutions are not known. Numerical methods are also often used when an approximate solution will yield results of sufficient accuracy with an economy of time and effort.

2-3. CONDUCTION IN ONE DIMENSION

The one-dimensional steady-state processes are the most simple, because the condition imposed upon the temperature distribution is an ordinary differential equation. The temperature is a function of only one space variable. Such one-dimensional processes occur in extensive slabs, such as building walls; in cylindrical elements, such as pipes and tubes; and in spherical elements, such as a nuclear-reactor pressure vessel. In this section each of these three cases is considered for substances having a uniform conductivity. Conduction in a slab is also considered for a material of temperature-dependent thermal conductivity.

Flat Surface. Consider steady-state conduction through a flat plate of thickness L which has a uniform thermal conductivity k. The two surface temperatures are t_1 and t_2. A coordinate system is chosen as shown in Fig. 2-2a. The differential equation, the Laplace equation in one dimension, and the boundary conditions are written:

$$\frac{d^2 t}{dx^2} = 0 \qquad \begin{array}{ll} \text{at } x = 0 & t = t_1 \\ \text{at } x = L & t = t_2 \end{array}$$

The general solution is obtained:

$$d\left(\frac{dt}{dx}\right) = 0 \qquad \frac{dt}{dx} = C_1$$

$$dt = C_1 \, dx \qquad t = C_1 x + C_2$$

The constants are evaluated from the boundary conditions:

at $x = 0$ $\qquad\qquad t_1 = C_2$

at $x = L$ $\qquad\qquad t_2 = C_1 L + C_2 \qquad C_1 = \dfrac{t_2 - t_1}{L}$

The solution is

$$t = (t_2 - t_1)\frac{x}{L} + t_1 \tag{2-8}$$

This is seen to be a linear change from t_1 to t_2 through the plate and is plotted in Fig. 2-2b.

The heat-flow rate per unit area is computed from the temperature distribution, Eq. (2-8), using Fourier's law of conduction, Eq. (1-3):

$$q'' = -k\frac{\partial t}{\partial x} \qquad (1\text{-}3)$$

$$\frac{dt}{dx} = \frac{t_2 - t_1}{L}$$

$$q'' = -\frac{k}{L}(t_2 - t_1) = \frac{k}{L}(t_1 - t_2) \quad (2\text{-}9)$$

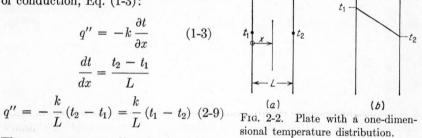

(a)   (b)
FIG. 2-2. Plate with a one-dimensional temperature distribution.

The temperature gradient is seen to be a constant. The heat-flow equation is seen to be identical with Eq. (1-2). The heat-flow rate for a plate of area A is

$$q = k\frac{A}{L}(t_1 - t_2) \tag{2-10}$$

where kA/L is a characteristic of the plate and is called its conductance. The conductance per unit plate area is k/L.

Example 2-1. A 4- by 5-ft concrete slab 6 in. thick, having a thermal conductivity of 1.5 Btu/hr ft °F, has its two surfaces maintained at 120 and 80°F, respectively. For steady-state conduction, find the heat-transfer rate through the slab.

The flux per unit area is

$$q'' = \frac{k}{L}(t_1 - t_2) = \frac{1.5 \times 12}{6}(120 - 80) = 120 \text{ Btu/hr ft}^2$$

The total heat-transfer rate is

$$q = q''A = 120 \times 4 \times 5 = 2400 \text{ Btu/hr}$$

Cylindrical Conduction Regions. The next case considered is a long cylindrical element of uniform thermal conductivity, as shown in Fig. 2-3. If the conduction process is in steady state and if the conditions specified on each of the two surfaces are independent of θ and z, the process is one-dimensional. That is, the temperature distribution depends only upon r. If temperatures of t_1 and t_2 are specified at r_1 and r_2, the relevant differential equation [from Eq. (2-6)] and boundary conditions are as follows:

$$\frac{d^2t}{dr^2} + \frac{1}{r}\frac{dt}{dr} = 0 \qquad \begin{array}{ll} \text{at } r = r_1 & t = t_1 \\ \text{at } r = r_2 & t = t_2 \end{array}$$

The general solution is obtained by substituting p for dt/dr. The differential equation then becomes

$$\frac{d}{dr}(p) + \frac{p}{r} = 0$$

Multiplying through by $r \, dr$, we have

$$r \, dp + p \, dr = d(pr) = 0$$

$$pr = \frac{dt}{dr}r = C_1$$

This result is rewritten, integrated again, and the constants determined from the boundary conditions:

$$dt = \frac{C_1}{r}dr$$

$$t = C_1 \ln r + C_2$$

at $r = r_1$
$$t_1 = C_1 \ln r_1 + C_2$$

at $r = r_2$
$$t_2 = C_1 \ln r_2 + C_2$$

$$C_1 = \frac{t_2 - t_1}{\ln (r_2/r_1)} \qquad C_2 = \frac{t_1 \ln r_2 - t_2 \ln r_1}{\ln (r_2/r_1)}$$

$$t = \frac{1}{\ln (r_2/r_1)}[(t_2 - t_1)\ln r + t_1 \ln r_2 - t_2 \ln r_1] \qquad (2\text{-}11)$$

This distribution is seen to be logarithmic and is plotted in Fig. 2-3 for $t_1 > t_2$. The slope decreases in magnitude from r_1 to r_2, indicating that the heat flux per unit area decreases as r increases. This is consistent with the fact that the total heat flux per unit cylinder length must be independent of r and that the area for conduction increases with r. The heat-transfer rate per unit area and the total conduction rate per unit cylinder length are calculated:

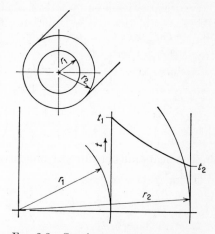

$$q'' = -k \frac{dt}{dr} = -\frac{k(t_2 - t_1)}{r \ln (r_2/r_1)}$$

$$= \frac{k(t_1 - t_2)}{r \ln (r_2/r_1)}$$

$$\frac{q}{L} = q''2\pi r = \frac{2\pi k(t_1 - t_2)}{\ln (r_2/r_1)} \quad (2\text{-}12)$$

FIG. 2-3. Steady-state temperature distribution in a cylindrical element.

The conductance of the cylindrical wall is the coefficient of $(t_1 - t_2)$.

Note that the expression for the heat-flow rate for a cylinder is different from that for a flat plate. However, for small values of $(r_2 - r_1)/r_1$, this conductance becomes essentially equal to $A_m k/\Delta r$, where A_m is the conductance area at the average radius.

Spherical Conduction Regions. The case of a spherical element of inside radius r_1 and outside radius r_2 is solved for steady-state conduction and surface temperatures of t_1 and t_2. The differential equation [from Eq. (2-7)] and boundary conditions are

$$\frac{d^2t}{dr^2} + \frac{2}{r}\frac{dt}{dr} = 0 \qquad \begin{matrix} \text{at } r = r_1 & t = t_1 \\ \text{at } r = r_2 & t = t_2 \end{matrix}$$

Again, dt/dr is replaced by p. The result is multiplied by $r^2\,dr$ and integrated:

$$r^2\,dp + p(2r\,dr) = d(r^2 p) = 0$$

$$r^2 p = C_1 \qquad \text{or} \qquad p = \frac{dt}{dr} = \frac{C_1}{r^2}$$

$$t = -\frac{C_1}{r} + C_2$$

The constants are determined and substituted into the general solution:

at $r = r_1$ $$t_1 = -\frac{C_1}{r_1} + C_2$$

at $r = r_2$ $$t_2 = -\frac{C_1}{r_2} + C_2$$

$$-C_1 = \frac{t_1 - t_2}{1/r_1 - 1/r_2} \qquad C_2 = \frac{t_2/r_1 - t_1/r_2}{1/r_1 - 1/r_2}$$

$$t = \frac{1}{1/r_1 - 1/r_2}\left(\frac{t_1 - t_2}{r} + \frac{t_2}{r_1} - \frac{t_1}{r_2}\right) \tag{2-13}$$

The heat-transfer rate per unit area and the total heat-transfer rate are found:

$$q'' = -k\frac{dt}{dr} = \frac{k(-C_1)}{r^2} = \frac{k(t_1 - t_2)}{r^2(1/r_1 - 1/r_2)}$$

$$q = 4\pi r^2 q'' = \frac{4\pi k(t_1 - t_2)}{1/r_1 - 1/r_2} \tag{2-14}$$

The conductance of the spherical shell is the coefficient of $(t_1 - t_2)$ in Eq. (2-14). For thin shells [i.e., with $(r_2 - r_1)/r_1$ very small] the conductance becomes $A_m k/\Delta r$, where A_m is the conductance area at the average radius.

Example 2-2. The spherical pressure vessel of a small homogeneous reactor is to have a 2-ft ID and a 3-ft OD and to be made of a steel having a thermal conductivity of 24.2 Btu/hr ft °F. The outside surface of the vessel is to be sufficiently well insulated so that the heat loss through the insulation will be 120 Btu/hr ft² of area, based upon the outside surface of the pressure vessel. If the inside surface of the pressure vessel is to be at 700°F, let us find the outside surface temperature.

The total conduction rate through the spherical shell is

$$q = 4\pi r_2^2 q_2'' = \frac{4\pi k(t_1 - t_2)}{1/r_1 - 1/r_2}$$

Therefore,

$$t_1 - t_2 = \frac{r_2 q_2''(r_2/r_1 - 1)}{k} = \frac{1.5 \times 120(\frac{3}{2} - 1)}{24.2} = 3.3°F$$

$$t_2 = t_1 - \Delta t = 700 - 3.3 = 696.7°F$$

Variable Thermal Conductivity. If the thermal conductivity of the material which makes up the conduction region varies significantly in the region, the preceding equations do not apply directly. The Laplace equation is not valid in such a circumstance. The proper differential equation is determined from the general conduction equation, Eq. (2-1), for a steady-state conduction process (without internal generation of energy). The equation and boundary conditions are

$$\frac{d}{dx}\left(k\,\frac{dt}{dx}\right) = 0 \qquad \begin{array}{ll} \text{at } x = 0 & t = t_1 \\ \text{at } x = L & t = t_2 \end{array}$$

where k may be a function of x and t.

A solution is presented below for the plate conduction problem for the case wherein the thermal conductivity is a function of temperature, that is,

$$k = f(t) \tag{2-15}$$

The differential equation is integrated and the constants are determined. Integrating,

$$k\,\frac{dt}{dx} = C_1$$

$$\int_{t_1}^{t} k\,dt = C_1 \int_0^x dx = C_1 x$$

From $t = t_2$ at $x = L$,

$$\int_{t_1}^{t_2} k\,dt = C_1 L$$

$$C_1 = \frac{1}{L}\int_{t_1}^{t_2} k\,dt = -k_m\,\frac{t_1 - t_2}{L}$$

$$k_m = \frac{1}{t_1 - t_2}\int_{t_1}^{t_2} k\,dt \tag{2-16}$$

where k_m is defined as the integrated average value of k from t_1 to t_2. For a linear variation of k with t this is equal to the average of k_1 and k_2.

The temperature distribution is given by

$$\int_{t_1}^{t} k\,dt = -k_m(t_1 - t_2)\,\frac{x}{L}$$

This may not be written explicitly until the relation between k and t is specified.

The heat flux and the total heat-flow rate for the plate may be found from the result of the first integration:

$$q'' = -k\,\frac{dt}{dx} = -C_1 = \frac{k_m(t_1 - t_2)}{L} \tag{2-17}$$

$$q = \frac{k_m A}{L}(t_1 - t_2) \tag{2-18}$$

These relations are identical with the previous result for uniform thermal conductivity, Eq. (2-10), except that the thermal conductivity which appears is the integrated average value.

The cylindrical and spherical cases may be analyzed in a similar fashion. These results are presented for a linear variation of k with t in Jakob (1949). The heat-transfer equations which result are identical with Eqs. (2-12) and (2-14), respectively, except that the thermal conductivity is replaced by the average of its values at t_1 and t_2.

2-4. CONDUCTION WITH GENERATION IN ONE DIMENSION

Energy generation in a conduction region modifies considerably the temperature distribution from that which would apply for simple conduction. If q''', the generation rate per unit volume, is positive, the temperature levels are higher than for simple conduction, and the directions of heat flow may be reversed if the distributed source is sufficiently strong. In the analysis of such a case, these features are introduced when the Laplace equation is replaced by the Poisson equation as the differential equation governing the temperature distribution.

Numerous types of distributed energy-generation processes occur in practice. Electric current flowing in a conductor results in dissipation, due to electrical resistance. Induction heating introduces the energy into the material in a distributed way. Chemical reactions may occur in a material and result in either positive or negative generation, depending upon whether the reaction is exothermic or endothermic. In nuclear-reactor fuel elements, moderator, shielding, etc., there is a generation due to the deceleration and absorption of neutrons and other fission products and due to the absorption of gamma radiation.

The examples of generation processes given above indicate the several ways in which the strength of the distributed source, q''', may vary in conduction regions. If the current density in an electrical conductor is uniform and if the resistivity does not vary with temperature, then q''' is uniform throughout the conductor. Chemical-reaction rates, however, are usually sharply temperature-dependent. In an exothermic reaction the more remote parts of the reaction region have a higher temperature, a higher reaction rate, and, therefore, a larger q'''. The generation rate in this circumstance depends upon the local temperature. The radiation shield of a nuclear reactor has a generation rate which varies with location but is essentially independent of temperature. The absorption and deceleration rate would be a maximum at the inside face and would decrease (perhaps exponentially) to a minimum at the outside face.

The generation rate, then, may be constant or variable over the conduction region and may depend upon local temperature, location, or upon both of these. This section treats the problems of uniform generation rate, generation dependent linearly upon temperature, and generation dependent upon location, for steady-state processes. The plate, cylinder, and tube are analyzed for uniform generation. The plate is considered for the cases of temperature- and location-dependent generation rates. In all cases the thermal conductivity is taken as constant over the conduction region.

Uniform, Distributed Generation. The steady-state temperature distribution and heat-transfer rate are to be found for a plate of thickness L and surface temperatures of t_1 and t_2. Energy is assumed generated at a uniform rate q''' throughout the plate. The differential equation is (2-5) in one dimension:

$$\frac{d^2t}{dx^2} + \frac{q'''}{k} = 0 \qquad \begin{array}{ll} \text{at } x = 0 & t = t_1 \\ \text{at } x = L & t = t_2 \end{array}$$

The solution is obtained and constants evaluated:

$$\frac{dt}{dx} + \frac{q'''}{k}x = C_1$$

$$t + \frac{q'''}{k}\frac{x^2}{2} = C_1 x + C_2$$

$$C_2 = t_1 \qquad C_1 = \frac{t_2 - t_1}{L} + \frac{q'''L}{2k}$$

$$t = \frac{q'''L^2}{2k}\left[\frac{x}{L} - \left(\frac{x}{L}\right)^2\right] + (t_2 - t_1)\frac{x}{L} + t_1 \qquad (2\text{-}19)$$

The temperature distribution reduces to Eq. (2-8) for $q''' = 0$ and may be interpreted as a linear distribution, with the following parabolic term added:

$$\frac{q'''}{k}\frac{L^2}{2}\left[\frac{x}{L} - \left(\frac{x}{L}\right)^2\right]$$

The distribution is rewritten in generalized form as

$$\frac{t - t_2}{t_1 - t_2} = \frac{q'''L^2}{2k(t_1 - t_2)}\left(1 - \frac{x}{L}\right)\frac{x}{L} + \left(1 - \frac{x}{L}\right) = B\frac{x}{L}\left(1 - \frac{x}{L}\right) + \left(1 - \frac{x}{L}\right)$$

$$(2\text{-}20)$$

This relation is plotted in Fig. 2-4 for various values of B.

The local heat flux is equal to minus the product of k and the local temperature gradient:

$$q'' = -k\frac{dt}{dx} = -k\left(C_1 - \frac{q'''}{k}x\right) = -k\left(\frac{t_2 - t_1}{L} + \frac{q'''L}{2k} - \frac{q'''x}{k}\right)$$

$$= k\left[\frac{t_1 - t_2}{L} - \frac{q'''L}{k}\left(\frac{1}{2} - \frac{x}{L}\right)\right] \qquad (2\text{-}21)$$

For $q''' = 0$ this expression reduces to Eq. (2-9) for the plate without generation. The second term, preceded by a minus sign, is the influence of generation on heat flux. For example, for $(t_1 - t_2)$ and q''' positive, sufficiently large values of q''' can reverse the direction of q''. This can be seen in Fig. 2-4 from the changes of the slope of the curves as B increases.

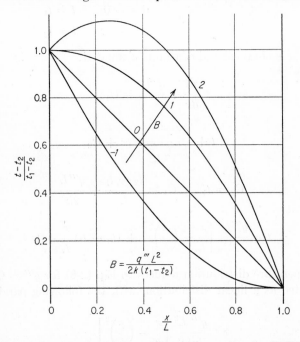

Fig. 2-4. Temperature distribution in a plate with a uniformly distributed source.

Example 2-3. Two large steel plates at temperatures of 200 and 160°F are separated by a steel rod 1 ft long and 1 in. in diameter. The rod is welded to each plate. The space between the plates is filled with insulation, which also insulates the lateral faces of the rod. Because of a voltage difference between the two plates, current flows through the rod, dissipating electrical energy at a rate of 25 Btu/hr. The maximum temperature in the rod and the heat flux at each end are to be determined. For the rod, $k = 26$ Btu/hr ft °F.

The insulation of the lateral face of the rod assures zero radial temperature gradients. Therefore, the temperature field is one-dimensional and is equivalent to that found in a plate under similar conditions. The strength of the source is found:

$$V = \frac{\pi D^2 L}{4} = \frac{\pi}{4 \times 144} = 0.00545 \text{ ft}^3$$

$$q''' = \frac{q}{V} = \frac{25}{0.00545} = 4590 \text{ Btu/hr ft}^3$$

The heat-flow rates are found for each end from Eq. (2-21):

At $x = 0$,

$$q = \frac{\pi}{4} D^2 q'' = \frac{\pi}{4} D^2 k \left(\frac{t_1 - t_2}{L} - \frac{q''' L}{2k} \right) = \frac{26\pi}{4 \times 144} \left(40 - \frac{4590}{2 \times 26} \right)$$

$$= 0.142(40 - 88.3) = -6.8 \text{ Btu/hr}$$

At $x = L$,

$$q = \frac{\pi D^2}{4} k \left(\frac{t_1 - t_2}{L} + \frac{q''' L}{2k} \right) = 0.142(40 + 88.3) = 18.2 \text{ Btu/hr}$$

The heat flows out of both ends, which means that the maximum temperature occurs within the rod. The location and magnitude of the maximum are found from Eq. (2-20):

$$\frac{d}{d(x/L)} \left(\frac{t - t_2}{t_1 - t_2} \right) = \frac{d}{d(x/L)} \left[\left(B \frac{x}{L} + 1 \right) \left(1 - \frac{x}{L} \right) \right]$$

$$= - \left(B \frac{x}{L} + 1 \right) + B \left(1 - \frac{x}{L} \right) = 0$$

and

$$\left(\frac{x}{L} \right)_m = \frac{B - 1}{2B}$$

Therefore,

$$\frac{t_m - t_1}{t_2 - t_1} = \frac{B(B - 1)}{2B} \left(1 - \frac{B - 1}{2B} \right) + 1 - \frac{B - 1}{2B} = \frac{(B + 1)^2}{4B}$$

$$B = \frac{q''' L^2}{2k(t_1 - t_2)} = \frac{4590}{2 \times 26 \times 40} = 2.21$$

$$\frac{t_m - t_2}{t_1 - t_2} = \frac{(2.21 + 1)^2}{4 \times 2.21} = 1.167 \quad \text{and} \quad t_m = 206.7°\text{F}$$

The temperature distribution in a tube or cylindrical element subject to a uniform, distributed source may be found from the Poisson equation in cylindrical coordinates. For conditions independent of θ and z,

$$\frac{d^2 t}{dr^2} + \frac{1}{r} \frac{dt}{dr} + \frac{q'''}{k} = 0$$

Replacing dt/dr by p and multiplying through by $r\,dr$, we have

$$r\,dp + p\,dr + \frac{q'''}{k}\,r\,dr = d(rp) + \frac{q'''}{2k}\,d(r^2) = 0$$

$$rp + \frac{q'''}{2k}\,r^2 = C_1$$

This may be written as

$$dt = -\frac{q'''}{2k}\,r\,dr + C_1\frac{dr}{r}$$

and, therefore,

$$t = -\frac{q'''}{4k}\,r^2 + C_1\ln r + C_2 \tag{2-22}$$

Considering first a tube of inside and outside radii a and b with inside and outside surface temperatures maintained at t_1 and t_2, the boundary conditions are

at $r = a$ $\qquad\qquad\qquad\qquad$ $t = t_1$

at $r = b$ $\qquad\qquad\qquad\qquad$ $t = t_2$

The constants are evaluated and substituted into Eq. (2-22):

$$t_1 = -\frac{q'''}{4k}\,a^2 + C_1\ln a + C_2$$

$$t_2 = -\frac{q'''}{4k}\,b^2 + C_1\ln b + C_2$$

$$C_1 = \frac{(q'''/4k)(b^2 - a^2) - (t_1 - t_2)}{\ln(b/a)}$$

$$C_2 = t_2 + \frac{q'''}{4k}\,b^2 - C_1\ln b$$

$$\frac{t - t_2}{t_1 - t_2} = \frac{q'''b^2}{4k(t_1 - t_2)}\left[\left(1 - \frac{a^2}{b^2}\right)\frac{\ln(r/b)}{\ln(b/a)} - \left(1 + \frac{r^2}{b^2}\right)\right] - \frac{\ln(r/b)}{\ln(b/a)} \tag{2-23}$$

The heat-flow rate is determined from the temperature gradient.

The general solution, Eq. (2-22), is next applied to a solid rod of radius b maintained at t_o on its surface. One boundary condition is

at $r = b$ $\qquad\qquad\qquad\qquad$ $t = t_o$

Two conditions are necessary for a second-order differential equation; that is, there are two constants, C_1 and C_2, to be determined. The other condition is evident upon inspection of the general solution (2-22). Since for uniform generation the temperature at $r = 0$ must be finite, the coefficient of $\ln r$ must be zero. The constant C_2 is evaluated, and the temperature distribution is

$$t - t_o = \theta = \frac{q'''b^2}{4k}\left(1 - \frac{r^2}{b^2}\right) \tag{2-24}$$

where θ, called the temperature excess, is the amount by which the local temperature exceeds that at the surface. The maximum temperature excess (at $x = 0$) and the temperature-excess ratio are

$$\theta_0 = \frac{q'''b^2}{4k}$$

$$\phi = \frac{\theta}{\theta_0} = 1 - \frac{r^2}{b^2} \tag{2-25}$$

Variable, Distributed Generation. The next case to be considered is a plate subject to a temperature-dependent, distributed generation process. Such a circumstance would occur, for example, in a material through which an electric current is passing if the electrical resistivity of the material varies considerably with temperature. In this analysis a linear dependence of q''' upon temperature is assumed for a plate having both surfaces at t_L:

$$q''' = q_L'''[1 + \beta(t - t_L)] = q_L'''(1 + \beta\theta)$$

where q_L''' is the generation rate at t_L and β denotes the fractional change of q''' per degree of temperature change. θ is the temperature excess $(t - t_L)$.

Since both surfaces are at t_L, the temperature distribution is symmetric about the midplane. Placing the origin at the midplane will result in simple relations. In addition, the thickness of the plate is taken as $2L$ for convenience (see Fig. 2-5a). The symmetry of the temperature distribution results in the second boundary condition being a zero temperature gradient at $x = 0$. The equation and boundary conditions are

$$\frac{d^2t}{dx^2} + \frac{q'''}{k}[1 + \beta(t - t_L)] = 0 \qquad \begin{array}{ll} \text{at } x = 0 & \dfrac{dt}{dx} = 0 \\[2mm] \text{at } x = L & t = t_L \end{array}$$

These relations may be expressed in terms of $\theta = (t - t_L)$:

$$\frac{d^2\theta}{dx^2} + \frac{q_L'''}{k}(1 + \beta\theta) = 0$$

or
$$\frac{d^2\theta}{dx^2} + r + s\theta = 0$$

where
$$r = \frac{q'''_L}{k} \quad \text{and} \quad s = \beta \frac{q'''_L}{k}$$

At $x = 0$
$$\frac{d\theta}{dx} = 0$$

at $x = L$
$$\theta = 0$$

Integration is simply performed if $(r + s\theta)$ is replaced by θ':

$$\frac{d^2\theta'}{dx^2} + s\theta' = 0$$

The solution is

$$\theta' = r + s\theta = C'_1 \cos (x\sqrt{s}) + C'_2 \sin (x\sqrt{s})$$

$$\theta = C_1 \cos (x\sqrt{s}) + C_2 \sin (x\sqrt{s}) - \frac{r}{s}$$

$$\frac{d\theta}{dx} = -C_1\sqrt{s} \sin (x\sqrt{s}) + C_2\sqrt{s} \cos (x\sqrt{s})$$

$$\left(\frac{d\theta}{dx}\right)_0 = 0 = C_2\sqrt{s} \quad \text{and} \quad C_2 = 0$$

$$\theta_L = 0 = C_1 \cos (L\sqrt{s}) - \frac{r}{s} \quad \text{and} \quad C_1 = \frac{r}{s \cos (L\sqrt{s})}$$

Therefore,
$$\theta = \frac{1}{\beta} \left[\frac{\cos (x\sqrt{s})}{\cos (L\sqrt{s})} - 1 \right] \tag{2-26}$$

This temperature-distribution expression has several interesting features. The temperature excess is a maximum at $x = 0$ and decreases to zero at $x = L$. However, for $L\sqrt{s} = \pi/2$, the temperature excess is infinite for all x. Since s is the measure of the temperature effect upon the local generation rate, the condition $L\sqrt{s} < \pi/2$ sets a limit on temperature dependence beyond which arbitrarily high temperatures and destruction of the plate result. This circumstance can be interpreted as the result of a temperature dependence of sufficient magnitude that the temperature rise necessary to cause the generated energy to be conducted to the surface causes an increase in generation rate which is too large to be conducted away. This limitation in terms of q'''_L and β is

$$LV_s = L \sqrt{\frac{\beta q'''}{k}} < \frac{\pi}{2}$$

or
$$\beta q'''_L < \left(\frac{\pi}{2}\right)^2 \frac{k}{L^2}$$

For a temperature dependence less than the limiting value, the midplane temperature excess θ_0 and the temperature-excess-ratio distribution are

$$\theta_0 = \frac{1}{\beta}\left[\frac{1}{\cos(LV_s)} - 1\right]$$

$$\phi = \frac{\theta}{\theta_0} = \frac{\cos(xV_s) - \cos(LV_s)}{1 - \cos(LV_s)} \tag{2-27}$$

The temperature distribution, expressed as an excess ratio, varies between zero and one. The form of the curve is relatively insensitive to LV_s. Curves for various values of LV_s are plotted in Fig. 2-5b.

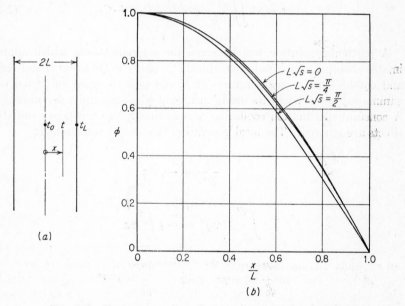

Fig. 2-5.   Temperature-dependent energy generation in a plate.

The cylindrical and spherical cases of one-dimensional temperature-dependent generation are more complicated. The governing differential equations are of the Bessel form. The solutions are given in Jakob (1949) for a uniform surface temperature. Temperature-excess-ratio distributions are presented. A limiting temperature dependence is found, as in the plate case above.

The rate of generation due to a distributed source may also vary over the conduction region in a manner independent of temperature. Such a circumstance would result, for example, for a chemical reaction in which the concentration of reactants was nonuniform, in an electrical conductor in which the current density was nonuniform owing to geometric effects, or for reactor elements wherein the reaction, absorption, and deceleration characteristics were independent of temperature.

The equations for the case of a location-dependent generation rate in a plate are

$$q''' = f(x)$$

$$\frac{d^2t}{dx^2} + \frac{f(x)}{k} = 0$$

$$t = -\iint \frac{f(x)}{k} (dx)^2 + C_1 x + C_2 \qquad (2\text{-}28)$$

A particular solution will be given for a circumstance which approximates absorption in a radiation shield. A plate of thickness L and inside and outside surface temperatures of t_1 and t_2 is assumed subjected to a gamma-ray intensity at its inside surface of q_0'' energy units per unit time. A constant attenuation coefficient γ is assumed, and secondary radiation effects are ignored. The local generation rate is first determined:

$$\frac{dq''}{q''} = -\gamma \, dx$$

$$\int_{q_0''}^{q''} d \ln q'' = -\gamma \int_0^x dx$$

$$\ln \frac{q''}{q_0''} = -\gamma x \qquad \text{or} \qquad \frac{q''}{q_0''} = e^{-\gamma x}$$

$$q''' = -\frac{dq''}{dx} = \gamma q'' = \gamma q_0'' e^{-\gamma x}$$

The temperature distribution is derived:

$$\frac{d^2t}{dx^2} + \frac{\gamma q_0''}{k} e^{-\gamma x} = 0 \qquad \begin{array}{ll} \text{at } x = 0 & t = t_1 \\ \text{at } x = L & t = t_2 \end{array}$$

$$\frac{dt}{dx} = \frac{q_0''}{k} e^{-\gamma x} + C_1$$

$$t = -\frac{q_0''}{\gamma k} e^{-\gamma x} + C_1 x + C_2$$

$$t - t_1 = \frac{q_0''}{\gamma k} \left[(1 - e^{-\gamma x}) - \frac{x}{L}(1 - e^{-\gamma L}) \right] - (t_1 - t_2)\frac{x}{L} \qquad (2\text{-}29)$$

The conduction heat flux may be determined from the first derivative of the temperature distribution.

The foregoing analysis is limited to energy-generation processes which are distributed over the conduction region and which result in a temperature field which may be described in terms of one space coordinate. If a concentrated source is present, the methods are somewhat different; the Laplace equation applies, with heat-flux boundary conditions established by the strength of the source. The reader is referred to Jakob (1949) and Carslaw and Jaeger (1959) for such an analysis. Multidimensional temperature fields often arise in conjunction with generation. Numerous solutions are available for these cases, and reference may be made to Jakob (1949), Carslaw and Jaeger (1959), and Schneider (1955).

2-5. MULTIDIMENSIONAL CONDUCTION

If the description of the temperature field requires two or three space coordinates, the problem of obtaining a solution may be quite difficult and may involve the use of more sophisticated mathematical techniques. For complicated geometry and boundary conditions, it may not even be possible or practical to obtain convenient solutions. However, many problems of importance have been solved analytically. This section presents a solution of one of the first cases analyzed by Fourier in the classical treatise which established the theory of conduction heat transfer. The Langmuir equations for thick-walled boxes are also discussed.

Method of Separation of Variables. Many mathematical techniques have been used to obtain solutions for particular heat-conduction cases in which partial differential equations arise. In recent analyses the technique of separation of variables and the method of the Laplace transform have been most widely used. In the present section a solution is obtained for a two-dimensional conduction region employing the method of separation of variables. The method of separation of variables proceeds from the assumption that the solution of the problem (i.e., the temperature distribution) is a function of x, y, and z which is separable into a product of functions, each involving only x, y, or z. That is,

$$t = f(x,y,z) = X(x)Y(y)Z(z)$$

$$= XYZ \tag{2-30}$$

where X, Y, and Z are, respectively, functions only of x, y, and z. The solutions of linear equations such as the Laplace and Fourier equations have this property for many types of boundary and initial conditions.

The function $Z(z)$ is not present in the two-dimensional case considered here; t is equal to the product of $X(x)$ and $Y(y)$. This expression for t is substituted into the Laplace equation:

$$\frac{\partial^2 t}{\partial x^2} + \frac{\partial^2 t}{\partial y^2} = \frac{\partial^2 (XY)}{\partial x^2} + \frac{\partial^2 (XY)}{\partial y^2} = Y\frac{d^2 X}{dx^2} + X\frac{d^2 Y}{dy^2} = 0$$

or

$$\frac{1}{X}\frac{d^2 X}{dx^2} = -\frac{1}{Y}\frac{d^2 Y}{dy^2}$$

This last equation has an interesting feature. Apparently, the left-hand side may be a function only of x and the right-hand side only of y. However, since x and y may vary independently of each other, the two sides of the equation would vary independently of each other if they were, respectively, functions of x and y. Therefore, they are not functions of x and y but are equal to the same constant, say λ^2.† Therefore,

$$\frac{d^2 X}{dx^2} - \lambda^2 X = 0 \qquad \frac{d^2 Y}{dy^2} + \lambda^2 Y = 0$$

These ordinary differential equations may be integrated. The results are

$$X = C_1 e^{i\lambda x} + C_2 e^{-i\lambda x}$$

$$Y = Ce^{\lambda y} + De^{-\lambda y}$$

Using the relation $e^{\pm i\lambda x} = \cos \lambda x \pm i \sin \lambda x$, the first relation is rewritten as

$$X = A \cos \lambda x + B \sin \lambda x$$

We have as a solution, therefore,

$$t = XY = (A \cos \lambda x + B \sin \lambda x)(Ce^{\lambda y} + De^{-\lambda y}) \tag{2-31}$$

This result is now applied to a particular problem.

---

† A constant $-\lambda^2$ is equally acceptable. The two cases are capable of satisfying different boundary conditions.

Conduction in a Strip. Consider the conduction region shown in Fig. 2-6 which occupies the region $0 \leq x \leq L$ and $y \geq 0$. It is assumed that there is no conduction in the z direction; this condition would result, for example, if the region was a strip insulated on the top and bottom surfaces. The solution will be presented for the case of the two edges maintained at t_o and the bottom maintained at a temperature t_1. The differential equation and boundary conditions are written in terms of temperature excess θ as

$$\frac{\partial^2 \theta}{\partial x^2} + \frac{\partial^2 \theta}{\partial y^2} = 0 \qquad (2\text{-}32)$$

1. $x = 0$ and $x = L$ \qquad $\theta = t - t_o = 0$

2. $y = 0, 0 < x < L$ \qquad $\theta_1 = t_1 - t_o$

3. $\lim_{y \to \infty} \theta = 0$

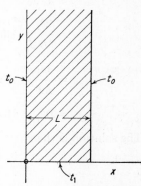

FIG. 2-6. Semi-infinite strip.

Equation (2-31) is a solution of Eq. (2-32). The boundary conditions are used to determine A, B, C, and D in Eq. (2-31). Boundary condition 1 shows that $A = 0$ because $\cos 0° = 1$ and θ must be zero at $x = 0$. Similarly, $\sin \lambda x$ must be zero at $x = L$; that is, λL must be an integral multiple of π:

$$\lambda L = n\pi \qquad \lambda = \frac{n\pi}{L}$$

Condition 3 shows that $C = 0$. Equation (2-31) is now

$$\theta = BD e^{-(n\pi/L)y} \sin\left(\frac{n\pi}{L} x\right) = E e^{-(n\pi/L)y} \sin\left(\frac{n\pi}{L} x\right)$$

This expression satisfies the differential equation for any integral value of n equal to or greater than zero, and the result for zero is trivial. Therefore, since the sum of any two solutions of a linear differential equation is also a solution, the general solution is obtained by summing all possible solutions:

$$\theta = \sum_{n=1}^{\infty} E_n e^{-(n\pi/L)y} \sin\left(\frac{n\pi}{L} x\right)$$

Boundary condition 2 is used to evaluate the E_n. At $y = 0$ the expression is

$$\theta_1 = \sum_{n=1}^{\infty} E_n \sin\left(\frac{n\pi}{L} x\right) \qquad 0 < x < L$$

This is recognized as the Fourier sine series expansion of a constant θ_1 in the interval 0 to L. The constants E_n are the Fourier coefficients for such an expansion and are given by

$$E_n = \frac{2}{L} \int_0^L \theta_1 \sin\left(\frac{n\pi}{L}x\right) dx$$

$$= \frac{2\theta_1}{L} \int_0^L \sin\left(\frac{n\pi}{L}x\right) dx = -\frac{2\theta_1}{L}\left(\frac{L}{n\pi}\right) \cos\left(\frac{n\pi}{L}x\right)\Big|_0^L$$

$$= \frac{4\theta_1}{n\pi} \qquad \text{for } n = 1, 3, 5, \ldots$$

$$= 0 \qquad \text{for } n = 2, 4, 6, \ldots$$

The solution is then

$$\theta = \frac{4\theta_1}{\pi} \sum_{n=1,3,5}^{\infty} \frac{e^{-(n\pi/L)y}}{n} \sin\left(\frac{n\pi}{L}x\right)$$

This may be written in closed form as

$$\theta = \frac{2\theta_1}{\pi} \arctan \frac{\sin\left[(\pi/L)x\right]}{\sinh\left[(\pi/L)y\right]} \qquad (2\text{-}33)$$

where

$$\sinh\left(\frac{\pi}{L}y\right) = \tfrac{1}{2}(e^{(\pi/L)y} - e^{-(\pi/L)y})$$

The nature of the solution may be visualized by noting that isothermals are given by

$$\frac{\sin\left[(\pi/L)x\right]}{\sinh\left[(\pi/L)y\right]} = \tan\left(\frac{\pi}{2}\frac{\theta}{\theta_1}\right) = \text{constant} = C$$

$$\sin\left(\frac{\pi}{L}x\right) = \frac{C}{2}(e^{(\pi/L)y} - e^{-(\pi/L)y})$$

The isothermals are plotted in Fig. 2-7 for various values of θ/θ_1.

The multidimensional case considered here is one of the simplest. Many solutions have been obtained for more complicated circumstances. Carslaw and Jaeger (1959) and Jakob (1949) give comprehensive summaries of these results.

Langmuir's Equations. Thick-walled boxes, right-rectangular parallele-pipeds, are often encountered, and analytic solutions are not available. Langmuir et al. (1913) presented relations, based upon measurements with electrical analogues, which permit the calculation of the heat-conduction rate through the walls of rectangular-sided boxes of various configurations. Such analogue methods are discussed in detail in Chap. 13.

The Langmuir relations apply to boxes whose walls are of uniform thickness L. For a given geometry, the heat-transfer rate is proportional to the thermal conductivity and to the temperature difference and is inversely

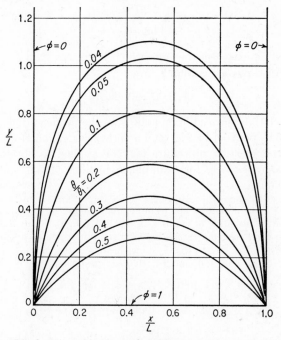

Fig. 2-7.   The location of isothermals in the conduction region of Fig. 2-6.

proportional to the wall thickness L. An effective area A_e, which is a function of geometry, is defined in the following equality:

$$q = \frac{A_e k}{L}(t_1 - t_2) \tag{2-34}$$

Langmuir determined the relations between A_e and the parallelepiped geometry. In the following relations, A_1 and A_2 are the inside and outside surface areas, and l_i is the length of an inside edge (there are three different values of l_i in a given example). Four cases are considered:

Case 1.   All l_i less than $2L$ and greater than $L/5$:

$$A_e = A_1 + 0.54L\Sigma y + 1.2L^2 \tag{2-35}$$

where Σy is the sum of the lengths of the 12 inside edges.

Case 2.   One of the l_i less than $L/5$:

$$A_e = A_1 + 0.465L\Sigma y + 0.35L^2 \tag{2-36}$$

where Σy is the sum of the edges which are greater than $L/5$.

Case 3.   Two of the l_i less than $L/5$:

$$A_e = \frac{2.78Ll_{\max}}{\log (A_2/A_1)} \tag{2-37}$$

where $l_{\max}$ is the length of the edge which is greater than $L/5$.

Case 4.   All three l_i less than $L/5$:

$$A_e = 0.79\sqrt{A_1 A_2} \tag{2-38}$$

The first relation is based upon adding to the inside surface an edge correction of $0.54L$ per foot of edge and a corner correction of $0.15L^2$ for each corner.   This correction procedure may be applied to obtain expressions for additional cases [see, for example, Schneider (1955) and Jakob and Hawkins (1957)].

Example 2-4.   A small pottery kiln of inside dimensions 2 by 2 by 3 ft has 1-ft-thick walls, floor, and ceiling made of firebrick ($k = 0.9$ Btu/hr ft °F).   In steady state, the inside and outside surface temperatures are 1300 and 110°F, and we wish to estimate the kilowatt requirement for the electric resistance heaters in the kiln.

Since $L = 1$ ft, the l_i are 1, 1, and 2 ft, and case 1 applies.

$$A_1 = 2 \times 1 + 4 \times 2 = 10 \text{ ft}^2 \qquad \Sigma y = 4 \times 1 + 4 \times 1 + 4 \times 2 = 16 \text{ ft}$$

$$A_e = 10 + 0.54 \times 1 \times 16 + 1.2 \times 1 = 19.84 \text{ ft}^2$$

$$q = \frac{19.84 \times 0.9 \times 1190}{1} = 21{,}200 \text{ Btu/hr, or } 6.23 \text{ kw}$$

2-6. NUMERICAL METHODS IN STEADY-STATE CONDUCTION

The preceding sections of this chapter consider techniques which are used in analyzing various steady-state conduction circumstances.   The analysis is relatively simple in one-dimensional cases.   In multidimensional circumstances considerable mathematical difficulty arises, and with complicated boundary conditions, a useful solution may not be obtainable.

In order to circumvent the mathematical difficulty, various numerical methods have been developed which may be used to obtain approximate solutions.   For steady-state conduction, the "numerical method" is the technique whereby the temperatures at a network of points are determined from the equations which relate them.   One widely used technique, called the "relaxation method," was developed by Southwell and coworkers.   The method was adapted to the approximate determination of stresses in complicated structures. Stresses are assumed for all members in a structure. The amount by which the sum of stresses differs from zero at any junction point is made up for by a "constraining" support. The proper stresses result when these constraints for all junction points are "relaxed" to essentially zero by a numerical technique.

Emmons (1943) applied these ideas to the solution of steady and unsteady heat-conduction problems. In numerous subsequent publications new techniques and calculation procedures were introduced. See Dusinberre (1949) for a summary of heat-transfer techniques and Allen (1954) for general steady-state methods. The present section considers the various equations which apply to numerical solutions of steady-state conduction and demonstrates the application of the relaxation technique. Section 3-5 is devoted to the application of numerical methods to unsteady-state problem solution, and problems with more complicated boundary conditions are considered in Sec. 11-7.

The Finite-difference Equation. The equations which govern numerical solutions are more easily understood if the analytical and numerical methods are contrasted. For an analytical solution, the differential equation, which is valid for every point in the conduction region, is solved for the temperature distribution throughout the region. The numerical method uses an algebraic equation, which applies to only a network of points in the conduction region, to estimate the temperature at these points. These are different types of results and are used differently.

Since most one-dimensional steady conduction problems are readily solved analytically, the techniques of numerical methods are developed for multidimensional conduction (in isotropic materials having uniform thermal conductivity). The Poisson equation, which is the general equation, is replaced by its equivalent "finite-difference" form, which in turn governs the numerical calculations. This finite-difference form is developed for the network point o in Fig. 2-8a. The Poisson equation is

$$\frac{\partial^2 t}{\partial x^2} + \frac{\partial^2 t}{\partial y^2} + \frac{\partial^2 t}{\partial z^2} + \frac{q'''}{k} = 0 \qquad (2\text{-}5)$$

The second derivatives are estimated in terms of the six temperatures to which t_o is directly related.

Consider, as shown in Fig. 2-8b, the function $u = f(v)$. The first derivative at point b is estimated as the change in u divided by the change in v:

$$\frac{du}{dv} \approx \frac{\Delta u_1 + \Delta u_2}{2\,\Delta v} = \frac{u_c - u_a}{2\,\Delta v} \qquad (2\text{-}39)$$

The first term of the error equation for this estimate is of the order of $(\Delta v)^3$ times the third derivative of u with respect to v.

An estimate of the second derivative at b is obtained by estimating the first derivative in each of the two intervals, 1 and 2, and dividing their difference by the distance between the two points where these estimates apply, that is, at the centers of the two intervals:

$$\frac{d^2 u}{dv^2} \approx \frac{\Delta u_2/\Delta v - \Delta u_1/\Delta v}{\Delta v} = \frac{\Delta u_2 - \Delta u_1}{(\Delta v)^2}$$

$$= \frac{(u_c - u_b) - (u_b - u_a)}{(\Delta v)^2} = \frac{u_a + u_c - 2u_b}{(\Delta v)^2} \tag{2-40}$$

The first term in the error equation for this estimate is of the order of $(\Delta v)^4$ times the fourth derivative. These error considerations show the desirability of using small intervals in estimating.

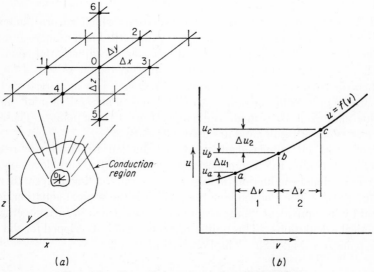

FIG. 2-8.   Network for numerical-method analysis.

The above estimate of a second derivative is used to replace the derivatives in Eq. (2-5). The curve in Fig. 2-8b can be looked upon, for example, as the trace of t versus x at constant y and z. From Fig. 2-8a, values of u_a, u_b, and u_c become t_1, t_o, and t_3, and Δv becomes Δx. Therefore,

$$\frac{\partial^2 t}{\partial x^2} \approx \frac{(t_3 - t_o)/\Delta x - (t_o - t_1)/\Delta x}{\Delta x} = \frac{t_1 + t_3 - 2t_o}{(\Delta x)^2} \tag{2-41}$$

This argument is applied to directions y and z in turn. Equation (2-5) may be replaced by the following finite-difference estimate, where q_o''' is the generation rate at point o.

$$\frac{t_1 + t_3 - 2t_o}{(\Delta x)^2} + \frac{t_2 + t_4 - 2t_o}{(\Delta y)^2} + \frac{t_5 + t_6 - 2t_o}{(\Delta z)^2} + \frac{q_o'''}{k} = 0 \qquad (2\text{-}42)$$

If $\Delta x = \Delta y = \Delta z$,

$$t_1 + t_2 + t_3 + t_4 + t_5 + t_6 - 6t_o + \frac{q_o'''(\Delta x)^2}{k} = 0 \qquad (2\text{-}43)$$

For two-dimensional conduction regions the equation becomes

$$t_1 + t_2 + t_3 + t_4 - 4t_o + \frac{q_o'''(\Delta x)^2}{k} = 0 \qquad (2\text{-}44)$$

The Relaxation Method. The finite-difference equation is the basis of the numerical method. The equation applies to every network point and establishes a relation between the temperature at any point and the temperatures at the surrounding points. That is, the equation expresses the temperature at every point in terms of its surrounding temperatures. Since, in any given problem, one such equation may be written for each network point, there are as many equations as unknown temperatures. The solution of this system of equations is the estimate of the temperature distribution.

The principal difficulty in the use of the numerical method arises in the solution of the system of equations. Typically the number of grid points is too large for an exact solution of these equations. We recall that the number of operations in obtaining a solution to n equations of this type is proportional to n^3. Therefore, approximate answers are obtained by various numerical procedures carried out in various ways. The relaxation method discussed here is one of these numerical procedures and is demonstrated in a scheme suitable for rapid hand calculation. Many different procedures have been used for machine calculations. These are not considered here. The reader is referred to books concerned with such computational techniques.

In the relaxation procedure, the temperatures at the grid points are guessed. These guesses do not, in general, satisfy the finite-difference equations for the network points. That is, the left-hand side in Eq. (2-43) [or (2-44)] does not sum to zero. The amount of this sum at any point is termed the "residual," R, at that point. For example, in three dimensions,

$$t_1 + \cdots + t_6 - 6t_o + \frac{q_o'''(\Delta x)^2}{k} = R_o \qquad (2\text{-}45)$$

Each point has its residual, and the solution is approached by reducing the residuals toward zero by altering the temperatures in the network. The smaller and more randomly distributed the residuals are, the more accurate the estimate of the solution.

Several observations about the behavior of residuals may be made from Eq. (2-45). For three-dimensional processes an increase in the temperature at a point reduces the residual at the point by 6° and increases the residual at adjacent points by 1°. If a network point is on a plane or line of symmetry, changes of temperatures at adjacent points may require special procedures with respect to residuals. The generation term may be zero, and if not zero, it may depend upon temperature t_o or upon location.

The numerical method will be demonstrated by an example. Consider a 2- by 2-ft metal duct insulated ($k = 0.1$ Btu/hr ft °F) as shown in Fig. 2-9a. The temperature distribution and heat loss per unit length will be found for inside and outside insulation temperatures of 1100 and 100°F. The accuracy of the results is higher with smaller grid sizes, and this effect will be demonstrated by comparing the results for grid sizes of $\sqrt{2}$, $\sqrt{2}/2$, and $\sqrt{2}/4$ ft.

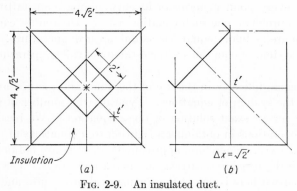

FIG. 2-9. An insulated duct.

The solution need not be carried out for the whole region. The smallest representative portion is the part between adjacent planes of symmetry. That is one-eighth of the cross section for this geometry. For $\Delta x = \Delta y$ and $q_o''' = 0$, the residual equation is

$$t_1 + t_2 + t_3 + t_4 - 4t_o = R_o$$

With $\Delta x = \sqrt{2}$ ft, there is only one unknown temperature, t', and this may be found directly:

$$1100 + 1100 + 100 + 100 - 4t' = 0$$

$$t' = 600°F$$

Halving the grid size produces six network points of unknown temperature. The temperatures are guessed by using the previous result and estimating the positions of the isothermals (see Fig. 2-10a). In order to

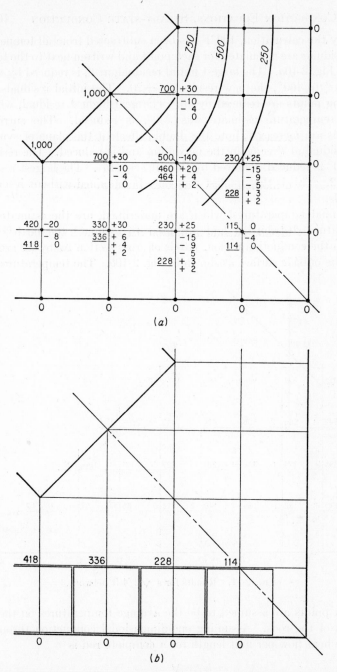

FIG. 2-10. The relaxation method applied to the geometry of Fig. 2-9. (a) $\Delta x = \sqrt{2}/2$, relaxation procedure. (b) Rods for heat-flow calculation.

simplify the calculation, 100°F has been subtracted from all temperatures. The residuals are calculated for each point and written next to the temperature in Fig. 2-10a. The largest initial residual, at t', is reduced by overcorrecting t' to 460°; the new residual is +20. The initial residuals at surrounding points are reduced by 40. The next-highest residual, where the initial temperature estimate was 330°, is reduced. The surrounding residuals are increased; note the double effect at the plane of symmetry. The residual at t' is again the maximum and is reduced. The residual at $t = 230°$ is reduced, followed by that at $t = 115°$. The largest residual is now +2. This is the smallest that may be obtained without resorting to decimals.

The final temperatures, which are underlined, are the estimate of the temperature distribution and are used to estimate the heat-flow rate through the conduction region. Rods of cross section Δx by Δx are placed along the outside surface as shown in Fig. 2-10b. The temperatures at the

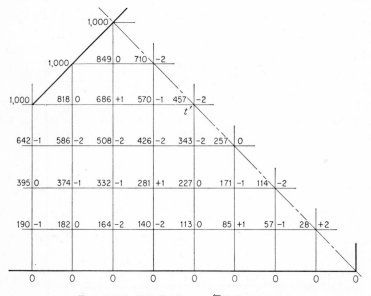

FIG. 2-11.   Results for a $\sqrt{2}/4$-ft network.

network points are assumed to be the average temperatures on the inside surfaces of the rods. Assuming one-dimensional conduction through the rod, the heat flow per unit length for a complete rod is

$$\frac{k \, \Delta x \, \Delta t}{\Delta x} = k \, \Delta t$$

The total heat flow per unit length is the sum through all rods, times 8 for the whole region. Note that a $\frac{1}{2}$ appears for the half rod at the plane of symmetry.

$$\frac{q}{L} = 8k[\tfrac{1}{2}(418 - 0) + (336 - 0)$$
$$+ (228 - 0) + (114 - 0)]$$
$$= 710 \text{ Btu/hr ft}$$

The heat-flow estimate for the $\sqrt{2}$-ft grid, Fig. 2-9b, is

$$\frac{q}{L} = 8k[\tfrac{1}{2}(1000 - 0) + (500 - 0)]$$
$$= 800 \text{ Btu/hr ft}$$

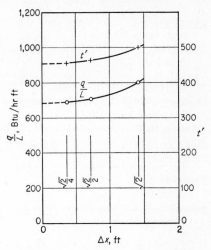

FIG. 2-12.   Dependence of temperature distribution and heat-transfer rate upon network size.

Better estimates of the temperature distribution and heat flow may be obtained by using an even smaller grid. The resulting distribution for $\Delta x = \sqrt{2}/4$ ft is shown in Fig. 2-11. The heat-flow estimate is 690 Btu/hr ft. This distribution and heat-flow rate may be verified by the reader. Comparison of t' and the heat-flow rate for the various solutions shows a large change in the first halving of the grid size and a small change in the second. These trends are clearer in Fig. 2-12. The extrapolation to a Δx of zero is an estimate of the exact solution.

NOTATION

c	specific heat
k	thermal conductivity
q''	heat flux
q'''	energy-generation rate per unit volume
t	temperature
α	thermal diffusivity
β	temperature coefficient of electrical resistivity
γ	gamma-ray attenuation coefficient
θ	temperature excess
ρ	density of mass
τ	time
ϕ	a ratio of two temperature excesses

REFERENCES

Allen, D. N. de G.: "Relaxation Methods," McGraw-Hill Book Company, Inc., New York, 1954.
Carslaw, H. S., and J. C. Jaeger: "Conduction of Heat in Solids," 2d ed., Oxford University Press, New York, 1959.
Dusinberre, G. M.: "Numerical Analysis of Heat Flow," McGraw-Hill Book Company, Inc., New York, 1949.
Emmons, H. W.: *Trans. ASME*, vol. 65, p. 607, 1943.
Jakob, M.: "Heat Transfer," vol. 1, John Wiley & Sons, Inc., New York, 1949.
——— and G. A. Hawkins: "Elements of Heat Transfer," 2d ed., John Wiley & Sons, Inc., New York, 1957.
Langmuir, I., E. Q. Adams, and F. S. Meikle: *Trans. Am. Electrochem. Soc.*, vol. 24, p. 53, 1913.
Schneider, P. J.: "Conduction Heat Transfer," Addison-Wesley Publishing Company, Reading, Mass., 1955.

PROBLEMS

1. Using the relations between cartesian and cylindrical coordinates, derive Eq. (2-6) from Eq. (2-3).

2. Using cylindrical coordinates, show that the steady-state differential equation for a distributed source in a material of uniform conductivity, where temperature is a function only of radius, is

$$\frac{d^2t}{dr^2} + \frac{1}{r}\frac{dt}{dr} + \frac{q'''}{k} = 0$$

3. For the conditions of Prob. 2, show that, if k is variable, the differential equation is

$$\frac{1}{r}\frac{d}{dr}\left(rk\frac{dt}{dr}\right) + q''' = 0$$

4. A round rod of radius b has the following initial temperature distribution:

$$t = A[8b^4 + (x^4 + y^4) - 3b^2(x^2 + y^2)]$$

At zero time, find in what portion of the rod cross section the temperature is decreasing with time.

5. Compare the heat fluxes which would result from a 10°F temperature difference across 1-in. layers of steel, concrete, sand, mahogany, and felt.

6. A wall is constructed of a 6-in. layer of concrete with a 1-in. layer of lime plaster on the inside and a 2-in. limestone facing on the outside.

a. Find the conductance of each layer per unit area and, for steady-state conduction, the ratio of the temperature differences across the plaster and limestone facing to that across the concrete.

b. For a total temperature difference of 30°F across the wall, find each of the temperature differences and the heat flux.

7. A $\frac{3}{4}$-in. schedule 80 steel pipe has inside and outside surface temperatures of 200 and 160°F. Find the heat-flow rate per unit pipe length and the flux per unit inside area and per unit outside area.

8. Consider a long tube of inside and outside diameters a and b with a uniform thermal conductivity. Under what conditions is the following expression for heat flow per unit tube length accurate within 4 per cent?

$$\frac{q}{L} = \frac{2ak}{a-b}(t_1 - t_2)$$

9. The two surfaces of a 4- by 6-ft plate 2 in. thick are at 140 and 100°F. Find the total heat-flow rate if the thermal conductivity has the following dependence upon t, in typical units:

$$k = 3.2(1 + 0.005t + 1.2 \times 10^{-4}t^2)$$

10. A lake surface is covered by a 3-in. layer of ice on a day when the air temperature is 10°F. A thermocouple embedded near the upper surface of the ice layer indicates a temperature of 24°F. Assuming steady-state conduction in the ice and no liquid cooling, find the heat loss from the lake per acre of surface. What is the conductance of the ice layer?

11. Consider a cylindrical element of inside and outside diameters a and b with the inside and outside temperature levels t_1 and t_2. For a linear variation of k with t,

$$k = k_o(1 + \beta t)$$

show that Eq. (2-12) is correct if k is replaced by its average value.

12. A wall of thickness L is made of a material whose thermal conductivity varies with temperature as follows: $k = k_o t^2$.

a. Find an expression for the steady heat conduction through the wall per unit area, that is, q'', if the two surfaces are maintained at t_1 and t_2.

b. If we wish to write q'' as the product of the temperature difference and a mean thermal conductivity divided by L, at what temperature must this conductivity be calculated so that such an equation will give the right result?

c. Sketch the temperature distribution for $t_1 > t_2$.

13a. For a plate of thickness L having surface temperatures of t_1 and t_2 and a linear variation of k with t, that is,

$$k = k_o (1 + \beta t)$$

find the expression for the temperature distribution.

b. For a concrete slab 8 in. thick having $t_1 = 100°F$, $t_2 = 50°F$, $k_o = 1.05$ Btu/hr ft °F, and $\beta = 0.01$ °F^{-1}, compute the heat flux and plot the actual temperature distribution and the distribution that would apply for a uniform k, equal to the average value.

14. A copper rod $\frac{1}{4}$ in. in diameter and 3 ft long runs between two large bus bars. The rod is insulated on its lateral surface against the flow of heat and electric current. The bus bars will be at 60°F. What is the maximum current the rod may carry if its temperature is not to exceed 300°F at any point? Assume that the electrical resistivity of copper is constant at 1.72×10^{-6} ohm cm.

15. A small dam, which may be idealized as an extensive plate 4 ft thick, is to be completely poured in a short period of time. The hydration of the concrete results in the equivalent of a distributed source of constant strength 7 Btu/hr ft^3. If both dam surfaces are at 60°F, find the maximum temperature to which the concrete will be subjected, assuming a simple conduction process in steady state. $k = 0.7$ Btu/hr ft °F.

16. For a plate of thickness L having a distributed source of uniform strength q''' and equal surface temperatures t_o, derive an expression from Poisson's equation for the maximum temperature in the plate. Find an expression for $(t - t_o)/(t_m - t_o)$, where t_m is the maximum temperature in the plate.

17. An electrical conductor consists of a copper wire $\frac{1}{4}$ in. in diameter covered with a $\frac{1}{2}$-ft layer of an insulating material having a thermal conductivity of 0.09 Btu/hr ft °F. The conductor passes through a pool of liquid which maintains the outside surface of the insulation at essentially 60°F. If the insulation temperature is not to exceed 100°F at any point, what is the maximum current the conductor may carry? Assume the resistivity of copper constant at 1.72×10^{-6} ohm cm.

18. For the maximum permissible current in Prob. 17, what is the highest temperature level in the copper conductor?

19. One method of determining inside surface convection coefficients for fluids flowing through tubes involves supplying the heat by passing electric current through the tube wall material between two electrodes welded to the tube at different points. The outside surface is insulated, and the inside heat flux to the fluid is computed from voltage and current measurements. The outside surface temperature is measured, and from this the inside surface temperature is computed, knowing the generation rate, tube dimensions, etc.

 a. Derive the relation for the inside surface temperature in terms of the outside surface temperature and other variables for a tube of ID, OD, and length (between electrodes) of a, b, and L, respectively.

 b. Compute the inside surface temperature for a run using a 1-in. ID, a 0.120-in. wall thickness, and a 5-ft-long stainless-steel tube for which the following data were obtained: outside temperature, 1000°F; voltage difference between electrodes, 100; current, 192 amp; and $k = 10$ Btu/hr ft °F for the tube material.

20. Repeat Prob. 14 for a temperature-dependent resistivity R for copper of

$$R = R_{60°\text{F}}[1 + \beta(t - 60)]$$
$$= 1.724 \times 10^{-6}[1 + 0.0022(t - 60)] \qquad \text{ohm cm}$$

What is the upper limit of current for the conditions specified?

21. A circular rod of length L, thermal conductivity k, and cross-sectional area A has the left and right ends maintained at temperatures of t_1 and t_2, respectively. A distributed source results in a generation rate which increases linearly from zero at the left end; that is, $q''' = bx$. The lateral surface of the rod is insulated.

 a. Derive the equation for the temperature distribution in the rod.

 b. Develop the conditions under which a temperature maximum will appear between the ends of the rod. Sketch such a distribution and the resulting flux distribution.

22. The iron thermal shield of a nuclear reactor may be idealized as an infinite flat plate 5 in. thick. A neutron flux at the inner surface of 7×10^{13} cm^{-2} sec^{-1} produces a net heat release per unit volume which decreases exponentially from 6 watts/cm³ at the inside surface to half that value 1 in. from the inside surface. If both surfaces of the shield are to be maintained at 100°F, find the location of the maximum temperature in the shield and its value.

23. Consider the pressure shell of a nuclear reactor as being a large flat metal plate of thickness s. The gamma-ray heating rate within the plate per unit volume and time will vary exponentially with x, where the origin for x is at the inside face:

$$q''' = q''\gamma e^{-\gamma x}$$

The constants γ and q'' are, respectively, the absorption coefficient and the gamma-ray intensity at the inside surface.

 a. If the inside surface of the shell is adiabatic and the outside surface is maintained at t_s, find the temperature-excess distribution through the shell.

b. Calculate the heat flux at the outside shell surface due to gamma-ray absorption within the shell material.

24. For a strip of infinite length and subject to the temperature conditions of Fig. 2-6, prove that the slope of the isothermals is zero at $x = L/2$, for all θ/θ_1, and zero and infinite at $x = 0$ and L, for $\theta/\theta_1 = 0$ and $\theta/\theta_1 = 1$, respectively.

25. For the temperature distribution referred to in the preceding problem, find the equation for the adiabatic surfaces in the strip.

26. For the circumstance referred to in Prob. 24, show that the heat-flow rate across the base of the strip is infinite. Explain this result and indicate how the temperature boundary conditions adjust themselves in a practical circumstance to avoid the requirement for an infinite heat-flow rate.

27. A radioactive sample is to be stored in a protective box with 3-in.-thick walls and inside dimensions of $\frac{1}{2}$ by $\frac{1}{2}$ by 2 in. The radiation is primarily gamma radiation which is completely absorbed at the inside surface of the box wall. This energy is conducted through the walls of the box. The walls are made of regranulated cork ($k = 0.04$ Btu/hr ft °F) encased in thin metal. The outside surface of the box will be at 70°F. If the inside surface temperature may not exceed 130°F, what is the maximum permissible sample radiation rate in joules per hour?

28. A wall 2 in. thick is strengthened on the outside surface by ribs 2 in. thick and 3 in. high. The distance between ribs is 2 in. If the inside and outside temperatures are 450 and 50°F, respectively, find the heat flow through the wall per square foot of flat wall area. Use a $\frac{1}{2}$- by $\frac{1}{2}$-in. network. Compare the conductance per unit area of this wall with that of a similar wall without stiffeners. $k = 0.5$ Btu/hr ft °F.

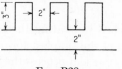

FIG. P28

29. A tall chimney made of brick ($k = 0.4$ Btu/hr ft °F) has inside and outside cross-sectional dimensions of 4 by 2 ft and 8 by 8 ft. The passage is centered. If the inside and outside surfaces are at 500 and 100°F, respectively, find the rate of heat loss per foot of chimney height. Use a 1- by 1-ft network.

30. For the passage shown in Fig. P30, compute the rate of heat transfer per unit length and the temperature distribution for surface temperatures of 500 and 100°F. Use a 6-in.-square grid. $k = 0.513$ Btu/hr ft °F.

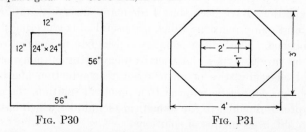

FIG. P30   FIG. P31

31. A 2- by 2-ft conduit carrying heated gases is insulated with 85 per cent magnesia, as shown in Fig. P31. The inside and outside surfaces of the insulation are at 200 and 70°F. Using a 4- by 4-in. grid, find the heat loss per foot of conduit length.

CHAPTER 3

Unsteady-state Conduction

3-1. UNSTEADY-STATE PROCESSES

The solution of unsteady-state problems is in general more difficult than the solution of steady-state problems because of the additional independent variable, time. The temperature is a function of position in the conduction region, but, in addition, this distribution changes with time. If this change in temperature is periodic, the process is called periodic. Nonperiodic processes are called transients.

The solution is approached by stating the boundary conditions (which may be time-dependent) and the simplest form of differential equation applicable. In addition, in a transient process the initial temperature distribution throughout the conduction region must be given. The problem then amounts to finding how this distribution changes with time.

The necessary differential equation depends upon the process. If the conduction region is isotropic and has a uniform thermal conductivity, Eq. (2-2) applies. If no distributed source is present, the Fourier equation applies. This is given as Eq. (2-3) for cartesian coordinates and as Eqs. (2-6) and (2-7) for cylindrical and spherical coordinates.

These equations have been solved for many unsteady-state conduction processes, and many relations which are useful in engineering design have been established. The present chapter considers a number of solutions of problems of various types and thereby demonstrates many of the techniques and characteristics of unsteady-state conduction analysis. Since many problems cannot be reduced to a practical solution, the last section of the chapter is devoted to the numerical techniques which have been developed to obtain estimates of solutions.

In this chapter several one-dimensional transient and periodic solutions are presented. The separation-of-variables technique, which applies to linear differential equations, is employed. The relevant differential equation for conduction regions of uniform thermal conductivity is the Fourier equation. In one dimension it becomes

$$\frac{\partial^2 t}{\partial x^2} = \frac{1}{\alpha} \frac{\partial t}{\partial \tau} \tag{3-1}$$

The solution to a particular problem is a function of x and τ which may in general be written as

$$t = f(x,\tau) = X(x)F(\tau) \tag{3-2}$$

Substituting this into Eq. (3-1), we have

$$FX'' = \frac{1}{\alpha} XF' \quad \text{or} \quad \frac{X''}{X} = \frac{1}{\alpha} \frac{F'}{F}$$

As a result of the definitions of X and F, the left-hand side may be a function only of x and the right-hand side only a function of τ. Since x and τ are independent, neither side is a function of x or τ and, therefore, both sides are equal to a constant λ^2 or $-\lambda^2$.

$$X'' = \pm\lambda^2 X$$

$$F' = \pm\lambda^2 F$$

The solutions of these equations are

for $+\lambda^2$ 　　　　　　　$X = C_1 e^{\lambda x} + C_2 e^{-\lambda x}$ 　　　　　　　(3-3)

for $-\lambda^2$ 　　　　　　　$X = C_3' e^{i\lambda x} + C_4' e^{-i\lambda x}$

　　　　　　　　　　　　$= C_3 \cos \lambda x + C_4 \sin \lambda x$ 　　　　　　　(3-4)

for $\pm\lambda^2$ 　　　　　　　$F = C_5 e^{\pm\alpha\lambda^2\tau}$ 　　　　　　　(3-5)

These forms anticipate the various types of problems which may be encountered. Equation (3-3) includes exponential distributions, and Eq. (3-4) permits infinite series expansions of distributions. Equation (3-5) may be an exponential decay of temperature, or a periodic case if λ^2 is an imaginary quantity.

3-2. TRANSIENT PROCESSES

In this section, several transient processes are considered. Transients are relatively common in engineering design, and an accurate knowledge of the temperature variation is often necessary. Circumstances frequently arise in which the success of the design depends upon the accurate prediction of temperature levels in some critical part. For example, in devices intended to operate only a relatively short time in high-temperature surroundings, it is not always necessary to design for the steady-state case. Substantial economies in materials, etc., may result from designing only for the conditions reached during the transient period when successful functioning is required. Rocket and missile components provide examples of such devices. Transient characteristics may also be important in devices which are intended to operate in steady state but which change from one operating level to another.

The cases considered here indicate various kinds of solutions and demonstrate transient behavior for different types of geometry and conditions.

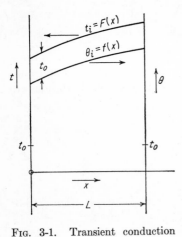

The first case is a plate with an initial temperature distribution which suddenly has both surfaces changed to some thereafter constant value t_o. The second case analyzed is that of an extensive solid, initially at t_i, whose surface temperature is suddenly changed to t_o. The third example is similar to the first. A plate initially at t_i throughout is suddenly immersed in a fluid at temperature t_e and exchanges heat with the fluid by convection. For this last temperature condition the solutions for a cylinder and for a sphere are also given. In each of these cases the boundary conditions are independent of time.

FIG. 3-1. Transient conduction in a plate.

Transient in a Plate. The first case is a plate of thickness L which is assumed of infinite extent, in order to make the process one-dimensional. The plate has an initial temperature distribution of $t_i = F(x)$ (see Fig. 3-1). At $\tau = 0$, the temperatures of the two surfaces are changed to t_o. We wish to find the subsequent distribution in the plate as a function of time. In order to simplify the analysis, the problem is stated and solved in terms of temperature excess θ. The local temperature excess is the amount by which the local temperature differs from t_o. The problem statement is

$$\frac{\partial^2 \theta}{\partial x^2} = \frac{1}{\alpha}\frac{\partial \theta}{\partial \tau}$$

at $\tau = 0$ $\qquad \theta_i = F(x) - t_o = f(x) \qquad$ for $0 \le x \le L$

for $\tau > 0$ $\qquad \theta = 0 \qquad$ at $x = 0$ and $x = L$

Since the temperature variation with time is not periodic, the separation

variable λ^2 in the equations of Sec. 3-1 is a real number. Since the temperature decays with time, the exponent of e in Eq. (3-5) must be negative.
Therefore, Eq. (3-4) is used for X, and the following is a solution:

$$\theta = C_5 e^{-\alpha\lambda^2\tau}(C_3 \cos \lambda x + C_4 \sin \lambda x) \tag{3-6}$$

Since $\theta = 0$ at $x = 0$ for all $\tau > 0$, C_3 must be zero. Similarly, $C_4 \sin \lambda x$
must be zero at $x = L$ for all $\tau > 0$. Since C_4 may not be zero, $\sin \lambda L$ must
be zero. This occurs for $\lambda L = n\pi$, where n is any integer. The solution,
then, is the sum of all particular solutions:

$$\theta = \sum_{n=1,2}^{\infty} C_n e^{-(n\pi/L)^2\alpha\tau} \sin \frac{n\pi}{L} x \tag{3-7}$$

The initial condition (at $\tau = 0$) determines the C_n:

$$\theta_i = f(x) = \sum_{n=1,2}^{\infty} C_n \sin \frac{n\pi}{L} x$$

This is a Fourier sine series expansion of $f(x)$. The coefficients are given by

$$C_n = \frac{2}{L} \int_0^L f(x') \sin \frac{n\pi}{L} x' \, dx' \tag{3-8}$$

Equations (3-7) and (3-8) constitute a solution of the problem when $f(x)$ is
specified.

If the initial temperature-excess distribution is uniform and equal to θ_i,
the constants are evaluated as

$$C_n = \frac{2\theta_i}{L} \int_0^L \sin \frac{n\pi}{L} x' \, dx' = 0 \qquad \text{for } n = 0, 2, 4, \ldots$$

$$= \frac{4\theta_i}{n\pi} \qquad \text{for } n = 1, 3, 5, \ldots$$

The solution is

$$\frac{\theta}{\theta_i} = \frac{4}{\pi} \sum_{n=1,3}^{\infty} \frac{e^{-(n\pi/L)^2\alpha\tau}}{n} \sin \frac{n\pi}{L} x \tag{3-9}$$

The heat flux may be calculated as follows:

$$q'' = -k \frac{\partial\theta}{\partial x} = -\frac{4k\theta_i}{L} \sum_{n=1,3}^{\infty} e^{-(n\pi/L)^2\alpha\tau} \cos \frac{n\pi}{L} x \tag{3-10}$$

This is seen to be zero for all τ at $x = L/2$ and infinite at $\tau = 0$ for $x = 0$.

Example 3-1.   A concrete wall 20 in. thick, initially at 60°F throughout, has its exposed faces suddenly raised to 85°F.   We wish to find the midplane temperature and surface heat flux after 6 hr.

$$\rho = 100 \text{ psf} \qquad c = 0.205 \text{ Btu/lb }°\text{F} \qquad k = 0.41 \text{ Btu/hr ft }°\text{F}$$

Equations (3-9) and (3-10) apply:

$$\alpha = \frac{k}{\rho c} = 2 \times 10^{-2} \text{ ft}^2/\text{hr} \qquad \left(\frac{\pi}{L}\right)^2 \alpha = 7.1 \times 10^{-2} \text{ hr}^{-1}$$

$$\theta_i = 60 - 85 = -25°\text{F}$$

At $x = L/2$,

$$\theta = \frac{4\theta_i}{\pi} \sum_{n=1,3}^{\infty} \frac{e^{-7.1 \times 10^{-2} n^2 \tau}}{n} \sin \frac{n\pi}{2}$$

$$= \frac{4\theta_i}{\pi} \left(e^{-0.426} - \frac{e^{-3.84}}{3} + \frac{e^{-10^{-2} n^2 \tau}}{5} - \cdots \right)$$

$$= \frac{4\theta_i}{\pi} \left(0.653 - \frac{0.0215}{3} + \cdots \right) = -20.6$$

$$\theta = t - t_i = -20.6 \qquad t = -20.6 + 85 = 64.4°\text{F}$$

$$q'' = -\frac{4k\theta_i}{L} \sum_{n=1,3}^{\infty} e^{-7.1 \times 10^{-2} n^2 \tau} \cos 0° = \frac{4k\theta_i}{L} \sum_{n=1,3}^{\infty} e^{-7.1 \times 10^{-2} n^2 \tau}$$

$$= -\frac{4k\theta_i}{L} (0.653 + 0.0215 + \cdots) = 16.1 \text{ Btu/hr ft}^2$$

Transient in a Semi-infinite Solid.   Consider next a solid which extends from $x = 0$ to infinity, as indicated in Fig. 3-2.   The temperature is initially t_i throughout, and the surface temperature is changed to t_o at $\tau = 0$. The temperature in the solid decays to t_o with time.   The statement, in terms of temperature excess, is

$$\frac{\partial^2 \theta}{\partial x^2} = \frac{1}{\alpha} \frac{\partial \theta}{\partial \tau}$$

at $\tau = 0$ $\theta = t_i - t_o = \theta_i$ for $x \geq 0$

for $\tau > 0$ $\theta = 0$ at $x = 0$

A real value of λ^2 is necessary since no periodic temperature changes arise. A negative exponent is required in Eq. (3-5); therefore, Eq. (3-4) is used:

$$\theta = C_5 e^{-\alpha \lambda^2 \tau} (C_3 \cos \lambda x + C_4 \sin \lambda x)$$

The second condition yields $C_3 = 0$, but since no condition at L is specified, all values of λ are permissible.   Summing all possibilities, we have

$$\theta = \int_0^{\infty} C_\lambda e^{-\alpha \lambda^2 \tau} \sin \lambda x \, d\lambda \tag{3-11}$$

The methods of determining C_λ from the initial condition are involved,

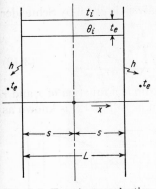

FIG. 3-4. Transient conduction in a plate with surface convection.

The arguments used in the first case in this section again lead to Eq. (3-6) as a solution for this case. The condition at $x = 0$, of a zero derivative, is first applied:

$$\frac{\partial \theta}{\partial x} = C_5 e^{-\alpha \lambda^2 \tau}(-C_3 \lambda \sin \lambda x + C_4 \lambda \cos \lambda x)$$

This is zero at $x = 0$ if $C_4 = 0$ for $\lambda \neq 0$. Therefore,

$$\theta = C e^{-\alpha \lambda^2 \tau} \cos \lambda x \qquad (3\text{-}13)$$

The last boundary condition is applied to determine the permissible values of λ:

$$\frac{\partial \theta}{\partial x} = -C e^{-\alpha \lambda^2 \tau} \lambda \sin \lambda x = -\frac{\theta}{\cos \lambda x} \lambda \sin \lambda x$$

$$\left(\frac{\partial \theta}{\partial x}\right)_s = -\lambda \theta_s \tan \lambda s = -\frac{h}{k} \theta_s$$

Therefore,

$$\cot \lambda s = \frac{k}{h} \lambda = \frac{k}{hs} p$$

or

$$\cot p = \frac{p}{hs/k} = \frac{p}{N_{\text{Bi}}} \qquad (3\text{-}14)$$

where $p = \lambda s$. The dimensionless quantity hs/k is called the Biot modulus (or number). There are an infinite number of values of p, called p_j, which satisfy Eq. (3-14), and these values depend upon the Biot modulus. That is, a different set of p_j is found for each value of the Biot modulus. The roots of Eq. (3-14) may be estimated by plotting $\cot p$ and p/N_{Bi} versus p and finding the intersections as shown in Fig. 3-5.

The first three roots are indicated for several different N_{Bi}. We note that for $N_{\text{Bi}} = \infty$, $h = \infty$, and $\theta_s = 0$. The values of p_j are $\pi/2$, $3\pi/2$, $5\pi/2$, etc. This is the first case solved in the present section, and the solution is Eq. (3-9). The present case, therefore, includes the previous one.

Various investigators have calculated the roots of Eq. (3-14) for various N_{Bi}. Jakob (1949) lists the first five roots as calculated by Groeber. Schneider (1955) lists the same information determined with higher accuracy.

Since each root of Eq. (3-14) satisfies Eq. (3-13), the complete solution

and only the result is presented here. This analysis is given
(1955) and leads to the following solution:

$$\frac{\theta}{\theta_i} = \frac{2}{\sqrt{\pi}} \int_0^{x/2\sqrt{\alpha\tau}} e^{-x'^2}\, dx' = f\left(\frac{x}{2\sqrt{\alpha\tau}}\right)$$

This result shows that the temperature-excess ratio is a functio
only in the combination $x/2\sqrt{\alpha\tau}$. The function in Eq. (3-12)

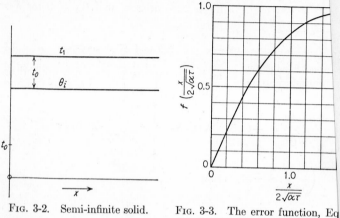

FIG. 3-2. Semi-infinite solid.   FIG. 3-3. The error function, Eq
                                       (tabulated in Table A-13).

the Gauss error integral or as the probability integral and is p
Fig. 3-3 and tabulated in Table A-13.

Transient in a Plate, with Surface Resistance. The last case c
here is a plate of thickness L, or of half thickness s, initially at t_i thr
which is suddenly, at $\tau = 0$, placed in contact with a fluid at t_e. Co
occurs between the surface and the fluid, and the rate of heat tra
unit of surface area is equal to the surface coefficient h times the d
between the surface and fluid temperatures. In Fig. 3-4 the m
which is a plane of symmetry, is placed at $x = 0$ for convenienc
solution. The statement, in terms of θ, is

$$\frac{\partial\theta^2}{\partial x^2} = \frac{1}{\alpha}\frac{\partial\theta}{\partial\tau}$$

at $\tau = 0$ $\theta = t_i - t_e = \theta_i$ for $-s \leq x \leq s$

for $\tau \geq 0$ $\dfrac{\partial\theta}{\partial x} = 0$ at $x = 0$, because of symmetry

for $\tau > 0$ $\dfrac{\partial\theta}{\partial x} = -\dfrac{h}{k}\theta$ at $x = s$

for the temperature distribution is obtained by summing over all roots for any given value of N_{Bi}:

$$\theta = \sum_{\lambda} C_{\lambda} e^{-\alpha\lambda^2\tau} \cos \lambda x = \sum_{j=1,2}^{\infty} C_j e^{-p_j(2\alpha\tau/s^2)} \cos\left(p_j \frac{x}{s}\right)$$

The constants C_j are determined from the initial condition, that is,

$$\theta_i = \sum_{j=1,2}^{\infty} C_j \cos\left(p_j \frac{x}{s}\right) = C_1 \cos\left(p_1 \frac{x}{s}\right) + C_2 \cos\left(p_2 \frac{x}{s}\right) + \cdots$$

This is an expansion of θ in an infinite series. The coefficients may be

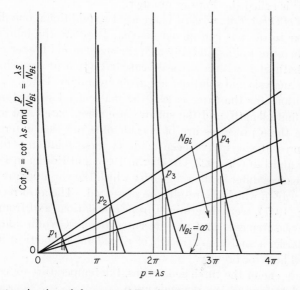

Fig. 3-5. Determination of the roots of Eq. (3-14), that is, the eigenvalues of the case of transient conduction in an infinite plate of thickness $2s$.

evaluated by multiplying both sides by $\cos[p_m(x/s)]$ and integrating from $x = 0$ to $x = s$. It can be shown that for $m \neq j$,

$$\int_0^s C_j \cos\left(p_m \frac{x}{s}\right) \cos\left(p_j \frac{x}{s}\right) dx = 0$$

The term for which $m = j$ is not equal to zero, and the equation for C_j is therefore

$$\int_0^s \theta_i \cos\left(p_j \frac{x}{s}\right) dx = \int_0^s C_j \cos^2\left(p_j \frac{x}{s}\right) dx$$

Successive values of m are taken, and each C_j is evaluated. The general result, valid for all j, is

$$C_j = \theta_i \frac{\displaystyle\int_0^s \cos\left(p_j \frac{x}{s}\right) dx}{\displaystyle\int_0^s \cos^2\left(p_j \frac{x}{s}\right) dx} = \frac{2 \sin p_j}{p_j + \sin p_j \cos p_j} \qquad (3\text{-}15)$$

The solution is

$$\frac{\theta}{\theta_i} = \sum_{j=1,2}^{\infty} \frac{2 \sin p_j \cos [p_j(x/s)]}{p_j + \sin p_j \cos p_j} e^{-p_j^2(\alpha\tau/s^2)} \qquad (3\text{-}16)$$

where $\alpha\tau/s^2$ is called the Fourier number.

Solutions of Other Transients. There are two additional one-dimensional cases similar to the one considered above. They are the infinite cylinder and the sphere (of radii s) initially at t_i throughout and immersed at $\tau = 0$ in a fluid bath at t_e with a surface heat-convection process characterized by h. The analysis and solutions are given by Jakob (1949).

The solutions for the three cases—the plate of infinite extent, the cylinder of infinite length, and the sphere—are complicated and awkward to use. Since these processes are of considerable practical interest, several graphical presentations have been made of these solutions—for example, by Gurney and Lurie in 1923, Groeber in 1925, and Heisler in 1947. These three approaches differ in the range over which the variables are considered and in the way in which the results are presented. The most recent graphs, by Heisler (1947), were determined from calculations and from electrical-analogue measurements and are presented here. Certain additional features of Heisler's analysis, although of considerable practical importance, are omitted here for brevity.

Given any one of the three geometries, the temperature-excess ratio θ/θ_i [see Eqs. (3-14) and (3-16)] depends upon

$$\frac{x}{s}, \qquad N_{\text{Bi}} = \frac{hs}{k}, \quad \text{and } N_{\text{Fo}} = \frac{\alpha\tau}{s^2}$$

The following relations therefore apply for each geometry:

$$\frac{\theta_o}{\theta_i} = f_1(N_{\text{Bi}}, N_{\text{Fo}}) \qquad \text{where } \theta_o = \theta \text{ at } \frac{x}{s} = 0 \qquad (3\text{-}17)$$

$$\frac{\theta}{\theta_i} = f_2\left(\frac{x}{s}, N_{\text{Bi}}, N_{\text{Fo}}\right) \qquad (3\text{-}18)$$

The first relation is presented in Figs. 3-6 to 3-8 for the three geometries for $0.01 \leq N_{\text{Bi}} \leq \infty$ and $0.001 \leq \theta_o/\theta_i \leq 1.0$. Analysis shows that the form of the temperature distribution in the solid depends primarily upon geometry and N_{Bi}. That is, the θ/θ_o distribution is essentially independent of N_{Fo}, which is the time variable. Therefore, for each geometry, θ/θ_o is plotted for various values of x/s (or r/s) versus $1/N_{\text{Bi}}$ in Figs. 3-9 to 3-11. Finally, in Fig. 3-12, a one-line plot of θ_o/θ_i versus $mN_{\text{Fo}}N_{\text{Bi}}$ is presented which is valid for $N_{\text{Fo}} > 0.2$ and $N_{\text{Bi}} < 0.01$, where m is a function of geometry. This last graph applies to the case of a relatively low convective coefficient h. In this circumstance the convection process on the surface governs the process. This case is solved explicitly in Sec. 11-5 in connection with thermometer temperature response. A mass of volume V and surface area A is considered with negligible internal resistance to heat transfer.

Example 3-2. We wish to consider the heating problem for a missile reentering the denser layers of the atmosphere at a very high velocity. The nose section is formed of $\frac{1}{4}$-in.-thick stainless-steel plate and is not cooled on the inside surface. As a first approximation, the effective temperature of the air surrounding the nose region is considered to be uniformly 4000°F, and the surface coefficient is estimated at 300 Btu/hr ft^2 °F. Assuming that the steel nose section is initially at a uniform temperature of 100°F, we wish to estimate the maximum permissible time in these surroundings if the maximum metal temperature is not to exceed 2000°F. Radiation effects will be neglected. This problem may be idealized as a $\frac{1}{4}$-in.-thick flat plate with one surface adiabatic and the other surface subjected to the surrounding conditions. Since the midplane of the circumstance leading to Eq. (3-16) is adiabatic, that solution applies, with $s = \frac{1}{4}$ in. The following constant values of properties are employed:

$$\rho = 490 \text{ lb/ft}^3 \qquad c = 0.106 \text{ Btu/lb °F} \qquad k = 30 \text{ Btu/hr ft °F}$$

$$\alpha = \frac{30}{0.106 \times 490} = 0.578 \text{ ft}^2/\text{hr} = 0.1606 \times 10^{-3} \text{ ft}^2/\text{sec}$$

$$\theta_i = 100 - 4000 = -3900°$$

The maximum temperature is at the surface: $\theta_s = 2000 - 4000 = -2000°$.

$$N_{\text{Bi}} = \frac{hs}{k} = \frac{300 \times 1}{30 \times 4 \times 12} = 0.208$$

From Fig. 3-9, $\theta_s/\theta_o = 0.92$,

$$\frac{\theta_o}{\theta_i} = \frac{\theta_o}{\theta_s}\frac{\theta_s}{\theta_i} = \frac{1}{0.92}\left(\frac{-2000}{-3900}\right) = 0.557$$

From Fig. 3-6, $N_{\text{Fo}} = \frac{\alpha\tau}{s^2} = 3.0$,

$$\tau = \frac{3.0s^2}{\alpha} = \frac{3.0 \times 1}{4^2 \times 12^2 \times 0.1606 \times 10^{-3}} = 8.1 \text{ sec}$$

When the exposed-surface temperature is 2000°F, the inside surface temperature is

$$\theta_o = t_o - t_e = \frac{\theta_s}{0.92} = \frac{-2000}{0.92} = -2170$$

$$t_o = 4000 - 2170 = 1830°\text{F}$$

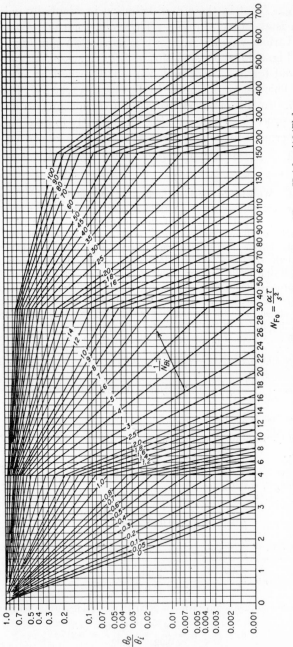

$N_{Fo} = \dfrac{\alpha \tau}{s^2}$

$\dfrac{\theta_0}{\theta_i}$

$\dfrac{1}{N_{Bi}}$

FIG. 3-6. Midplane temperature for a plate of infinite extent. [*From Heisler* (1947).]

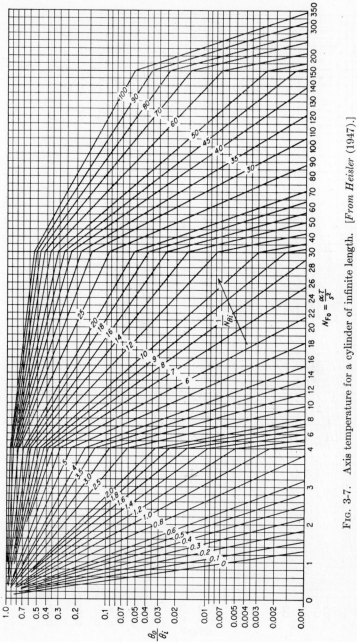

FIG. 3-7. Axis temperature for a cylinder of infinite length. [*From Heisler* (1947).]

$N_{Fo} = \dfrac{\alpha \tau}{s^2}$

$\dfrac{\theta_0}{\theta_i}$

N_{Bi}

61

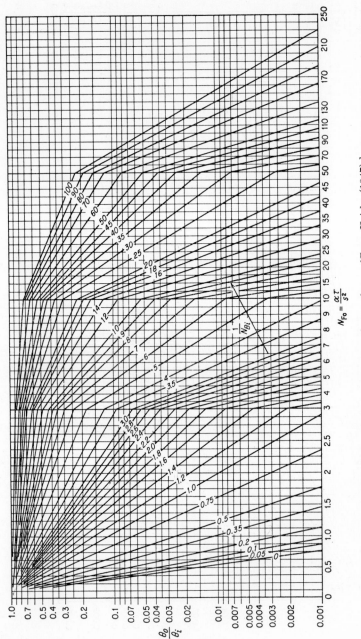

$N_{Fo} = \dfrac{\alpha \tau}{s^2}$

$\dfrac{1}{N_{Bi}}$

$\dfrac{\theta_0}{\theta_i}$

FIG. 3-8. Center temperature for a sphere. [*From Heisler* (1947).]

62

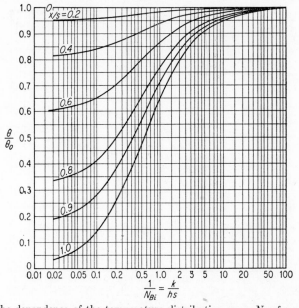

Fig. 3-9. The dependence of the temperature distribution upon N_{Bi} for a plate of infinite extent. [*From Heisler* (1947).]

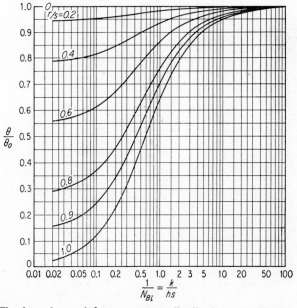

Fig. 3-10. The dependence of the temperature distribution upon N_{Bi} for a cylinder of infinite length. [*From Heisler* (1947).]

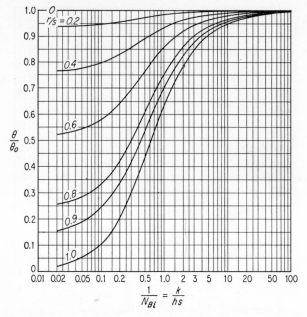

FIG. 3-11. The dependence of the temperature distribution upon N_{Bi} for a sphere. [*From Heisler* (1947).]

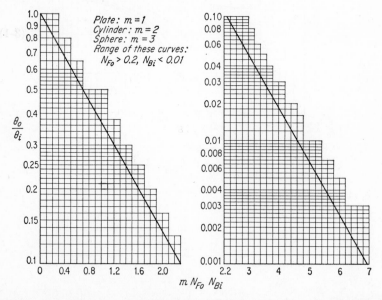

FIG. 3-12. Midpoint temperatures for plates, cylinders, and spheres for relatively high surface resistance. [*From Heisler* (1947).]

3-3. PERIODIC PROCESSES

In many circumstances heat-conduction processes are encountered in which the boundary conditions are time-dependent. The appearance of a time dependence in the boundary conditions usually complicates the solution, and several special mathematical techniques have been developed for such cases.

The present section considers two examples of one particular type of problem, the type wherein a time-dependent boundary temperature varies sinusoidally. In such a circumstance any nonperiodic temperature variations initially present are quickly dampened out, and the temperature variation becomes periodic at all points in the conduction region. Such unsteady-state problems are called periodic.

The temperature distribution is derived for a semi-infinite solid subjected to a sinusoidal temperature variation on its exposed face. The results are given for an analysis of a semi-infinite solid with its exposed face in contact with a fluid whose temperature varies sinusoidally. These two solutions indicate many interesting features of such processes.

Consider a semi-infinite solid at a uniform average temperature throughout, whose surface temperature varies sinusoidally about this average value. The statement of the problem in terms of temperature excess is

$$\frac{\partial^2 \theta}{\partial x^2} = \frac{1}{\alpha}\frac{\partial \theta}{\partial \tau} \tag{3-1}$$

$$\theta = \theta_a \cos \omega\tau \qquad \text{at } x = 0$$

The temperature variation with time is periodic, and only an imaginary exponent of e in Eq. (3-5) will produce such a solution. Since the "angular velocity" of the periodic variation must be ω, the quantity λ^2 must be

$$\lambda^2 = \frac{i\omega}{\alpha}$$

Therefore, $\lambda = \pm \sqrt{\dfrac{i\omega}{\alpha}} = \pm\sqrt{i}\,\sqrt{\dfrac{\omega}{\alpha}} = \pm(1 + i)\sqrt{\dfrac{\omega}{2\alpha}}$

Equation (3-3) may be used for X in this case, and the following is the solution:

$$\theta = Ce^{-i\omega\tau}\left\{C_1 \exp\left[\pm i(1+i)\sqrt{\frac{\omega}{2\alpha}}x\right] + C_2\exp\left[\mp i(1+i)\sqrt{\frac{\omega}{2\alpha}}x\right]\right\}$$

$$= A\exp\left[i\left(\omega\tau \mp \sqrt{\frac{\omega}{2\alpha}}x\right)\right]\exp\left(\mp\sqrt{\frac{\omega}{2\alpha}}x\right)$$

$$+ B\exp\left[-i\left(\omega\tau \pm \sqrt{\frac{\omega}{2\alpha}}x\right)\right]\exp\left(\pm\sqrt{\frac{\omega}{2\alpha}}x\right)$$

Neither the plus nor the minus sign is consistent with the requirements that temperatures must be finite, unless either A or B is zero. Setting $B = 0$,

$$\theta = \exp\left(\mp\sqrt{\frac{\omega}{2\alpha}}x\right)\left[a_1\cos\left(\omega\tau \mp \sqrt{\frac{\omega}{2\alpha}}x\right) - a_2\sin\left(\omega\tau \mp \sqrt{\frac{\omega}{2\alpha}}x\right)\right]$$

The plus sign in the exponent is inadmissible, and the boundary condition (at $x = 0$) requires that $a_2 = 0$ and $a_1 = \theta_a$. Therefore, the solution is

$$\theta = \theta_a\, e^{-(\sqrt{\omega/2\alpha})x}\cos\left(\omega\tau - \sqrt{\frac{\omega}{2\alpha}}x\right) \qquad (3\text{-}19)$$

The types of conduction processes for which this is a solution have many interesting characteristics. We note that the coefficient of the cosine term in Eq. (3-19) is the local amplitude and that this amplitude decays very fast, exponentially. This characteristic is shown in Fig. 3-13. As a result of this rapid decay of periodic disturbances, the equations for semi-infinite solids may often be applied to thick plates.

The temperature varies periodically everywhere. The distance between adjacent maxima at any instant in time, called the wavelength λ, may be found as the difference in x which will cause a difference of 2π in the argument of the cosine at any given value of τ:

$$\Delta\left(\omega\tau - \sqrt{\frac{\omega}{2\alpha}}x\right) = \sqrt{\frac{\omega}{2\alpha}}\Delta x = \sqrt{\frac{\omega}{2\alpha}}\lambda = 2\pi$$

$$\lambda = 2\pi\sqrt{\frac{2}{\alpha\omega}} \qquad (3\text{-}20)$$

The velocity of the waves may be found as the distance between local maxima divided by the period, which is the time necessary for a crest to travel this distance:

$$v = 2\pi\frac{\sqrt{2\alpha/\omega}}{2\pi/\omega} = \sqrt{2\alpha\omega} \qquad (3\text{-}21)$$

This result shows that thermal waves are propagated at a velocity which depends upon the characteristics of the material, α, and upon the frequency of the disturbance. This is in contrast with the propagation of sound in a gas for which the velocity is independent of frequency.

The heat flux at $x = 0$ is also periodic:

$$q_0'' = -k \left(\frac{\partial \theta}{\partial x}\right)_0 = k\theta_a \sqrt{\frac{\omega}{\alpha}} \left(\cos \omega \tau + \frac{\pi}{4}\right)$$

The flux and temperature variations are 45° out of phase with each other. The flux leads. We note that the net heat input per cycle is zero. Also, from the temperature-distribution function, Eq. (3-19), the time average temperature excess at all x is zero.

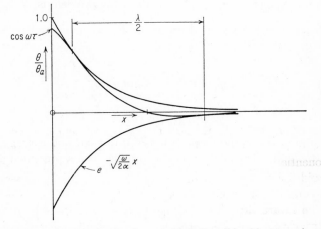

FIG. 3-13. Temperature distribution in a semi-infinite solid subject to a sinusoidal temperature fluctuation at the surface.

Example 3-3. Estimate the depth to which frost penetrates in the ground at a latitude where the yearly surface temperature variation may be considered sinusoidal, with maximum and minimum surface temperatures of 75 and 25°F. We shall compute the time lag of the temperature wave at the maximum depth of frost penetration. We shall assume that the water content of the soil is sufficiently low so that the latent heat of fusion and the change in properties may be ignored. Typical properties of soil are

$$k = 0.6 \text{ Btu/hr ft } °F \qquad c = 0.20 \text{ Btu/lb } °F \qquad \rho = 90 \text{ lb/ft}^3$$

The average temperature is everywhere 50°F. The amplitude of the variation at the surface is $\theta_a = 75 - 50 = 25°$. The amplitude where the local minimum temperature of 32°F is found is $\theta_a = 50 - 32 = 18°$. The "angular velocity" of the variation and the thermal diffusivity of soil are

$$\omega = \frac{2\pi}{365 \times 24} \text{ radians/hr} \qquad \alpha = \frac{k}{\rho c} = 0.0333 \text{ ft}^2/\text{hr}$$

From Eq. (3-19), the relation between surface and local amplitude is

$$\theta'_a = \theta_a e^{-(\sqrt{\omega/2\alpha})x}$$

and $x = \sqrt{\dfrac{2\alpha}{\omega}}\ln\dfrac{\theta_a}{\theta'_a} = \sqrt{\dfrac{2 \times 0.0333 \times 365 \times 24}{2\pi}}\ln\dfrac{25}{18} = 3.18 \text{ ft}$

The time necessary for the local minimum to be propagated from the surface to x is the distance divided by the velocity of propagation:

$$\tau = \frac{x}{\sqrt{2\alpha\omega}} = \frac{1}{\omega}\ln\frac{\theta_a}{\theta'_a} = \frac{365 \times 24}{2\pi}\ln\frac{25}{18} = 459 \text{ hr, or } 19.1 \text{ days}$$

The next case considered is a periodic process with thermal resistance at the exposed surface of the solid. If the exposed face of a semi-infinite solid is in contact with a fluid whose temperature varies sinusoidally and the convection coefficient is h, the statement of the problem is

$$\frac{\partial^2\theta}{\partial x^2} = \frac{1}{\alpha}\frac{\partial\theta}{\partial\tau}$$

at $x = 0$ $q''_0 = -k\,\dfrac{\partial\theta}{\partial x} = h(\theta - \theta_e)$

$$\theta_e = t_e - t_m = \theta_{a,e}\cos\omega\tau$$

where t_e and t_m are, respectively, the instantaneous and average temperatures of the fluid. The analysis of this problem is not presented here. The solution is

$$\theta = a\theta_{a,e}e^{-(\sqrt{\omega/2\alpha})x}\cos\left(\omega\tau - \sqrt{\frac{\omega}{2\alpha}}x - b\right) \qquad (3\text{-}22)$$

where $a = \sqrt{\dfrac{1}{2e^2 + 2e + 1}}$

$$b = \arctan\frac{e}{e+1}$$

$$e = \sqrt{\frac{k\omega\rho c}{2h^2}}$$

The factor a in Eq. (3-22) indicates the dampening of the amplitude due to the surface resistance of the convection process. A large surface resistance, that is, a small h, leads to large values of e and small values of a. There is an additional lag angle b for the temperature variation which applies even at $x = 0$.

The two foregoing cases by no means exhaust the number of analytic solutions of conduction problems with time-dependent boundary conditions. For summaries of additional periodic solutions the reader is referred to Jakob (1949). For transient conduction, Carslaw and Jaeger (1959), Jakob (1949), Schneider (1955), Boelter et al. (1948), and Ingersoll et al. (1954) present many cases.

3-4. UNSTEADY-STATE CONDUCTION WITH GENERATION AND MULTIDIMENSIONAL CASES

The present section considers several more complicated conduction cases which are of considerable practical importance but for which the techniques of the preceding sections are not directly applicable. However, it is shown that these cases may be reduced to a combination of various simpler cases either by a suitable change of variable or by a transformation of the problem. Such procedures are often employed to obtain solutions.

Transient with Distributed Generation. The first case is a transient in an extensive plate subject to a distributed source internal to the material. Such processes arise, for example, in transients in nuclear-reactor elements and shields and in induction heating.

A relatively simple particular case is that of an extensive plate initially uniformly at t_i, which, for $\tau > 0$, has its surfaces held at t_o and is subjected to a uniform generation rate q''' throughout. This case is treated by replacing the temperature variable by the sum of two new variables, each of which satisfies certain conditions of the problem.

The differential equation is written from Eq. (2-2) with the relevant initial and boundary conditions:

$$\frac{\partial^2 \theta}{\partial x^2} + \frac{q'''}{k} = \frac{1}{\alpha}\frac{\partial \theta}{\partial \tau} \qquad (3\text{-}23a)$$

at $\tau = 0$ $\theta_i = t_i - t_o$ for $0 \leq x \leq L$

for $\tau > 0$ $\theta = 0$ at $x = 0$ and $x = L$

The use of a product solution is not permissible here. The effects of the variables x and τ may not be separated in this way because of the additional term q'''/k. Instead, the variable θ is replaced by $\theta_1 + \theta_2$, where θ_1 is taken to be a function only of x. The differential equation and boundary conditions become

$$\frac{\partial^2 \theta_2}{\partial x^2} + \frac{d^2 \theta_1}{dx^2} + \frac{q'''}{k} = \frac{1}{\alpha}\frac{\partial \theta_2}{\partial \tau} \qquad (3\text{-}23b)$$

at $\tau = 0$ $\qquad$ $\theta_2 = \theta_i - \theta_1 = f(x)$ $\qquad$ for $0 \leq x \leq L$

for $\tau > 0$

$\qquad$ $\theta_1 = 0$ $\qquad$ at $x = 0$ and $x = L$

$\qquad$ $\theta_2 = 0$ $\qquad$ at $x = 0$ and $x = L$

The mathematical justification for replacing θ by θ_1 and θ_2 may be seen by noting that the sum of the statements for θ_1 and θ_2 is the statement for θ. This argument is developed on page 29 of Carslaw and Jaeger (1959).

The function θ_1 does not depend upon time and is chosen to satisfy

$$\frac{d^2\theta_1}{dx^2} + \frac{q'''}{k} = 0 \tag{3-24}$$

Integrating this equation and applying the boundary conditions on θ_1, we have

$$\theta_1 = -\frac{q'''}{k}\frac{x^2}{2} + C_1 x + C_2$$

$$C_2 = 0 \qquad C_1 = \frac{q'''L}{2k}$$

$$\theta_1 = \frac{q'''}{2k}(Lx - x^2) \tag{3-25}$$

The statement for θ_2 is

$$\frac{\partial^2\theta_2}{\partial x^2} = \frac{1}{\alpha}\frac{\partial\theta_2}{\partial\tau} \tag{3-26}$$

at $\tau = 0$ $\qquad$ $\theta_2 = \theta_i - \frac{q'''}{2k}(Lx - x^2) = f(x)$ $\qquad$ for $0 \leq x \leq L$

for $\tau > 0$ $\qquad$ $\theta_2 = 0$ $\qquad$ at $x = 0$ and $x = L$

This statement for θ_2 is identical to that for θ in Sec. 3-2 for the transient in the plate of thickness L. The solution for θ_2 is, therefore, Eq. (3-7), with constants determined as indicated in Eq. (3-8), where $f(x) = \theta_i - \theta_1$. The constants are evaluated as follows:

$$C_n = \frac{2}{L}\int_0^L \left[\theta_i - \frac{q'''}{2k}(Lx' - x'^2)\right]\sin\left(\frac{n\pi}{L}x'\right)dx'$$

$$= \frac{4\theta_i}{n\pi} - \frac{4q'''L^2}{kn^3\pi^3} \qquad \text{for } n = 1, 3, 5, \ldots$$

The solution for θ is then

$$\theta = \theta_1 + \theta_2 = \frac{q'''L^2}{2k}\left[\frac{x}{L} - \left(\frac{x}{L}\right)^2\right]$$

$$+ \frac{4}{\pi}\sum_{n=1,3}^{\infty}\frac{\theta_i - q'''L^2/kn^2\pi^2}{n}\left(e^{-(n\pi^2/L)\alpha\tau}\right)\sin\left(\frac{n\pi}{L}x\right) \quad (3\text{-}27)$$

Note that, for $q''' = 0$, this reduces to Eq. (3-9), as it must. At long times the series disappears, and the solution reduces to Eq. (2-19), with $t_1 = t_2 = t_o$, which was derived for steady-state conduction in a plate with a uniform, distributed source.

Multidimensional Transients. The unsteady-state conduction analyses discussed thus far in this chapter apply to one-dimensional circumstances. In multidimensional cases a more complicated differential equation must be satisfied. However, many such problems may be solved by combining one-dimensional solutions. The technique is demonstrated for a particular case below.

Consider a long bar of square cross section (L by L), initially at t_i throughout, whose surface temperature is suddenly changed to t_o. The problem statement is

$$\frac{\partial^2\theta}{\partial x^2} + \frac{\partial^2\theta}{\partial y^2} = \frac{1}{\alpha}\frac{\partial\theta}{\partial\tau} \quad (3\text{-}28)$$

at $\tau = 0$ $\theta = \theta_i$ for $0 \leq x \leq L$ and $0 \leq y \leq L$

for $\tau > 0$ $\theta = 0$ for $x = 0$ and $x = L$

                              for $y = 0$ and $y = L$

The differential equation and boundary conditions are satisfied by a function of x, y, and τ:

$$\theta = \theta(x,y,\tau)$$

A simpler form of solution may be shown to apply. If $\theta(x,y,\tau)$ is taken equal to a product of two functions $\theta_x(x,\tau)$ and $\theta_y(y,\tau)$, it may be shown that if both θ_x and θ_y are solutions of the one-dimensional equation (3-1), then θ is a solution of Eq. (3-28).

$$\theta(x,y,\tau) = \theta_x(x,\tau)\theta_y(y,\tau) = \theta_x\theta_y \quad (3\text{-}29)$$

Substituting Eq. (3-29) into Eq. (3-28) and rearranging, we have

$$\theta_y\frac{\partial^2\theta_x}{\partial x^2} + \theta_x\frac{\partial^2\theta_y}{\partial y^2} = \frac{\theta_y}{\alpha}\frac{\partial\theta_x}{\partial\tau} + \frac{\theta_x}{\alpha}\frac{\partial\theta_y}{\partial\tau}$$

$$\left(\frac{\partial^2\theta_x}{\partial x^2} - \frac{1}{\alpha}\frac{\partial\theta_x}{\partial\tau}\right) + \left(\frac{\partial^2\theta_y}{\partial y^2} - \frac{1}{\alpha}\frac{\partial\theta_y}{\partial\tau}\right) = 0$$

Thus, $\theta = \theta_x \theta_y$ satisfies Eq. (3-28) if θ_x and θ_y each satisfy Eq. (3-1).

The solution for θ is then the product of the solutions of the following two problems:

For θ_x
$$\frac{\partial^2 \theta_x}{\partial x^2} = \frac{1}{\alpha} \frac{\partial \theta_x}{\partial \tau}$$

at $\tau = 0$ $\qquad$ $\theta_x = \sqrt{\theta_i}$ $\qquad$ for $0 \leq x \leq L$

for $\tau > 0$ $\qquad$ $\theta_x = 0$ $\qquad$ for $x = 0$ and $x = L$

For θ_y
$$\frac{\partial^2 \theta_y}{\partial y^2} = \frac{1}{\alpha} \frac{\partial \theta_y}{\partial \tau}$$

at $\tau = 0$ $\qquad$ $\theta_y = \sqrt{\theta_i}$ $\qquad$ for $0 \leq y \leq L$

for $\tau > 0$ $\qquad$ $\theta_y = 0$ $\qquad$ for $y = 0$ and $y = L$

These combined boundary conditions amount to those of the original statement, following Eq. (3-28).

The above one-dimensional problems are solved in Sec. 3-2. Equation (3-9), with θ_i replaced by $\sqrt{\theta_i}$, is θ_x. The function for θ_y is obtained by replacing θ_i with $\sqrt{\theta_i}$ and x with y. The solution to these problems is also included in the general case of a plate with convection on its surfaces. The condition of an infinite convection coefficient repeats the previous solution and is plotted on Heisler's charts.

The above technique has been applied to compute the midpoint temperature transient for many two- and three-dimensional cases. Curves of such transients are reproduced in McAdams (1954), Schneider (1955), Eckert and Drake (1959), and Carslaw and Jaeger (1959).

3-5. NUMERICAL METHODS IN UNSTEADY-STATE CONDUCTION

Numerical methods are discussed in Sec. 2-6 and applied to steady-state conduction problems. The present section considers numerical methods applied to unsteady-state processes. Section 2-6 and the present section treat only pure conduction. Consideration of problems involving combined conduction, convection, and radiation is deferred to Chap. 11.

Numerical methods are applied to unsteady-state cases in a quite different manner from that used in steady-state cases. In steady state, the distribution is determined for a network of points by using residual equations. The temperature distribution is adjusted to the boundary conditions. In unsteady state, the problem is to find the temperature distribution as a function of time, starting from a given initial temperature distribution, or its equivalent. The numerical method determines this distribution for a network of points in the conduction region, at various subsequent times. That is, starting from the given initial distribution of temperature, a subsequent distribution is determined, and from this a subsequent one, etc. Therefore, the equations which guide the calculation at any given value of time τ are those which permit the determination of the distribution at time $\tau + \Delta\tau$ from the distribution at time τ.

The Finite-difference Equation. The calculation equations are determined by replacing the derivatives of temperature in the differential equation by estimates of their value. The result, called a "finite-difference equation," is developed below for an isotropic substance having a uniform and constant thermal conductivity. The relevant differential equation is

$$\frac{\partial^2 t}{\partial x^2} + \frac{\partial^2 t}{\partial y^2} + \frac{\partial^2 t}{\partial z^2} + \frac{q'''}{k} = \frac{1}{\alpha}\frac{\partial t}{\partial \tau} \tag{2-2}$$

Equations (2-39) and (2-40) are estimates of the first and second derivatives appearing in Eq. (2-2). The first derivative in Eq. (2-2) is of t with respect to τ, and the estimate is in terms of the previous and subsequent temperatures, that is,

$$\frac{\partial t}{\partial \tau} \approx \frac{t_c - t_a}{2\,\Delta\tau}$$

This is an inconvenient estimate. For example, in starting a solution from an initial distribution, t_b is given with t_a unspecified. Therefore, the estimate of the derivative is based entirely upon the right interval (see Fig. 2-8b) and is used throughout the calculation process. That is,

$$\frac{\partial t}{\partial \tau} \approx \frac{t_c - t_b}{\Delta\tau} \tag{3-30}$$

Taking a general conduction region, covered by a network of points, as in Fig. 2-8a, the finite-difference estimate of Eq. (2-2) is written

$$\frac{t_1 + t_3 - 2t_o}{\Delta x^2} + \frac{t_2 + t_4 - 2t_o}{\Delta y^2} + \frac{t_5 + t_6 - 2t_o}{\Delta z^2} + \frac{q_o'''}{k} = 1\frac{t_{o,\Delta\tau} - t_o}{\alpha\,\Delta\tau}$$

where $t_{o,\Delta\tau}$ is the temperature at point o after a time interval $\Delta\tau$ and q_o''' is the local energy-generation rate per unit volume and time. If $\Delta x = \Delta y = \Delta z$, we have

$$t_1 + t_2 + t_3 + t_4 + t_5 + t_6 - 6t_o + \frac{q_o'''\,\Delta x^2}{k} = \frac{\Delta x^2}{\alpha\,\Delta\tau}(t_{o,\Delta\tau} - t_o)$$

$$= M(t_{o,\Delta\tau} - t_o)$$

where
$$M = \frac{\Delta x^2}{\alpha\,\Delta\tau}$$

Solving for $t_{o,\Delta\tau}$,

$$t_{o,\Delta\tau} = \frac{1}{M}(t_1 + t_2 + t_3 + t_4 + t_5 + t_6) + \left(1 - \frac{6}{M}\right)t_o + \frac{q_o''' \, \Delta x^2}{kM} \quad (3\text{-}31)$$

The equivalent relations for the two- and one-dimensional cases are

$$t_{o,\Delta\tau} = \frac{1}{M}(t_1 + t_2 + t_3 + t_4) + \left(1 - \frac{4}{M}\right)t_o + \frac{q_o''' \, \Delta x^2}{kM} \quad (3\text{-}32)$$

$$t_{o,\Delta\tau} = \frac{1}{M}(t_1 + t_2) + \left(1 - \frac{2}{M}\right)t_o + \frac{q_o''' \, \Delta x^2}{kM} \quad (3\text{-}33)$$

Equations (3-31) to (3-33) are the equations whereby a given initial distribution may be used to calculate later distributions. The temperatures $t_1, t_2, \ldots, t_6$ are used to compute the value of t_o after a time interval $\Delta\tau$ has elapsed. This procedure is applied to every point in the network to give the complete distribution after $\Delta\tau$. The process is then repeated to give the distribution after $2\,\Delta\tau$, etc., until the desired information has been obtained.

The size of network chosen for a problem affects the accuracy of the estimate of the derivatives and, therefore, the accuracy of the result. This matter is discussed in Sec. 2-6. In general, the smaller the intervals Δx and $\Delta\tau$, the better. However, these intervals may not be chosen in a completely arbitrary manner, no matter how small the interval. Noting that the coefficients of the temperatures in Eqs. (3-31) to (3-33) indicate the magnitude of the effect of the various temperatures upon $t_{o,\Delta\tau}$, we must conclude that none of these coefficients may be negative. A negative coefficient would mean that a high temperature at point o or in its vicinity would produce a low subsequent temperature at point o. Therefore, a coefficient of zero is the minimum acceptable value. In order for the coefficient of t_o to be equal to or greater than zero,

$$M \geq 2 \quad \text{for one-dimensional cases}$$

$$M \geq 4 \quad \text{for two-dimensional cases}$$

$$M \geq 6 \quad \text{for three-dimensional cases}$$

Therefore, a choice of network spacing Δx fixes a maximum permissible value for the time interval $\Delta\tau$.

Calculation of a Transient. The foregoing equations are the basis of the numerical techniques for unsteady-state problems and may be adapted for hand or machine calculation or for graphical procedures. The first

application will be for a one-dimensional transient for $q''' = 0$ and with
the value of M chosen to permit the simplest procedure. The minimum
value of 2 is chosen for M, and the proper equation (3-33) becomes

$$t_{o,\Delta\tau} = \frac{t_1 + t_2}{2} \qquad\qquad (3\text{-}34)$$

This very simple result amounts to the statement that the subsequent temperature at point o is the average of the preceding temperatures at the
adjacent points. This result is the basis of what is often called the Schmidt-
Binder method and is applied below to a particular transient case.

A 12-in.-thick wall, initially at 50°F throughout, suddenly has one face
raised to 114°F; the other face is perfectly insulated. The thermal diffusivity of the material is 0.250 ft^2/hr. We shall estimate the temperature
distribution after 45 min. A Δx of 3 in. results in the network shown in
Fig. 3-14a. The adiabatic condition on the right face may be met by placing another wall of equal thickness on the right side, which is subjected to

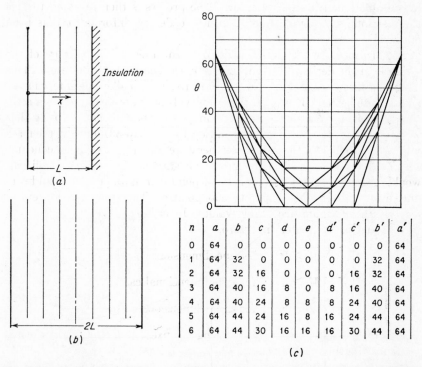

n	a	b	c	d	e	d'	c'	b'	a'
0	64	0	0	0	0	0	0	0	64
1	64	32	0	0	0	0	0	32	64
2	64	32	16	0	0	0	16	32	64
3	64	40	16	8	0	8	16	40	64
4	64	40	24	8	8	8	24	40	64
5	64	44	24	16	8	16	24	44	64
6	64	44	30	16	16	16	30	44	64

(c)

FIG. 3-14. Application of the numerical method to a transient in a wall. (a) Wall.
(b) Equivalent circumstance. (c) Graphical and numerical calculation of the temperature distribution.

the same temperature conditions. For $\Delta x = 3$ in. the time interval for $M = 2$ is

$$M = 2 = \frac{\Delta x^2}{\alpha \, \Delta \tau} \qquad \Delta \tau = \frac{\Delta x^2}{2\alpha} = \frac{3^2}{12^2 \times 2 \times 0.25} = \frac{1}{8} \, \text{hr}$$

Therefore, six time intervals, or repetitions, will be required to reach 45 min.

The calculation is carried out both graphically and numerically in Fig. 3-14c in terms of $\theta = t - t_i$. Each temperature is the average of the previous ones at adjacent points.

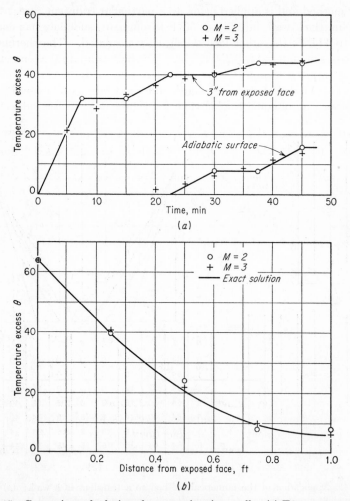

FIG. 3-15. Comparison of solutions for a transient in a wall. (a) Temperature changes with time. (b) Temperature distribution at 30 min.

In the list of values in Fig. 3-14c we note certain of the unreasonable results of having chosen $M = 2$. The temperature at any given point increases and then remains constant over an interval before increasing again. This is seen in Fig. 3-15a, where θ_b and θ_e are plotted against time. The points are joined by lines. The heat flux would show the same characteristic. The temperature distributions at various times, in Fig. 3-14c, are also unrealistic.

Greatly improved results may be obtained by an almost equally simple calculation technique if $M = 3$ is used. Equation (3-33) then indicates that the subsequent temperature at point o is the average of the preceding temperatures at all three points:

$$t_{o,\Delta\tau} = \frac{t_o + t_1 + t_2}{3} \tag{3-35}$$

The time interval is now

$$\Delta\tau = \frac{\Delta x^2}{3\alpha} = \frac{1}{12}\,\mathrm{hr}$$

Eight steps are required. These are carried out in Table 3-1, and the results are plotted in Fig. 3-15, along with the results of the exact solution

TABLE 3-1. NUMERICAL SOLUTION OF A ONE-DIMENSIONAL TRANSIENT

n	a	b	c	d	e	d'	c'	b'	a'
0	64	0	0	0	0	0	0	0	64
1	64	21.3	0	0	0	0	0	21.3	64
2	64	28.4	7.1	0	0	0	7.1	28.4	64
3	64	33.2	11.8	2.4	0	2.4	11.8	33.2	64
4	64	36.3	15.8	4.7	1.6	4.7	15.8	36.3	64
5	64	38.7	18.9	7.4	3.7	7.4	18.9	38.7	64
6	64	40.5	21.7	10.0	6.2	10.0	21.7	40.5	64
7	64	42.1	24.1	12.6	8.7	12.6	24.1	42.1	64
8	64	43.4	26.3	15.1	11.3	15.1	26.3	43.4	64
9	64	44.6	28.3	17.6	13.8	17.6	28.3	44.6	64

from Eq. (3-9).* The change from $M = 2$ to $M = 3$ made a great improvement in the form of the temperature results, and the results for $M = 3$ are in closer agreement with the exact solution.

The preceding problem was merely used as an example of the application of the numerical method. The exact solution of the same problem is given

* Note that the boundary conditions which led to that solution were somewhat different but may be converted to a form identical with the present problem if L is taken equal to 24 in.

in Sec. 3-2. However, multidimensional unsteady-state problems are often encountered for which exact solutions are not known, are too difficult to obtain, or are too complicated for convenient use. In such circumstances the numerical method is a simple and convenient substitute. A two-dimensional problem is solved in the following example. In Sec. 11-7, the numerical techniques required for more complicated circumstances are considered, and references are given for other discussions of this topic.

Example 3-4. A long concrete structural element of 6- by 8-in. cross section is initially at 60°F throughout. Two adjacent faces of the element are suddenly raised to 160°F; the other two faces are insulated. We wish to find the time required for the minimum temperature in the element to rise to 90°F and for the average temperature of the element material to become 120°F. A Δx of 2 in. will be used.

For an M of 4 (the minimum permissible value) and $\alpha = 0.0158$ ft^2/hr, the time interval is

$$M = 4 = \frac{\Delta x^2}{\alpha \, \Delta \tau} \qquad \Delta \tau = 0.11 \text{ hr}$$

The calculation equation is

$$t_{o,\Delta\tau} = \frac{t_1 + t_2 + t_3 + t_4}{4}$$

The adiabatic-surface condition may be simulated by considering instead an element of four times the size with symmetric boundary conditions. The calculations in terms of temperature excess, where $\theta_s = 100$°F, are carried out in the accompanying table to the extent necessary. Only the interior points are listed. The letters in parentheses at the head of each column are an indication of which temperatures are averaged for that point. The last column is the average temperature computed by weighting the temperature at each point according to the area it represents. For example, t_g represents Δx^2, and t_m represents $\Delta x^2/4$.

n	a (ssbc)	b (ascf)	c (bsdg)	d (csch)	e (safi)	f (ebgj)	g (fchk)	h (gdgm)	i (seie)	j (ifkf)	k (jgmg)	m (khkh)	τ, hr	$\bar{\theta}$
0	0	0	0	0	0	0	0	0	0	0	0	0	0	
1	50	25	25	25	25	0	0	0	25	0	0	0	0.11	
2	62.5	44	44	37.5	44	12.5	6.5	6.5	37.5	6.5	0	0	0.22	
3	72	55	47	48.5	53	25	16	12.5	48.5	15.5	5	3	0.33	
4	77	61	55	51.5	61	35	22.5	21	55.5	26	12	9	0.44	60.2
5	...	...	...	58	...	...	31	26	...	24.5	20	16.5	0.55	
6	...	...	...	...	...	...	...	34	...	...	28	23	0.66	
7	...	...	...	...	...	...	...	...	...	...	...	31	0.77	

An average temperature excess of 60.2°F is achieved at 0.44 hr. The minimum temperature is at point m. Using a linear interpolation, $\theta = 30$°F is achieved at 0.76 hr.

NOTATION

M	the reciprocal of the grid Fourier number
N_{Bi}	Biot number
N_{Fo}	Fourier number
p_j	eigenvalues, solutions of Eq. (3-14)
q''	heat flux
q'''	energy-generation rate per unit volume
t	temperature
α	thermal diffusivity
θ	temperature excess
τ	time
ω	frequency of a periodic process, radians per unit time

REFERENCES

Boelter, L. M. K., V. H. Cherry, H. A. Johnson, and R. C. Martinelli: "Heat Transfer Notes," University of California Press, Berkeley, Calif., 1948.

Carslaw, H. S., and J. C. Jaeger: "Conduction of Heat in Solids," 2d ed., Oxford University Press, New York, 1959.

Eckert, E. R. G., and R. M. Drake, Jr.: "Heat and Mass Transfer," 2d ed., McGraw-Hill Book Company, Inc., New York, 1959.

Heisler, M. P.: *Trans. ASME*, vol. 69, p. 227, 1947.

Ingersoll, L. R., O. J. Zobel, and A. C. Ingersoll: "Heat Conduction," The University of Wisconsin Press, Madison, Wis., 1954.

Jakob, M.: "Heat Transfer," vol. 1, John Wiley & Sons, Inc., New York, 1949.

McAdams, W. H.: "Heat Transmission," 3d ed., McGraw-Hill Book Company, Inc., New York, 1954.

Schneider, P. J.: "Conduction Heat Transfer," Addison-Wesley Publishing Company, Reading, Mass., 1955.

PROBLEMS

1. Wide oak boards 1 in. thick are to be heated from an initial temperature of 60°F by hanging them in a steam-filled enclosure.

a. If the steam condenses at 212°F on both surfaces and if the surface resistance is neglected, plot the board midplane temperature vs. time in minutes.

b. Estimate the time necessary for the midplane temperature to reach 180°F.

$$\rho = 42 \text{ lb/ft}^3 \qquad c = 0.33 \text{ Btu/lb °F} \qquad k = 0.105 \text{ Btu/hr ft °F}$$

2. A plate of thickness δ initially has a sinusoidal temperature distribution varying from t_o at $x = 0$ to t_m at $x = \delta/2$ and to t_o at $x = \delta$. If the surfaces of the plate are held at t_o for subsequent times, find the temperature distribution as a function of time.

3a. For a plate of thickness D, initially at t_a throughout, with surface temperatures suddenly changed to t_b and thereafter maintained constant, derive an expression relating average plate temperature to time.

b. For the circumstance of Prob. 1, estimate the time necessary for the average temperature of the oak board to reach 180°F.

4. A plate initially has a linear temperature distribution, from t_a at the left face to t_b at the right face. The two surface temperatures are suddenly changed to a thereafter constant value t_o. Find the relation between temperature, location within the plate material, and time.

5. A concrete wall 2 ft thick is initially at 60°F throughout. Its surface temperatures are suddenly changed to 100°F. From the appropriate solution and from the solution for a semi-infinite solid, plot temperature versus $\ln \tau$ for a point 3 in. from one surface and for the midpoint. If a 1 per cent error in temperature change is permissible, find the conditions under which the proper solution may be replaced by the simpler semi-infinite solid solution.

$$k = 1.00 \text{ Btu/hr ft °F} \qquad \alpha = 0.016 \text{ ft}^2/\text{hr}$$

6. A semi-infinite solid initially at a uniform temperature t_a is suddenly subjected to a thereafter constant surface temperature t_b.

a. Find the velocity at which the temperature disturbance is propagated through the solid.

b. If the velocity of propagation is defined as the propagation rate of a temperature increase of 1 per cent of $(t_b - t_a)$, determine the velocity of propagation.

7. Steel plates being thinned by rolling must be periodically reheated. How long must plates 3 in. thick which are at 1000°F be kept in a furnace surrounding at 1600°F, $h = 30$ Btu/hr ft^2 °F, in order to reach a minimum metal temperature of 1300°F?

$$k = 20 \text{ Btu/hr ft °F} \qquad \alpha = 0.37 \text{ ft}^2/\text{hr}$$

8. For the conditions of Prob. 7, how long must the plate be kept in the furnace in order to reach an average metal temperature of 1300°F?

9. Long cylindrical billets of brass 4 in. in diameter are heated to 1100°F preparatory to an extrusion process. If the minimum metal temperature permissible for extrusion is 900°F, how long may these billets stand in 80°F surroundings if the surface coefficient is 15 Btu/hr ft^2 °F? What is the temperature at the cylinder axis at this time?

$$\alpha = 1.1 \text{ ft}^2/\text{hr} \qquad k = 65 \text{ Btu/hr ft °F}$$

10. Large ingots of steel may be approximated by a flat plate 2 ft thick. The temperature of the ingot material is uniform at 600°F when the molds are removed. In surroundings at 60°F, how long will it take for the maximum metal temperature to reach 150°F if the convection coefficient is 12 Btu/hr ft^2 °F? What is the surface temperature at this time?

$$k = 20 \text{ Btu/hr ft °F} \qquad \alpha = 0.37 \text{ ft}^2/\text{hr}$$

11. The nozzle of a rocket engine is made of a ceramic material $\frac{1}{2}$ in. thick having the properties listed below. The combustion gases passing through the nozzle are at a temperature of 3400°F, and a convection coefficient of 1000 Btu/hr ft^2 °F is expected. If the maximum operating temperature the ceramic material will stand is 2700°F, find the permissible engine operating period if the initial material temperature is 100°F. The nozzle wall may be approximated by a flat plate with the unexposed surface being considered adiabatic.

$$k = 10.3 \text{ Btu/hr ft °F} \qquad \rho = 150 \text{ lb/ft}^3 \qquad c = 0.2 \text{ Btu/lb °F}$$

12. A 4-in. concrete building wall is insulated on its inside surface. The wall is in equilibrium with the outside air at 60°F when the outside-air temperature changes to 40°F in a very short period. Find the temperatures of the outside and inside surfaces of the wall after 2 hr and after 6 hr. Estimate the amount of heat transferred to the air per square foot of wall area during the first 2 hr. The convection coefficient is 2.0 Btu/hr ft^2 °F.

$$k = 1.1 \text{ Btu/hr ft °F} \qquad \alpha = 0.017 \text{ ft}^2/\text{hr}$$

13. Steel wire is being reduced to a diameter of 0.10 in. by being drawn through a die at 3 fps. Because of cold working in the die, the wire temperature is raised to 300°F. Neglecting axial conduction inside the wire, find the distance along the wire from the die at which the wire temperature has been reduced to 180°F if the surface loses heat to the surroundings at 60°F according to a convection coefficient of 7.0 Btu/hr ft^2 °F.

14. Steel spheres of 3 in. diameter, heated to 500°F, are to be cooled by immersion in an oil bath which is at 100°F. A convection coefficient of 70 Btu/hr ft^2 °F is expected. Find the surface and midpoint temperatures for times of 10 sec and 1 and 6 min after immersion.

$$k = 19 \text{ Btu/hr ft °F} \qquad \alpha = 0.35 \text{ ft}^2/\text{hr}$$

15. In one frequently used method of measuring convection coefficients for fluid flow normal to cylindrical elements, heated cylinders at a high temperature are placed in the flow, and the temperature variation with time is measured at the cylinder axis. A long, solid copper cylinder of 1 in. diameter, with an initially uniform temperature of 160°F, is to be placed in streams of fluids with temperatures of 60°F. Find the convection coefficient for two circumstances, the axis temperature reduced to 110°F in 2.5 min and in 4.0 sec. Discuss the differences between these two transient processes.

$$\rho = 558 \text{ lb/ft}^3 \qquad c = 0.092 \text{ Btu/lb °F} \qquad k = 224 \text{ Btu/hr ft °F}$$

16. For a semi-infinite solid subjected to a sinusoidal variation in surface temperature:

a. Find the depth at which the amplitude of the temperature variation is one-*a*th the surface value.

b. What are the relative damping rates of two disturbances, one being twice the frequency of the other?

c. Prove that the net heat flow per cycle is zero at all locations.

d. Derive an expression for the heat input at $x = 0$ for the positive half of the heat-flow cycle.

e. Prove that the instantaneous maxima of the temperature distribution through the solid are not the local temperature maxima.

17. Find the conditions under which the solution for a sinusoidal temperature variation at the surface of an infinite solid may be applied to a plate of thickness L subject to a temperature variation on one of its two surfaces, the other surface being adiabatic, if temperature fluctuations of the order of 1 per cent in the semi-infinite solid solution may be considered negligible.

18. At a certain latitude the daily variation in the surface temperature of the earth may be considered sinusoidal with 4°F amplitude. Find the wavelength and the velocity of the wave. At what depth will the amplitude be reduced to 1°F?

$$\alpha = 0.012 \text{ ft}^2/\text{hr}$$

19. The thermal diffusivity of soil is to be estimated at a given location by noting the propagation characteristics of the diurnal temperature variation of the soil. This variation is assumed to be due to a sinusoidal variation in surface temperature. Thermocouple junctions are buried at depths of 1 and 4 in.

a. If the temperature maximum at 1 in. depth occurs at 3 P.M. and the maximum at 4 in. depth at 5 P.M., compute the thermal diffusivity of the soil.

b. If the maximum and minimum temperatures at 1 in. are 63 and 57°F, find the amplitude of the variation at the surface and the average surface temperature.

20. A semi-infinite solid is subjected to a surface temperature variation $t_s = \theta_a \sin \omega\tau + t_o$. Derive the expression relating temperature to location and time.

21. Repeat Prob. 17 for the case of a sinusoidal variation of the temperature of a fluid in contact with the surface of the semi-infinite solid.

22. A thick concrete retaining wall is in contact with air on its exposed side. If, during a particular season, the daily temperature variation of the air may be assumed to be sinusoidal over the range 50 to 80°F, find the variation in temperature at the surface of the wall and at a point 2 in. inside the wall. The expected convection coefficient is 2.0 Btu/hr ft² °F.

$$\alpha = 0.016 \text{ ft}^2/\text{hr} \qquad k = 1.0 \text{ Btu/hr ft °F}$$

23. A plate, initially at t_i throughout, is suddenly subjected to surface temperatures of t_o and to a uniform distributed source of strength q'''.

a. Derive an expression for the heat flux at the surface for all times and determine the value of the heat flux as $\tau \to \infty$.

b. Determine the form of the transient temperature distribution and locate any maxima or minima in the distribution.

24. A long, square bar (2*s* by 2*s* in cross section), initially at t_i throughout, is suddenly immersed in a fluid at t_o. Assume that the surface resistance to heat transfer is negligible compared with the internal resistance. Plot from the Heisler charts the midpoint temperature excess (divided by $\theta_i = t_i - t_o$) vs. a dimensionless time variable. Use logarithmic coordinates.

25. Repeat Prob. 24 for a cube having sides of length 2*s*.

26. A long, square steel bar (2 by 2 in.), initially at 300°F throughout, is immersed in water at 60°F. Neglecting surface resistance, find the immersion time necessary to reduce the maximum temperature in the bar to 90°F.

27. Repeat Prob. 26 for a steel cube of size 4 by 4 by 4 in.

28. Repeat Prob. 26 using a numerical method with $M = 4$ and 5 and $\Delta x = \frac{1}{8}$ in. Compare the two solutions.

29. Repeat Prob. 1 using a numerical method with $M = 2$ and 3 and $\Delta x = \frac{1}{3}$ in.

30. A steel plate 6 in. thick is taken from a furnace with a uniform metal temperature of 800°F. The plate remains in air at 60°F for 20 min; the convection coefficient is 25 Btu/hr ft² °F. The plate is then immersed in water at 60°F, and a negligible surface resistance may be assumed. Find the necessary immersion time to reduce the maximum metal temperature to 140°F.

$$\alpha = 0.35 \text{ ft}^2/\text{hr} \qquad k = 20 \text{ Btu/hr ft °F}$$

31. A concrete wall 16 in. thick initially has a sinusoidal temperature distribution, being 60°F at both surfaces and 90°F at the center. If the left and right surfaces are suddenly changed to 40 and 70°F, respectively, find the time necessary for the maximum temperature in the wall to be reduced to 75°F, using a numerical technique. Use $M = 3$ and $\Delta x = 2$ in.

32. A metal pressure vessel of a reactor may be idealized as a flat plate 2 in. thick. In operation the inside surface of the vessel will be adiabatic, and the outside surface will be maintained at 500°F by circulating a coolant. During normal periods of reactor operation the vessel wall is subjected to an irradiation which may be approximated by a uniformly distributed source of strength 3.68×10^5 Btu/hr ft³. We are interested in the transient temperature distribution in the vessel wall as a function of time for an abrupt start-up to full normal operating level. Assume that the material is initially at 500°F throughout.

$$\alpha = 0.5 \text{ ft}^2/\text{hr} \qquad k = 40 \text{ Btu/hr ft °F}$$

a. Using a $\frac{1}{2}$-in. grid and the simplest calculation procedure, find the temperature distribution after 25 sec.

b. Find the location and magnitude of the maximum temperature in the wall after steady state has been achieved.

33. A long 1- by 1-ft square metal duct is insulated with a 6-in. layer of 85 per cent magnesia. The initial temperature of the insulation is 60°F throughout. A high-temperature fluid suddenly begins flowing through the duct, changing the temperature of the inside surface of the insulation to a thereafter constant temperature of 460°F. The outside surface temperature remains constant at 60°F. Use a 2-in. grid.

a. Determine the temperature distribution and heat-transfer rate after steady state has been achieved.

b. For the transient process plot the heat-loss rate from the outside surface vs. time, from the beginning of the process until 80 per cent of the steady-state value has been achieved.

$$\rho = 10 \text{ lb/ft}^3 \qquad c = 0.2 \text{ Btu/lb °F}$$

CHAPTER 4

Thermal-radiation Phenomena

4-1. THERMAL RADIATION AND EMISSIVE POWER

One of the basic mechanisms by which energy is transferred between regions of different temperature is called radiation. This mechanism is distinguished from conduction and convection by the fact that it does not depend upon the presence of an intermediate material to act as a carrier of energy. On the contrary, a radiation-transfer process between two regions is usually impeded by the presence of a material in the space between. The radiation energy-transfer process is explained as the consequence of energy-carrying electromagnetic waves. These waves are emitted by atoms and molecules of matter as the result of various changes in their energy content. The amount and characteristics of the radiant energy emitted by a quantity of material depend primarily upon the nature of the material, its microscopic arrangement, and its absolute temperature. The rate of emission of energy is assumed to be independent of the surroundings. However, the net energy-transfer rate depends upon the temperatures and spatial relationships of the various materials involved in the radiation-transfer process.

A wide variety of radiant energy-discharge processes are known. The various kinds of discharge are promoted by many means—for example, by bombardment with high-energy particles, by the occurrence of a chemical reaction, by an electric discharge, or by the incidence of relatively low energy radiation of particular wavelengths. One type of discharge process of special interest in connection with heat-transfer phenomena is that which arises as the result of the thermal motion of molecules. This type of radiant energy is called thermal radiation. Thermal radiation is composed of waves of many wavelengths and is amenable to relatively simple laws. Many of the radiation-exchange processes by which appreciable amounts of energy are transferred between surfaces are thermal in nature.

The rate of thermal radiant energy emission by a surface is directly dependent upon its absolute temperature. The relation between the energy-emission rate and the temperature is very simple if the surface is "black." A surface is called "black" if it will absorb all incident radiation. Let us denote the total rate of energy emission per unit area of black surface to the hemispherical region above it by the symbol W_b. The relation is then

$$W_b = \sigma T^4 \tag{4-1}$$

This equation is usually called the Stefan-Boltzmann law and may be derived from thermodynamic considerations or from a fundamental radiation expression developed by Planck and called the Planck law. For a clear presentation of the thermodynamic argument see Cork (1942). The constant σ is a true natural constant; it does not vary from surface to surface. Its value in English units is 0.1713×10^{-8} Btu/hr ft^2 °R if the units of W_b are chosen as Btu/hr ft^2 and the units of temperature as degrees Rankine.

4-2. THE PLANCK DISTRIBUTION LAW

The generally accepted distribution law for a black surface is the one developed by Planck:

$$W_{b,\lambda} = \frac{2\pi hc^2 \lambda^{-5}}{e^{ch/k\lambda T} - 1} \tag{4-2}$$

where λ is the wavelength, T is the absolute temperature, c is the velocity of light, and h and k are the Planck and Boltzmann constants. The constants are

$$c = 2.9979 \times 10^{10} \text{ cm/sec}$$

$$h = 6.6236 \times 10^{-27} \text{ erg/sec}$$

$$k = 1.3802 \times 10^{-16} \text{ erg/°K}$$

The symbol $W_{b,\lambda}$ denotes the monochromatic emissive power and is defined as the energy emitted per unit surface area at wavelength λ per unit wavelength interval around λ. That is, the rate of energy emission in the interval $d\lambda$ is equal to $W_{b,\lambda} \, d\lambda$.

The Planck distributions for the two temperatures 1500 and 2000°R are shown as curves a and b in Fig. 4-1.* For any temperature the distribution curve has a maximum value. The value of λ for which this maximum occurs may be found by determining $\partial W_{b,\lambda}/\partial\lambda$ from Eq. (4-2) and finding what value of λ between zero and infinity will make the derivative zero. The result is

$$\lambda = \frac{0.2898}{T} \qquad \text{or} \qquad \lambda T = 0.2898 \text{ cm °K} \tag{4-3}$$

* For another interesting method of presenting the Planck distribution see Dunkle (1954).

The Planck law of radiant energy distribution is connected to the Stefan-Boltzmann emissive power W_b by the following relation:

$$W_b = \sigma T^4 = \int_0^\infty W_{b,\lambda}\, d\lambda \qquad (4\text{-}4)$$

Evaluation of the integral, after substituting in $W_{b,\lambda}$ from Eq. (4-2), yields

$$W_b = \frac{2\pi^5 k^4}{15 c^2 h^3}\, T^4$$

Therefore, the value of σ may be computed from the other fundamental constants. The resulting value is the one given after Eq. (4-1). The value of σ has been repeatedly estimated by direct experiment, and these values are consistently somewhat higher than the one obtained by the application of Eq. (4-4).

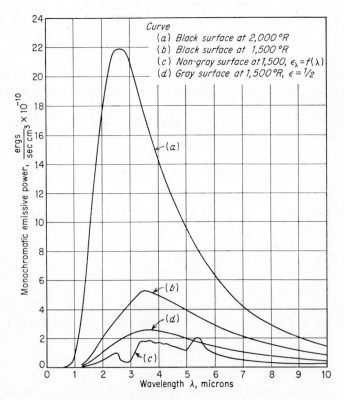

FIG. 4-1.   Monochromatic emissive power.

havior of a gray surface, compared with that of a black surface, is the same at all wavelengths. The monochromatic emissive power of a gray surface at 1500°R having an emissivity of 0.5 is shown as curve d in Fig. 4-1. In heat-transfer calculations, gray-surface characteristics are often assumed because several important classes of surfaces are approximately gray. In addition, the resulting simplicity is desirable. For most materials the assumption of grayness is unavoidable, because of the absence of information relating ϵ_λ and λ.

Just as actual surfaces do not emit as readily as black surfaces, they do not completely absorb radiant energy which falls upon them. Some of the incident energy is absorbed, some is perhaps transmitted, and the remainder is reflected. These tendencies are characterized by quantities which are defined as follows: the absorptivity α is defined as the fraction of the incident radiation which is absorbed; τ and ρ are, respectively, the fractions of the incident radiation which are transmitted and reflected. Clearly,

$$\alpha + \tau + \rho = 1 \qquad (4\text{-}8)$$

For an opaque surface, $(\alpha + \rho) = 1$, and for a black surface, $\alpha = 1$. However, no really black surfaces exist; even lampblack has an absorptivity of less than 0.95. There are many types of transmission and reflection processes; for example, reflection may be specular or diffuse.

The absorptivity, transmissivity, and reflectivity characteristics of a given surface, like its emissivity, are dependent upon the material, the conditions of the surface, and the temperature level. Further, α, τ, and ρ may be different for different wavelength intervals of the incident radiation. A result of such a dependence is that α, τ, and ρ depend upon the temperature and emission characteristics of the source of the incident radiant energy. Many examples of such behavior are known. Numerous common surfaces—for example, concrete, porcelain, and paper—have a higher absorptivity for low- than for high-frequency radiation. As a result, their total, or integrated, absorptivity is much higher for radiation emitted from a high-temperature surface. Allowance for these characteristics would introduce formidable complications into radiant exchange calculations. However, because of the scarcity of reliable information concerning the nature of these variations, α, τ, and ρ are usually assumed constant at whatever values are available.

4. KIRCHHOFF'S LAW

A useful relation between the emissivity and absorptivity of any opaque surface may be developed directly from thermodynamic considerations. Consider an enclosure with a small hole of area ΔA_a in its side. Assume

4-3. RADIATION PROPERTIES

Different substances and surfaces show various divergences
Stefan-Boltzmann and Planck laws. From considerations pr
Sec. 4-4, we shall see that W_b and $W_{b,\lambda}$ are the maximum emiss
for any given surface temperature. Actual surfaces emit and
readily and are called "nonblack." The emissive power of a
surface at temperature T to the hemispherical region above it i

$$W = \epsilon W_b = \epsilon \sigma T^4$$

where ϵ is less than 1.0 and is called the hemispherical emis
emissivity is in general a function of the material, of the con
surface, and perhaps even of the temperature of the surface.

The monochromatic emissive power of a nonblack surface
written as

$$W_\lambda = \epsilon_\lambda W_{b,\lambda} = \epsilon_\lambda \frac{2\pi h c^2 \lambda^{-5}}{e^{ch/k\lambda T} - 1}$$

where ϵ_λ is called the monochromatic hemispherical emissivit
that ϵ_λ is less than 1.0 and that ϵ_λ may be a function of the m
face condition, the temperature, and even the wavelength
chromatic emissive power of a hypothetical surface at 150(
ϵ_λ is a function of λ is shown in Fig. 4-1 as curve c.

There is clearly a relation between ϵ and ϵ_λ. We have th
pression, similar to Eq. (4-4):

$$W = \int_0^\infty W_\lambda \, d\lambda$$

From Eqs. (4-5) and (4-6), we may write

$$W = \epsilon \sigma T^4 = \int_0^\infty \epsilon_\lambda W_{b,\lambda} \, d\lambda$$

or

$$\epsilon = \frac{1}{\sigma T^4} \int_0^\infty \epsilon_\lambda W_{b,\lambda} \, d\lambda$$

One type of monochromatic-emissivity characteristic
portance because of the simplicity of the resulting relati
ϵ_λ. If ϵ_λ does not depend upon λ, then Eq. (4-7) may
follows:

$$\epsilon = \frac{1}{\sigma T^4} \int_0^\infty \epsilon_\lambda W_{b,\lambda} \, d\lambda = \frac{\epsilon_\lambda}{\sigma T^4} \int_0^\infty W_{b,\lambda} \, d\lambda = \epsilon_\lambda$$

Surfaces having this radiation characteristic are called

that the surfaces forming the enclosure are in temperature equilibrium, that is, all surfaces are at the same temperature level T. Let us imagine that a small black surface at the same temperature T and of area ΔA_b equal to ΔA_a is brought up to close the hole in the enclosure wall. If ΔA_b is small compared with the sum of all the other areas making up the enclosure, it is clear that all the energy emitted by ΔA_b, that is, $\sigma T^4 \Delta A_b$, will be absorbed by the surfaces of the enclosure directly and by repeated reflection, even though these surfaces may be poor absorbers. Therefore, practically none of $\sigma T^4 \Delta A_b$ will return to ΔA_b. Now, in order to avoid a violation of the second law of thermodynamics, the radiation coming across ΔA_a from the enclosure must equal $\sigma T^4 \Delta A_b$ and, therefore, $\sigma T^4 \Delta A_a$. Otherwise thermal equilibrium would spontaneously disappear, and energy would be flowing from a lower- to a higher-temperature region of its own accord. We see, therefore, that the hemispherical emissive power of the opening ΔA_a is equal to that of a black surface at T. Since neither the shape of the enclosure nor the location of ΔA_a was specified, it is clear that the rate of radiant energy reception per unit area on any relatively small surface is the same no matter where it is placed in the enclosure and that this intensity is σT^4.

In order to determine the relation between the emissivity and absorptivity of any arbitrary opaque surface, imagine a small specimen of area ΔA of surface temperature T to be introduced into an enclosure also at the same temperature. The rate of radiant energy emission by the surface is $\epsilon \sigma T^4 \Delta A$, from Eq. (4-5). The rate of energy reception from the enclosure surfaces is $\sigma T^4 \Delta A$, by the argument of the preceding paragraph. The amount of energy absorbed would be $\alpha \sigma T^4 \Delta A$, from the definition of α. Since thermal equilibrium may not spontaneously disappear, $\epsilon \sigma T^4 \Delta A = \alpha \sigma T^4 \Delta A$ and, therefore, $\epsilon = \alpha$. It is also true that the same relation holds for monochromatic emissivities and absorptivities, that is, $\epsilon_\lambda = \alpha_\lambda$.

The above development is important because it reduces by one the number of independent radiation characteristics of a surface. Radiation intensities may be inferred from measurements of absorption rates. A caution is necessary, however, in the interpretation of $\epsilon = \alpha$. The proof shows that the emissivity for radiant emission at a temperature T equals the absorptivity for radiation coming from a black surface at the same temperature. If the two surface temperatures are different, the emissivity of a surface may not be equal to its absorptivity for the incident radiation.

4-5. DIFFUSE RADIATION

The foregoing discussion relates to total hemispherical radiation from surfaces, that is, to the total rate of radiant energy passage across a fictitious hemispherical surface directly above the emitting surface. No regard is given to the way in which the energy is distributed over such a hemispherical surface. However, the nature of the distribution of energy in the region above an emitting surface has an important effect upon the rates of heat transfer in various geometric arrangements. For example, if the radiant emission is concentrated along the normals to a surface, there is no radiant heat transfer to surfaces not lying along these normals, even though these surfaces may themselves be radiating to the original surface.

Very early in the study of radiation phenomena the question of energy distribution was investigated. One result of these investigations was the formulation of a law of radiant energy distribution subsequently called Lambert's law. This law may be stated as follows. Consider any small radiating surface dA_1. Erect a hemisphere above this surface, using the surface as its center. The law states that the intensity of radiant energy over the surface of this hemisphere varies as the cosine of the angle between the normal to the radiating surface and the line joining the radiating surface to the point of the spherical surface. That is, if dI_o is the intensity directly above dA_1, then dI, the intensity at any other point, is $dI_o \cos \theta$, where θ is the angle between the normal and the line joining dA_1 and that point. The phrase "intensity at a point" refers to the rate of radiant energy reception per unit area on an area dA_2 at the point, the area dA_2 being arranged perpendicular to the incident radiation. We see that the Lambert intensity variation is equivalent to the assumption that the radiation from a surface in a direction other than normal occurs as if it came from an equivalent area having the same emissive power (per unit area) as the original surface. This equivalent area is obtained by projecting the original area upon a plane normal to the direction of radiation.

Black surfaces obey the Lambert law exactly. The law holds approximately for many actual radiation processes and even for reflection processes. Much everyday observation supports the law. For example, often a body of equal, high temperature on all its surfaces will produce an image through a lens system, such as that of the eye, of equal intensity over the whole image area. This means that the amount of radiation received by the lens system from any element of surface dA is proportional to the projection of dA onto a plane normal to the line joining dA and the lens system. Or, stating it in another way, the amount of radiation from dA which contributes to the image is $dA \cos \theta$ times the normal intensity from dA. Examples of images of approximately constant intensity include the sun, the elements of electric heaters, and metal and other objects in furnaces.

Lambert's law, however, has many exceptions and is therefore not actually a law. A preferable approach is to use the term "diffuse radiation" to refer to the kind of radiation processes which behave according to Lambert's law. The expression $dI = dI_o \cos \theta$ is then the basic definition of diffuse radiation from a surface dA.

In order to obtain a quantitative idea of the radiation intensity above a black or gray surface dA_1, it is necessary to relate dI_o to the hemispherical emissive power of dA_1, that is, $W_1 \, dA_1$. This is done by equating $W_1 \, dA_1$ to the rate of energy passage through the hemisphere of radius r above dA_1 with its center at dA_1. In Fig. 4-2, the intensity is constant over dA_2 when a ring is chosen as shown. Therefore,

$$dq_{dA_2} = dI_o \cos \theta \, dA_2 = dI_o \, 2\pi r^2 \sin \theta \cos \theta \, d\theta$$

and
$$W_1 \, dA_1 = \epsilon W_b \, dA_1 = \int_{A_2} dq_{dA_2} = \int_0^{\pi/2} 2\pi \, dI_o \, r^2 \sin \theta \cos \theta \, d\theta$$

$$= 2\pi \, dI_0 \, r^2 \left[\frac{\sin^2 \theta}{2} \right]_0^{\pi/2} = \pi \, dI_o \, r^2 \tag{4-9}$$

Therefore,

$$dI_o = \frac{W_1}{\pi r^2} \, dA_1 \qquad \text{or} \qquad I_o = \frac{W_1}{\pi r^2} \qquad \text{per unit area at 1} \tag{4-10}$$

$$dI = \frac{W_1}{\pi r^2} \, dA_1 \cos \theta \qquad \text{or} \qquad I = \frac{W_1}{\pi r^2} \cos \theta \qquad \text{per unit area at 1} \tag{4-11}$$

These results show that the normal intensity is $W_1/\pi r^2$ per unit area at 1 and that the intensity at $\theta = 90°$ is zero. A result of this intensity distribu-

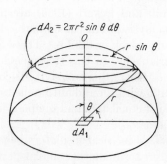

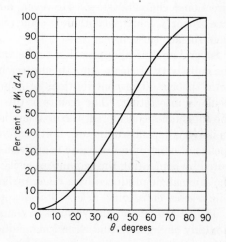

FIG. 4-2. Radiation to a hemispherical surface.

FIG. 4-3. Percentage of $W_1 \, dA_1$ encountering the hemispherical surface between 0° and θ.

tion and of geometric considerations is that half of the radiant energy emitted by dA_1 passes through the area of the hemisphere between $0°$ and $\theta = 45°$. Percentages for other values of θ may be seen in Fig. 4-3.

An alternative but equivalent way of looking at the radiation process from dA_1 to dA_2 is to compute dq_{dA_2} as due to the solid angle $d\omega$ subtended by dA_2 from an equivalent radiating area $\cos\theta\, dA_1$. This equivalent area produces a normal intensity I_n per unit area per unit solid angle equal to that of the original area dA_1 in its normal direction. A solid angle is a cone, and the unit of measure is the steradian. The number of steradians represented by a given solid angle is equal to the area subtended by the angle on a unit sphere. For example, the measure of the solid angle subtended by dA_2 at dA_1 in Fig. 4-2 is $dA_2/r^2 = 2\pi \sin\theta\, d\theta$. Clearly, I_n is equal to $I_o r^2$ or W_1/π. Therefore,

$$dq_{dA_2} = I_n\, dA_1 \cos\theta\, d\omega = I_o\, dA_1\, r^2 \cos\theta\, d\omega$$

$$= dI_o\, 2\pi r^2 \sin\theta \cos\theta\, d\theta \tag{4-12}$$

4-6. PROPERTIES OF IDEAL AND ACTUAL SURFACES

The hemispherical emissivity as defined in Eq. (4-5) is not a simple property for many surfaces. In general its value depends markedly upon the mechanical and chemical condition of the surface. Also, for many substances the value of the emissivity varies quite sharply with temperature. In addition, many substances do not emit diffusely but exhibit strong directional characteristics. However, despite the complexity of the surface property, emissivity, there is some regularity in the way its value varies from surface to surface.

Several analytical approaches to the value and nature of the variation of the emissivity of clean, smooth surfaces have been made from electromagnetic theory. The contributions of Schmidt and Eckert (1935) are particularly interesting. The results of this analysis are discussed here. For the substances considered, the emission is not black or diffuse. Therefore, emissivity depends upon an additional variable θ. In this treatment one speaks of emissivities at various angles as ϵ_θ, where this emissivity is computed by comparing the radiant intensity at θ with the radiant intensity at the same angle produced by a black surface of equal area and temperature. The normal emissivity, at $\theta = 0$, is denoted as ϵ_0.

The results of the analysis are as follows. Electrical insulators behave similarly as a group, and electrical conductors form another similar group. The insulators generally have high normal emissivities and low emissivities at large values of θ (see Fig. 4-4 for a typical case). The assumption of diffuse radiation would be a reasonable one in this circumstance. For conductors, the normal emissivity is quite low and increases with θ as shown in Fig. 4-5.

The resulting hemispherical-emissivity values for insulators, ϵ_i, are consistently higher than the values for conductors, ϵ_m. Figure 4-6 summarizes the results. The hemispherical and normal emissivities are directly related. Normal emissivities of conductors lie between 0 and about 0.4 and of insulators between 0.4 and 1.0. The ratio of hemispherical to normal emissivity is plotted against normal emissivity. The analytical approach indicates that very low values of ϵ_m may be expected and that ϵ_m increases rather sharply and approximately linearly with temperature. A discussion of other contributions to this theory is given in Jakob (1949).

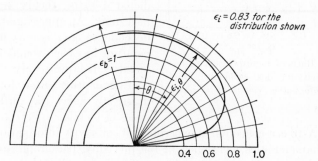

FIG. 4-4.   Emissivity distribution of an electrical insulator.

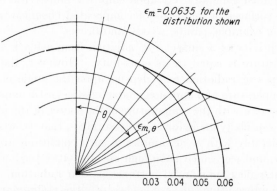

FIG. 4-5.   Emissivity distribution of an electrical conductor.

Experimental determinations of surface properties are in good agreement with theory. Although most measurements are of absorptivity, such values are simply related to emissivity by Kirchhoff's law. The relation between the hemispherical and normal emissivities is close to the theoretical prediction, and this indicates that insulators and thick oxide films are at least approximately diffuse radiators. The emissivity of many light-

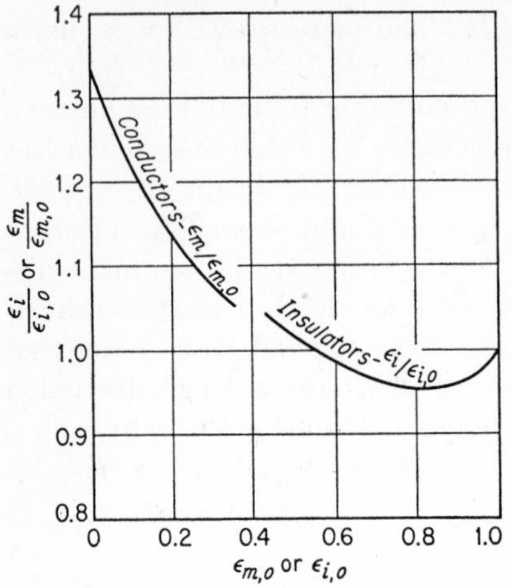

FIG. 4-6. Ratio of hemispherical to normal emissivity for ideal surfaces. [Adapted from information contained in Jakob (1949).]

colored insulators decreases with temperature, and the emissivity of many dark-colored ones increases slightly. This is in part an effect of the variation of monochromatic emissivity ϵ_λ with λ. The variation is not great, however, and average values are sufficiently accurate over a considerable temperature range. For conductors with clean, smooth surfaces the very low values predicted by the theory have been measured. An approximately linear dependence of emissivity upon temperature has been found for many metals. However, very thin oxide coatings or other surface fouling may drastically affect the surface properties of metals.

Table A-10 is a collection of experimental emissivity information. Many of the characteristics mentioned in the preceding paragraph are evident from these data. For surfaces whose nature is complicated by roughness or films, one must generally rely upon empirical emissivities. This is also true for the surfaces of materials of complicated chemical or mechanical structure—for example, paints, woods, and bricks.

The absorptivity of a surface for radiation from a black surface at the same temperature is equal to its emissivity. However, the absorptivity for other types of radiation may depend upon the angle of incidence or upon the temperature and emission characteristics of the emitting surface. The variation of α with the temperature of the source of the incident radiation may be especially great for nongray surfaces, that is, where α_λ $(= \epsilon_\lambda)$ varies considerably with λ. Examples of such conditions are paper, light paints, snow, and ice, which have high absorptivities for low-temperature radiation but reflect substantial portions of solar radiation. Some recent experimental information concerning absorptivities is summarized by Giedt (1957).

The foregoing discussion indicates the complexity of the factors which affect radiation heat-transfer rates. Unfortunately, however, it is impractical to formulate a general approach to problem solution which includes an allowance for all these effects. The resulting equations would be too complicated, and the use of the technique would require extensive property information which is not usually available. The alternative approximate analysis which is normally used is based upon certain assumptions. These include, for example, the assumptions that radiation and reflection are diffuse, that $\alpha = \epsilon$, and that the surfaces are gray. In the event that these assumptions are not reasonable, the results must be qualified.

4-7. ABSORPTION AND RADIATION CHARACTERISTICS OF GASES

Radiation phenomena in gases are quite different from those involving solids, in that gases are not opaque. Therefore, the nature of absorption and emission processes depends upon the interior state of the gas body and upon the geometry of the body. In addition, emission and absorption tendencies vary widely from gas to gas, and few, if any, gases may be called "gray," that is, $\epsilon_\lambda = f(\lambda)$. Most gases absorb and radiate only in narrow bands of wavelength.

Fortunately, many gases of technical importance are relatively transparent to thermal radiation in temperature ranges of common engineering interest, and their presence can sometimes be ignored in computing transfer rates. However, certain important gases enter appreciably into radiation exchange even at pressures and temperatures which are normal in conventional processes. The gases which have these low-temperature radiation characteristics are similar, in that the constituent molecules are nonsymmetric and are polar. These gases include O_3, CO_2, H_2O, CO, SO_2, and many hydrocarbons. Various nonpolar, symmetric molecules, such as those of O_2, N_2, and H_2, do not enter appreciably into low-temperature radiation processes.

The subject of gas radiation transfer is a special one requiring as detailed an analysis as that for radiation transfer between opaque surfaces. Therefore, only the latter kind of problem is considered here. The reader is referred to Jakob (1949) and McAdams (1954) for the techniques used in connection with gas radiation analysis.

NOTATION

c	velocity of light
h	Planck constant
I	intensity of radiation, per unit area or per unit solid angle
k	Boltzmann constant
T	absolute temperature
W	total hemispherical emissive power per unit area
W_b	total hemispherical emissive power of a "black" surface, per unit area
W_λ	monochromatic hemispherical emissive power per unit area
$W_{b,\lambda}$	monochromatic hemispherical emissive power for a "black" surface, per unit area

α	absorptivity
α_λ	monochromatic hemispherical absorptivity
ϵ	hemispherical emissivity
ϵ_i	hemispherical emissivity of an insulator
ϵ_m	hemispherical emissivity of a conductor
ϵ_θ	directional emissivity
ϵ_λ	monochromatic hemispherical emissivity
θ	angle from the normal to an element of surface
λ	wavelength
ρ	reflectivity
σ	universal constant for black-body radiation
τ	transmissivity
ω	solid angle

REFERENCES

Cork, J. M.: "Heat," 2d ed., John Wiley & Sons, Inc., New York, 1942.

Dunkle, R. V.: *Trans. ASME*, vol. 76, p. 549, 1954.

Giedt, W. H.: "Principles of Engineering Heat Transfer," D. Van Nostrand Company, Inc., Princeton, N.J., 1957.

Jakob, M.: "Heat Transfer," vol. 1, John Wiley & Sons, Inc., New York, 1949.

McAdams, W. H.: "Heat Transmission," 3d ed., McGraw-Hill Book Company, Inc., New York, 1954.

Schmidt, E., and E. Eckert: *Forsch. Gebiete Ingenieurw.*, vol. 6, p. 175, 1935.

PROBLEMS

1. Prove that the maximum value of the monochromatic emissive power given by the Planck equation occurs at a wavelength λ, in centimeters, equal to $0.2898/T$, in degrees Kelvin.

2. Determine whether or not $W_{b,\lambda}$, given by Eq. (4-2), increases with temperature for all wavelengths λ.

3. For radiation according to the Planck expression for a black surface, find the ratio of the monochromatic emissive power at 3000 and 1500°R for an ultraviolet wavelength of 10^{-5} cm and for an infrared wavelength of 10^{-2} cm.

4. For a black surface, prove that the monochromatic emissive power is zero for $\lambda = 0$ and $\lambda = \infty$ for all temperatures.

5a. For the Planck distribution, show that $W_{b,\lambda}/T^5$ is not a function of both λ and T separately but merely of their product λT.

b. Plot this function in metric units on ln-ln coordinates for the range of λT (in micron degrees Kelvin) from 1000 to 20,000.

6. Consider a differential area dA which emits diffusely and a large plane parallel to it and directly above it a distance D. Let us denote as o the point at which the normal from dA passes through the large plane. Find the intensity of the radiation per unit area of dA as a function of x, the distance from o to the arbitrary point.

7. In the geometric circumstance presented in Prob. 6, find the fraction of the total energy emitted from dA which (a) falls on a disk of radius R centered at o on the plane above dA; (b) falls on a disk as in part a, which disk subtends a unit solid angle about dA.

8. The inside surfaces of a large furnace are at 1600°F and are made of a material having an emissivity of 0.60 at this temperature. Find the radiant intensity and rate of radiant energy loss through a small, 1-in.-diameter opening in the furnace wall. Describe the nature of the radiation at the opening.

9. If the solar constant, the radiant energy per unit time and area of surface normal to the sun's rays, is taken as 429 Btu/hr ft² corrected for atmospheric absorption, estimate the effective sun surface temperature, assuming a black surface. The sun's radius is 430×10^3 miles; the diameter of the earth's orbit is 186×10^6 miles.

10. If the surface of the sun behaves as a black surface at 11,000°R, find the fraction of the sun's total energy emission which is in the visible range, 0.38 to 0.76 μ (μ denotes microns, 10^{-4} cm).

11. A furnace whose inside surface temperature is 500°F is located in a room having surface temperatures of 70°F. Find the net rate of radiant energy transfer per unit area across a small opening in the furnace wall.

12. A blackened metal sphere of 1 in. diameter is suspended in a large evacuated enclosure with blackened surfaces for experimentation with radiation quantities. If the sphere and enclosing-surface temperatures are maintained at 300 and 70°F, respectively, estimate the rate of energy loss from the sphere, neglecting convection and assuming the surface of the sphere to be black.

13. The emissivities in Table A-10 are normal values (i.e., at $\theta = 0$). Employing the results of the theory for insulators, estimate the error incurred in assuming these normal emissivities equal to hemispherical values for cuprous oxide, cast-iron plate, and paper.

14. Repeat Prob. 13 for polished silver and polished cast iron.

15. For the directional emissivity distribution shown in Fig. 4-4, draw a polar plot of the intensity variation on a hemispherical surface a unit distance from the emitting surface. The emitting surface is at a temperature of 600°R. Calculate the intensity in English units per unit area of emitting surface. Add to this plot the intensity distribution for a diffuse emitting surface having the same hemispherical emissivity.

16. A particular infrared detector is sensitive to all radiation with a wavelength less than 2 μ. If the voltage output of the detector is directly proportional to the total amount of radiation received from the radiation source in this wavelength range, find how the detector output varies with the temperature of the source of the incident radiation. Consider only the low-temperature range, that is, less than 600°R, from a black and from a gray surface.

CHAPTER 5

Energy Exchange
by Thermal Radiation

5-1. DIFFUSE RADIATION BETWEEN SURFACES

The foregoing chapter considers various aspects of the radiation characteristics of surfaces. Several relations between the rates and distribution of radiation and the various properties of surfaces are discussed. The present chapter deals with certain of the techniques which have evolved for the estimation of heat-transfer rates resulting from thermal radiation between surfaces having various geometries, radiation characteristics, and orientations with respect to one another.

The techniques discussed herein are often used in engineering calculations and are preferred because of their relative simplicity and clarity. However, the simplicity is purchased at a price. Certain assumptions are required, and some of the assumed conditions are not strictly met in many situations of practical importance. The result, then, is that the calculated results in such circumstances must be considered quite approximate and these results must be carefully interpreted. The alternative procedure is to return to the nature of the basic phenomena and to develop new techniques which do not require the questionable assumptions. This second approach is often out of the question when time or economic considerations are admitted.

The assumptions which will be made are the following. All surfaces will be considered to be either gray or black. Radiation and reflection processes will be assumed to be diffuse. Each surface will be assumed to have uniform properties over its whole extent. The absorptivity of a surface will be taken equal to its emissivity and independent of the temperature of the source of the incident radiation. Initially, all objects engaged in radiation exchange will be considered thick enough to be opaque; that is, $\tau = 0$ and, therefore, $\rho = 1 - \alpha$. The material, if any, occupying the space between radiating surfaces will be assumed neither to emit nor to absorb radiation.

The Angle Factor. Several preliminary ideas will be developed here for subsequent use. The "interception," or "angle," factor is a convenient concept. This factor is a function of the geometric relation between two surfaces which may exchange energy by diffuse radiation. The numerical value of the factor in a given circumstance is the measure of how large one surface looms in the surroundings of another. In terms of two surfaces, 1 and 2, the angle factor from surface 1 to surface 2, F_{12}, is defined as the fraction of the radiant energy emitted by surface 1 which falls directly upon 2 (i.e., is intercepted by 2). The angle factor from 2 to 1 is similarly defined merely by interchanging the roles of 1 and 2. This second angle factor will not, in general, be numerically equal to the first. However, an important and simple relation between the two values will be subsequently developed.

The definition of the angle factor clearly indicates that it is a function of the relation of at least two areas and is not generally a function of the nature of one area alone. The only exception arises when some of the radiant energy emitted from a surface may directly strike that same surface. In that case one could say that the surface "sees" itself and that the angle factor from the surface to itself is greater than zero. It is also clear from the definition that the sum of the angle factors from any surface to all of its surroundings is equal to one.

The utility of the idea of an angle factor is found in computing energy-transfer rates. If, for example, there are two surfaces A_1 and A_2 which may exchange energy by radiation, we may compute the amount of the radiant emission of surface A_1 which goes directly to A_2 as

$$q_{1\text{-}2} = F_{12}W_1A_1 \qquad (5\text{-}1)$$

where F_{12} is the angle factor from 1 to 2. The advantage in this form lies in the fact that F_{12} is a function only of geometry. It should be emphasized that more than F_{12} of W_1A_1 may get to surface A_2 if reflecting surfaces are present.

It is possible to develop a general method of determining the numerical value of angle factors. Consider surfaces A_1 and A_2 in Fig. 5-1. The problem is to develop expressions for the values of F_{12} and F_{21} in terms of the characteristics of the geometric arrangement. Consider first the angle factor dF from dA_1 to dA_2. The energy

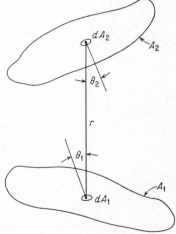

FIG. 5-1.   Determination of angle factors.

emitted by dA_1 is $W_1 \, dA_1$. The intensity of this radiation at dA_2 is $dI_1 = (W_1/\pi r^2) \, dA_1 \cos \theta_1$, from Eq. (4-11). Therefore, the amount intercepted by dA_2 is equal to dI_1 times the effective area of dA_2, that is, $\cos \theta_2 \, dA_2$.

$$dq_{dA_1\text{-}dA_2} = dI_1 \cos \theta_2 \, dA_2 = \frac{W_1 \, dA_1}{\pi r^2} \cos \theta_1 \cos \theta_2 \, dA_2 \qquad (5\text{-}2)$$

The angle factor is then

$$dF_{dA_1\text{-}dA_2} = \frac{dq_{dA_1\text{-}dA_2}}{W_1 \, dA_1} = \frac{\cos \theta_1 \cos \theta_2 \, dA_2}{\pi r^2} \qquad (5\text{-}3)$$

Similarly, for dF from dA_2 to dA_1, we have

$$dq_{dA_2\text{-}dA_1} = dI_2 \cos \theta_1 \, dA_1 = \frac{W_2 \, dA_2}{\pi r^2} \cos \theta_2 \cos \theta_1 \, dA_1 \qquad (5\text{-}4)$$

$$dF_{dA_2\text{-}dA_1} = \frac{dq_{dA_2\text{-}dA_1}}{W_2 \, dA_2} = \frac{\cos \theta_1 \cos \theta_2 \, dA_1}{\pi r^2} \qquad (5\text{-}5)$$

These expressions are valid for any choice of dA_1 and dA_2 on A_1 and A_2 as long as dA_1 and dA_2 "see" each other, that is, as long as both θ_1 and θ_2 are equal to or less than 90°. If either θ_1 or θ_2 is greater than 90°, both dF values are taken as zero, even though Eqs. (5-3) and (5-5) may assign values other than zero.

The angle factor from dA_1 to A_2, $F_{dA_1\text{-}A_2}$, is computed by summing up the values of $dF_{dA_1\text{-}dA_2}$ over all elements of A_2 seen from dA_1.

$$F_{dA_1\text{-}A_2} = \int_{A_2} dF_{dA_1\text{-}dA_2} = \int_{A_2} \frac{\cos \theta_1 \cos \theta_2 \, dA_2}{\pi r^2} \qquad (5\text{-}6)$$

Finally, the value of F_{12} is obtained by averaging $F_{dA_1\text{-}A_2}$ over A_1:

$$F_{12} = \frac{1}{A_1} \int_{A_1} F_{dA_1\text{-}A_2} \, dA_1 = \frac{1}{A_1} \int_{A_1} \left(\int_{A_2} \frac{\cos \theta_1 \cos \theta_2 \, dA_2}{\pi r^2} \right) dA_1 \quad (5\text{-}7)$$

Similarly, for the angle factors from dA_2 and A_2 to A_1, we have

$$F_{dA_2\text{-}A_1} = \int_{A_1} dF_{dA_2\text{-}dA_1} \, dA_1 = \int_{A_1} \frac{\cos \theta_1 \cos \theta_2 \, dA_1}{\pi r^2} \qquad (5\text{-}8)$$

$$F_{21} = \frac{1}{A_2} \int_{A_2} F_{dA_2\text{-}A_1} \, dA_2 = \frac{1}{A_2} \int_{A_2} \left(\int_{A_1} \frac{\cos \theta_1 \cos \theta_2 \, dA_1}{\pi r^2} \right) dA_2 \quad (5\text{-}9)$$

It is necessary to emphasize again that dA_1 and dA_2 contribute to the value of an angle factor only if they see each other. Therefore, the operations of integration are to extend only over regions for which this is true.

Example 5-1.   Find the angle factor from a small flat surface dA_1 to a disk of diameter D directly above it a distance R. dA_1 and A_2 are parallel.   Choose dA_2 as a ring of width dx.   Therefore, $dA_2 = 2\pi x\, dx$.   Note that $\theta_1 = \theta_2$ for all x.

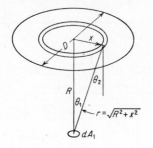

$$dF_{dA_1\text{-}dA_2} = \frac{\cos^2 \theta}{\pi r^2}\, dA_2$$

$$\cos \theta = \frac{R}{\sqrt{R^2 + x^2}} \qquad r^2 = R^2 + x^2$$

$$dF_{dA_1\text{-}dA_2} = \frac{R^2 2\pi x\, dx}{(R^2 + x^2)\pi(R^2 + x^2)} = R^2\,\frac{d(x^2)}{(R^2 + x^2)^2}$$

$$F_{dA_1\text{-}A_2} = R^2 \int_{A_2} \frac{d(x^2)}{(R^2 + x^2)^2} = R^2 \int_0^{D/2} \frac{d(x^2)}{(R^2 + x^2)^2} = -R^2\,\frac{1}{R^2 + x^2}\bigg]_0^{D/2}$$

$$= \frac{D^2}{4R^2 + D^2}$$

Note also that the value of $F_{A_2\text{-}dA_1}$ is

$$F_{A_2\text{-}dA_1} = F_{dA_1\text{-}A_2}\,\frac{dA_1}{A_2} = \frac{4D^2}{(4R^2 + D^2)\pi D^2}\, dA_1 = 0$$

The angle factor from the area dA_1' composed of both sides of dA_1, that is, $dA_1' = 2\,dA_1$, would be $\frac{1}{2}F_{dA_1\text{-}A_2}$.

The Determination of Angle Factors.   A very useful reciprocity relation is evident from the form of Eqs. (5-3) and (5-5).   It is clear that

$$dF_{dA_1\text{-}dA_2}\, dA_1 = dF_{dA_2\text{-}dA_1}\, dA_2$$

A more useful form of this relation results from Eqs. (5-7) and (5-9).   If both equations are written as double integrals and if the order of integration is changed in either one of the equations and both sides of the first equation are multiplied by A_1 and both sides of the second equation by A_2, we see that the right-hand sides of the equations are identical.   Therefore

$$F_{12}A_1 = F_{21}A_2 \qquad\qquad (5\text{-}10)$$

This demonstration of the reciprocity relation is valid only if the order of integration in Eq. (5-7) or (5-9) may be interchanged. However, the conditions under which the integrals may be so manipulated will not be

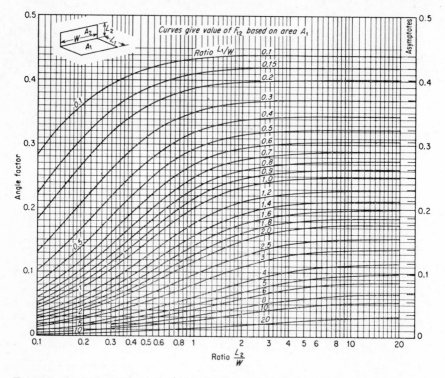

FIG. 5-2. Angle factors between perpendicular rectangular areas with a common edge. [*From Mackey et al.* (1943).]

developed, since a rigorous proof of Eq. (5-10) may be carried out more easily in another manner which shows that Eq. (5-10) is valid under all conditions for diffuse radiation.

Certain conclusions about angle factors are evident. The numerical value of the angle factor does not depend upon the emissivities of the surfaces involved. The angle-factor expressions derived above apply only for diffuse radiation, and the reciprocity relation is not generally true for non-diffuse radiation characteristics. The value of the angle factor between two surfaces does not depend in any way upon the presence of other surfaces if the other surfaces are not between the initial two. If surface 1 sees surfaces 1, 2, 3, . . ., n, it is clear that

$$F_{1\text{-}1,2,3,\ldots,n} = F_{11} + F_{12} + F_{13} + \cdots + F_{1n} \qquad (5\text{-}11)$$

If surfaces $1, 2, 3, \ldots, n$ form an enclosure, we have

$$F_{11} + F_{12} + F_{13} + \cdots + F_{1n} = 1$$
$$F_{21} + F_{22} + F_{23} + \cdots + F_{2n} = 1 \qquad (5\text{-}12)$$
$$\cdot \cdot \cdot \cdot \cdot \cdot \cdot \cdot \cdot \cdot \cdot \cdot \cdot$$
$$F_{n1} + F_{n2} + F_{n3} + \cdots + F_{nn} = 1$$

The reciprocity relation may be written between any two surfaces i and j as

$$F_{ij}A_i = F_{ji}A_j \qquad (5\text{-}13)$$

In general, if there are n surfaces, there are $\sum_{i=1}^{n-1} i = \dfrac{n(n-1)}{2}$ different reciprocity relations among the n^2 individual angle factors. If, in addition, the n surfaces form an enclosure, there are n more relations of the form of Eqs. (5-12) relating the n^2 angle factors. The result is that $n^2 - \{[n(n-1)]/2 + n\} = [n(n-1)]/2$ individual angle factors must be found

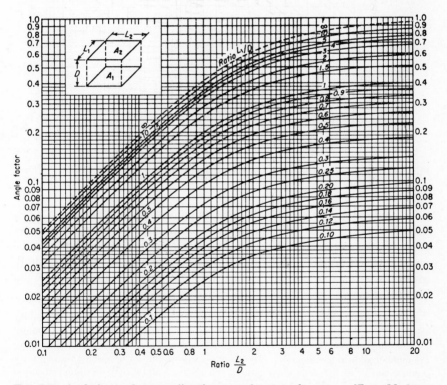

Fig. 5-3. Angle factors between directly opposed rectangular areas. [*From Mackey et al.* (1943).]

from geometric considerations. If no surface of the enclosure sees itself, we have $F_{11} = 0$, $F_{22} = 0$, etc., for n more relations. Therefore, the number of unknowns would now be $[n(n-1)]/2 - n = (n^2 - 3n)/2$. In many problems additional simplifications occur; for example, several angle factors may be known to be equal from symmetry conditions.

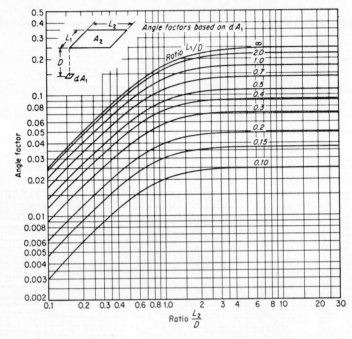

Fig. 5-4. Angle factor between a differential area and a parallel rectangle. [*From Mackey et al.* (1943).]

The determination of the numerical value of the angle factor in a given situation may be quite difficult and time-consuming if the integrations must actually be carried out. For certain geometries the calculation may be avoided by referring to charts which have been presented in various publications [see, for example, Mackey et al. (1943) and Hamilton and Morgan (1952)]. Several typical charts are reproduced in Figs. 5-2 to 5-5.

Example 5-2. As an example of the calculation of angle factors, let us determine all the significant angle factors between the walls of a rectangular room which has no openings. Let the dimensions of the room be H in height, D in depth, and W in width. The surfaces are numbered as in the diagram. There are 6 surfaces, but let us assume that surfaces 5 and 6 will be at the same temperature. Therefore, 5 and 6 may be combined into a new designation, 7. We have now only 5 individual surfaces, one of which, 7, sees itself. There are n^2, or 25, individual angle factors. There are 5 relations of the type of Eqs.

(5-12) between them and $[n(n-1)]/2 = 10$ reciprocity relations. This leaves $25 - 5 -$
$10 = 10$ factors undetermined. However, $F_{11} = F_{22} = F_{33} = F_{44} = 0$ reduces the num-

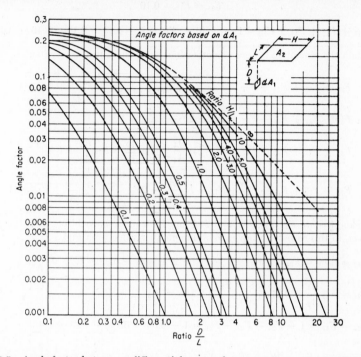

FIG. 5-5. Angle factor between a differential area and a perpendicular rectangle. [*From Mackey et al.* (1943).]

ber to 6. Consideration of the figure gives 3 more relations: $F_{43} = F_{23}$, $F_{41} = F_{21}$, and
$F_{47} = F_{27}$. The undetermined number is now only 3, and these must be found from the

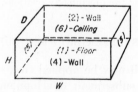

geometric relation of the areas. A relatively simple approach would be to find F_{12} and
F_{13} from Fig. 5-2 and F_{42} from Fig. 5-3. For room dimensions of $H = 8$ ft, $D = 24$ ft,
and $W = 16$ ft, we find

$$F_{12} = F_{21}\frac{A_2}{A_1} = 0.31\,\frac{8 \times 16}{24 \times 16} = 0.10$$

$$F_{13} = F_{31}\frac{A_3}{A_1} = 0.32 \times \frac{8 \times 24}{16 \times 24} = 0.16 \quad \text{and} \quad F_{42} = 0.06$$

The angle factors from 1 to 4 and 7, F_{14} and F_{17}, are found as follows:

$$F_{14} = F_{12} = 0.10$$

$$F_{17} + F_{12} + F_{14} + F_{13} = 1 \quad \text{and} \quad F_{17} = 1 - 0.10 - 0.10 - 0.16 = 0.64$$

To obtain the remaining factors, the other four sums equal to 1 are written

for 2 $\quad F_{21} + F_{23} + F_{24} + F_{27} = 1 = F_{21} + F_{32}\dfrac{A_3}{A_2} + F_{24} + F_{27}$

for 3 $\quad F_{31} + F_{32} + F_{34} + F_{37} = F_{31} + 2F_{32} + F_{37} = 1$

for 4 $\quad F_{41} + F_{42} + F_{43} + F_{47} = 1 = F_{14}\dfrac{A_1}{A_4} + F_{24}\dfrac{A_2}{A_4} + F_{32}\dfrac{A_3}{A_2} + F_{27}$

for 7 $\quad F_{71} + F_{72} + F_{73} + F_{74} + F_{77} = F_{17}\dfrac{A_1}{A_7} + 2F_{27}\dfrac{A_2}{A_7} + F_{37}\dfrac{A_3}{A_7} + F_{77} = 1$

The unknowns are F_{27}, F_{32}, F_{37}, and F_{77}, and the equations could be solved for them. However, in this case it is simpler to obtain another value from Fig. 5-2.

$$F_{32} = 0.11 = F_{34} \qquad F_{37} = 1 - F_{31} = 2F_{32} = 1 - 0.32 - 0.22 = 0.46$$

$$F_{23} = F_{32}\frac{A_3}{A_2} = 0.11 \times \frac{8 \times 24}{8 \times 16} = 0.165 = F_{43}$$

$$F_{27} = F_{47} = 1 - F_{24} - F_{23} - F_{21} = 1 - 0.06 - 0.165 - 0.31 = 0.46$$

$$F_{77} = 1 - F_{71} - 2F_{72} - F_{73} = 1 - (F_{17}A_1 + 2F_{27}A_2 + F_{37}A_3)\frac{1}{A_7}$$

$$= 1 - (0.64 \times 16 \times 24 + 2 \times 0.46 \times 8 \times 16 + 0.46 \times 8 \times 24)\frac{1}{24 \times 24}$$

$$= 0.22$$

Any other values may be found from reciprocity relations.

5-2. RATE OF ENERGY TRANSFER BETWEEN SURFACES

The foregoing ideas will now be applied to a series of arrangements of radiating surfaces. The subsequent development will rest upon the assumptions previously made and listed in Sec. 5-1. Additional assumptions will be stated as required.

Consider a surface of area A_1 and emissivity ϵ_1 at a uniform temperature T_1 (see Fig. 5-6). The rate of emission from the surface is $W_1A_1 = \epsilon_1 W_{b1}A_1$, and the net rate of heat loss from the surface will be equal to this amount if the surroundings are black and at absolute zero and if the surface does not irradiate itself. If the surface does irradiate itself, then F_{11}

of W_1A_1 will encounter A_1 again, $\epsilon_1 F_{11}$ of W_1A_1 will be absorbed, and $(1 - \epsilon_1)F_{11}$ of W_1A_1 will be reflected. Now, if it is assumed that the radiation incident upon A_1, that is, $F_{11}W_1A_1$, is uniformly distributed over A_1 and, further, that the reflection of $(1 - \epsilon_1)F_{11}W_1A_1$ is diffuse, then F_{11} may be used as the angle factor for the reflected radiation. The result is therefore that $(1 - \epsilon_1)F_{11}^2 W_1 A_1$, or $(1 - \epsilon_1)F_{11}^2$ of W_1A_1, again encounters A_1 after the first reflection. The amount of W_1A_1 absorbed is $\epsilon_1(1 - \epsilon_1)F_{11}^2$. The amount of W_1A_1 absorbed after the second reflection

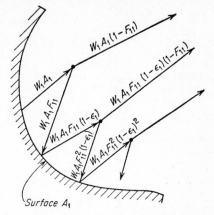

FIG. 5-6. Radiation interchanges for a single surface.

is $\epsilon_1(1 - \epsilon_1)^2 F_{11}^3$. This process may be carried on through successive steps, and the expression for the net rate of loss from A_1 is

$$q_1 = W_1 A_1 - W_1 A_1 [\epsilon_1 F_{11} + \epsilon_1 F_{11}^2 (1 - \epsilon_1) + \epsilon_1 F_{11}^3 (1 - \epsilon_1)^2$$

$$+ \epsilon_1 F_{11}^4 (1 - \epsilon_1)^3 + \cdots]$$

$$= W_1 A_1 \left\{ 1 - \epsilon_1 F_{11} \sum_{n=0}^{\infty} [F_{11}(1 - \epsilon_1)]^n \right\}$$

$$= W_1 A_1 \left[1 - \frac{\epsilon_1 F_{11}}{1 - F_{11}(1 - \epsilon_1)} \right]$$

$$= \epsilon_1 A_1 \sigma T_1^4 \frac{1 - F_{11}}{1 - F_{11}(1 - \epsilon_1)} \qquad (5\text{-}14)$$

This relation is also valid for the case of $\epsilon_1 = 1$.

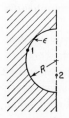

Example 5-3. Consider a hemispherical cavity of radius $R = 1$ in. on the plane surface of a material at 60°F having an emissivity of 0.5. We shall calculate q_1 of the hemispherical surface and the effective emissivity ϵ_e of the cavity. The effective emissivity is the emissivity of the equivalent surface, that is, of the area of the hemisphere projected onto its base, which would produce the same intensity of radiation.

The necessary angle factors, F_{11} and the angle factor to the opening, can be found by imagining the opening closed by a fictitious surface 2. For an enclosure one may write

$$F_{11} + F_{12} = 1 \qquad F_{22} + F_{21} = 1 = F_{21}$$

Also, $$F_{12}A_1 = F_{21}A_2 = A_2 \quad \text{and} \quad F_{12} = \frac{A_2}{A_1}$$

Therefore, $$F_{11} = 1 - F_{12} = 1 - \frac{A_2}{A_1}$$

$$\frac{A_2}{A_1} = \frac{\pi r^2}{4\pi r^2/2} = 0.5 \quad \text{and} \quad F_{12} = 0.5 \qquad F_{11} = 0.5$$

Equation (5-14) applies:

$$q_1 = W_1A_1 \frac{1 - F_{11}}{1 - F_{11}(1 - \epsilon_1)}$$

$$= \frac{0.5 \times 0.1713 \times 10^{-8} \times 520^4 \times 2\pi \times 1^2 \times 0.5}{144(1 - 0.5 \times 0.5)} = 1.82 \text{ Btu/hr}$$

$$q_1 = \epsilon_e \frac{W_1}{\epsilon_1} A_2 = \frac{W_1A_1F_{12}}{1 - (1 - F_{12})(1 - \epsilon_1)}$$

$$\epsilon_e = \frac{\epsilon_1 A_1 F_{12}}{A_2[1 - (1 - F_{12})(1 - \epsilon_1)]} = \frac{\epsilon_1}{1 - (1 - F_{12})(1 - \epsilon_1)}$$

Note that this relation is general and applies to any cavity. Now, for the hemispherical one,

$$\epsilon_e = \frac{\epsilon_1}{1 - \frac{1}{2}(1 - \epsilon_1)} = \frac{2\epsilon_1}{\epsilon_1 + 1} = \frac{2 \times 0.5}{0.5 + 1} = 0.667$$

At this point, it is desirable to form some impression of how important subsequent reflection terms are and what their contribution is to the magnitude of the heat-transfer rate. The amounts of the various components for the case in Example 5-3 will be determined. The amount absorbed, expressed as a percentage of W_1A_1, of the radiation initially intercepted by A_1 is 25.0 per cent. The amounts absorbed by A_1 from the first and second reflections are 6.25 and 1.56 per cent, respectively, when expressed as a percentage of W_1A_1. Or, looking at it another way, the change in q_1 caused by assuming that all the radiation reflected after the second incidence misses A_1 and is lost is only 1 per cent. These magnitudes indicate that in many cases it is possible to ignore certain effects of reflections without great error. This fact is often very useful in connection with more complicated problems.

The next more complicated case in which energy transfers are to be considered is that involving two surfaces, A_1 and A_2, which see each other but which may not form an enclosure. Since the portions of the surroundings of A_1 which are not occupied by A_2 are not to be specified, the assumption will be made that they absorb all radiation coming to them and emit none.

The simplest case of two surfaces is the one in which A_1 and A_2 do not see themselves and are black. The rates of emission from A_1 and A_2 are $W_{b1}A_1$ and $W_{b2}A_2$, and the net rate of loss from A_1 is $W_{b1}A_1$ minus the amount of $W_{b2}A_2$ which is intercepted by A_1. Therefore, the rate of radiant energy loss from A_1 is

$$q_1 = W_{b1}A_1 - W_{b2}A_2F_{21} = W_{b1}A_1 - W_{b2}A_1F_{12} = A_1\sigma(T_1{}^4 - T_2{}^4F_{12})$$

$$(5\text{-}15)$$

Similarly, for A_2 the rate of loss is

$$q_2 = W_{b2}A_2 - W_{b1}A_1F_{12} = A_2\sigma(T_2{}^4 - T_1{}^4F_{21}) \qquad (5\text{-}16)$$

If A_1 and A_2 are both black and A_1 sees itself, we have

$$q_1 = W_{b1}A_1 - W_bA_1F_{11} - W_{b2}A_2F_{21}$$

$$= W_{b1}A_1(1 - F_{11}) - W_{b2}A_1F_{12} = A_1\sigma[T_1{}^4(1 - F_{11}) - T_2{}^4F_{12}]$$

$$(5\text{-}17)$$

As a demonstration of the reflection method of calculation of rates of heat loss from a gray surface in the presence of other gray surfaces, two surfaces A_1 and A_2 will be taken which may not form an enclosure and do not see themselves. Again, the unspecified surroundings are assumed to absorb all radiation and to emit none. The net rate of loss from A_1 is equal to W_1A_1 minus any absorption of the radiation that reaches A_1. The radiation reaching A_1 arises in two ways. First, F_{12} of W_1A_1 hits A_2, and $(1 - \epsilon_2)F_{12}$ is reflected. Some of this is returned to A_1 to be absorbed and reflected. Some of this reflected radiation hits A_2 and is partially reflected to A_1, etc. Similarly, F_{21} of W_2A_2 hits A_1, and $F_{21}\epsilon_1$ of W_2A_2 is absorbed. The remainder is reflected to A_2, and some is reflected again to A_1, where partial absorption occurs, etc. Therefore, q_1 is W_1A_1 minus the contribution of these two effects. Consideration of the following table will explain the method of finding the fraction of W_2A_2 which is absorbed by A_1.

Partial Absorption of W_2A_2 by A_1

Hits A_1	Absorbed by A_1	Reflected by A_1	Reflected by A_2
F_{21}	ϵ_1F_{21}	$(1 - \epsilon_1)F_{21}$	$(1 - \epsilon_1)(1 - \epsilon_2)F_{12}F_{21}$
$(1 - \epsilon_1)(1 - \epsilon_2)F_{12}F_{21}{}^2$	$\epsilon_1(1 - \epsilon_1)(1 - \epsilon_2)F_{12}F_{21}{}^2$	$(1 - \epsilon_1)^2(1 - \epsilon_2)F_{12}F_{21}{}^2$	$(1 - \epsilon_1)^2(1 - \epsilon_2)^2F_{12}{}^2F_{21}{}^2$
$(1 - \epsilon_1)^2(1 - \epsilon_2)^2F_{12}{}^2F_{21}{}^3$	$\epsilon_1(1 - \epsilon_1)^2(1 - \epsilon_2)^2F_{12}{}^2F_{21}{}^3$	etc.	

The fraction of W_2A_2 absorbed by A_1 is

$$\epsilon_1 F_{21}[1 + (1 - \epsilon_1)(1 - \epsilon_2)F_{12}F_{21} + (1 - \epsilon_1)^2(1 - \epsilon_2)^2 F_{12}{}^2 F_{21}{}^2 + \cdots]$$

$$= \epsilon_1 F_{21} \sum_{n=0}^{\infty} [(1 - \epsilon_1)(1 - \epsilon_2)F_{12}F_{21}]^n = \frac{\epsilon_1 F_{21}}{1 - (1 - \epsilon_1)(1 - \epsilon_2)F_{12}F_{21}}$$

$$(5\text{-}18a)$$

The fraction of W_1A_1 absorbed by A_1 is found by a similar technique as

$$\epsilon_1(1 - \epsilon_2)F_{12}F_{21} \sum_{n=0}^{\infty} [(1 - \epsilon_1)(1 - \epsilon_2)F_{12}F_{21}]^n$$

$$= \frac{\epsilon_1(1 - \epsilon_2)F_{12}F_{21}}{1 - (1 - \epsilon_1)(1 - \epsilon_2)F_{12}F_{21}} \quad (5\text{-}18b)$$

These results are combined to obtain the rate of loss of energy from surface A_1.

$$q_1 = \frac{A_1\{W_1[1 - F_{12}F_{21}(1 - \epsilon_2)] - \epsilon_1 W_2 F_{12}\}}{1 - (1 - \epsilon_1)(1 - \epsilon_2)F_{12}F_{21}} \quad (5\text{-}19)$$

The expression for q_2 can be derived from the above by merely interchanging subscripts.

The effect of subsequent reflection terms upon the magnitude of q_1 is indicated by the following results calculated for two surfaces for which $F_{12} = F_{21} = 0.4$ and $\epsilon_1 = \epsilon_2 = 0.7$. Such a value of emissivity is typical of many common materials. The effect upon q_1 of the partial return of W_1A_1 to A_1 is 3.4 per cent of W_1A_1. The change in the value of q_1 caused by ignoring all but the first absorption effect is only 0.05 per cent of W_1A_1. Considering now the effect on q_1 of the amount of W_2A_2 absorbed by A_1, the calculation indicates that a total of 28.4 per cent of W_2A_2 is eventually absorbed by A_1. The error caused in q_1 by ignoring repeated reflection, that is, by including only the amount absorbed by A_1 of the directly incident radiation from A_2, is 0.4 per cent of W_2A_2. Including only the effect of the directly incident and the return of part of the first reflection causes an error of only 0.002 per cent of W_2A_2. Several reasonable conclusions are indicated for surfaces having relatively high emissivities. The first is that in a rate-of-loss calculation from a surface it may be sufficiently accurate to consider the first reflection back from other surfaces of the emission of the initial surface. Further, to obtain the effect of the emissive power of other surfaces, it may be necessary to account only for the amount of the radiation absorbed which is initially incident upon the surface of interest, plus, perhaps, the amount of the first reflection which in part returns and is partially absorbed by the surface. These approximations make the approach much simpler in fairly complicated problems and yield an approximate solution of some problems which would otherwise be too complicated for the successive-reflection method of analysis.

As a case involving more than two areas—for example, $A_1, A_2, \ldots, A_n$—consider the rate of loss from A_1 when all surfaces are black:

$$q_1 = W_1 A_1 - W_1 A_1 F_{11} - W_2 A_2 F_{21} - W_3 A_3 F_{31} - \cdots - W_n A_n F_{n1}$$

$$= A_1 [W_1 (1 - F_{11}) - W_2 F_{12} - \cdots - W_n F_{n1}] \tag{5-20}$$

A more complicated case would be three gray surfaces, A_1, A_2, and A_3, which may not form an enclosure and do not see themselves. The problem is, for example, to compute q_1. The approach is similar to that used for two gray surfaces. However, the process is much more complicated, since each reflection gives rise to two more reflections. Therefore, the number of terms involved increases quickly, and the resulting complications are considerable. These difficulties may be avoided by making the approximations shown to be reasonable above.

5-3. RADIATION EXCHANGE BETWEEN THE SURFACES OF AN ENCLOSURE

The relations developed in the preceding section may be applied to enclosures where it is possible to form an enclosure of the number and types of surfaces specified. Many enclosures are more complicated. However, the relations developed for surfaces not forming an enclosure are in some cases more complicated than those for enclosures with the same number and types of surfaces, because additional relations apply between angle factors for enclosures [see Eqs. (5-12)].

One of the simplest enclosures is that formed by two black surfaces one of which, A_2, sees itself. The heat-transfer relations may be written as

$$q_1 = A_1 W_1 - A_2 W_2 F_{21}$$

$$q_2 = A_2 W_2 (1 - F_{22}) - A_1 W_1 F_{12}$$

These may be simplified by noting the following relations between angle factors:

$$F_{21} + F_{22} = 1 \qquad F_{21} A_2 = F_{12} A_1 \qquad \text{and} \qquad F_{12} = 1$$

Therefore, $\qquad F_{21} = \dfrac{A_1}{A_2} \qquad$ and $\qquad \dfrac{A_1}{A_2} = 1 - F_{22}$

$$q_1 = A_1 W_1 - A_2 W_2 F_{21} = A_1 (W_1 - W_2) = A_1 \sigma (T_1{}^4 - T_2{}^4) \tag{5-21}$$

$$q_2 = A_2 W_2 (1 - F_{22}) - A_1 W_1 F_{12} = A_2 W_2 \frac{A_1}{A_2} - A_1 W_1$$

$$= A_1 (W_2 - W_1) = A_1 \sigma (T_2{}^4 - T_1{}^4) \tag{5-22}$$

Note that $q_1 = -q_2$. This will always be true in an enclosure made up of only two surfaces. This equality is merely a result of the more general relation which holds for any enclosure of n surfaces:

$$\sum_{i=1}^{n} q_i = 0 \qquad (5\text{-}23)$$

The next more complicated enclosure, and a type of considerable practical importance, is one similar to the above but with gray surfaces. The circumstance is diagramed in Fig. 5-7. The rate of loss from A_1 is W_1A_1, minus the part of W_1A_1 which returns and is absorbed, minus the amount of W_2A_2 which is absorbed by A_1. The processes of summing these effects are carried out below:

PARTIAL ABSORPTION OF W_1A_1 BY A_1

Hits A_1	Absorbed by A_1	Reflected, plus the amount which misses A_1
$(1 - \epsilon_2)F_{21}$	$(1 - \epsilon_2)F_{21}\epsilon_1$	$(1 - \epsilon_2) - (1 - \epsilon_2)F_{21}\epsilon_1 = (1 - \epsilon_2)(1 - F_{21}\epsilon_1)$
$(1 - \epsilon_2)^2 F_{21}(1 - F_{21}\epsilon_1)$	$(1 - \epsilon_2)^2 F_{21}(1 - F_{21}\epsilon_1)\epsilon_1$	$(1 - \epsilon_2)^2(1 - F_{21}\epsilon_1)^2$
$(1 - \epsilon_2)^3 F_{21}(1 - F_{21}\epsilon_1)^2$	$(1 - \epsilon_2)^3 F_{21}(1 - F_{21}\epsilon_1)^2 \epsilon_1$	etc.

The fraction of W_1A_1 absorbed by A_1 is

$$(1 - \epsilon_2)F_{21}\epsilon_1[1 + (1 - \epsilon_2)(1 - F_{21}\epsilon_1) + (1 - \epsilon_2)^2(1 - F_{21}\epsilon_1)^2 + \cdots]$$

$$= (1 - \epsilon_2)F_{21}\epsilon_1 \sum_{n=0}^{\infty} [(1 - \epsilon_2)(1 - F_{21}\epsilon_1)]^n = \frac{(1 - \epsilon_2)F_{21}\epsilon_1}{1 - (1 - \epsilon_2)(1 - F_{21}\epsilon_1)}$$

PARTIAL ABSORPTION OF W_2A_2 BY A_1

Hits A_1	Absorbed by A_1	Reflected, plus the amount which missed A_1
F_{21}	$F_{21}\epsilon_1$	$(1 - F_{21}\epsilon_1)$
$(1 - \epsilon_2)(1 - F_{21}\epsilon_1)F_{21}$	$(1 - \epsilon_2)(1 - F_{21}\epsilon_1)F_{21}\epsilon_1$	$(1 - \epsilon_2)(1 - F_{21}\epsilon_1)^2$
$(1 - \epsilon_2)^2(1 - F_{21}\epsilon_1)^2 F_{21}$	$(1 - \epsilon_2)^2(1 - F_{21}\epsilon_1)^2 F_{21}\epsilon_1$	etc.

The fraction of W_2A_2 absorbed by A_1 is

$$F_{21}\epsilon_1[1 + (1 - \epsilon_2)(1 - F_{21}\epsilon_1) + \cdots] = \frac{F_{21}\epsilon_1}{1 - (1 - \epsilon_2)(1 - F_{21}\epsilon_1)}$$

The expression for q_1 is, therefore,

$$q_1 = W_1 A_1 - W_1 A_1 \frac{(1 - \epsilon_2) F_{21} \epsilon_1}{1 - (1 - \epsilon_2)(1 - F_{21} \epsilon_1)}$$

$$- W_2 A_2 \frac{F_{21} \epsilon_1}{1 - (1 - \epsilon_2)(1 - F_{21} \epsilon_1)}$$

This simplifies to

$$q_1 = \frac{A_1 \sigma (T_1^4 - T_2^4)}{\dfrac{1}{\epsilon_1} + \dfrac{A_1}{A_2}\left(\dfrac{1}{\epsilon_2} - 1\right)} \tag{5-24}$$

In certain circumstances this equation can be considerably simplified. For example, consider A_1 to be a small box or sphere in a large enclosure such as a room. Since $A_1 \ll A_2$, $A_1/A_2 \approx 0$ and

$$q_1 = A_1 \epsilon_1 \sigma (T_1^4 - T_2^4) \tag{5-25}$$

This same expression results when the enclosure surface is relatively black, that is, $(1/\epsilon_2 - 1) \approx 0$.

Consider now an enclosure formed by n black surfaces which may or may not see themselves. The expression for q_j for any surface j will be given:

$$q_j = W_j A_j - \sum_{i=1}^{n} W_i A_i F_{ij} = A_j \left(W_j - \sum_{i=1}^{n} W_i F_{ji} \right) \tag{5-26}$$

For enclosures made up of three or more nonblack surfaces the reflection method is extremely complicated if energy quantities are followed through

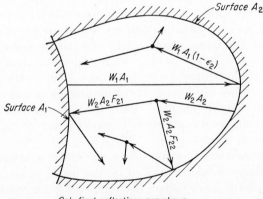

Only first reflections are shown

FIG. 5-7. Radiation interchanges for an enclosure consisting of two surfaces.

all reflections. Other methods of analysis have been developed for such complicated enclosures. A convenient general method which is consistent with the variables and definitions used in this chapter was recently presented by Gebhart (1957) and is discussed in Sec. 5-5. Another method, employing techniques of network analysis, was presented by Oppenheim (1956).

Example 5-4. Find the rate of radiant heat transfer between two concentric spherical surfaces 6 and $6\frac{1}{4}$ in. in diameter when the temperature of the inner surface is 500°F and the temperature of the outer surface is 200°F. The inner and outer spheres have surface emissivities of 0.7 and 0.9, respectively.

For $A_1 \approx A_2$,

$$q_1 = -q_2 = \frac{A_1\sigma(T_1^4 - T_2^4)}{\dfrac{1}{\epsilon_1} + \dfrac{A_1}{A_2}\left(\dfrac{1}{\epsilon_2} - 1\right)} \approx \frac{A_1\sigma(T_1^4 - T_2^4)}{\dfrac{1}{\epsilon_1} + \dfrac{1}{\epsilon_2} - 1}$$

$$= \frac{\pi6^2 \times 0.1713 \times 10^{-8}(960^4 - 660^4)}{144\left(\dfrac{1}{0.7} + \dfrac{1}{0.9} - 1\right)} = 575 \text{ Btu/hr}$$

5-4. SURFACES WITH SPECIAL CHARACTERISTICS

The derivations and developments thus far in this chapter pertain to the type of surface that has the same assigned temperature at all points. In addition, if the transfer process is in steady state, each surface is assumed to be an energy source (or sink). That is, each surface is assumed to be supplied with (or relieved of) energy at a rate sufficient to keep its temperature constant at the assigned value. Certain other types of surfaces are encountered in practical problems. There are three types of frequent importance: openings, windows, and surfaces in radiation balance. An opening absorbs all incident radiation and contributes none (of itself). The window absorbs, transmits, reflects, and emits radiant energy. A surface in radiant balance is defined as one which is adiabatic from the radiation point of view. Such a surface exchanges radiant energy with other surfaces and has a temperature which results from the amount of radiation absorbed and from its tendency to reradiate. That is, for a surface in radiation balance, a temperature level is attained at which the rate of radiant emission is equal to the rate of absorption. Therefore, $q = 0$. An example of the first type of surface would be an opening in the wall of a furnace. A surface in radiation balance would be formed by the inside surface of a well-insulated wall or by the inside surface of a furnace wall for which the conduction loss through the wall is balanced by the convection gain from furnace gases on the inside face of the wall.

The first of these cases, that of an opening into the enclosure, is treated without additional assumptions or qualifications. The opening is imagined to be closed by a surface A_e which is arranged so as to intercept any radiation which would otherwise pass through the opening. The q_e is determined as before, except that A_e does not emit if the surrounding region beyond the opening, that is, outside the enclosure, is at a relatively low temperature compared with the temperature levels in the enclosure. However, if the surroundings are at a relatively high temperature, the radiant transfer into the enclosure must be taken into account. In the case that the surroundings are, in turn, a large enclosure with all surfaces at approximately the same temperature T_s, the rate of radiant energy flow across A_e, from the surroundings into the enclosure, is equal to the rate of emission of a black surface of area A_e at a temperature T_s, that is, $A_e \sigma T_s^4$ (see the Kirchhoff law argument in Sec. 4-4).

As a typical analysis of the rate of loss through an opening, consider the relatively simple case of an enclosure formed of n black surfaces and one opening of effective area A_e into a region of relatively low temperature. The net radiation transfer across A_e is written as

$$q_e = W_1 A_1 F_{1e} + W_2 A_2 F_{2e} + \cdots + W_n A_n F_{ne}$$

$$= A_e \sum_{i=1}^{n} F_{ei} W_i \qquad (5\text{-}27)$$

If the surfaces are not black, the effect of repeated reflections must be accounted for. The presence of a window would be treated in a similar fashion.

The presence of one or more surfaces in radiation balance among those forming an enclosure requires certain modifications in the heat-loss expressions for those surfaces which are not zero-net-flux surfaces. As previously indicated, the condition that must be satisfied in order for a surface A_a to be in radiation balance is that the rate of emission, $W_a A_a$, be equal to the total rate of absorption from all incident radiation. This means that the temperature of this surface, T_a, must have a high enough value for this to be true. Under this condition, $q_a = 0$. The expression for q_a could be used to determine W_a and, therefore, T_a.

However, the use of a heat-loss equation to determine W_a, from which the desired values of q_1, q_2, etc., could be obtained, would be a very complicated and, under most conditions, an unnecessary procedure. Under our previous assumptions, all reflections are diffuse and are uniformly distributed over the reflecting surface. The same is true of any radiation emitted by a surface. It is clear, then, that all radiant energy coming from a surface, whether emitted or reflected, comes uniformly from all elements of that surface and is diffuse in nature. Therefore, there is no difference between considering a given amount of radiation as having been entirely reflected and considering it as having been partly reflected and partly absorbed, with the absorbed part having in turn been diffusely emitted. Since distributed, diffuse reflection and diffuse reemission of an equal amount of energy may be assumed for each component of the radiation incident upon a surface in radiation balance, we are justified in treating such surfaces as complete diffuse reflectors, regardless of the actual surface emissivity. With this qualification, enclosures having radiation-balanced surfaces are treated as before.

As an example of the determination of the heat-loss expression for one of the surfaces having a net flux in an enclosure, the result for the case of one radiation-balanced surface, A_a, which may see itself, and three other black surfaces, A_1, A_2, and A_3, which do not see themselves, is presented in Eq. (5-28). No approximations regarding subsequent reflections are necessary; the blackness of A_1, A_2, and A_3 limits the number of terms to a manageable quantity.

$$q_1 = W_1 A_1 - W_2 A_2 F_{21} - W_3 A_3 F_{31} - W_a A_a F_{a1}$$

But for the surface in radiation balance

$$W_a A_a = W_1 A_1 F_{1a} + W_2 A_2 F_{2a} + W_3 A_3 F_{3a} + W_a A_a F_{aa}$$

Eliminating $W_a A_a$ and using reciprocity relations, we have

$$q_1 = A_1(W_1 - W_2 F_{12} - W_3 F_{13})$$

$$- \frac{F_{1a}(A_1/A_a)}{1 - F_{aa}} (W_1 A_1 F_{1a} + W_2 A_2 F_{2a} + W_3 A_3 F_{3a}) \quad (5\text{-}28)$$

Similar expressions for still more complicated enclosures may be determined. Many more complicated circumstances arise in practical problems; for example, it may be necessary to consider an enclosure made up of all four kinds of components discussed here: radiation-balanced surfaces, source-sink surfaces, openings, and windows. This type of problem may be individually considered by making assumptions for each surface similar to those discussed in the foregoing pages. Caution is necessary in making approximations in cases of successive reflections. The magnitude of subsequent reflection contributions depends upon the values of angle factors and emissivities as well as upon the number of reflections.

Example 5-5. Consider a room 16 ft deep, 16 ft wide, and 8 ft high heated by a radiant floor panel which will maintain a floor surface temperature of 85°F. The ceiling and two adjacent side walls of the room are interior partitions and therefore may be considered to have zero net radiant flux. The other two adjacent walls are exterior walls, and from consideration of their different construction it is estimated that the inside surface temperature of one wall will be 55°F and that of the other wall will be 60°F. Let us consider the rate of floor surface loss if all surfaces are assumed black. The surfaces are numbered as shown in the figure. Surface 1 is the floor, and the remaining

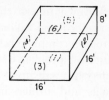

source-sink surfaces are denoted as 2 and 3. Therefore, $A_a = A_4 + A_5 + A_6$. This enclosure is one composed of three source-sink surfaces which do not see themselves and one surface in radiation balance. Therefore, the equation derived above applies:

$$W_1A_1 = 0.1713 \times 10^{-8} \times 545^4 \times A_1 = 151.1A_1 = 3.869 \times 10^4$$

$$W_2A_2 = 0.1713 \times 10^{-8} \times 515^4 \times A_2 = 120.5A_2 = 1.542 \times 10^4$$

$$W_3A_3 = 0.1713 \times 10^{-8} \times 520^4 \times A_3 = 125.3A_3 = 1.604 \times 10^4$$

$$F_{12} = F_{13} = 0.145 \qquad \text{from Fig. 5-2}$$

$$F_{1a} = F_{14} + F_{15} + F_{16} = 1 - F_{12} - F_{13} = 1 - 2F_{12} = 0.71$$

$$F_{23} = 0.15 \qquad F_{21} = 0.29 \qquad \text{from Fig. 5-2}$$

$$F_{2a} = F_{3a} = 1 - F_{21} - F_{23} = 1 - 0.15 - 0.29 = 0.56$$

$$F_{aa} = 1 - F_{a1} - F_{a2} - F_{a3} = 1 - \frac{F_{1a}A_1 + F_{2a}A_2 + F_{3a}A_3}{A_a} = 0.36$$

$$q_1 = 16 \times 16(151.1 - 120.5 \times 0.145 - 125.3 \times 0.145)$$

$$- \frac{0.71 \times 10^4 \times (16 \times 16/16 \times 32)}{1 - 0.36} (3.869 \times 0.71 + 1.542 \times 0.56$$

$$+ 1.604 \times 0.56)$$

$$= 29{,}670 - 25{,}010 = 4660 \text{ Btu/hr}$$

5-5. A UNIFIED METHOD FOR RADIATION-EXCHANGE CALCULATIONS

The methods of analysis discussed in Secs. 5-2 and 5-3 are limited in their application to black surfaces or to the very simplest arrangements involving gray surfaces. The present section is devoted to a discussion of a general method of analysis which was developed by Gebhart (1957 and 1959). This technique treats all diffuse-radiation circumstances, including those which involve special features such as windows, openings, and surfaces in radiant balance. The method as discussed below applies unchanged to arrangements of any complexity.

In preceding sections, q was defined as the net rate of energy loss from a surface due to radiation exchanges. Clearly this quantity has no significance unless the complete radiant surroundings of the surface are specified and taken into account in calculating q. The surface of interest and its complete radiant surroundings constitute, in effect, an "enclosure," and all problems are, in this sense, enclosure problems. This enclosure may be made up of some very special surfaces, for example, windows, openings, and surfaces in radiation balance (that is, surfaces having a net radiation loss or gain of zero). The present analysis considers the complete enclosure and presents a general method of calculating the net rate of energy loss, due to radiation processes, for any of the surfaces.

The Absorption Factor. Consider a group of n gray surfaces, $A_1, A_2, \ldots,$ A_n, which form an enclosure. We wish to find the rate of radiant energy loss of any one of the surfaces, say A_j. This rate of loss, q_j, will be equal to the emission rate of A_j, that is, $W_j A_j$, minus the total rate of radiant energy absorption by A_j from any source whatsoever. All the surfaces of the enclosure may emit energy, and we must sum up the amount absorbed at A_j after direct incidence or after any path of reflection or re-reflection. The ith surface, of area A_i, emits at a rate $W_i A_i$. Portions of this energy may arrive at A_j by many very complicated parallel reflection processes. We shall define an absorption factor B_{ij} as the total fraction of the emission of A_i which is absorbed by A_j. For example, B_{1j} is the fraction of $W_1 A_1$ which is absorbed at A_j. The net rate of loss from the jth surface is then

$$q_j = W_j A_j - B_{1j} W_1 A_1 - B_{2j} W_2 A_2 - \cdots - B_{jj} W_j A_j - \cdots - B_{nj} W_n A_n$$

$$= W_j A_j - \sum_{i=1}^{n} B_{ij} W_i A_i \qquad (5\text{-}29)$$

where j may be taken as any one of the n surfaces of the enclosure. Note that in general B_{jj} is not zero; some of $W_j A_j$ may be reabsorbed at A_j.

The Determination of Absorption Factors. The n values of B_{ij} necessary to compute q_j may be found by summing absorption rates at j due to the emission rates of $A_1, A_2, \ldots, A_n$. For example, $W_1 A_1$ is emitted at A_1 and reaches the n surfaces in fractions indicated by the angle factors F_{11}, $F_{12}, \ldots, F_{1n}$. The amount $F_{1j}\epsilon_j$ is absorbed by A_j, and $F_{1j}\rho_j$ is reflected. In general, $F_{1i}\rho_i$ is reflected by the ith surface. Now, the fraction of $F_{1i}\rho_i$ which is absorbed at A_j is the same as the fraction of $W_i A_i$ which is absorbed at A_j if the incident energy $F_{1i} W_1 A_1$ is uniformly distributed over A_i and is diffusely reflected. Assuming uniform distribution, the fraction of $W_1 A_1$ absorbed at A_j because of reflection off A_i is then $B_{ij} F_{1i}\rho_i$. Writing out this result for $A_1, A_2, \ldots, A_n$, the total fraction of $W_1 A_1$ absorbed at A_j, that is, B_{1j}, is

$$B_{1j} = F_{1j}\epsilon_j + F_{11}\rho_1 B_{1j} + F_{12}\rho_2 B_{2j} + F_{13}\rho_3 B_{3j} + \cdots + F_{1n}\rho_n B_{nj}$$

For each of the other surfaces a similar relation may be written:

$$B_{2j} = F_{2j}\epsilon_j + F_{21}\rho_1 B_{1j} + F_{22}\rho_2 B_{2j} + F_{23}\rho_3 B_{3j} + \cdots + F_{2n}\rho_n B_{nj}$$

$$B_{3j} = F_{3j}\epsilon_j + F_{31}\rho_1 B_{1j} + F_{32}\rho_2 B_{2j} + F_{33}\rho_3 B_{3j} + \cdots + F_{3n}\rho_n B_{nj}$$

$$\cdots \cdots \cdots \cdots \cdots \cdots \cdots \cdots \cdots \cdots \cdots \cdots \cdots$$

$$B_{nj} = F_{nj}\epsilon_j + F_{n1}\rho_1 B_{1j} + F_{n2}\rho_2 B_{2j} + F_{n3}\rho_3 B_{3j} + \cdots + F_{nn}\rho_n B_{nj}$$

A total of n linear equations is obtained. Transposing, rearranging, and introducing $F_{rs}\rho_s = \alpha_{rs}$, we have a more convenient form:

$$
\begin{aligned}
(\alpha_{11}-1)B_{1j} &+ \alpha_{12}B_{2j} &&+ \alpha_{13}B_{3j} &&+ \cdots + \alpha_{1n}B_{nj} &&+ F_{1j}\epsilon_j = 0 \\
\alpha_{21}B_{1j} &+ (\alpha_{22}-1)B_{2j} &&+ \alpha_{23}B_{3j} &&+ \cdots + \alpha_{2n}B_{nj} &&+ F_{2j}\epsilon_j = 0 \\
\alpha_{31}B_{1j} &+ \alpha_{32}B_{2j} &&+ (\alpha_{33}-1)B_{3j} &&+ \cdots + \alpha_{3n}B_{nj} &&+ F_{3j}\epsilon_j = 0 \\
&\cdots \cdots \cdots \cdots \cdots \cdots \cdots \cdots \\
\alpha_{n1}B_{1j} &+ \alpha_{n2}B_{2j} &&+ \alpha_{n3}B_{3j} &&+ \cdots + (\alpha_{nn}-1)B_{nj} &&+ F_{nj}\epsilon_j = 0
\end{aligned}
$$

$$(5\text{-}30)$$

This set of n equations may be solved for the n unknowns B_{1j}, B_{2j}, ..., B_{nj}. The above set of equations is valid, with the same coefficients, for any choice of j, that is, 1, 2, ..., n. Therefore, Eqs. (5-29) and (5-30) may be applied to any surface of the enclosure.

For the jth surface the general absorption factor B_{ij} is written from Eqs. (5-30) as the ratio of two n-by-n determinants formed from the coefficients and constants of the equations in the usual manner:

$$B_{ij} = \frac{D_{ij}}{D} \qquad (5\text{-}31)$$

Consideration of Eqs. (5-30) shows that the determinant D in the denominator, formed of the coefficients of the B_{ij}, is the same for all B_{ij}. The determinant in the numerator is merely D altered by replacing the ith column with minus the constants of Eqs. (5-30).

Comparison of Eq. (5-29) for a gray-surface enclosure with Eq. (5-20) for a black-surface enclosure provides a means of relating absorption factors to angle factors. The absorption factor is a generalized angle factor which applies to circumstances involving gray surfaces.

There are certain necessary relations between the n^2 absorption factors of an n-surface enclosure just as there are between the n^2 angle factors [see Eqs. (5-12) and (5-13)]. Since all the emission of A_i is absorbed by A_1, A_2, ..., A_n,

$$\sum_{j=1}^{n} B_{ij} = 1 \qquad (5\text{-}32)$$

The following reciprocity relation is proved by Gebhart (1957):

$$B_{ij}\epsilon_i A_i = B_{ji}\epsilon_j A_j \tag{5-33}$$

These necessary relations reduce the n^2 absorption factors to $n(n-1)/2$ independent ones which must be found from Eqs. (5-30). Equations (5-32) and (5-33) may also be used to reduce Eq. (5-29) to a simpler form for some calculations.

The above treatment is, strictly speaking, limited to those enclosures for which the surfaces are arranged so as to cause a uniform distribution over each surface of the radiation incident upon it from any other surface. Only a limited number of special arrangements have this characteristic. In a particular problem the simplest possible choice of surfaces may result in an arrangement for which the distribution is far from uniform over one or more of the surfaces. In such a case the accuracy of the heat-transfer estimates may be improved by further subdividing the surfaces, since the above method applies to any number of surfaces. However, the work required to obtain a solution increases rapidly with the number of surfaces, and a balance must be found which is consistent with the importance of the problem in hand.

Special Surfaces in Enclosures. All types of diffuse-radiation processes are included under the "enclosure" method discussed above, and surfaces having special characteristics are treated by being assigned consistent properties. An opening is treated as an equivalent area A_e with a reflectivity of zero. If energy enters the enclosure through the opening, A_e is assigned an equivalent temperature; otherwise its temperature is taken as zero. If the loss through the opening is desired, q_e is found. A window in the enclosure is assigned its actual properties.

A surface in radiant balance is one for which radiant emission is balanced by radiant absorption. Such a surface, of extent A_a, is simulated for the calculation of the rate of loss for any other surface by assigning to it a reflectivity of 1.0 and an emissivity of 0. The absorption factors are then found from Eqs. (5-30) by using these values. If the temperature of A_a is desired, the values of B_{ia} are found by using the actual properties of A_a. The B_{ia} are then substituted into the following relation for q_a to find W_a and T_a:

$$q_a = 0 = W_a A_a - \sum_{i=1}^{n} B_{ia} W_i A_i \tag{5-34}$$

The above general method may also be applied to enclosures containing gray absorbing and emitting media [see Gebhart (1957)].

Example 5-6. A cubical kiln 4 ft wide is heated by circulating combustion gases behind one wall. These combustion gases maintain the inside surface of this wall at 2000°F.

The wall opposite the heated one has a 1- by 1-ft centered opening. The angle factor from the opening to the heated wall is 0.23. The removable floor is covered with small metal pieces. The objects and floor are at 1400°F and may be assumed to form a black surface of 16 ft². The remaining three walls and ceiling are in radiant balance. The walls and ceiling have emissivities of 0.9. We shall compute the rate of radiant energy loss from the heated wall and the rate of radiant energy loss through the opening.

The surfaces are numbered as shown in the figure. The surfaces in radiant balance are combined as A_4, having a reflectivity of 1.0. The angle factors are found:

$$F_{11} = 0 \qquad F_{12} = 0.23 \qquad F_{13} = 0.193 \qquad F_{14} = 0.577$$

$$F_{21} = 0.0144 \qquad F_{22} = 0 \qquad F_{23} = 0.20 \qquad F_{24} = 0.786$$

$$F_{31} = 0.0120 \qquad F_{32} = 0.20 \qquad F_{33} = 0 \qquad F_{34} = 0.788$$

$$F_{41} = 0.0092 \qquad F_{42} = 0.20 \qquad F_{43} = 0.20 \qquad F_{44} = 0.591$$

$$\rho_1 = 0 \qquad \rho_2 = 0.1 \qquad \rho_3 = 0 \qquad \rho_4 = 1.0$$

q_1 will be found first. The equations for B_{11}, B_{21}, B_{31}, and B_{41} are written with the $\alpha_{rs} = F_{rs}\rho_s$ values as the coefficients. Note that the α_{r1} and α_{r3} are zero because ρ_1 and ρ_3 are zero.

$$-B_{11} + 0.023B_{21} + \quad 0 \quad + 0.577B_{41} + 0 \qquad = 0$$

$$0 \quad - \quad B_{21} + \quad 0 \quad + 0.786B_{41} + 0.0144 = 0$$

$$0 \quad + \quad 0.02B_{21} - B_{31} + 0.788B_{41} + 0.0120 = 0$$

$$0 \quad + \quad 0.02B_{21} + \quad 0 \quad - 0.409B_{41} + 0.0092 = 0$$

B_{11} need not be found because $W_1 = 0$. Similarly, B_{41} will not be computed because $\epsilon_4 = 0$ and, therefore, $W_4 = 0$. We have, then, $B_{21} = 0.0333$ and $B_{31} = 0.0308$.

$$q_1 = W_1A_1 - B_{11}W_1A_1 - B_{21}W_2A_2 - B_{31}W_3A_3 - B_{41}W_4A_4$$

$$= B_{21}W_2A_2 - B_{31}W_3A_3$$

$$= -\sigma(0.0333 \times 0.9 \times 2460^4 \times 4 \times 4 + 0.0308 \times 1.0 \times 1860^4 \times 4 \times 4)$$

$$= -40{,}500 \text{ Btu/hr}$$

This is negative and, therefore, a gain. This is the rate of energy loss through the opening. The loss for the heated wall is

$$q_2 = W_2A_2 - B_{12}W_1A_1 - B_{22}W_2A_2 - B_{32}W_3A_3 - W_{42}W_4A_4$$

$$= (1 - B_{22})W_2A_2 - B_{32}W_3A_3$$

The values of B_{22} and B_{32} are found from the following equations as 0.360 and 0.173.

$$-B_{12} + 0.023B_{22} + \quad 0 \quad + 0.577B_{42} + 0.189 = 0$$

$$0 \quad - \quad B_{22} + \quad 0 \quad + 0.786B_{42} + 0 \quad\quad = 0$$

$$0 \quad + \quad 0.02B_{22} - B_{32} + 0.788B_{42} + 0.180 = 0$$

$$0 \quad + \quad 0.02B_{22} + \quad 0 \quad - 0.409B_{42} + 0.180 = 0$$

$$q_2 = \sigma[(1 - 0.360)0.9 \times 2460^4 \times 4 \times 4 - 0.173 \times 1.0 \times 1860^4 \times 4 \times 4]$$

$$= 520{,}000 \text{ Btu/hr}$$

Since $\Sigma q = 0$, the radiant gain of the floor is $520{,}000 - 40{,}500 = 479{,}500$ Btu/hr.

5-6. RADIATION SURFACE COEFFICIENT

In order to obtain simple expressions for use in heat-transfer calculations, numerous quantities are defined which, when inspected carefully, have rather complicated characteristics. The example to be discussed here is the radiation surface coefficient h_r. Consider a surface A_1 at a temperature T_1 surrounded by an enclosure composed of surfaces having assignable temperatures. The enclosure may be filled with a fluid with an average temperature t_f. A convection process occurs between A_1 and the fluid, and the rate of loss by convection from A_1 to the fluid is connected to the other relevant variables by

$$q_{c,1} = A_1 h_c(t_1 - t_f) \tag{5-35}$$

where h_c, the convection coefficient, is a measure of the vigor of the convection process. Now, parallel to this convection process and somewhat independent of it, A_1 loses energy by radiation to the enclosure surfaces and perhaps to the fluid as well. A convenience results from writing a similar relation for the radiation process:

$$q_{r,1} = A_1 h_r(t_1 - t_f) \tag{5-36}$$

This is the definition of h_r. The result is that the total loss from A_1 may be written as

$$q_{t,1} = A_1(h_c + h_r)(t_1 - t_f) = A_1 h(t_1 - t_f) \tag{5-37}$$

The potential convenience of such a method is evident upon comparing the simplicity of Eq. (5-36) with the complexity of, for example, Eq. (5-24). However, one must investigate the meaning of h_r and indicate how numerical values are to be found in various circumstances. This will be done for the relatively simple radiation case wherein A_1 does not see itself and is completely surrounded by a surface A_2 at T_2. The expression for q_1 is therefore Eq. (5-24), and, equating this to Eq. (5-36), the value of h_r is found as

$$h_r = \frac{\sigma(T_1{}^4 - T_2{}^4)}{\left[\dfrac{1}{\epsilon_1} + \dfrac{A_1}{A_2}\left(\dfrac{1}{\epsilon_2} - 1\right)\right](t_1 - t_f)} \qquad (5\text{-}38)$$

If T_2 is not equal to T_f, there is little advantage in using h_r. Assuming that $T_2 = T_f$ and that $A_1 \ll A_2$, a more useful result is found:

$$h_r = \frac{\sigma\epsilon_1(T_1{}^4 - T_f{}^4)}{T_1 - T_f} = \sigma\epsilon_1(T_1{}^2 + T_f{}^2)(T_1 + T_f) \qquad (5\text{-}39)$$

If, in addition, $(T_1 - T_f) \ll T_1$, the difference in fourth powers may be approximated by $4T_{av}{}^3\,(T_1 - T_f)$. This is sufficiently accurate in many problems. Therefore,

$$h_r = 4\sigma\epsilon_1 T_{av}{}^3 \qquad (5\text{-}40)$$

Values of h_r may then be computed from this relatively simple form for use in equations like (5-37). An important result of these steps is that q_1 is written as directly proportional to Δt rather than to $\Delta(T^4)$.

NOTATION

B_{ij}	absorption factor between surfaces i and j
F_{ij}	angle (or interception) factor between surfaces i and j
h_c	convection coefficient
h_r	radiation surface coefficient
n	number of surfaces in an enclosure
q_j	net rate of radiant energy loss from surface j
T	absolute temperature
W	total hemispherical emissive power per unit area
W_b	total hemispherical emissive power of a "black" surface
α_{rs}	$F_{rs}\rho_s$
ϵ	hemispherical emissivity
θ	angle from the normal to an element of surface
ρ	reflectivity
σ	universal constant for black-body radiation

REFERENCES

Gebhart, B.: *ASME Paper* 57-A-34, 1957.
——: *Trans. ASHRAE*, vol. 65, p. 321, 1959.
Hamilton, D. C., and W. R. Morgan: *NACA Tech. Note* 2836, 1952.
Mackey, C. O., L. T. Wright, Jr., R. E. Clark, and N. R. Gay: Radiant Heating and Cooling, pt. I, *Cornell Univ. Eng. Exp. Sta. Bull.* 32, 1943.
Oppenheim, A. K.: *Trans. ASME*, vol. 78, p. 725, 1956.

PROBLEMS

1. Find the angle factor from a differential area dA (flat) to a sphere of radius a whose center lies on the normal from dA at a distance D from dA.

2. Consider a spherical surface of radius a enclosed by another spherical surface of larger radius b.

a. How many angle factors are there in the enclosure formed by the two spherical surfaces?

b. Do the values of these angle factors depend upon whether or not the spheres are concentric? Explain.

c. Determine the values of each of the angle factors in terms of the enclosure dimensions.

3. Between the surfaces of a cubical enclosure there are 36 individual angle factors. How many different numerical values are there among these 36? Find them.

4. Consider the enclosure formed by a hemispherical surface of radius R and its circular base. Find all significant angle factors if (*a*) the base is divided into two equal areas by a diameter; (*b*) the base is divided into two areas, one being a disk of radius r.

5. For the enclosure described in Prob. 4, composed of a hemisphere and its base, find the angle factors from a very small opening in the hemispherical surface to the total base and to the hemispherical surface.

6. The surface of an oxidized copper plate has on it a hemispherical cavity of radius r. Find the fraction of the radiant energy emitted by the surface of the cavity which escapes through the cavity opening. List all necessary assumptions.

7. In a certain manufacturing process, 3- by 3-ft plates at 200°F are to be held at that temperature between operations by suspending them parallel to, and at a distance of 1 ft from, a 3- by 3-ft heater plate. The heater plate is to be maintained at 470°F on its exposed face by electric heaters embedded in the surface and is to be insulated on its other face. Assuming that radiant energy gains from the surroundings are negligible, compute the rate of radiant energy loss or gain from both surfaces if they are both black. Compute the heating efficiency, defined as the net amount of radiant energy absorbed by the plate in process divided by the amount of energy supplied to the electric heaters if convection effects on the heater plate are ignored.

8. Repeat Prob. 7 if both surfaces are gray and have an emissivity of 0.7.

9. Consider a small spherical earth satellite, 2 ft in diameter, circling the earth (radius approximately 4000 miles) at a distance of 200 miles from the surface. The satellite surface is heavily oxidized aluminum and is to be at 0°F. Let us assume that the average earth surface temperature is 60°F and that the earth may be considered "black." We are interested in the net rate of loss of energy from the sphere by thermal-radiation processes when it is in the shadow of the earth.

a. Find the angle factors between the earth and the satellite.

b. Find the rate of thermal-radiation loss from the satellite if the part of the satellite surroundings not occupied by the earth is considered black and at 0°R.

c. Repeat part *b* for the unoccupied surroundings assumed to be at an "effective" temperature of 250°R and black.

10. Assume that the plate with the cavity described in Prob. 6 is at 440°F and is located in a relatively large enclosure whose average surface temperature is 80°F. Find the rate of energy loss by radiation from the cavity surface per square foot of projected area. Find the rate of energy loss by radiation from the flat surface per square foot of flat-plate surface.

11. A kiln whose average inside surface temperature is 2200°F has a small square opening (6 by 6 in.) in one of its 12-in.-thick walls. Assuming that the sides of the opening may be considered to be in radiant balance, find the rate of radiant energy loss through the opening.

12. A kiln of cubical interior shape, 12 ft on a side, is heated by means of a combustion process behind one of the side walls. The inside face of this heated wall is at 2400°F. The contents of the kiln, or load, may be approximated by a hemispherical solid that has a radius of 6 ft and is centered on the floor. If all the other wall surfaces may be considered to be in radiant balance, we are interested in the rate of radiant energy gain by the load when its average surface temperatures are 60 and 1400°F. Assume that the heated wall is faced with fire clay and that the surfaces of the objects making up the load are black. Use 0.1 as an estimate of the angle factor from the hemispherical surface to the heated wall.

13. A cubically shaped room, 10 ft on a side, is to be heated by means of water coils in the floor which maintain a surface temperature of 80°F. The ceiling is to be at 50°F, and the four walls are to be at 60°F. With this temperature information, there are three significant areas: the floor A_1, the ceiling A_2, and the remainder A_3.

   a. Calculate all angle factors.

   b. If all surfaces are black, find the rate of heat loss from the floor by radiation.

   c. The radiant loss from A_1 goes to A_2 and A_3. What percentage goes to A_2?

14. Consider the wedge-shaped cavity formed by two long strips joined along one edge as shown in Fig. P14. Surface 1 is 1 ft wide and $\epsilon_1 = 0.4$. The plane of the open-

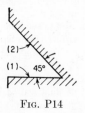

FIG. P14

ing is perpendicular to surface 1; that is, the width of surface 2 is $\sqrt{2}$ ft. Surface 1 is at 1540°F, and surface 2 is assumed to be in radiant balance. The surroundings are at 40°F.

   a. Determine all the angle factors, without the use of charts if possible.

   b. Find the expressions for the rates of loss from the cavity and from surface 1 per foot of cavity length. Are these expressions valid if surface 1 is black?

   c. Compute the rate of loss from surface 1 for the conditions given above.

   d. Describe how to estimate the temperature of surface 2.

15. A 16- by 16-ft room 8 ft high is heated by circulating warm water through tubes embedded in the ceiling which maintain a ceiling surface temperature of 90°F. Consider three surfaces: the ceiling, A_c; the walls, A_w; and the floor, A_f.

   a. Find all the angle factors between the three surfaces.

   b. For wall and floor temperatures of 60°F and black surfaces throughout, compute the rates of loss by thermal radiation from the ceiling, walls, and floor.

   c. If the walls are at 60°F and the floor is adiabatic, find its temperature and the rates of loss from the ceiling and walls.

16. Consider an enclosure of area A_2 with a plane opening of area A_1 in its side.

a. If the enclosure walls are gray ($\epsilon_2 = 0.5$) and are at a temperature T, find an expression for the intensity of radiant energy at the opening due to the enclosure.

$$A_1 = 1 \text{ ft}^2 \qquad A_2 = 100 \text{ ft}^2$$

b. For an enclosure surface temperature of 140°F, compare the numerical value of the intensity at the opening with the intensity that would be assumed to prove the Kirchhoff "law" in Sec. 4-4.

17. Estimate the equilibrium temperature of a spherical satellite 30 in. in diameter in the sun and in eclipse at an altitude of 500 miles, neglecting convection effects. The earth's diameter and average surface temperature may be taken as 8000 miles and 59°F, and the surface may be considered black. A solar constant of 429 Btu/hr ft^2 is expected. The satellite's surface emissivity is 0.10, and an internal energy-generation rate of 30 Btu/hr due to internal equipment is expected. A uniform surface temperature is to be assumed.

18. Using the techniques presented in Sec. 5-5, derive the relation for the rate of loss from one of two gray surfaces forming an enclosure if one of the surfaces sees itself. Compare the result with Eq. (5-24).

19. Do as requested in Prob. 18 for the circumstance wherein both of the gray surfaces may see themselves. Reduce the result to the form of Eq. (5-24) and compare.

20. An empty cubical kiln 4 ft wide is heated by circulating combustion gases behind one wall. These gases keep the inside surface of the wall at 2000°F. The floor surface temperature is 900°F, and the remaining three walls and ceiling are in radiant balance. Calculate the temperature of the surfaces in radiant balance. The floor is black; the walls and ceiling have an emissivity of 0.9.

21. If the wall opposite the heated wall in the kiln of Prob. 20 has a 1- by 1-ft centered opening, find the temperature of the surfaces in radiant balance. Neglect radiant energy entering the kiln through the opening. The angle factor from the opening to the heated wall is 0.23.

22. A room 16 ft wide, 24 ft long, and 8 ft high is to be heated by circulating warm water through coils in the floor. One long wall, labeled surface 3, is an outside wall with an inside surface temperature of 55°F and an emissivity of 0.90. The inside surface temperatures and emissivities of the other room surfaces are given below:

Other long wall:	70°F, 1.0
Ceiling (surface 2):	65°F, 0.80
End walls:	70°F, 1.0
Floor (surface 1):	85°F, 0.90

Neglecting all room openings, compute the rate of energy loss by radiation from the floor. As an approximation, combine the three inside walls into one surface.

23. Two surfaces, A_1 at T_1 and A_2 at T_2, form an enclosure, and both may see themselves. A_1 is black, and A_2 is gray. Assuming diffuse-radiation processes *in vacuo* and uniform distribution, develop an expression for the rate of radiant energy loss for each surface. Reduce the results to a form which involves F_{11} and a minimum of other enclosure quantities.

24. The wall of a container for storing very low temperature liquids is to be constructed of two sheets of metal separated by a distance L. The space between the sheets is to be evacuated. Assume that the distance L is small compared with the size of the plates. Consider only radiation transfer and a fixed temperature difference between the two sheets.

a. Find the ratio of heat gain through the wall for polished aluminum and for sheet-steel surfaces.

b. It is suggested that the radiation gain would be reduced by subdividing the space with sheets of metal foil. If the space is divided into n spaces in this way, plot the ratio of the heat gain with n spaces and with the single space versus n.

25. An enclosure is made up of two surfaces, A_1 and A_2 (at T_1 and T_2), and one surface in radiant balance A_a (which may see itself). If $F_{11} = F_{22} = 0$, find the absorption factors B_{11}, B_{12}, B_{21}, and B_{22}. Reduce the expressions to the simplest possible forms.

26. For the enclosure of Prob. 25, find B_{11} and B_{12} if A_2 may see itself ($F_{11} = 0$). Reduce the expressions to the simplest possible forms.

27. Calculate the absorption factor between the two end surfaces of a cylindrical enclosure if the end surfaces are black and the connecting cylindrical surface is in radiant balance. Carry out this calculation for values of the height-diameter ratio between 0 and 2 and plot the results. For the value of 2 subdivide the cylindrical surface into two parts for greater accuracy.

28. Repeat Prob. 27 for two directly opposed black square surfaces connected by surfaces in radiant balance. Carry out the calculation for values of the ratio of spacing to length of a side of the square between 0 and 2. For the value of 2 subdivide the surfaces in radiant balance into two parts for greater accuracy.

29. A radiation source is to be built, as shown in the diagram, for an experimental study of radiation. The base of the hemisphere is to be covered by a circular plate having a centered hole of radius $R/2$. The underside of the plate is to be held at 540°F

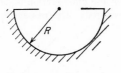

FIG. P29

by heaters embedded in its surface. The heater surface is black. The hemispherical surface is well insulated on the outside. Assume gray, diffuse processes and uniform distribution.

a. Find the ratio of the radiant intensity at the opening to the intensity of emission at the surface of the heated plate.

b. Find the radiant energy loss through the opening in Btu/hr for $R = 1.0$ ft.

c. Find the temperature of the hemispherical surface.

30. For the cavity to which Prob. 14 refers, surface A_1 is at 40°F and is black. Surface A_2 is at 240°F and has an emissivity of 0.4. The enclosure may be assumed to be at a temperature of absolute zero.

a. Determine all angle factors, without the use of charts, if possible.

b. Find the rates of radiant energy loss from A_1 and A_2 and from the cavity per foot of cavity length.

31. A 4- by 4-ft solar collector is designed as shown in the diagram. Fluid circulation tubes are embedded in the back of the collector plate (emissivity 1.00), and the whole assembly is insulated on the bottom side. The space between the collector plate and the $\frac{1}{8}$-in.-thick glass cover is evacuated to a pressure of 10^{-2} mm Hg. The glass has $\alpha = 0.05$ and $\tau = 0.88$ for high-temperature radiation and $\alpha = 0.90$ and $\tau = 0.05$ for low-temperature radiation. We wish to consider the case wherein the collector is horizontal and the sun is directly overhead. The solar intensity is to be 400 Btu/ft^2 hr.

Because of the large plate area, the effects of the connecting walls may be ignored. The cooling-fluid circulation rate will be adjusted to keep the collector-plate surface temperature at 140°F.

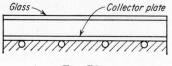

FIG. P31

  a. Neglecting all convection and conduction effects, find the glass temperature.

  b. Find the radiant energy gain rate for the collector plate.

  32. The surface of a metal plate has 50 per cent of its area covered with hemispherical cavities having an average diameter of 0.01 in. The rest of the surface is flat. If the metal of which the plate is made has a total hemispherical emissivity of 0.20, find the "effective" emissivity of the plate surface, assuming diffuse behavior.

  33. A cubical enclosure is to be heated by coils embedded in the floor which will maintain a floor surface temperature of 90°F. The floor surface emissivity is 0.80. One wall is at 60°F and has an emissivity of 0.90. The remaining three walls and ceiling are at 70°F and are black.

  a. Find the rate of radiant energy loss from the floor.

  b. Discuss any special assumptions or approximations made in the analysis.

  34. In a very long passage of the cross section shown, A_1 at T_1 is gray, A_2 at T_2 is black, and A_3 at T_3 is well-insulated. The passage is evacuated. Assuming uniform

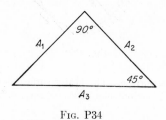

FIG. P34

distribution and diffuse processes, derive an expression for the rate of radiant energy loss for each surface in the enclosure and reduce the results to the form which involves the minimum number of enclosure quantities.

CHAPTER 6

Fluid Flow Processes

6-1. DESCRIPTION OF FLUID FLOW

Circumstances wherein heat (or mass) is transferred from surfaces to fluids in motion are called convection processes. The transfer rate depends primarily upon the nature of the fluid flow process, upon the velocity distribution in the fluid, and upon the properties of the fluid. So important are these effects that the principal difficulty in solving convection problems arises in solving the flow problem. Many types of convection are too difficult for even the most sophisticated methods, and much of the currently important information on heat and mass transfer and fluid flow has been obtained by experimentation. The present chapter considers the nature of fluid flow and presents the experimental results and analytic techniques which have been widely applied for convection analysis.

As an example of a process which includes many of the effects important in convection, consider the flow of an incompressible fluid normal to the axis of a long circular cylinder, as shown in Fig. 6-1a. The undisturbed fluid approaches at a velocity of U_∞. For an inviscid fluid the streamlines (lines tangent to the local velocity) diverge around the cylinder and converge again behind, as shown in Fig. 6-1b. The velocity at the surface is zero at the forward stagnation point, increases to $2U_\infty$ at 90°, and decreases again to zero at the rear stagnation point. The pressure decreases from the stagnation value p_o at the forward stagnation point to a minimum at 90° and then increases again to p_o. The drag force is zero.

For an actual viscous fluid, the process is quite different for the flow conditions commonly encountered in engineering practice. First, the fluid does not slip over the surface. The fluid in contact with the surface is at rest. As we proceed out, normal to the surface on the front half of the cylinder, the velocity increases rapidly to a higher value. In this region of large velocity gradients the effects of viscosity are very important. This portion of the flow is called the "boundary region." As a result of the momentum loss due to viscous effects in the boundary region, the flow does not follow around the back side of the cylinder but separates from the surface near the minimum pressure point. This occurs at approximately 90° for a wide range of conditions. The region behind the cylinder is separated flow and is a region of relatively low, varying velocity and low pressure.

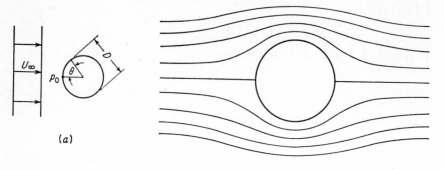

(a)

(b)

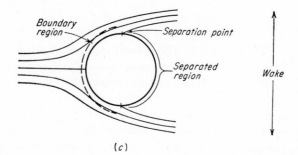

(c)

FIG. 6-1. Flow normal to a long cylinder. (a) Flow circumstance. (b) Inviscid flow. (c) Flow of a viscous fluid.

The downstream wake is a region of confused and turbulent flow. The effects of viscosity are of primary importance on the front half of the cylinder, and separation governs the process on the back half. Such a flow pattern results in appreciable drag.

Since fluids resist the rate of shear inherent in velocity gradients, shear stresses arise which are connected to the rate of shear by the viscosity. Consider two plates having a relative velocity U separated by a distance h. The space between is filled with a fluid. In the absence of acceleration and pressure gradients, the velocity distribution shown in Fig. 6-2 will result. (Recall that fluids do not slip in contact with solid surfaces.) The adjacent laminae of fluid in the space slide past each other, producing a rate of shear indicated by the gradient of u in the y direction. The shear stress which forces this rate of shear acts in a horizontal plane between adjacent laminae and is at least approximately proportional to the rate of shear:

$$\tau \propto \frac{du}{dy}$$

If, for a given fluid, the proportionality is exact, the fluid is called "newtonian." In this event a coefficient of viscosity μ is defined as the proportionality constant. Its value depends upon the nature of the fluid and upon its state:

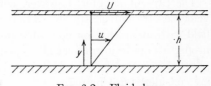

$$\tau = \mu \frac{du}{dy} \qquad (6\text{-}1)$$

Many fluids are approximately newtonian, and Eq. (6-1) is the basis

FIG. 6-2.   Fluid shear.

of much of the theory of viscous fluid flow. However, this relation is used in a more general form. The shear stress in a velocity field is equal to the viscosity times the rate of angular deformation of a fluid element.

The dimensions of viscosity are the product of stress (force per unit area) and time. In an M, L, T system this becomes M/LT. For metric and English units the results are

$$\frac{\text{g mass}}{\text{cm sec}} - \text{poise} \qquad \text{and} \qquad \frac{\text{lb mass}}{\text{ft sec}} - \frac{\text{lb}}{\text{ft sec}}$$

In an F, M, L, T system the results are

$$\frac{(\text{g force}) \text{ sec}}{\text{cm}^2} - \frac{\text{g sec}}{\text{cm}^2} \qquad \text{and} \qquad \frac{(\text{lb force}) \text{ sec}}{\text{ft}^2} - \frac{\text{lb sec}}{\text{ft}^2}$$

The first system is used throughout this book. For such units of μ, the conversion factor g_o must be introduced if τ is to be in lb force/ft^2, that is,

$$\tau = \frac{\mu}{g_o} \frac{du}{dy} \qquad \text{psf}$$

In English units $g_o = 32.17$ (lb mass) ft/(lb force) sec^2.

In fluid flow equations viscosity often appears divided by the fluid density. This combined quantity is called the kinematic viscosity and has the units shown below:

$$\nu = \frac{\mu}{\rho} \qquad \text{ft}^2/\text{sec} \qquad (6\text{-}2)$$

Numerous other characteristics of flow processes are important in determining rates of heat and mass transfer, friction losses, etc. Flow may be steady or unsteady. If unsteady, it may still be laminar, characterized by the laminae of fluid remaining distinct; or it may be turbulent, characterized by relatively violent and chaotic mixing processes which are described in terms of time average values. For either laminar or turbulent flow the velocity levels may be sufficiently high for compressibility effects in gases, for appreciable energy dissipation due to viscous effects in any fluid, and even for chemical effects induced by temperature increases resulting from compressibility and/or viscous-dissipation effects.

The present chapter, however, considers only processes for which the velocities are sufficiently low so that fluid elements move through the flow field with unvarying (or constant) properties. It is also assumed that the properties are uniform over all elements of the flow field. The more complicated aspects of flow which give rise to important temperature effects are considered in Chap. 7.

6-2. MASS CONTINUITY AND MOMENTUM EQUATIONS

Fluid flows in such a way that mass, momentum, and energy are conserved throughout the flow field. That is, a balance for each of these quantities must be satisfied everywhere. In addition, in the absence of chemical reaction, each chemical species must be conserved. In the present section the conditions for conservation of mass and of momentum will be derived for a fluid flow field having uniform and constant fluid properties ρ and μ. Constant density applies for incompressible fluids in a small temperature range and in the absence of appreciable diffusion of chemical species.

An x, y, z coordinate system is established in a fluid flow field. A differential element of volume ($dx\,dy\,dz$) is taken at an arbitrary point x, y, z (see Fig. 6-3). The state of the fluid and its transport properties at x, y, z are denoted by t, p, ρ, μ, and k. The velocity $\mathbf{V}$ at x, y, z is expressed in terms of its components u, v, and w in the x, y, and z directions, respectively.

For a constant, uniform-density fluid, the mass inside the volume ($dx\,dy\,dz$) must be constant for both steady and unsteady flow processes. Therefore, the sum of the rates of flow across the six faces of the element must be zero. The mass rate of flow in the x direction at x, y, z is (ρu) per unit area or ($\rho u\,dy\,dz$) for the element. The difference in mass-flow rate through the two faces perpendicular to the x direction is, therefore,

$$\frac{\partial}{\partial x}(\rho u\,dy\,dz)\,dx = dx\,dy\,dz\,\frac{\partial(\rho u)}{\partial x} = \rho\,dx\,dy\,dz\,\frac{\partial u}{\partial x}$$

The similar results for the y and z directions are

$$\frac{\partial}{\partial y}(\rho v\,dx\,dz)\,dy = \rho\,dx\,dy\,dz\,\frac{\partial v}{\partial y}$$

and

$$\frac{\partial}{\partial z}(\rho w\,dx\,dy)\,dz = \rho\,dx\,dy\,dz\,\frac{\partial w}{\partial z}$$

The continuity equation for the flow of a constant, uniform-density fluid is obtained by setting the sum of these three quantities equal to zero:

$$\frac{\partial u}{\partial x} + \frac{\partial v}{\partial y} + \frac{\partial w}{\partial z} = 0 = \text{div } \mathbf{V} \tag{6-3}$$

For variable density the sum of the mass rates of flow is set equal to the

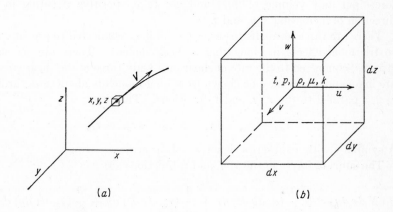

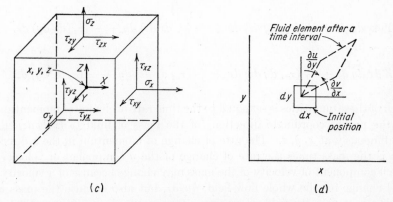

FIG. 6-3. Description of flow and stresses. (a) Typical volume element. (b) Conditions at x, y, z. (c) Shear and normal stresses. (d) Shear of an element.

time rate of mass decrease in volume $(dx\ dy\ dz)$. The result is

$$\frac{\partial(\rho u)}{\partial x} + \frac{\partial(\rho v)}{\partial y} + \frac{\partial(\rho w)}{\partial z} = -\frac{\partial \rho}{\partial \tau} \tag{6-4}$$

The condition of conservation of momentum, that is, the balance of forces and momentum changes, is next applied to the fluid instantaneously in the volume element $(dx\ dy\ dz)$. Since a balance may be written in each direction, x, y, and z, three equations result. The forces which must be accounted for in the balances are shown in Fig. 6-3c for three of the six faces. For each face one normal stress and two shear stresses are sufficient to describe the total force on the face. A body force, which may arise from gravitational, electrical, or magnetic effects, is shown in terms of its components X, Y, Z located at x, y, z. These are defined as the body forces per unit volume of fluid and are taken positive if acting in the direction of increasing x, y, and z.

There are three normal stresses, σ_x, σ_y, and σ_z, connected to pressure and to frictional effects in elongating a fluid element. There are six shear stresses, connected to the rate of shearing. Only three of the shear stresses are independent, as may be shown by taking moments about axes through x, y, z parallel to the x, y, and z directions. That is,

$$\tau_{xy} = \tau_{yx} \qquad \tau_{xz} = \tau_{zx} \qquad \tau_{yz} = \tau_{zy}$$

A symbol τ with a subscript denotes a shear stress.

The sums of forces in the x, y, and z directions are

$$X\ dx\ dy\ dz + \frac{\partial}{\partial x}(\sigma_x\ dy\ dz)\ dx + \frac{\partial}{\partial y}(\tau_{yx}\ dx\ dz)\ dy + \frac{\partial}{\partial z}(\tau_{zx}\ dx\ dy)\ dz$$

$$Y\ dx\ dy\ dz + \frac{\partial}{\partial x}(\tau_{xy}\ dy\ dz)\ dx + \frac{\partial}{\partial y}(\sigma_y\ dx\ dz)\ dy + \frac{\partial}{\partial z}(\tau_{zy}\ dx\ dy)\ dz$$

$$Z\ dx\ dy\ dz + \frac{\partial}{\partial x}(\tau_{xz}\ dy\ dz)\ dx + \frac{\partial}{\partial y}(\tau_{yz}\ dx\ dz)\ dy + \frac{\partial}{\partial z}(\sigma_z\ dx\ dy)\ dz$$

Each of these quantities is set equal to the time rate of change of momentum (in the proper coordinate direction) of the mass of fluid $(\rho\ dx\ dy\ dz)$ instantaneously at x, y, z. The rate of change of momentum in the x direction is the mass times the rate of change of the u component of velocity. The u component of velocity of the mass may change because of a velocity-level change for the whole flow field, $\partial u/\partial \tau$, but also because the mass is flowing in a velocity field whose instantaneous gradients in u, indicated by $\partial u/\partial x$, $\partial u/\partial y$, and $\partial u/\partial z$, are not zero. The fluid flows in the x direction at the rate of u and is, therefore, experiencing a velocity change per unit time, due to the velocity component u and velocity gradient $\partial u/\partial x$, equal to $u(\partial u/\partial x)$. Since u may also vary with y and z, motions in the y and z directions produce similar components, $v(\partial u/\partial y)$ and $w(\partial u/\partial z)$. The total time rate of change of the u component of the velocity of the fluid mass is, therefore,

$$\frac{\partial u}{\partial \tau} + u\frac{\partial u}{\partial x} + v\frac{\partial u}{\partial y} + w\frac{\partial u}{\partial z} = \frac{Du}{D\tau} \tag{6-5a}$$

where the total quantity, called the "substantive" or "particle" derivative, is denoted by the special symbol. The particle derivative evaluates the actual acceleration the particle is subject to while traveling along a streamline in a velocity field whose characteristics are described in terms of the usual types of derivatives.

The y- and z-direction accelerations are

$$\frac{\partial v}{\partial \tau} + u\frac{\partial v}{\partial x} + v\frac{\partial v}{\partial y} + w\frac{\partial v}{\partial z} = \frac{Dv}{D\tau} \tag{6-5b}$$

$$\frac{\partial w}{\partial \tau} + u\frac{\partial w}{\partial x} + v\frac{\partial w}{\partial y} + w\frac{\partial w}{\partial z} = \frac{Dw}{D\tau} \tag{6-5c}$$

The time rates of change of the components of momentum are

$$\rho\,dx\,dy\,dz\,\frac{Du}{D\tau} \qquad \rho\,dx\,dy\,dz\,\frac{Dv}{D\tau} \qquad \text{and} \qquad \rho\,dx\,dy\,dz\,\frac{Dw}{D\tau}$$

The three force-momentum balances are then

$$\rho\frac{Du}{D\tau} = X + \frac{\partial \sigma_x}{\partial x} + \frac{\partial \tau_{yz}}{\partial y} + \frac{\partial \tau_{zx}}{\partial z} \tag{6-6a}$$

$$\rho\frac{Dv}{D\tau} = Y + \frac{\partial \tau_{xy}}{\partial x} + \frac{\partial \sigma_y}{\partial y} + \frac{\partial \tau_{zy}}{\partial z} \tag{6-6b}$$

$$\rho\frac{Dw}{D\tau} = Z + \frac{\partial \tau_{xz}}{\partial x} + \frac{\partial \tau_{yz}}{\partial y} + \frac{\partial \sigma_z}{\partial z} \tag{6-6c}$$

The independent shear-stress quantities τ_{xy}, τ_{yz}, and τ_{xz} are related to the rates of shear in the xy, yz, and xz planes, respectively. In Fig. 6-3d, deformation due to shearing in the xy plane is shown. The angular-deformation rate is multiplied by the viscosity to obtain τ_{xy}. The other relations are similarly written:

$$\tau_{xy} = \mu \left(\frac{\partial u}{\partial y} + \frac{\partial v}{\partial x} \right) = \tau_{yx} \qquad (6\text{-}7a)$$

$$\tau_{yz} = \mu \left(\frac{\partial v}{\partial z} + \frac{\partial w}{\partial y} \right) = \tau_{zy} \qquad (6\text{-}7b)$$

$$\tau_{xz} = \mu \left(\frac{\partial u}{\partial z} + \frac{\partial w}{\partial x} \right) = \tau_{zx} \qquad (6\text{-}7c)$$

The normal stresses σ_x, σ_y, and σ_z were taken as positive outward and are equal to minus the pressure plus a viscous effect due to the rate of elongation of the element. The evaluation of this term is omitted here. The results are

$$\sigma_x = -p + 2\mu \frac{\partial u}{\partial x} \qquad (6\text{-}8a)$$

$$\sigma_y = -p + 2\mu \frac{\partial v}{\partial y} \qquad (6\text{-}8b)$$

$$\sigma_z = -p + 2\mu \frac{\partial w}{\partial z} \qquad (6\text{-}8c)$$

Equations (6-7) and (6-8) are substituted into Eqs. (6-6), the indicated differentiations are carried out, and the resulting equations, called the Navier-Stokes equations for an incompressible fluid, are written as follows:

$$\rho \frac{Du}{D\tau} = X - \frac{\partial p}{\partial x} + \mu \left(\frac{\partial^2 u}{\partial x^2} + \frac{\partial^2 u}{\partial y^2} + \frac{\partial^2 u}{\partial z^2} \right) = X - \frac{\partial p}{\partial x} + \mu \nabla^2 u \qquad (6\text{-}9a)$$

$$\rho \frac{Dv}{D\tau} = Y - \frac{\partial p}{\partial y} + \mu \left(\frac{\partial^2 v}{\partial x^2} + \frac{\partial^2 v}{\partial y^2} + \frac{\partial^2 v}{\partial z^2} \right) = Y - \frac{\partial p}{\partial y} + \mu \nabla^2 v \qquad (6\text{-}9b)$$

$$\rho \frac{Dw}{D\tau} = Z - \frac{\partial p}{\partial z} + \mu \left(\frac{\partial^2 w}{\partial x^2} + \frac{\partial^2 w}{\partial y^2} + \frac{\partial^2 w}{\partial z^2} \right) = Z - \frac{\partial p}{\partial z} + \mu \nabla^2 w \qquad (6\text{-}9c)$$

The four quantities in each equation are acceleration, body force, pressure force, and viscous force.

The Navier-Stokes equations for typical compressible fluids differ only in the normal stresses, which each have the following additive term in Eqs. (6-8):

$$-\tfrac{4}{3}\mu \ \text{div } \mathbf{V}$$

This is zero for incompressible fluids [see Eq. (6-3)]. This derivation may be studied in Schlichting (1955) or Kay (1957).

For flow which may be assumed inviscid, the last term in each Navier-Stokes equation disappears, and we have the Euler equations, which lead directly to the familiar Bernoulli equation.

The set of four equations (6-3) and (6-9) govern the nature of the velocity distribution in a uniform, constant-density flow field. They apply to steady and to unsteady flow. If sufficient boundary (and initial-flow) conditions are given to specify a problem, these four equations yield the distributions in space (and time) of the four quantities u, v, w, and p. These distributions are the solution of the problem.

Boundary conditions are determined for each particular problem. However, two general conditions apply in all cases. First, the fluid velocity component normal to a solid surface is zero at the fluid-solid interface. Second, for the "continuum" flow to which the above equations apply, the fluid velocity component tangential to the surface at the fluid-solid interface is also invariably taken equal to zero. That is, the fluid is not believed to slide in contact with the surface; the fluid always adheres to the surface. This principle, called the "no-slip hypothesis," has been supported by numerous experimental observations and by the successful predictions of the analyses based upon the hypothesis.

6-3. LAMINAR FLOW SOLUTIONS

There is no known general solution for the continuity and Navier-Stokes equations. However, many solutions of immense practical value have been obtained from these equations for certain particular circumstances in which the equations may be simplified. Numerous flow circumstances have been solved in detail. The present section considers two simple cases of steady, laminar flow: flow between infinite parallel plates (Couette flow) and flow in a circular tube. In the subsequent two sections one of the most important applications of the general equation, called boundary-layer theory, is considered.

Couette Flow. Consider two plates separated by a distance d, as shown in Fig. 6-4a. The bottom one is stationary, and the upper one moves at a constant velocity U. The space between the plates is filled with a fluid having properties ρ and μ. The coordinate system is chosen as shown. We assume that the fluid is subjected to a pressure gradient only in the x direction. The gradient will be constant because of the uniform spacing of the plates. Therefore, $v = 0$. Also, $w = 0$. The continuity equation (6-3) gives

$$\frac{\partial u}{\partial x} = 0$$

Therefore, u is a function only of y. The Navier-Stokes equations (6-9)

apply in a very simple form. The acceleration and body forces are zero.
Equations (6-9b) and (6-9c) disappear entirely, because the gradients and
velocity components are zero. Equation (6-9a) remains, in the simple form,

$$0 = -\frac{\partial p}{\partial x} + \mu \frac{\partial^2 u}{\partial y^2} \quad \text{or} \quad \frac{dp}{dx} = \mu \frac{d^2 u}{dy^2}$$

since p and u depend only upon x and y, respectively. The no-slip condition gives the necessary two boundary conditions:

at $y = 0$ $\qquad\qquad\qquad\qquad\qquad$ $u = 0$

at $y = d$ $\qquad\qquad\qquad\qquad\qquad$ $u = U$

The equation is solved and the constants evaluated:

$$u = \frac{1}{\mu}\left(\frac{dp}{dx}\right)\frac{y^2}{2} + C_1 y + C_2$$

$$C_2 = 0 \qquad C_1 = \frac{1}{d}\left(U - \frac{1}{\mu}\frac{dp}{dx}\frac{d^2}{2}\right)$$

$$u = \frac{1}{\mu}\left(-\frac{dp}{dx}\right)\frac{d^2}{2}\left(\frac{y}{d}\right)\left(1 - \frac{y}{d}\right) + \frac{y}{d}U$$

$$= N\left(\frac{y}{d}\right)\left(1 - \frac{y}{d}\right) + \frac{y}{d}U \qquad\qquad\qquad (6\text{-}10)$$

where $\qquad\qquad\qquad N = \frac{1}{\mu}\left(-\frac{dp}{dx}\right)\frac{d^2}{2} \qquad\qquad\qquad (6\text{-}11)$

This solution has many interesting features. If the pressure gradient is
zero, N is zero, and a linear distribution results, as shown in Fig. 6-4c.
The fluid is merely pulled along because of its adherence to the upper plate.
At the other extreme, $U = 0$, the flow is induced entirely by the pressure
gradient, and the parabolic distribution shown in Fig. 6-4b results. Various
values of N correspond to various pressure gradients. The general case of
neither U nor N equal to zero may be obtained by adding the $N = 0$ curve
of Fig. 6-4c to the curve of Fig. 6-4b drawn for a particular N. Several such
curves are plotted in Fig. 6-4c. For sufficiently adverse pressure gradients,
that is, $N/U < -1$, velocities in both directions may be found in the cross
section. For sufficiently favorable gradients, that is, $N/U > 1$, velocities
greater than U occur.

The above results may be used to obtain the relationship between pressure loss and average flow velocity for flow between stationary parallel

plates. For $U = 0$, the velocity distribution is

$$u = \frac{1}{\mu}\left(-\frac{dp}{dx}\right)\frac{d^2}{2}\left(\frac{y}{d}\right)\left(1 - \frac{y}{d}\right)$$

This parabolic velocity distribution is symmetric about the center of the passage. Therefore, the maximum u_m occurs at $y/d = \frac{1}{2}$ and is

$$u_m = \frac{1}{\mu}\left(-\frac{dp}{dx}\right)\frac{d^2}{8}$$

The relation between the average velocity V and the maximum velocity u_m could be obtained by integrating or by noting that the average height of a symmetric parabolic section is two-thirds of its maximum height:

$$V = \tfrac{2}{3}u_m = \frac{1}{\mu}\left(-\frac{dp}{dx}\right)\frac{d^2}{12}$$

or

$$\left(-\frac{dp}{dx}\right) = \frac{12\mu V}{d^2} = \frac{24}{\rho V d/\mu}\left(\frac{1}{d}\right)\frac{\rho V^2}{2}$$

If pressure is converted to force units and $\rho V d/\mu$ is denoted by N_{Re}, the

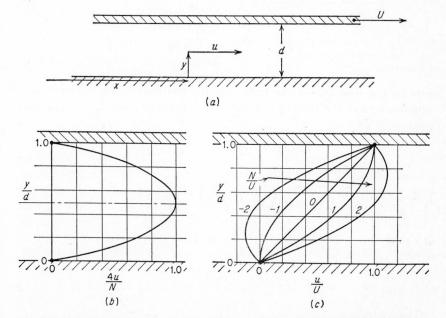

Fig. 6-4. Laminar flow between infinite plates. (a) Two plates at uniform separation. (b) Distribution of velocity, upper plate at rest. (c) Distribution of velocity, upper plate in motion.

passage Reynolds number, the equation becomes

$$\left(-\frac{dp}{dx}\right) = \frac{24}{N_{\text{Re}}}\left(\frac{1}{d}\right)\frac{\rho V^2}{2g_o} = f\left(\frac{1}{d}\right)\frac{\rho V^2}{2g_o} \tag{6-12}$$

where f is the flow "friction factor." This is the form in which flow-loss equations are usually written.

Flow in a Circular Tube. The same type of analysis may be applied to the developed, steady, laminar flow of a fluid through a circular tube of radius R. Only an axial pressure gradient need be considered, and nonaxial velocity components are zero. The no-slip condition at the wall is symmetric about the tube axis; therefore, the velocity distribution is also symmetric. The continuity and Navier-Stokes equations are most simply applied to this case in their cylindrical-coordinate form.

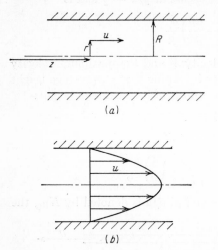

FIG. 6-5. Laminar flow through a circular tube. (a) Coordinate system. (b) Velocity distribution.

Taking r as the distance from the tube axis, the velocity parallel to the axis as u, and z as the coordinate in the direction of the tube axis, the continuity and Navier-Stokes equations yield the following result. The boundary conditions are also written.

$$\frac{\partial u}{\partial z} = 0 \qquad \text{that is} \qquad u = f(r)$$

$$\mu\left(\frac{d^2u}{dr^2} + \frac{1}{r}\frac{du}{dr}\right) = \frac{dp}{dz}$$

at $r = 0$ $\dfrac{du}{dr} = 0$

at $r = \dfrac{d}{2}$ $u = 0$

The solution is

$$u = \frac{1}{\mu}\left(-\frac{dp}{dz}\right)\frac{R^2}{4}\left[1 - \left(\frac{y}{R}\right)^2\right] \tag{6-13}$$

This parabolic distribution is plotted in Fig. 6-5b. The maximum velocity may be found from Eq. (6-13), and we note that the average velocity V is one-half the maximum velocity. That is, the average height of a paraboloid of revolution is one-half its maximum height:

$$V = \frac{u_m}{2} = \frac{1}{\mu}\left(-\frac{dp}{dz}\right)\frac{R^2}{8} = \frac{1}{\mu}\left(-\frac{dp}{dz}\right)\frac{D^2}{32}$$

This result is rewritten in the form of Eq. (6-12) as

$$\left(-\frac{dp}{dz}\right) = \frac{32\mu V}{D^2} = \frac{64}{N_{\text{Re}}}\frac{1}{D}\frac{\rho V^2}{2g_o} = f\frac{1}{D}\frac{\rho V^2}{2g_o} \tag{6-14}$$

This equation provides the relation between pressure loss, Reynolds number, diameter, and a quantity proportional to dynamic pressure for steady, laminar flow in a circular tube. Laminar flow in a tube results for flow Reynolds numbers less than about 2000.

Example 6-1. Oil, having a viscosity of 0.025 lb/ft sec and a density of 50 lb/ft³, flows through a 1-in.-ID tube at a rate of 0.2 cfs. We wish to find the Reynolds number, the maximum velocity, and the pressure gradient due to viscous effects.

$$V = \frac{Q}{A} = \frac{0.20}{\pi/144} = 9.17 \text{ fps} \qquad \frac{VD\rho}{\mu} = \frac{9.17 \times 50}{12 \times 0.025} = 1530$$

$$u_m = 2V = 18.34 \text{ fps}$$

$$f = \frac{64}{1530} = 0.0418 \qquad \frac{\rho V^2}{2g_o} = 65.3 \text{ psf}$$

$$\left(-\frac{dp}{dx}\right) = f\frac{1}{D}\frac{\rho V^2}{2g_o} = 0.0418 \times 12 \times 65.3 = 32.7 \text{ psf/ft}$$

6-4. LAMINAR BOUNDARY-LAYER EQUATIONS

The boundary-layer concept, initiated by Prandtl in 1904 but little applied for several subsequent decades, has been widely used in recent years to obtain solutions to many important problems. At the base of this concept lies the principle that, for many conditions of flow of a viscous fluid over a surface, the effects of fluid viscosity and of the no-slip surface condition are important only in a very narrow region adjacent to the surface. This region is called the "boundary region," and the layer of affected fluid is called the "boundary layer."

The boundary-layer interpretation is valid only for portions of the surface for which the main flow remains attached, that is, unseparated.

We shall see subsequently that the boundary layer is thin compared with the significant dimension of the body for high Reynolds number flows.

If the conditions for the boundary-region hypothesis are met, the flow field may be separated into two regions: the main flow, which is inviscid and is described by the simpler Euler equations; and the boundary region, in which the Navier-Stokes equations apply. Prandtl showed that, because of the nature of flow in thin layers, the Navier-Stokes equations could be

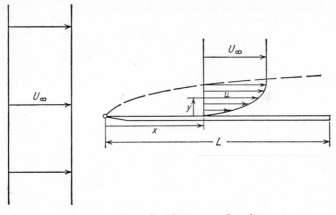

FIG. 6-6.   Boundary layer on a flat plate.

reduced to a much simpler form, called the "boundary-layer equations." The complete solution of a problem then proceeds by solving the main inviscid flow field, by the methods of hydrodynamics. The resulting pressure distribution is then applied to the boundary layer to solve the boundary-layer equations.

The boundary-layer equations are developed below. For simplicity, consider two-dimensional flow over a flat plate at zero angle of incidence, as diagramed in Fig. 6-6. The stream approaches at a uniform velocity U_∞. A boundary region forms in which the fluid is decelerated by viscous action. A v component of velocity arises. The local thickness of the boundary region is denoted by δ. The relevant Navier-Stokes equations, the continuity equation, and the boundary conditions are shown below. The pressure terms are zero for a flat plate but are retained for later reference.

$$u\frac{\partial u}{\partial x} + v\frac{\partial u}{\partial y} = -\frac{1}{\rho}\frac{\partial p}{\partial x} + \frac{\mu}{\rho}\left(\frac{\partial^2 u}{\partial x^2} + \frac{\partial^2 u}{\partial y^2}\right) \qquad (6\text{-}15a)$$

$$u\frac{\partial v}{\partial x} + v\frac{\partial v}{\partial y} = -\frac{1}{\rho}\frac{\partial p}{\partial y} + \frac{\mu}{\rho}\left(\frac{\partial^2 v}{\partial x^2} + \frac{\partial^2 v}{\partial y^2}\right) \qquad (6\text{-}15b)$$

$$\frac{\partial u}{\partial x} + \frac{\partial v}{\partial y} = 0 \qquad (6\text{-}16)$$

at $y = 0$ $\qquad\qquad u = 0 \qquad$ and $\qquad v = 0$

as $y \to \infty$ $\qquad\qquad u \to U_\infty$

These equations are simplified by determining the relative magnitudes of the various terms. First, the variables u, v, x, y, and δ are generalized:

$$x' = \frac{x}{L} \qquad y' = \frac{y}{L} \qquad \delta' = \frac{\delta}{L} \qquad u' = \frac{u}{U_\infty} \qquad v' = \frac{v}{U_\infty}$$

These substitutions are applied to Eqs. (6-15) and (6-16), and the results are rearranged to give

$$u' \frac{\partial u'}{\partial x'} + v' \frac{\partial u'}{\partial y'} = \frac{\mu}{\rho U_\infty L} \left(\frac{\partial^2 u'}{\partial x'^2} + \frac{\partial^2 u'}{\partial y'^2} \right) \qquad (6\text{-}17a)$$

$$\quad\; 1 \quad\; 1 \qquad \delta' \;\; \tfrac{1}{\delta'} \qquad\quad \delta'^2 \qquad\quad 1 \qquad\quad \tfrac{1}{\delta'^2}$$

$$u' \frac{\partial v'}{\partial x'} + v' \frac{\partial v'}{\partial y'} = \frac{\mu}{\rho U_\infty L} \left(\frac{\partial^2 v'}{\partial x'^2} + \frac{\partial^2 v'}{\partial y'^2} \right) \qquad (6\text{-}17b)$$

$$\quad\; 1 \;\; \delta' \qquad \delta' \;\; 1 \qquad\quad \delta'^2 \qquad\quad \delta' \qquad\quad \tfrac{1}{\delta'}$$

$$\frac{\partial u'}{\partial x'} + \frac{\partial v'}{\partial y'} = 0 \qquad (6\text{-}18)$$

at $y' = 0$ $\qquad\qquad u' = 0 \qquad$ and $\qquad v' = 0$

as $y' \to \infty$ $\qquad\qquad u' \to 1$

Since u' changes from 1 at $x' = 0$ to a small value at $x' = 1$, the derivative of u' with respect to x' is of order 1, that is,

$$\frac{\partial u'}{\partial x'} = O(1)$$

Therefore, from Eq. (6-18),

$$\frac{\partial v'}{\partial y'} = O(1)$$

Since v' changes from 0 to its maximum value as y' changes from 0 to δ', the above result may be integrated to give

$$v' = O(\delta')$$

The following estimates are made by similar arguments:

$$\frac{\partial^2 v'}{\partial y'^2} = O\left(\frac{1}{\delta'}\right) \qquad \frac{\partial u'}{\partial y'} = O\left(\frac{1}{\delta'}\right) \qquad \frac{\partial^2 u}{\partial y'^2} = O\left(\frac{1}{\delta'^2}\right)$$

$$\frac{\partial v'}{\partial x'} = O(\delta') \qquad \frac{\partial^2 v'}{\partial x'^2} = O(\delta') \qquad \frac{\partial^2 u'}{\partial x'^2} = O(1)$$

These estimates are written under the appropriate terms of Eqs. (6-17). The orders of the terms on the left-hand sides of Eqs. (6-17a) and (6-17b) are 1 and δ', respectively. Comparing the terms on the left- and right-hand sides of Eq. (6-17a), we see that if the viscous forces and momentum-transport rate are to be of the same order of magnitude, as is the case in the boundary region, the following quantity must be of order 1:

$$\left(\frac{\mu}{\rho U_\infty L}\right)\left(\frac{\partial^2 u'}{\partial x'^2} + \frac{\partial^2 u'}{\partial y'^2}\right) \approx \left(\frac{\mu}{\rho U_\infty L}\right)\frac{\partial^2 u'}{\partial y'^2} = O(1)$$

Therefore,
$$\frac{\mu}{\rho U_\infty L} = O(\delta'^2) \tag{6-19a}$$

This result shows that the boundary-layer thickness divided by the plate length is inversely proportional to the square root of the plate Reynolds number, $\rho U_\infty L/\mu$.

$$\frac{\delta}{L} \propto \frac{1}{\sqrt{\rho U_\infty L/\mu}} = \frac{1}{\sqrt{N_{\mathrm{Re},L}}} \tag{6-19b}$$

That is, a thin boundary region results for relatively high Reynolds number flow.

If the result in Eq. (6-19a) is introduced into Eq. (6-17b), we see that all terms in this equation are of order δ' or less. Therefore, this equation is of negligible importance compared with Eqs. (6-17a) and (6-18) for high Reynolds number flow. The resulting boundary-layer equations for a flat plate are written below with the necessary boundary conditions:

$$u\frac{\partial u}{\partial x} + v\frac{\partial u}{\partial y} = \nu\frac{\partial^2 u}{\partial y^2} \tag{6-20}$$

$$\frac{\partial u}{\partial x} + \frac{\partial v}{\partial y} = 0 \tag{6-21}$$

at $y = 0$ $u = 0$ and $v = 0$

as $y \to \infty$ $u \to U_\infty$

This type of analysis was carried out by Prandtl for a curved wall. The pressure terms were retained, and $\partial p / \partial y$ was shown to be of negligible magnitude. Therefore, the boundary-layer pressure field is a function only of x and is determined by the external inviscid flow field. The more general boundary-layer equations and boundary conditions are

$$u \frac{\partial u}{\partial x} + v \frac{\partial u}{\partial y} = -\frac{1}{\rho} \frac{dp}{dx} + v \frac{\partial^2 u}{\partial y^2} \tag{6-22}$$

$$\frac{\partial u}{\partial x} + \frac{\partial v}{\partial y} = 0 \tag{6-23}$$

at $y = 0$ $u = 0$ and $v = 0$

as $y \to \infty$ $u \to U(x)$ where $-\frac{1}{\rho} \frac{dp}{dx} = U(x) \frac{dU(x)}{dx}$

Tollmien, in 1931, repeated the analysis for curved surfaces to determine the effect of changes in the local radius of curvature R on the boundary-layer approximations. The effect was shown to be negligible if R does not change too rapidly with x, that is, if dR/dx is small.

A similar boundary-layer reduction of the Navier-Stokes equations for compressible flow may be carried out. However, the question of compressible flow is left to the next chapter.

The effect of boundary-layer theory is, then, to reduce the problem from one of solving Eqs. (6-15) and (6-16) over the total flow field to a problem of solving the Euler equations outside the boundary region and Eqs. (6-22) and (6-23) inside the boundary region. Since inviscid flow solutions are often known or obtainable and since Eqs. (6-22) and (6-23) may be solved with reasonable accuracy, considerable success has been achieved with the boundary-layer method of analysis.

6-5. LAMINAR BOUNDARY-LAYER SOLUTIONS

In order to demonstrate the use of the boundary-layer concept and to show the detailed nature of boundary-layer flow, one of the simplest cases, that of a flat plate at zero angle of incidence, is considered in detail.

The principal difficulty in the use of a set of equations such as (6-22) and (6-23) is their partial differential form. The components u and v each apparently vary with x and y independently. However, because of the form of boundary-layer equations, it is often possible (for some boundary conditions) to determine a new variable η which combines the effects of x and y

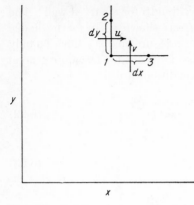

FIG. 6-7. Relation between the velocity components and the stream function.

and reduces the two partial differential equations to one ordinary differential equation. That is, if η is properly chosen, as a combination of x and y, u may become a function only of η. Such a variable is called a "similarity variable," and the velocity distributions at all points along the surface are similar when expressed in terms of η.

The Boundary Layer on a Flat Plate. Prandtl showed that such a transformation is possible for the flat-plate case, Eqs. (6-20) and (6-21) with the relevant boundary conditions. Since u increases from zero at $y = 0$ to U_∞ at $y \approx \delta$ and since δ is proportional to $\sqrt{vx/U_\infty}$, as suggested by Eq. (6-19b), we might expect u to be a function of x and y only in the following combination:

$$\eta = \frac{y}{\sqrt{vx/U_\infty}} = y\sqrt{\frac{U_\infty}{vx}} \tag{6-24}$$

The reduction of Eqs. (6-20) and (6-21) proceeds in the following way. The continuity equation may be integrated by defining a stream function $\psi(x,y)$ as the quantity whose difference between two points in the xy plane is equal to the average velocity of fluid flow through the space separating these points. Flow in the clockwise direction is considered positive. The relation between $\psi(x,y)$ and the velocity components u and v may be seen in Fig. 6-7. The change in $\psi(x,y)$ between points 1 and 2 is equal to u, and the change between points 1 and 3 is equal to $-v$:

$$\frac{\partial \psi(x,y)}{\partial y} dy = u\, dy \qquad \text{and} \qquad \frac{\partial \psi}{\partial y} = u$$

$$\frac{\partial \psi(x,y)}{\partial x} dx = -v\, dx \qquad \text{and} \qquad \frac{\partial \psi}{\partial x} = -v$$

Therefore, $\dfrac{\partial u}{\partial x} + \dfrac{\partial v}{\partial y} = \dfrac{\partial}{\partial x}\dfrac{\partial \psi}{\partial y} - \dfrac{\partial}{\partial y}\dfrac{\partial \psi}{\partial x} = 0$

and ψ, defined in this way, satisfies the continuity equation.

The stream function $\psi(x,y)$ is replaced by a function $f(\eta)$ of the similarity variable η:

$$\psi = \sqrt{\nu x U_\infty}\, f(\eta) \tag{6-25}$$

The velocity components and their derivatives are determined in terms of η and $f(\eta)$, from Eqs. (6-24) and (6-25), for substitution into Eq. (6-20):

$$u = \frac{\partial \psi}{\partial y} = \sqrt{\nu x U_\infty}\, \frac{\partial f(\eta)}{\partial y} = \sqrt{\nu x U_\infty}\, \frac{\partial f(\eta)}{\partial \eta}\frac{\partial \eta}{\partial y} = U_\infty f' \tag{6-26}$$

$$v = -\frac{\partial \psi}{\partial x} = -f(\eta)\frac{\partial \sqrt{\nu x U_\infty}}{\partial x} - \sqrt{\nu x U_\infty}\,\frac{\partial f(\eta)}{\partial \eta}\frac{\partial \eta}{\partial x}$$

$$= \frac{1}{2}\sqrt{\frac{\nu U_\infty}{x}}\,(\eta f' - f) \tag{6-27}$$

$$\frac{\partial u}{\partial x} = U_\infty \frac{\partial f'(\eta)}{\partial \eta}\frac{\partial \eta}{\partial x} = -\frac{U_\infty f'' y}{2}\sqrt{\frac{U_\infty}{\nu x^3}} = -\frac{U_\infty f'' \eta}{2x}$$

$$\frac{\partial u}{\partial y} = U_\infty \sqrt{\frac{U_\infty}{\nu x}}\, f''$$

Equation (6-20) becomes

$$ff'' + 2f''' = 0 \tag{6-28}$$

at $\eta = 0$ $f = 0$ and $f' = 0$

as $\eta \to \infty$ $f' \to 1$

The primes denote differentiation with respect to η. The boundary conditions are obtained from those for Eq. (6-20), using the relations between u, v, x, y, and f, η. For example, for $y = 0$, $\eta = 0$, and for $u = 0$, $f' = 0$.

Equation (6-28) is simpler than Eqs. (6-20) and (6-21). However, it is still very complicated, being of the third order and nonlinear. No exact, explicit solution is known.

Numerous approximate solutions have been obtained. The first was found by Blasius, in 1908, and employs a series expansion of the stream function. Computations by Howarth (1938) for surfaces with pressure gradients yield accurate information for the zero-angle-of-incidence case. The values of f, f', and f'' are presented as functions of η. The results are listed in Table 6-1. The velocity distributions are related to these values by Eqs. (6-26) and (6-27) and are plotted in Fig. 6-8.

TABLE 6-1. LAMINAR BOUNDARY-LAYER SOLUTION FOR A FLAT PLATE AT ZERO
ANGLE OF INCIDENCE *

η	f	$f' = u/U_\infty$	f''	$\frac{1}{2}(\eta f' - f)$
0	0	0	0.33206	0
0.2	0.00664	0.06641	0.33199	0.00332
0.4	0.02656	0.13277	0.33147	0.01328
0.8	0.10611	0.26471	0.32739	0.05283
1.2	0.23795	0.39378	0.31659	0.11730
1.6	0.42032	0.51676	0.29667	0.20325
2.0	0.65003	0.62977	0.26675	0.30469
2.4	0.92230	0.72899	0.22809	0.41364
2.8	0.23099	0.81152	0.18401	0.52064
3.2	1.56911	0.87609	0.13913	0.61719
3.6	1.92954	0.92333	0.09809	0.69723
4.0	2.30576	0.95552	0.06424	0.75816
4.4	2.69238	0.97587	0.03897	0.80073
4.8	3.08534	0.98779	0.02187	0.82803
5.0	3.28329	0.99155	0.01591	0.83723
5.2	3.48189	0.99425	0.01134	0.84411
5.6	3.88031	0.99748	0.00543	0.85279
6.0	4.27964	0.99898	0.00240	0.85712
6.4	4.67938	0.99961	0.00098	0.85906
6.8	5.07928	0.99987	0.00037	0.85992
7.2	5.47925	0.99996	0.00013	0.86023
7.6	5.87924	0.99999	0.00004	0.86034
8.0	6.27923	1.00000	0.00001	0.86039
8.4	6.67923	1.00000	0.00000	0.86039

* Arranged from the results of Howarth (1938).

The u and v distributions approach their asymptotic values rapidly, and u/U_∞ is within 1 per cent of 1.0 at $\eta = 5.0$. If the local boundary-layer thickness δ is defined as the distance out from the surface at which the velocity component u reaches 99 per cent of the free-stream value U_∞, we have

$$\eta = 5.0 = y \sqrt{\frac{U_\infty}{\nu x}} = \delta \sqrt{\frac{U_\infty}{\nu x}}$$

or

$$\frac{\delta}{x} = \frac{5.0}{\sqrt{U_\infty x/\nu}} = \frac{5.0}{\sqrt{N_{\mathrm{Re},x}}} \tag{6-29}$$

That is, the boundary-layer thickness, expressed as a fraction of the distance from the leading edge, is inversely proportional to the square root of $U_\infty x/\nu$, which is defined as the local boundary-layer Reynolds number. This quantity varies from zero at the leading edge to the plate Reynolds number at the trailing edge.

The shear stress at the surface of the plate $\tau_0(x)$ may be determined from the rate of fluid shear in the boundary layer at $y = 0$, that is, at $\eta = 0$:

$$\tau_0(x) = \mu \left(\frac{\partial u}{\partial y}\right)_0 = \mu U_\infty \sqrt{\frac{U_\infty}{\nu x}} f''(0) = 0.332 \mu U_\infty \sqrt{\frac{U_\infty}{\nu x}}$$

or

$$\frac{\tau_0(x)}{\rho U_\infty^2/2} = \frac{0.664}{\sqrt{N_{\text{Re},x}}} \tag{6-30}$$

The shear stress is seen to decrease with a thickening of the boundary layer at increasing x. The total drag F_D, per unit plate width, is found by integration:

$$F_D = \int_0^L \tau_0(x)\, dx = 0.664 \mu U_\infty \sqrt{\frac{U_\infty L}{\nu}} \tag{6-31}$$

The coefficient of drag of a body immersed in a flowing fluid is defined as the drag force divided by the product of the dynamic pressure and a significant area of the object under consideration. For a plate, the area is the

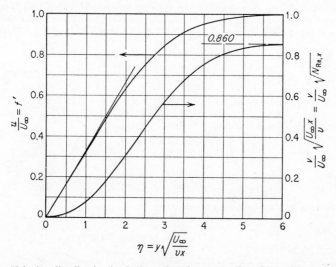

Fig. 6-8. Velocity distribution in the boundary layer on a flat plate. [*From the computations by Howarth* (1938).]

length times the width. The coefficient of drag becomes

$$C_D = \frac{F_D}{L(\rho U_\infty^2/2)} = \frac{1.328}{\sqrt{U_\infty L/\nu}} = \frac{1.328}{\sqrt{N_{\text{Re},L}}} \qquad (6\text{-}32)$$

The solution discussed above is of sufficient precision to satisfy the demands of accuracy of virtually any application of the results. The calculated results have been checked by numerous measurements of boundary-layer velocity distributions, shear-stress distributions, and total-drag characteristics. Such measurements are in very close agreement with the predicted behavior.

There is a limit to the use of the above results, however. They apply only for a laminar boundary layer. A laminar boundary layer becomes unstable at a high Reynolds number and undergoes a transition to a turbulent boundary layer. The upper limit of laminar flow is somewhat indistinct, depending upon the roughness of the surface and upon the level of the disturbances (or turbulence) in the free stream. For a smooth plate in a stream having the disturbance levels customarily encountered, transition occurs at a sufficient distance x from the leading edge to result in a local boundary-layer Reynolds number in the range 300,000 to 500,000. For very low turbulence streams, much higher transition Reynolds numbers have been observed. Transition is also delayed by a favorable pressure gradient.

Example 6-2. A plate 1 ft long is placed at zero angle of incidence in a stream of 60°F water moving at 3 fps. We shall find the velocity component parallel to the plate at the midpoint of the boundary layer, the maximum boundary-layer thickness, and the maximum value of the normal component of velocity at the trailing edge of the plate.

$$\mu = 2.72 \text{ lb/hr ft} \qquad \rho = 62.4 \text{ psf}$$

From Howarth's solution, the midpoint is at $\eta = 2.5$, at which $f' = 0.751$. Therefore,

$$\frac{u}{U_\infty} = 0.751 \qquad \text{and} \qquad u = 3 \times 0.751 = 2.25 \text{ fps}$$

The maximum value of δ occurs at $x = 1$ ft.

$$\frac{U_\infty L \rho}{\mu} = \frac{3 \times 1 \times 62.4 \times 3600}{2.72} = 248,000$$

$$\delta_L = \frac{5L}{\sqrt{N_{\text{Re},L}}} = \frac{5 \times 1}{498} = 0.0101 \text{ ft, or } 0.121 \text{ in.}$$

v increases with y to the following asymptote:

$$\frac{v_\infty}{U_\infty} \sqrt{\frac{U_\infty x}{v}} = 0.860$$

$$v_{\infty,L} = \frac{0.860 U_\infty}{\sqrt{N_{\text{Re},L}}} = \frac{0.860 \times 3}{498} = 0.00518 \text{ fps}$$

Laminar Boundary Layers with Pressure Gradients. Solutions of boundary-layer problems in the presence of a pressure gradient are somewhat more difficult and in some cases impossible. The differential equations (6-22) and (6-23) and the accompanying boundary conditions are more complicated. The proper similarity variable η is also more complicated. For some types of boundary conditions no similarity variable exists. A detailed consideration of this question is given by Schlichting (1955).

An important class of problems which possess a similarity variable involves the flow of fluid in the vicinity of the stagnation point of a wedge of included angle $\beta\pi$, as shown in Fig. 6-9a. For this flow the solution for an inviscid fluid indicates a velocity distribution at the surface of the wedge which varies as x^m, where m is related to the wedge-angle parameter β as follows:

$$U(x) = Cx^m \tag{6-33}$$

$$m = \frac{\beta}{2 - \beta} \tag{6-34}$$

The similarity variable for the boundary-layer equation for this case was determined by Falkner and Skan (1931) to be

$$\eta = y\sqrt{\frac{m + 1}{2} \frac{U(x)}{\nu x}} = y\sqrt{\frac{m + 1}{2} \frac{c}{\nu}}\, x^{(m-1)/2} \tag{6-35}$$

A generalized stream function f is again employed. Equations (6-22) and (6-23) and the associated boundary conditions reduce to

$$f''' + ff'' + \beta(1 - f'^2) = 0 \tag{6-36}$$

at $\eta = 0$ $\qquad\qquad$ $f = 0$ $\quad$ and $\quad$ $f' = 0$

as $\eta \to \infty$ $\qquad\qquad$ $f' \to 1$

This result reduces to that of the flat plate for $\beta = 0$. However, in general, the problem contains the parameter β. Therefore, a solution may be found for each value of β. Hartree (1937) determined solutions for various values of β from -0.1988 to 2.4. Negative values of β refer to corners which turn the flow away from the stream. The lowest value of β is for the minimum angle of turning, away from the flow, which produces flow separation. The u-component distributions for several wedge angles are shown in Fig. 6-9b.

Several values of β are of special interest. $\beta = 0$ is the flat plate; therefore, this distribution repeats that in Fig. 6-8. $\beta = 1.0$ is a plate perpendicular to the flow or, in fact, any surface normal to the flow at the stagnation point.

Boundary-layer solutions have been obtained for many additional two- and three-dimensional cases for compressible and incompressible fluids. The most recent general summary of these results is given by Schlichting (1960).

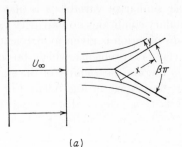

(a)

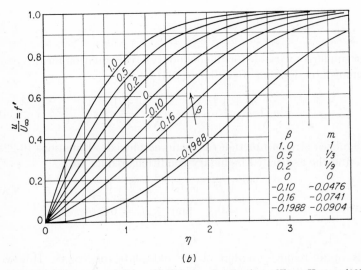

(b)

FIG. 6-9. (a) Flow over a wedge. (b) Velocity distribution. [From Hartree (1937).]

6-6. TURBULENCE AND TURBULENT EXCHANGE PROCESSES

The equations of motion derived in Sec. 6-2 apply to fluid flow processes in general. However, the boundary-layer equations and solutions discussed in preceding sections are for steady, laminar flow. Many, in fact most, of the transport processes which must be considered in engineering design involve unsteady and/or turbulent flow. Turbulent flow is inherently unsteady, in the sense that the velocity at any point in the fluid varies in time. In "steady," turbulent flow, this variation of velocity at each point occurs around a constant average value. The present section discusses this type of flow.

In a field of turbulently flowing fluid many flow disturbances are super-imposed upon the average velocity of motion. These disturbances may be looked upon as eddies of fluid moving with the stream. The flow field is composed of eddies of all sizes and velocities. The detailed description of a turbulent velocity field is in terms of the instantaneous values of the velocity components u, v, w over the flow field. The instantaneous value of each component may be written as its average value plus a fluctuating component, which is time-dependent:

$$u = \bar{u} + u' \tag{6-37}$$

$$v = \bar{v} + v' \tag{6-38}$$

$$w = \bar{w} + w' \tag{6-39}$$

The time average values of u', v', and w' are zero.

The magnitude of velocity fluctuation is a measure of the violence or intensity of the disturbances, and the following quantity is called the "intensity" of the turbulence:

$$i = \frac{\sqrt{\frac{1}{3}(\overline{u'^2} + \overline{v'^2} + \overline{w'^2})}}{V} \tag{6-40}$$

where V is the average velocity.

Intensity is only one aspect of a turbulent flow field. Many other quanti-ties have been defined that further characterize the nature of the disturb-ances. For example, it is often important to know whether or not the u', v', and w' disturbances at any given point are related to one another. Does the value of u' have any relation to the value of v' at any given time? Are u' and v' correlated? Correlation coefficients may be defined for each pair of components. The u', v' coefficient is shown below:

$$R = \frac{\overline{u'v'}}{\sqrt{\overline{u'^2}}\sqrt{\overline{v'^2}}} \tag{6-41}$$

If the characteristics of the turbulence are independent of direction, the field is said to be isotropic, and such correlation coefficients are zero. Free turbulence, that is, turbulent flow distant from surfaces, tends to be isotropic. In the presence of shear stresses nonzero correlations are found.

Another aspect of turbulence is the approximate physical size of the fluid particles in a flow disturbance. This quantity is measured by defining a scale of turbulence. General discussions of turbulence quantities and of

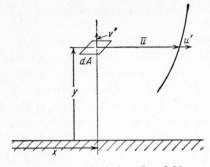

Fig. 6-10. Turbulent flow field.

characteristics of turbulence may be found in Corcoran, Opfell, and Sage (1956) and Knudsen and Katz (1958). A detailed summary of the nature of turbulence was recently published by Hinze (1959).

Since thermal energy, momentum, and mass are diffused in a flow stream by the disturbances which characterize turbulence, the simple expressions between flux and gradient, such as Eqs. (1-3) and (6-1), are inapplicable. These relations apply for molecular diffusion; the eddy processes produce an additional and additive transport process. In an early attempt to quantize the diffusion of momentum by eddy processes, Boussinesq defined an "eddy viscosity" A which relates the shear-stress equivalent of the momentum transport by turbulence to the gradient of the time average velocity:

$$\tau_t = A \frac{d\bar{u}}{dy} \tag{6-42}$$

However, A does not have the simplicity of the molecular viscosity μ. The latter is primarily a function of fluid state, whereas A depends primarily upon the nature of the turbulence, as is shown subsequently.

Consider turbulent flow parallel to a wall, as shown in Fig. 6-10. At point x, y consider the rate of flow of x-direction momentum toward the wall across area dA perpendicular to the y axis. The instantaneous velocity normal to dA is $-v = -v'$, since $\bar{v} = 0$. The mass rate of flow across dA is $-\rho v' \, dA$, and the x-direction momentum per unit mass is u. The rate of momentum transport is $-\rho v' u \, dA$ and is set equal to a shear-stress equivalent, called the turbulent shear stress, times the area dA:

$$\tau_t' \, dA = -\rho u v' \, dA$$

The average value of τ_t is found by averaging uv', assuming ρ constant.

$$\overline{\tau_t'} = \tau_t = -\rho \overline{uv'} = -\rho \overline{(\bar{u} + u')v'} = -\rho \overline{(\bar{u}v' + u'v')}$$

$$= -\rho(\overline{\bar{u}v'} + \overline{u'v'}) = -\rho(\bar{u}\bar{v}' + \overline{u'v'})$$

$$= -\rho \overline{u'v'} \tag{6-43}$$

Although both $\overline{u'}$ and $\overline{v'}$ are zero, $\overline{u'v'}$ is not necessarily zero. If values of u' and v' are connected, $\overline{u'v'}$ need not be zero. The correlation coefficient defined in Eq. (6-41) measures this characteristic of the flow field. Comparing Eqs. (6-42) and (6-43), the eddy viscosity becomes

$$A = -\frac{\overline{\rho u'v'}}{\dfrac{d\bar{u}}{dy}} \tag{6-44}$$

Clearly this quantity is primarily dependent upon the nature of the flow field, which depends in turn upon fluid properties and upon the geometry of the passage.

The total flux of momentum, thermal energy, and mass may be written as the sum of the molecular and eddy components. These relations are written below in terms of diffusivities:

$$\frac{\tau}{\rho} = \frac{\tau_m + \tau_t}{\rho} = (\nu + \epsilon_M)\frac{d\bar{u}}{dy} \tag{6-45}$$

$$\frac{q''}{\rho c_p} = \frac{q''_m + q''_t}{\rho c_p} = (\alpha + \epsilon_H)\frac{d\bar{t}}{dy} \tag{6-46}$$

$$m'' = m''_m + m''_t = (D + \epsilon_C)\frac{d\bar{C}}{dy} \tag{6-47}$$

where ϵ_M, ϵ_H, and ϵ_C are the eddy diffusivities of momentum, thermal energy, and chemical species, respectively.

The equation for the diffusion of a chemical species, (6-47), is based upon a form for the molecular diffusion of a chemical species similar to Eq. (1-3) for thermal energy and to Eq. (6-1) for momentum. That is,

$$m'' = -D\frac{dC}{dy}$$

where C is the local concentration of the diffusing species and m'' is the rate of diffusion in the y direction per unit area normal to y. D is the diffusion coefficient which has the dimensions of a diffusivity L^2/T if m'' and C are in similar units. The above relation for chemical (or mass) diffusion is limited to circumstances in which the concentration gradients are small. Diffusion coefficients D for the diffusion of gases and vapors in air are tabulated in Table A-12.

The formulations of Eqs. (6-45) to (6-47) are used in subsequent sections to infer temperature and concentration distributions from momentum-transport information.

6-7. TURBULENT FRICTION LOSS AND VELOCITY DISTRIBUTION

In Sec. 6-3 a solution was obtained for the velocity distribution and the friction-loss characteristics in steady, laminar flow in passages. These results for a circular tube are given by Eqs. (6-13) and (6-14). For flow Reynolds numbers above 2000, based upon tube diameter, turbulent flow may result. Turbulent flow is much more complicated, as is indicated in the preceding section. At present no solution has been obtained which proceeds directly from first principles, not even for the case of steady, turbulent flow in a circular tube. The present section considers such flow and discusses the Prandtl "mixing-length" hypothesis. This hypothesis leads to a velocity distribution and to the correlation of friction-loss behavior for smooth- and rough-walled tubes.

Any one of the relations between equivalent shear stress and velocity gradient formulated in the preceding section, Eq. (6-42), (6-43), or (6-45), can be used to find $\bar{u}$ as a function of y if the coefficient of the velocity gradient is known. The shear stress varies linearly across the passage, as may be shown by a force balance on the fluid element of radius r in Fig. 6-11a. For the developed flow of an incompressible fluid, there are no acceleration effects, and the pressure force acting upon πr^2 is equal to the shear force acting upon $2\pi r\,\Delta x$:

$$\left(-\frac{dp}{dx}\right)\Delta x\,\pi r^2 = \tau 2\pi r\,\Delta x \qquad \tau = \left(-\frac{dp}{dx}\right)\frac{r}{2}$$

or
$$\tau_o = \left(-\frac{dp}{dx}\right)\frac{D}{4} \qquad\qquad (6\text{-}48)$$

However, neither the eddy viscosity nor the eddy diffusivity can be specified in a general manner.

Mixing Length. In an early study of turbulent transport (1925), Prandtl attempted to circumvent this difficulty by evaluating the turbulent shear stress directly from an estimation of the quantity $\overline{u'v'}$. In an analogy to the transport of momentum by molecules moving over the distance of their mean free path λ, Prandtl assumed that, in turbulent flow, macroscopic quantities of fluid moved lateral to the principal velocity, thereby carrying momentum from one region to another. The typical path length l is called the "mixing length" and is connected to the average size of the turbulent eddies in the flow.

The relation between l, the distance a lump of fluid moves, and the velocity disturbance u' that this induces at y (in the x-direction velocity component) may be inferred from Fig. 6-11b. The quantity of fluid coming from

$(y + l)$ would, on the average, have a higher x-direction component of velocity and that from $(y - l)$ a lower x-direction component. The average difference, which is an estimate of u', is

$$u' \propto l \left| \frac{d\bar{u}}{dy} \right|$$

If the disturbance is looked upon as a rotating eddy moving with the flow, the velocity component of the disturbance in the y direction will be of the same order. That is,

$$v' \propto l \left| \frac{d\bar{u}}{dy} \right|$$

Inspection of the mixing mechanism shows that u' and v' are correlated, that is, interdependent. Fluid lumps coming from above have a negative v' but carry a positive u'. Conversely, those coming from below have a

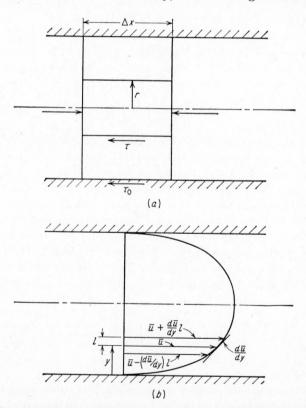

Fig. 6-11.   Developed turbulent flow in a circular passage.   (a) Forces on a fluid element. (b) Estimation of fluctuating components.

positive v' and carry a negative u'. Therefore, $\overline{u'v'}$ is not zero and is negative. An estimation of the turbulent shear stress, from Eq. (6-43), is, therefore,

$$\tau_t = -\rho\overline{u'v'} = k_1\rho l^2 \left(\frac{d\bar{u}}{dy}\right)^2 \tag{6-49}$$

where k_1 is a proportionality constant.

Equation (6-49) does not yield a velocity distribution until a value is determined for the unknown mixing length. Since l is associated with eddy size, Prandtl assumed that it increases linearly with distance from the wall, that is,
$$l = k_2 y$$

This assumption is introduced into Eq. (6-49), and τ is assumed to be essentially equal to τ_t, the turbulent contribution. The shear stress is assumed constant at τ_o, the wall value, and a differential equation results which may be integrated:

$$\tau_t = \tau_o = k_1 k_2{}^2 \rho y^2 \left(\frac{d\bar{u}}{dy}\right)^2$$

$$d\bar{u} = k \sqrt{\frac{\tau_o}{\rho}} \frac{dy}{y}$$

$$\bar{u} = k \sqrt{\frac{\tau_o}{\rho}} \ln y + C_1 \tag{6-50}$$

Many of the assumptions of this argument are questionable, and later treatments (by von Kármán in 1921 and G. I. Taylor in 1932) remove some of the objections. However, the Taylor theory yields essentially the same result. A more complicated relation results from the von Kármán theory, which, nevertheless, is also in close agreement with Eq. (6-50).

The Universal Velocity Distribution. Numerous measurements of velocity distributions in circular tubes have indicated that Eq. (6-50) fits the form of the distribution except in the region near the wall (where molecular-diffusion processes are not negligible). The distributions for various flow conditions are fitted by a single relation when $\bar{u}$ and y are generalized as follows:

$$\frac{\bar{u}}{u^*} = u^+ \quad \text{and} \quad \frac{yu^*}{\nu} = y^+ \quad \text{where } u^* = \sqrt{\frac{\tau_o}{\rho}}$$

Therefore,
$$u^+ = k \ln y^+ + C \tag{6-51}$$

Various observations on flow in smooth-walled tubes suggest that the flow immediately adjacent to the wall is laminar. In this event the following relation is integrated from the wall for $\tau = \tau_m = \tau_o$ assumed constant.

$$\frac{\tau}{\rho} = \frac{\tau_m}{\rho} = \frac{\tau_o}{\rho} = \nu \frac{du}{dy}$$

$$\frac{du}{\sqrt{\tau_o/\rho}} = du^+ = \sqrt{\frac{\tau_o}{\rho}\frac{dy}{\nu}} = dy^+$$

$$\int_0^{u^+} du^+ = u^+ = \int_0^{y^+} dy^+ = y^+$$

The region wherein this result applies is called the "laminar sublayer."

Between the laminar sublayer and the wholly turbulent core there is a "buffer" region in which molecular- and eddy-transport effects are of the same order of magnitude. Measurements show that the distribution in this region may be fitted by a relation of the form of Eq. (6-51), with constants different from those which apply in the turbulent core. These three relations, which comprise what is called the "universal velocity distribution," are given below with their regions of application, as suggested by von Kármán (1939).

$$u^+ = y^+ \qquad\qquad y^+ < 5 \qquad\qquad \text{primarily laminar} \qquad (6\text{-}52a)$$

$$u^+ = 5.0 \ln y^+ - 3.05 \qquad 5 < y^+ < 30 \qquad \text{laminar-turbulent} \qquad (6\text{-}52b)$$

$$u^+ = 2.5 \ln y^+ + 5.5 \qquad y^+ > 30 \qquad \text{primarily turbulent} \qquad (6\text{-}52c)$$

These relations are plotted in Fig. 6-12. Similar relations for turbulent flow in rough-walled tubes may be found in Schlichting (1955).

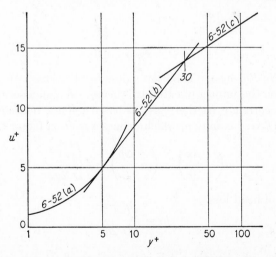

Fig. 6-12. The universal velocity distribution.

Example 6-3. Water having a kinematic viscosity of 0.94×10^{-5} ft²/sec flows through a smooth 2-in.-ID tube at a rate of 0.07 cfs. For this flow condition the wall shear stress may be taken as 0.05 psf. We wish to find the thickness of the laminar sublayer and of the buffer region and the ratio of the average to the maximum velocity.

$$u^* = \sqrt{\frac{\tau_o g_o}{\rho}} = 0.161 \text{ fps}$$

For y^+ of 5 and 30, the values of y are found:

$$y^+ = \frac{yu^*}{\nu} \qquad y = \frac{y^+ \nu}{u^*}$$

$$y_5 = \frac{5 \times 0.94 \times 10^{-5}}{0.161} = 0.000292 \text{ ft, or } 0.0035 \text{ in.}$$

$$y_{30} = 6y_5 = 0.00175 \text{ ft, or } 0.021 \text{ in.}$$

$$V = \frac{Q}{A} = 3.21 \text{ fps}$$

The maximum velocity occurs at the center, where y^+ is

$$y^+ = \frac{Du^*}{2\nu} = \frac{2 \times 0.161}{2 \times 12 \times 0.94 \times 10^{-5}} = 1430$$

$$u_m{}^+ = 2.5 \ln 1430 + 5.5 = 23.7 = \frac{u_m}{u^*}$$

$$u_m = 3.82 \text{ fps}$$

and
$$\frac{V}{u_m} = \frac{3.21}{3.82} = 0.84$$

This ratio is considerably different from the 0.5 which applies for laminar flow.

Flow Loss in Passages. The friction loss for developed turbulent flow in tubes has been the subject of extensive theoretical and experimental study. Attempts to correlate friction loss are based upon a relation, called the Fanning or D'Arcy equation, which defines a friction factor f.

$$\left(-\frac{dp}{dx}\right) = \left(-\frac{\Delta p}{L}\right) = f\frac{L}{D}\frac{\rho V^2}{2g_o} \tag{6-53a}$$

or, in terms of head loss,

$$h_l = f\frac{L}{D}\frac{V^2}{2g} \tag{6-53b}$$

where L is the tube length and V is the average fluid velocity.

Equation (6-53a) is in the same form as the analytical result for laminar flow, Eq. (6-14), for which the friction factor is merely $64/N_{Re}$. For turbulent flow the friction factor is also a function of the Reynolds number, but it depends as well upon the tube wall relative roughness, as measured by the equivalent magnitude of the roughness k_s divided by the tube diameter D. That is,

$$f = f\left(N_{Re}, \frac{k_s}{D}\right)$$

The relations between pressure gradient and shear stress, Eq. (6-48), and between shear stress and velocity distribution, Eqs. (6-52), provided Prandtl a means of determining the friction factor as a function of Reynolds number for smooth-walled tubes. The result is in very close agreement with experimental observations:

$$\frac{1}{\sqrt{f}} = 0.87 \ln N_{Re}\sqrt{f} - 0.8 \tag{6-54}$$

Similar relations have been obtained for completely turbulent flow, that is, for flow wherein the wall roughness protrudes through the laminar sublayer and buffer region into the turbulent core. An equation which covers the whole transition region between smooth-walled and completely turbulent flow was presented by Colebrook (1939). The two equations are

$$\frac{1}{\sqrt{f}} = -0.87 \ln \frac{k_s}{D} + 1.14 \qquad \text{completely turbulent} \tag{6-55}$$

$$\frac{1}{\sqrt{f}} = -0.87 \ln \left(\frac{k_s/D}{3.7} + \frac{2.51}{N_{Re}\sqrt{f}}\right) \qquad \text{transition} \tag{6-56}$$

Moody (1944) presented the foregoing functional relationships between the friction factor, Reynolds number, and relative roughness in graphical form. The four flow situations—laminar, turbulent with a smooth wall, transition, and completely turbulent—are included in the single plot. Moody plotted f versus N_{Re} with contours of constant relative roughness for a wide range of N_{Re}. The diagram is reproduced in Fig. 6-13. A transition zone is shown between smooth-walled and completely turbulent flow.

An equivalent roughness was determined for commercial pipes by comparing actual friction loss with that indicated by the equations which involve relative roughness k_s/D. This equivalent roughness is listed in Fig. 6-13 for several types of commercial piping.

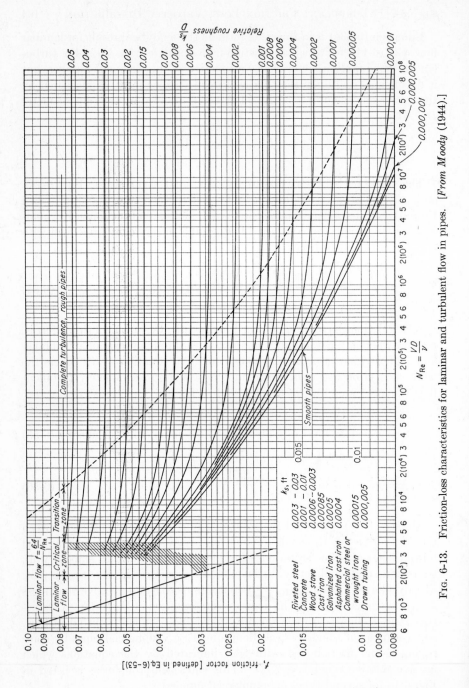

FIG. 6-13. Friction-loss characteristics for laminar and turbulent flow in pipes. [*From Moody* (1944).]

Example 6-4.   Air at 120 psia and 100°F flows at a rate of 2.0 lb/sec through a 4-in. nominal standard commercial steel pipe. We wish to find the pressure loss per 100 ft of length. The ID, density, and average velocity are found:

$$ID = 4.500 - 2 \times 0.237 = 4.026 \text{ in.}$$

$$\rho = \frac{p}{RT} = \frac{120 \times 144}{53.34 \times 560} = 0.578 \text{ lb/ft}^3$$

$$V = \frac{m}{\rho A} = 39.3 \text{ fps}$$

Assuming incompressible flow, the Reynolds number, friction factor, and flow loss are determined:

$$\mu = 0.0484 \text{ lb/hr ft} = 1.345 \times 10^{-5} \text{ lb/sec ft}$$

$$N_{Re} = \frac{DV\rho}{\mu} = \frac{4.026 \times 39.3 \times 0.578}{12 \times 1.345 \times 10^{-5}} = 565{,}000$$

$$\frac{k_s}{D} = \frac{0.00015 \times 12}{4.026} = 0.00045$$

$$f = 0.0173$$

$$\left(-\frac{dp}{dx}\right) = f \frac{1}{D} \frac{\rho V^2}{2g_o} = 7.14 \text{ psf/ft}$$

$$\Delta p = 714 \text{ psf/100 ft, or } 4.95 \text{ psi/100 ft}$$

The foregoing correlations of flow loss apply in particular to circular tubes. However, for square, rectangular, and other cross sections not too different from circular, the foregoing relations may be used if the diameter D is replaced by the equivalent diameter D_e of the noncircular cross section. The equivalent diameter is defined as four times the flow cross section divided by the flow perimeter upon which wall shear acts. Such a treatment is not accurate, however, for passages having sharp corners or high aspect ratios.

6-8. CHARACTERISTICS OF FLOW OVER BLUFF BODIES

In Sec. 6-1 the nature of the flow field around a bluff body, such as a cylinder, was discussed. The type of flow field indicated results for flow Reynolds numbers, based upon cylinder diameter, between approximately 40 and 4×10^5. Below 40, the wake is steady and laminar. Above approximately 4×10^5, the boundary layer formed on the front half of the cylinder becomes turbulent before the usual separation point is reached. This turbulent boundary layer adheres to the surface past the 90° location, and separation occurs farther back on the rear half of the cylinder. Similar results are found for many other shapes.

For the cylinder case, the drag has been determined analytically only for the very low Reynolds number range. However, the drag characteristics of many shapes have been measured over a wide range of conditions. The results are reduced to the form of a coefficient of drag, defined as the drag force divided by the product of the dynamic pressure of the stream and an area associated with the body, that is,

$$C_D = \frac{F_D}{A(\rho U_\infty^2/2g_o)} \qquad (6\text{-}57)$$

For bodies of infinite span, F_D is the force per unit span, and A is the thickness, diameter, or chord. For other bodies, a projected area is used. Thus, for a cylinder, $A = D$, and for a sphere, $A = \pi R^2$.

The drag coefficient is primarily dependent upon the flow Reynolds number. The relation is shown in Fig. 6-14 for a cylinder. The sudden decrease in C_D at the right results from a rearward shift in the point of separation due to transition to a turbulent boundary layer. This reduction in the extent of the separated area reduces the total drag by reducing the area upon which the low wake pressure acts.

Because of separation, the drag of a cylinder is relatively large. This may be seen by comparing the drag of a cylinder with that of a plate at zero angle of attack having equal surface area per unit span. The length of the plate in the direction of flow is

$$2L = \pi D \qquad L = \frac{\pi D}{2}$$

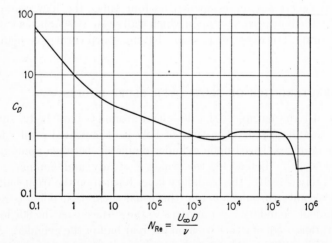

FIG. 6-14. Coefficient of drag for a circular cylinder normal to the flow.

The relation between the plate and cylinder Reynolds numbers is, therefore,

$$N_{\text{Re},P} = \frac{U_\infty L}{\nu} = \frac{\pi}{2} \frac{U_\infty D}{\nu} = \frac{\pi}{2} N_{\text{Re},C}$$

The cylinder drag is

$$F_{D,C} = C_{D,C} D \left(\frac{\rho U_\infty^2}{2 g_o} \right)$$

From Eq. (6-32), the total plate drag (two sides) is

$$F_{D,P} = \frac{1.328 \times 2L}{\sqrt{N_{\text{Re},P}}} \left(\frac{\rho U_\infty^2}{2 g_o} \right) = \frac{2.12L}{\sqrt{N_{\text{Re},C}}} \left(\frac{\rho U_\infty^2}{2 g_o} \right)$$

The ratio of cylinder and plate drag forces becomes

$$r = \frac{F_{D,C}}{F_{D,P}} = \frac{C_{D,C} D \sqrt{N_{\text{Re},C}}}{2.12L} = 0.30 C_{D,C} \sqrt{N_{\text{Re},C}}$$

For a cylinder Reynolds number of 10^4, $C_{D,C}$ is 1.1 and $r = 33$. That is, the cylinder drag is 33 times that of the plate. This large difference arises because of separation on the cylinder which causes a large pressure (or profile) drag. The plate has only frictional drag. If the cylinder and plate frictional-drag effects are assumed equal, the cylinder profile drag is seen to be approximately 97 per cent of the total drag.

Drag coefficients for various other common shapes are collected in Table 6-2. The effect of streamlining is to reduce the extent of separation.

TABLE 6-2. Coefficients of Drag of Various Shapes *

Shape and orientation to flow	Reynolds number range	C_D
Flat strip, normal to flow....	Greater than 10^3	1.95
Disk, normal to flow.........	Greater than 10^3	1.10
Hemispherical shell:		
Hollow upstream..........	Greater than 10^3	1.33
Hollow downstream.......	Greater than 10^3	0.34
Cylinder, normal to flow.....	10^3 to 2×10^5	1.10
	Greater than 5×10^5	~ 0.35
Sphere....................	10^3 to 2×10^5	0.45
	Greater than 3×10^5	~ 0.20
Model of airship...........	Greater than 2×10^5	0.04
Conventional airfoil at zero angle of attack	With boundary-layer transition	0.006

* Compiled from data in Hunsaker and Rightmire (1947) and Schlichting (1955).

The result may be seen by comparing values for various shapes. The effects of separation upon heat transfer are discussed in Chap. 7.

6-9. BOUNDARY-LAYER ANALYSIS BY THE INTEGRAL METHOD

The procedure of obtaining boundary-layer solutions was considered for two flow circumstances in Sec. 6-5. It is often quite difficult to obtain such a solution, and for many practical shapes the proper similarity variable is not known or does not exist. Therefore, the need for a substitute procedure of adequate accuracy is evident. Such a method, called the "integral method," has been developed. This method is based upon a boundary-layer momentum equation derived by von Kármán (1921).

The Momentum Equation. The momentum equation results from a force and momentum balance on the boundary layer and relates integrals of the velocity distribution to the wall shear stress, the boundary-layer pressure gradient, and the boundary-layer thickness. The method is applied by assuming the form of the velocity distribution (and perhaps also the surface shear stress) and then calculating from this the other quantities. Many difficult boundary-layer problems for both laminar and turbulent flow have been solved by this method, and the results are usually in close agreement with measurements. In the present section the momentum equation is developed for incompressible flow and is used to solve the flat-plate boundary-layer problem for both laminar and turbulent flow.

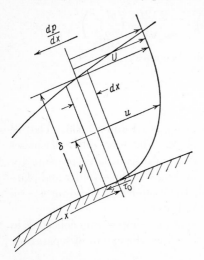

FIG. 6-15. Boundary-layer quantities.

In Fig. 6-15 a section of the boundary layer is shown at a distance x from the stagnation point. The local boundary-layer thickness δ is the distance out, normal to the surface, where the u component of velocity is essentially equal to the local free-stream velocity level U. A force-momentum balance is written for the element of thickness dx. The mass rate of flow in the boundary layer at x is

$$\int_0^\delta \rho u \, dy$$

The rate of momentum transport in the boundary layer is

$$\int_0^\delta (\rho u) u\, dy = \int_0^\delta \rho u^2\, dy$$

The momentum entering the boundary layer from the free stream in distance dx is

$$U \frac{d}{dx} \left(\int_0^\delta \rho u\, dy \right) dx$$

The total decrease in momentum in distance dx is

$$U \frac{d}{dx} \left(\int_0^\delta \rho u\, dy \right) dx - \frac{d}{dx} \left(\int_0^\delta \rho u^2\, dy \right) dx$$

$$= \rho\, dx \left[\frac{d}{dx} \left(\int_0^\delta U u\, dy \right) - \frac{dU}{dx} \int_0^\delta u\, dy - \frac{d}{dx} \int_0^\delta u^2\, dy \right]$$

$$= \rho\, dx \left\{ \frac{d}{dx} \left[\int_0^\delta (U - u) u\, dy \right] - \frac{dU}{dx} \int_0^\delta u\, dy \right\}$$

This is equal to the sum of the forces opposing the motion, that is, shear and pressure forces

$$\tau_o\, dx + \delta \frac{dp}{dx}\, dx$$

The momentum equation is, therefore,

$$\rho \frac{d}{dx} \left[\int_0^\delta (U - u) u\, dy \right] - \rho \frac{dU}{dx} \int_0^\delta u\, dy = \tau_o + \delta \frac{dp}{dx}$$

Since the Bernoulli equation for inviscid flow applies outside the boundary layer, the pressure gradient may be related to the gradient of U:

$$p + \frac{\rho U^2}{2} = \text{constant}$$

and

$$\frac{dp}{dx} + \rho U \frac{dU}{dx} = 0$$

Therefore,

$$\delta \frac{dp}{dx} = -\delta \rho U \frac{dU}{dx} = -\rho \frac{dU}{dx} \int_0^\delta U\, dy$$

The momentum equation becomes

$$\frac{d}{dx} \left[\int_0^\delta (U - u) u\, dy \right] + \frac{dU}{dx} \int_0^\delta (U - u)\, dy = \frac{\tau_o}{\rho} \tag{6-58}$$

This relation expresses τ_o in terms of the velocity distribution and the free-stream velocity gradient.

If the form of the velocity distribution inside the boundary layer may be assumed to be independent of x, that is, if

$$\frac{u}{U} = f\left(\frac{y}{\delta}\right) = f(\eta) \tag{6-59}$$

Eq. (6-58) may be written more simply. Considering the two terms on the left-hand side separately,

$$\frac{d}{dx}\left[\int_0^\delta (U - u)u\,dy\right] = \frac{d}{dx}\left[\delta U^2 \int_0^1 \left(1 - \frac{u}{U}\right)\left(\frac{u}{U}\right)d\left(\frac{y}{\delta}\right)\right]$$

$$= \int_0^1 \left(1 - \frac{u}{U}\right)\frac{u}{U}\,d\eta\left[\frac{d(\delta U^2)}{dx}\right]$$

$$= \int_0^1 (1 - f)f\,d\eta\left[\frac{d(\delta U^2)}{dx}\right] = \alpha\frac{d(\delta U^2)}{dx}$$

$$\frac{dU}{dx}\int_0^\delta (U - u)\,dy = \frac{dU}{dx}\,\delta U\int_0^1\left(1 - \frac{u}{U}\right)d\eta$$

$$= \frac{dU}{dx}\,\delta U\int_0^1 (1 - f)\,d\eta = \beta\,\delta U\frac{dU}{dx} = \frac{\beta\delta}{2}\frac{d(U^2)}{dx}$$

where $\quad \alpha = \int_0^1 (1 - f)f\,d\eta \quad$ and $\quad \beta = \int_0^1 (1 - f)\,d\eta$

The momentum equation becomes

$$\alpha\frac{d(\delta U^2)}{dx} + \frac{\beta\delta}{2}\frac{d(U^2)}{dx} = \frac{\tau_o}{\rho} \tag{6-60}$$

If it is assumed that the boundary-layer flow is laminar, the wall shear stress τ_o may be evaluated in terms of the derivative of $f(\eta)$:

$$\frac{\tau_o}{\rho} = \frac{\mu}{\rho}\left(\frac{\partial u}{\partial y}\right)_0 = \frac{U\mu}{\delta\rho}\left[\frac{\partial(u/U)}{\partial(y/\delta)}\right]_0 = \frac{U\mu}{\delta\rho}\left(\frac{df}{d\eta}\right)_0 = \frac{U\mu}{\delta\rho}f_0' \tag{6-61}$$

Flat-plate, Laminar Boundary Layer. For a laminar boundary layer on a flat plate at zero angle of incidence $U = U_\infty$, and Eqs. (6-60) and (6-61) apply in a very simple form:

$$\alpha U_\infty^2\frac{d\delta}{dx} = \frac{U_\infty\mu}{\delta\rho}f_0' \quad \text{or} \quad \delta\,d\delta = \frac{\mu f_0'\,dx}{U_\infty\alpha\rho}$$

At $x = 0$, $\delta = 0$; therefore,

$$\int_0^\delta \delta \, d\delta = \frac{\mu f_0'}{U_\infty \alpha \rho} \int_0^x dx = \frac{\delta^2}{2} = \frac{\mu f_0'}{U_\infty \alpha \rho} x = \frac{f_0'}{\alpha} \frac{\nu x}{U_\infty}$$

$$\frac{\delta}{x} = \frac{\sqrt{2f_0'/\alpha}}{\sqrt{N_{\text{Re},x}}} = \frac{C}{\sqrt{N_{\text{Re},x}}}$$

The shear stress, drag, and coefficient of drag are written from the preceding result:

$$\frac{\tau_0}{\rho U_\infty^2/2} = \frac{2\mu f_0' \sqrt{N_{\text{Re},x}}/\rho x U_\infty}{\sqrt{2f_0'/\alpha}} = \frac{\sqrt{2\alpha f_0'}}{\sqrt{N_{\text{Re},x}}}$$

$$F_D = \int_0^L \tau_0 \, dx = \sqrt{2\alpha f_0'} \sqrt{\mu \rho L U_\infty^3}$$

$$C_D = \frac{F_D}{L(\rho U_\infty^2/2)} = \frac{2\sqrt{2\alpha f_0'}}{\sqrt{N_{\text{Re},L}}}$$

Each of these results is identical in form to that obtained by the exact analysis.

The constants α and f_0' must be determined from an assumed velocity distribution of the form indicated in Eq. (6-59). It has been shown that the constants in the above equations are not very sensitive to the exact form of the chosen function. However, the method introduced by Pohlhausen to determine the proper form of the function will be discussed. In this method the conditions which the velocity distribution is known to satisfy are employed to determine the constants in a polynomial representation of $f(\eta)$:

$$\frac{u}{U} = f(\eta) = a_0 + a_1\eta + a_2\eta^2 + a_3\eta^3$$

It is known that

at $\eta = 0$ $f = 0$ and $f'' = 0$ [see Eq. (6-20)]

at $\eta = 1$ $f = 1$ and $f' = 0$

The constants are evaluated from these "compatibility" conditions to yield

$$\frac{u}{U} = f(\eta) = \tfrac{3}{2}\eta - \tfrac{1}{2}\eta^3 \qquad\qquad (6\text{-}62)$$

The values of α and f_0' are $\tfrac{39}{280}$ and $\tfrac{3}{2}$. The boundary-layer thickness, shear stress, drag, and coefficient of drag become

$$\frac{\delta}{x} = \frac{4.64}{\sqrt{N_{\mathrm{Re},x}}} \tag{6-63}$$

$$\frac{\tau_o}{\rho U_\infty^2/2} = \frac{0.646}{\sqrt{N_{\mathrm{Re},x}}} \tag{6-64}$$

$$F_D = 0.646\sqrt{\mu\rho L U_\infty^3} \tag{6-65}$$

$$C_D = \frac{1.292}{\sqrt{N_{\mathrm{Re},L}}} \tag{6-66}$$

These results are in close agreement with those obtained in the exact analysis [see Eqs. (6-29) to (6-32)].

Flat-plate, Turbulent Boundary Layer. For a turbulent boundary layer on a flat plate the method is similar. Equation (6-60) applies in its most simple form. However, for turbulent flow the shear stress may not be evaluated as in Eq. (6-61) unless a laminar layer is assumed near the wall for which an accurate velocity distribution is known. An alternative procedure is followed. α is evaluated from an assumed velocity distribution, the seventh-root law proposed by von Kármán for turbulent flow. The shear stress is evaluated from a correlation determined by Blasius from experimentally determined pressure-loss characteristics for flow in smooth pipes. This correlation has been carefully checked against the measured drag characteristics of plates.

$$\frac{u}{U} = \left(\frac{y}{\delta}\right)^{\frac{1}{7}} = (\eta)^{\frac{1}{7}} \tag{6-67}$$

$$\frac{\tau_o}{\rho U_\infty^2/2} = 0.045\left(\frac{\nu}{U_\infty\delta}\right)^{\frac{1}{4}} = C\left(\frac{\nu}{U_\infty\delta}\right)^{\frac{1}{4}} \tag{6-68}$$

Equation (6-60) is written and integrated from $x = 0$ and $\delta = 0$, assuming the boundary to be turbulent from the leading edge, where the thickness is negligible.

$$2\alpha\frac{d\delta}{dx} = \frac{\tau_o}{\rho U_\infty^2/2} = 0.045\left(\frac{\nu}{U_\infty\delta}\right)^{\frac{1}{4}} = C\left(\frac{\nu}{U_\infty\delta}\right)^{\frac{1}{4}}$$

$$\int_0^\delta \delta^{\frac{1}{4}}\,d\delta = \tfrac{4}{5}\delta^{\frac{5}{4}} = \frac{C}{2\alpha}\left(\frac{\nu}{U_\infty}\right)^{\frac{1}{4}}\int_0^x dx = \frac{C}{2\alpha}\left(\frac{\nu}{U_\infty}\right)^{\frac{1}{4}}x$$

$$\frac{\delta}{x} = \left(\frac{5C}{8\alpha}\right)^{\frac{4}{5}}\left(\frac{\nu}{U_\infty x}\right)^{\frac{1}{5}} = \frac{0.37}{\sqrt[5]{N_{\mathrm{Re},x}}} \tag{6-69}$$

The drag and coefficient of drag are evaluated by integrating Eq. (6-68):

$$C_D = \frac{0.072}{\sqrt[5]{N_{\text{Re},L}}} \tag{6-70}$$

These results are derived for a wholly turbulent boundary layer. However, since transition arises from an unstable laminar boundary layer, some portion of the leading edge of the plate will be subject to laminar flow. Therefore, the above results apply for large plate Reynolds numbers, for which the laminar portion will be a small fraction of the total length. For flows for which the laminar portion is a substantial part of the total length, composite expressions must be used.

The two applications of the momentum equation and integral method presented in this section are among the simplest examples of the use of this method. The technique has been used to solve many complicated flow problems. For an account of many cases the reader is referred to Schlichting (1955) and Eckert and Drake (1959). This method has also been applied to convection processes.

NOTATION

$\bar{C}$	time average value of concentration of a chemical species
C_D	coefficient of drag
D	chemical diffusivity (or molecular diffusivity of a chemical species)
f	friction factor
$f(\eta)$	stream function in terms of η
$f(\eta)$	velocity distribution, integral method
g_o	a conversion factor for units of force
h_l	head loss
i	intensity of turbulence
k_s	equivalent roughness
l	mixing length
m	velocity power-law exponent
m''	rate of diffusion of a chemical species, per unit area
N_{Re}	Reynolds number
$N_{\text{Re},x}$	local boundary-layer Reynolds number
p	pressure
q''	heat-transfer rate per unit area
R	correlation coefficient for turbulence
$\bar{t}$	time average value of temperature
u	component of velocity in the x direction
$\bar{u}$	time average value of the x component of velocity
u'	fluctuating component of the x component of velocity
u_m	maximum velocity of fluid
u^*	"friction velocity"
u^+	generalized velocity
U	velocity

v	component of velocity in the y direction
$\bar{v}$	time average value of the y component of velocity
v'	fluctuating component of the y component of velocity
V	average velocity of fluid
$\mathbf{V}$	vector velocity
w	component of velocity in the z direction
$\bar{w}$	time average value of the z component of velocity
w'	fluctuating component of the z component of velocity
X	body force per unit volume, in the x direction
y^{+}	generalized distance from the wall
Y	body force per unit volume, in the y direction
Z	body force per unit volume, in the z direction
α	thermal diffusivity (or molecular diffusivity of thermal energy)
α	parameter, the integral method
β	wedge-angle parameter
β	parameter, the integral method
δ	boundary-layer thickness
ϵ_C	eddy diffusivity of a chemical species
ϵ_H	eddy diffusivity of thermal energy
ϵ_M	eddy diffusivity of momentum
η	similarity variable
η	location variable, integral method
μ	absolute (or dynamic) viscosity
ν	kinematic viscosity (or molecular diffusivity of momentum)
ρ	density of mass
σ_{x_i}	normal stress
τ	time
τ	shear stress
τ_m	viscous shear stress
τ_o	shear stress at the wall
τ_t	shear-stress equivalent of momentum diffused by turbulence
$\tau_{x_i x_j}$	shear stress
ψ	stream function in terms of x and y

REFERENCES

Colebrook, C. F.: *J. Inst. Civil Engrs.*, vol. 11, p. 133, 1939.

Corcoran, W. H., J. B. Opfell, and B. H. Sage: "Momentum Transfer in Fluids," Academic Press, Inc., New York, 1956.

Eckert, E. R. G., and R. M. Drake, Jr.: "Heat and Mass Transfer," 2d ed., McGraw-Hill Book Company, Inc., New York, 1959.

Falkner, V. M., and S. W. Skan: *Phil. Mag.*, vol. 12, p. 865, 1931.

Hartree, D. R.: *Proc. Cambridge Phil. Soc.*, vol. 33, p. 223, 1937.

Hinze, J. O.: "Turbulence," McGraw-Hill Book Company, Inc., New York, 1959.

Howarth, L.: *Proc. Roy. Soc. (London)*, ser. A, vol. 164, p. 547, 1938.

Hunsaker, J. C., and B. G. Rightmire: "Engineering Applications of Fluid Mechanics," McGraw-Hill Book Company, Inc., New York, 1947.

Kay, J. M.: "Fluid Mechanics and Heat Transfer," Cambridge University Press, New York, 1957.

Knudsen, J. G., and D. L. Katz: "Fluid Dynamics and Heat Transfer," McGraw-Hill Book Company, Inc., New York, 1958.

Moody, L. F.: *Trans. ASME*, vol. 66, p. 671, 1944.

Schlichting, H.: "Boundary Layer Theory," McGraw-Hill Book Company, Inc., New York, 1955 (4th ed., 1960).

von Kármán, T.: *Z. angew. Math. Mech.*, vol. 1, p. 233, 1921: translated and reprinted as *NACA Tech. Mem.* 1092, 1921.

————: *Trans. ASME*, vol. 61, p. 705, 1939.

PROBLEMS

1. The absolute viscosity of air at 50°F is 0.0427 lb/hr ft.

a. Convert this viscosity to units of lb/sec ft, lb sec/ft^2, and poise.

b. Calculate the kinematic viscosity of air at 50°F and 14.7 psia in stokes and in English units.

2. If the velocity in Fig. 6-2 increases linearly from zero to a value of 1 fps at a distance of $\frac{1}{4}$ in. away from the plate, find the rate of shear and shear stress if the fluid is water at 60°F. Where does this shear stress act?

3. Plot a graph of the kinematic viscosity of air as curves of ν versus t with contours of constant pressure in the temperature range 40 to 400°F. Use pressure contours of 0.8, 1.0, 1.2, 1.4, 1.6, 1.8, and 2 atmospheres.

4. At 60°F mercury has a kinematic viscosity of 0.00118 stoke. Find its absolute viscosity in lb/hr ft.

5. List the following fluids in order of decreasing absolute viscosity and in order of decreasing kinematic viscosity. Compare the two lists. The fluids are water, air, mercury, light oil, alcohol, and oxygen. All fluids are at 60°F and 14.7 psia.

6. Starting with Eqs.(6-6),(6-7), and the proper forms of Eqs.(6-8), develop the Navier-Stokes equations for a compressible fluid having a uniform, constant viscosity. Reduce these results to the form applicable to incompressible fluids.

7a. For flow in the gravitational field with a strength indicated by an acceleration g, find the values of X, Y, and Z if the z axis is in the vertical direction.

b. For the circumstance in part *a*, develop the Bernoulli equation which relates changes in pressure, elevation, and velocity for incompressible, inviscid flow along a streamline.

8. Water at 60°F flows through a $\frac{1}{4}$-in.-ID circular tube at an average velocity of 1 fps.

a. Calculate the flow Reynolds number and the maximum fluid velocity.

b. Calculate the pressure gradient and the pressure loss for a section of tube 10 ft long.

9. For the flow of air at 60°F and 14.7 psia, compute the maximum value of the average velocity which is likely to result in laminar flow in a 1-in.-ID tube.

10. A wooden dam made of 1-in.-thick wood timbers placed horizontally has an opening, $\frac{1}{16}$ in. high and 10 ft long, between adjacent timbers along its lower edge. If water at 60°F stands 4 ft above the opening behind the dam, find the rate of leakage and the maximum water velocity in the flow passage. Find the friction factor for this flow.

11. An oil-lubricated journal bearing consists of a 6-in.-diameter shaft in a 6.020-in.-diameter sleeve. For shaft rotation at 1000 rpm with no load, find the necessary shaft torque. The properties of the oil are

$$\rho = 54 \text{ lb/ft}^3 \qquad \mu = 100 \text{ lb/hr ft}$$

12. Two extensive parallel plates, spaced at $\frac{1}{8}$ in., are placed at a 45° inclination. What flow rate of water at 60°F, in cubic feet per second, will result in a zero pressure gradient in the direction of flow?

13. A plate 1 ft long is placed at zero angle of attack in air at 14.7 psia and 60°F with a velocity of 10 fps. If the average thickness of the resulting boundary layer is 0.12 in., estimate the numerical value of each of the derivatives in the Navier-Stokes equations which apply for this flow circumstance. Use units of feet and seconds.

14. For the flow circumstance of the preceding problem, find (*a*) the boundary-layer thickness and the local shear stress at the middle and at the trailing edge of the plate; (*b*) the tangential and normal velocity components at the midpoint of the boundary layer at the trailing edge of the plate; (*c*) the drag coefficient and the total drag of the plate.

15. Consider a flat plate 2 ft long submerged in a stream of atmospheric-pressure air at 80°F moving at a velocity of 30 fps. The angle of attack is zero. For laminar flow, find (*a*) the boundary-layer thickness, v_∞, u at $y = \delta/2$, and τ_o, each at 1 and 2 ft from the leading edge; (*b*) the coefficient of drag and drag force for one side of the plate.

16a. Sketch the streamlines for laminar flow over a plate at zero angle of incidence.

b. Through the use of this field of streamlines, explain the variation of the normal velocity component over the boundary layer.

c. Show why the normal component of velocity may not approach zero at a large distance out, normal to the plate.

d. From the definitions of the streamline and of the stream function, show that streamlines are contours of constant values of the stream function.

17. Water flows in a turbulent manner through a rough-walled circular tube. The resulting velocity distribution, away from the wall, may be approximated by

$$\frac{\bar{u}}{\bar{u}_m} = \left(\frac{y}{R}\right)^{\frac{1}{10}}$$

where R is the radius of the tube and y is the distance from the wall. Find the distribution of eddy diffusivity across the passage.

18. Water at 80°F flows through a smooth 2-in.-ID pipe at a rate of 0.07 cfs.

a. Find the average velocity, the Reynolds number, and τ_o.

b. At what distance from the wall is u equal to the average velocity?

c. Estimate the thickness of the laminar sublayer and the buffer layer as a percentage of pipe radius.

19. Air at 50 psia and 60°F flows through a 4-in.-ID smooth-walled tube at an average velocity of 20 fps. For developed turbulent flow:

a. Find the friction loss for a length of 200 ft.

b. Plot the velocity distribution across the section and compare it with that which would characterize laminar flow at the same average velocity.

20. Oil flows through 0.5-in.-ID drawn tubing at a Reynolds number of 2500. Compare the friction loss and velocity distributions for laminar and for turbulent flow.

$$\mu = 0.03 \text{ lb/ft sec} \quad \text{and} \quad \rho = 50 \text{ lb/ft}^3$$

21. A 2000-ft-long 2-in.-OD power transmission line spans a river. Estimate the air drag on the line for 14.7 psia and 60°F and a 90-mph wind blowing perpendicular to the line.

22. Parachutes are to be designed for dropping equipment by air. If the equipment in question can withstand impact velocities of 20 mph, estimate the parachute diameter required for a 1-ton load.

23a. Develop an expression for the ratio of the drag forces for a long strip of width L placed normal and parallel to a stream of air moving at a velocity of U_∞ for $N_{Re} > 10^3$.

b. Comment upon the reasons for the appearance of the Reynolds number in this result.

c. Find the numerical value of the ratio for a 2-in. strip width in standard air moving at 10 fps.

24a. Write the boundary-layer momentum equation in terms of the local displacement thickness δ^*, which is defined as the sidewise displacement of the free stream due to viscous effects, and the momentum thickness θ, defined as the thickness of a layer of fluid in the free stream carrying the equivalent of the momentum deficiency in the boundary layer due to viscous effects.

b. Reduce this result to the simplest form that applies for a laminar boundary layer on a flat plate at zero angle of incidence.

25. Find the ratio of the displacement thickness (defined in the preceding problem) and the boundary-layer thickness for a flat plate, using the laminar velocity distribution assumed in Sec. 6-9.

26. For a laminar boundary layer on a flat plate, compute the boundary-layer thickness and coefficient of drag for a linear velocity distribution and for a sinusoidal velocity distribution, that is, for

$$\frac{u}{U_\infty} = \eta \quad \text{and} \quad \frac{u}{U_\infty} = \sin\frac{\pi}{2}\eta$$

Compare these results with those which resulted from assuming a cubic distribution.

27. It has been shown that for turbulent flow the seventh-root relation for the velocity distribution should be replaced by

$$\frac{u}{U} = \eta^{1/n}$$

where n increases with the flow Reynolds number. Using this result and the shear-stress correlation of Blasius, develop the expressions for thickness and for the coefficient of drag for a turbulent boundary layer on a flat plate.

28. Water at 60°F flows at 15 fps over a flat plate 3 ft long placed at zero angle of incidence in the stream. Compute the plate Reynolds number, the maximum boundary-layer thickness, and the total drag.

29. Air at 25 psia and 60°F flows at a velocity of 100 fps over a flat plate 1 ft long. Using the results of the approximate theory, compare the total drag and the maximum boundary-layer thickness for totally laminar and totally turbulent flow.

CHAPTER 7

Forced Convection

7-1. DESCRIPTION OF CONVECTION PROCESSES

A heat- (or mass-) transfer process whose rate is directly influenced by fluid motion is called a convection process. The heat may be finally transferred through the flowing material by conduction, but the conduction process is basically altered by relative motion in the fluid. Thermal energy and mass may be "convected" about the flow region by the motion of the fluid. For example, the disturbances connected with turbulence may have a large effect upon the transfer rate.

If the flow field is imposed, as in placing an object in a stream or in forcing a fluid through a pipe, the process is called forced convection. If, however, the fluid velocities arise as a result of density gradients resulting from heat or mass transfer, as for a domestic heating "radiator" or for a sun-heated road surface, the process is called natural (or free) convection. The present chapter treats forced convection, the subsequent one natural convection.

The nature of fluid flow and various methods of analyzing flow are considered in Chap. 6. Many different flow characteristics arise. Convection behavior depends primarily upon these characteristics, and convection processes are analyzed and classified on the basis of flow behavior. In this chapter the equations governing the temperature and chemical-species concentration distributions in a fluid are derived and applied. Turbulent transport is analyzed by employing a similarity theory, and experimental correlations of convection behavior are presented. High fluid velocities give rise to temperature effects due to fluid compression and due to high rates of energy dissipation as a result of the action of viscosity. Therefore, the convection characteristics are influenced. These effects are considered in some detail. For very low density fluids the ordinary "continuum" assumptions are not valid, and special techniques are required. The last section of the chapter discusses this matter.

176

7-2. ENERGY- AND MASS-DIFFUSION EQUATIONS

In Sec. 6-2 the continuity and momentum (Navier-Stokes) equations were derived for a constant, uniform density fluid by writing mass and force balances for the typical element ($dx\,dy\,dz$) in Fig. 6-3. Similar procedures are carried out below for the convection of thermal energy and mass. An energy balance results in a differential equation involving the temperature distribution. A balance for a particular chemical species yields a differential equation in terms of its concentration distribution.

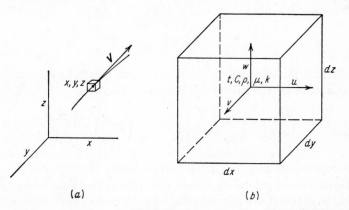

FIG. 7-1. Convection region. (a) Typical volume element. (b) Conditions at x, y, z.

These two relations are developed in this section for a fluid having a uniform, constant density (the effects of diffusion upon density are assumed negligible). The energy contributions due to compressibility and viscous dissipation are neglected here. These effects are considered in Secs. 7-8 and 7-9.

In order to write an energy balance, consider the element of mass instantaneously in volume ($dx\,dy\,dz$) centered at x, y, z, as shown in Fig. 7-1a and b. This element of mass is passing through point x, y, z at a velocity $\mathbf{V}$, and its time rate of temperature change is given by the particle derivative of temperature:

$$\frac{\partial t}{\partial \tau} + u\frac{\partial t}{\partial x} + v\frac{\partial t}{\partial y} + w\frac{\partial t}{\partial z} = \frac{Dt}{D\tau} \tag{7-1}$$

The significance and applicability of the particle derivative are discussed in Sec. 6-2, where it is used to evaluate the time rate of change of the velocity components u, v, and w of mass ($\rho\,dx\,dy\,dz$).

The rate of change of stored energy is the product of the specific heat, the mass, and the time rate of temperature change:

$$c\rho \, dx \, dy \, dz \, \frac{Dt}{D\tau}$$

This rate of energy increase must be equal to the net rate of energy gain due to conduction across the six faces of the element. The rate of energy conduction is related to the thermal conductivity and temperature gradient by Fourier's law of conduction, Eq. (1-3). The heat flux at x, y, z in the x direction is

$$q_x'' = -k \, \frac{\partial t}{\partial x} \tag{1-3}$$

The difference in the conduction rate across the two faces perpendicular to the x axis, with energy gained taken as positive, is

$$-\frac{\partial}{\partial x} \left(-k \, \frac{\partial t}{\partial x} \, dy \, dz \right) dx = \frac{\partial}{\partial x} \left(k \, \frac{\partial t}{\partial x} \right) dx \, dy \, dz$$

Similar expressions may be written for the y and z directions. The sum of these three rates of gain is set equal to the rate of change of energy storage to yield the differential equation governing the temperature distribution:

$$\rho c \, \frac{Dt}{D\tau} = \frac{\partial}{\partial x} \left(k \, \frac{\partial t}{\partial x} \right) + \frac{\partial}{\partial y} \left(k \, \frac{\partial t}{\partial y} \right) + \frac{\partial}{\partial z} \left(k \, \frac{\partial t}{\partial z} \right) \tag{7-2}$$

If k is uniform and constant, the equation is written more simply:

$$\frac{1}{\alpha} \frac{Dt}{D\tau} = \frac{1}{\alpha} \left(\frac{\partial t}{\partial \tau} + u \, \frac{\partial t}{\partial x} + v \, \frac{\partial t}{\partial y} + w \, \frac{\partial t}{\partial z} \right) = \nabla^2 t \tag{7-3}$$

where α is the thermal diffusivity of the fluid. The particle derivative is written out in Eq. (7-3), for later reference.

Comparison of Eq. (7-2) [or (7-3)] with that applicable to solid conduction, Eq. (2-1), indicates how the flow field, as described by velocity components u, v, and w, affects the temperature field.

The differential equation governing the distribution of the concentration C of one chemical species diffusing into another will be developed in its simplest form, the form which is strictly applicable only when thermal diffusion is negligible. In addition, the concentration level C will be assumed sufficiently low so that energy transports due to mutual diffusion may be ignored. With these assumptions, Eq. (7-3) is still the applicable energy equation.

The rate of gain in diffusing chemical species in the element of volume $(dx\,dy\,dz)$ is

$$dx\,dy\,dz\,\frac{DC}{D\tau}$$

This rate of gain is equal to the net rate of diffusion across the six faces of the element. The difference in the diffusion rate across the two faces perpendicular to the x axis is

$$-\frac{\partial}{\partial x}\left(-D\,\frac{\partial C}{\partial x}\,dy\,dz\right)dx$$

The sum of such rates of gain is set equal to the rate of gain of this chemical species in the volume element. The chemical diffusivity D is assumed uniform and constant.

$$\frac{1}{D}\frac{DC}{D\tau} = \frac{1}{D}\left(\frac{\partial C}{\partial \tau} + u\,\frac{\partial C}{\partial x} + v\,\frac{\partial C}{\partial y} + w\,\frac{\partial C}{\partial z}\right) = \nabla^2 C \qquad (7\text{-}4)$$

This differential equation is seen to be identical in form with that applying to the temperature distribution, Eq. (7-3). The chemical diffusivity is replaced by the thermal diffusivity, and the concentration is replaced by the temperature. This similarity is an expression of the observed similarity of heat-transfer and mass-diffusion behavior in many circumstances. It must be emphasized, however, that Eqs. (7-3) and (7-4) are valid only if the concentration of the diffusing species is low.

In the general convection circumstance in which heat and mass are diffusing, Eqs. (7-3) and (7-4) are combined with the continuity and Navier-Stokes equations (6-3) and (6-9) to describe the velocity (u, v, and w), pressure, temperature, and concentration distributions. Sufficient boundary conditions must be specified. For the temperature distribution, the boundary condition at a fluid-solid interface is similar to the no-slip condition applied to the velocity distribution. The temperature of the fluid immediately adjacent to the surface is taken equal to the temperature of the surface. An equivalent condition is often applied as a concentration boundary condition at the fluid-solid interface.

An interesting and important characteristic of convection analysis for a constant-density fluid is that the velocity and pressure distributions may be found from Eqs. (6-3) and (6-9) alone and do not depend upon the temperature and concentration distributions. The latter distributions, however, depend upon the velocity distribution, which must be known in order to solve Eqs. (7-3) and (7-4). This dependence makes it more difficult to solve convection problems than to solve flow problems. For this reason, and others, few convection problems of practical interest have been solved with the general equations. However, the boundary-layer forms of Eqs. (7-3) and (7-4) are much simpler and have been solved for many interesting and important cases. These equations are developed and applied in subsequent sections.

7-3. BOUNDARY-LAYER DIFFUSION EQUATIONS

The boundary-layer concept of Prandtl, which led to the laminar boundary-layer equations for the velocity distribution, has also been used to reduce Eqs. (7-3) and (7-4), for the temperature and concentration distributions, to simplified laminar boundary-layer forms. For an object placed in a fluid stream having a velocity U_∞, the temperature- and chemical-species diffusion effects occur primarily in a small boundary region near the surface, for unseparated flow.

The extent of the boundary region at any point is called the boundary-layer thickness. The various boundary-layer thicknesses—for velocity δ, for temperature δ_t, and for concentration δ_C—are not necessarily equal. The three diffusion processes may not be equally vigorous. Nevertheless, it is possible to obtain a boundary-layer equation for each distribution.

The temperature boundary-layer equation will be developed for the two-dimensional flow of an incompressible fluid over a surface. The stream is assumed to have a uniform, constant temperature t_∞ outside the boundary region. The surface is at t_o (see Fig. 7-2). The temperature differential

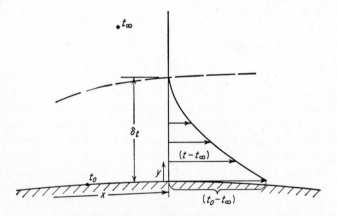

FIG. 7-2. Thermal boundary layer.

equation (7-3) is generalized, as were the Navier-Stokes equations in Sec. 6-4.

$$x' = \frac{x}{L} \qquad y' = \frac{y}{L} \qquad \delta' = \frac{\delta}{L} \qquad \delta_t' = \frac{\delta_t}{L}$$

$$u' = \frac{u}{U_\infty} \qquad v' = \frac{v}{U_\infty} \qquad \phi = \frac{t - t_\infty}{t_o - t_\infty}$$

$$u' \frac{\partial \phi}{\partial x'} + v' \frac{\partial \phi}{\partial y'} = \frac{\alpha}{U_\infty L} \left(\frac{\partial^2 \phi}{\partial x'^2} + \frac{\partial^2 \phi}{\partial y'^2} \right) \tag{7-5}$$

$$\quad 1 \quad 1 \qquad \delta' \quad \frac{1}{\delta_t'} \qquad\qquad 1 \qquad \frac{1}{\delta_t'}$$

From Sec. 6-4, v' is of order δ' and $u' = O(1)$. Since ϕ changes from 1 to 0 as y' changes from 0 to δ_t',

$$\frac{\partial \phi}{\partial y'} = O\left(\frac{1}{\delta_t'} \right) \qquad \text{and} \qquad \frac{\partial^2 \phi}{\partial y'^2} = O\left(\frac{1}{\delta_t'^2} \right)$$

ϕ changes from 0 upstream of the surface to order 1 as x' changes from 0 to 1. Therefore,

$$\frac{\partial \phi}{\partial x'} = O(1) \qquad \text{and} \qquad \frac{\partial^2 \phi}{\partial x'^2} = O(1)$$

Considering the orders of magnitude of the terms of Eq. (7-5), only the first term on the right may be neglected, since δ' and δ_t' may be of the same order. It is seen that the convection effects (left-hand side) and conduction effects (right-hand side) are of the same order of magnitude, as they are in the boundary layer, only if

$$\frac{\alpha}{U_\infty L} = O(\delta_t'^2) \tag{7-6a}$$

That is,

$$\delta_t'^2 \propto \frac{\alpha}{U_\infty L} = \left(\frac{\mu}{U_\infty L \rho} \right) \left(\frac{\alpha}{\nu} \right) = \frac{1}{N_{Re} N_{Pr}} = \frac{1}{N_{Pe}} \tag{7-6b}$$

A thin thermal boundary layer results from a high fluid flow Peclet number N_{Pe}.

The ratio of the temperature and velocity boundary-layer thicknesses is found from Eqs. (6-19b) and (7-6b):

$$\frac{\delta_t'}{\delta'} = \frac{\delta_t}{\delta} \propto \frac{1}{\sqrt{N_{Pr}}}$$

where N_{Pr} is the Prandtl number and is the ratio of the momentum and thermal diffusivities. The thicknesses are quite different for fluids having Prandtl numbers considerably different from 1.0.

The boundary-layer form of the temperature equation may be written from Eq. (7-5), with boundary conditions, as

$$u\frac{\partial t}{\partial x} + v\frac{\partial t}{\partial y} = \alpha\frac{\partial^2 t}{\partial y^2}$$
(7-7)

at $y = 0$ $t = t_o$ or $\phi = 1$

as $y \to \infty$ $t \to t_\infty$ and $\phi \to 0$

A similar equation applies to the concentration distribution for the two-dimensional flow of an incompressible fluid over a surface, as shown in Fig. 7-3. The stream is assumed to have a uniform concentration C_∞ outside the boundary region. A concentration C_o is maintained at the fluid-solid interface. This might occur, for example, if the surface was a sublimating solid or evaporating liquid having a uniform temperature over the whole surface.

The concentration boundary-layer thickness and concentration are generalized:

$$\delta_c' = \frac{\delta_c}{L} \quad \text{and} \quad C' = \frac{C - C_\infty}{C_o - C_\infty}$$

The generalized differential equation, from Eq. (7-4), is

$$u'\frac{\partial C'}{\partial x'} + v'\frac{\partial C'}{\partial y'} = \frac{D}{U_\infty L}\left(\frac{\partial^2 C'}{\partial x'^2} + \frac{\partial^2 C'}{\partial y'^2}\right)$$
(7-8)

$$\begin{array}{cccccc} 1 & 1 & & \delta' & \frac{1}{\delta_C'} & & 1 & & \frac{1}{\delta_C'^2} \end{array}$$

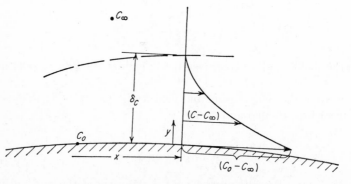

FIG. 7-3.   Concentration boundary layer.

Since C' changes from 1 to 0 as y' changes from 0 to δ'_c,

$$\frac{\partial C'}{\partial y'} = O\left(\frac{1}{\delta'_c}\right) \quad \text{and} \quad \frac{\partial^2 C'}{\partial y'^2} = O\left(\frac{1}{\delta'^2_c}\right)$$

Similarly,

$$\frac{\partial C'}{\partial x'} = O(1) \quad \text{and} \quad \frac{\partial^2 C'}{\partial x'^2} = O(1)$$

As for the temperature equation, only the first term on the right may be neglected. An estimate of the concentration boundary-layer thickness is obtained and compared with the velocity boundary-layer thickness δ:

$$\delta'^2_c \propto \frac{D}{U_\infty L} = \left(\frac{\mu}{U_\infty L \rho}\right)\left(\frac{D}{\nu}\right) = \frac{1}{N_{\text{Re}} N_{\text{Sc}}}$$

$$\frac{\delta_c}{\delta'} = \frac{\delta_c}{\delta} = \frac{1}{\sqrt{N_{\text{Sc}}}}$$

where N_{Sc} is the Schmidt number and is the ratio of the molecular diffusivities of momentum and chemical species.

The boundary-layer form of the concentration equation, with typical boundary conditions, is written below:

$$u \frac{\partial C}{\partial x} + v \frac{\partial C}{\partial y} = D \frac{\partial^2 C}{\partial y^2} \qquad (7\text{-}9)$$

at $y = 0$ $C = C_o$ (or $C' = 1$)

as $y \to \infty$ $C \to C_\infty$ (or $C' \to 0$)

The temperature and concentration boundary-layer equations (7-7) and (7-9) are of identical form. The boundary conditions, in terms of ϕ and C', are identical. Therefore, the ϕ and C' distributions are identical if $\alpha = D$, that is, if

$$\frac{\alpha}{D} = \left(\frac{\alpha}{\nu}\right)\left(\frac{\nu}{D}\right) = \frac{N_{\text{Sc}}}{N_{\text{Pr}}} = N_{\text{Le}} = 1$$

where N_{Le} is the Lewis number and is equal to the ratio of the thermal and chemical molecular diffusivities. Therefore, for a Lewis number of 1, the temperature and concentration distributions are identical, and an equation for the convection of heat applies also for the convection of mass for flow processes within the conditions of the assumptions made.

The two boundary-layer equations (7-7) and (7-9) apply to laminar boundary layers with arbitrary pressure gradients. These equations also apply to circumstances in which the temperature and/or concentration is not uniform over the whole fluid-solid surface. Solutions of the equations are discussed in subsequent sections. The effects of viscous dissipation and compressibility are added to the energy equation in Secs. 7-8 and 7-9.

7-4. CONVECTION SOLUTIONS FOR A LAMINAR BOUNDARY LAYER

Laminar boundary layers occur in many important applications, and the techniques of boundary-layer analysis have been applied to many circumstances. Solutions of the boundary-layer equations are called "exact" solutions. Such results have been obtained for the isothermal flat plate for ordinary conditions as well as for the extreme conditions wherein compressibility, the temperature dependence of the transport properties μ and k, and viscous dissipation are important. Various other shapes and conditions have been analyzed as well. These results have been of incalculable value, yielding design information in many circumstances for which controlled experimental studies are impractical or impossible.

The present section considers several relatively simple circumstances to which the incompressible boundary-layer equations, developed in the preceding section, may be applied with sufficient accuracy. The heat-transfer analysis for a flat plate at zero angle of incidence is carried out for fluids having a Prandtl number of 1.0. The results are then given for fluids of arbitrary Prandtl number. Then, by simple analogy, the heat-transfer results are extended to the diffusion of a chemical species for the circumstance wherein thermal diffusion is negligible and for which thermal energy transport due to diffusion may be ignored. These are the conditions under which the boundary-layer equations which were developed in the preceding section, Eqs. (7-7) and (7-9), may be applied to mass diffusion.

Flat Plate, Prandtl Number of 1.0. Consider a flat plate at temperature t_o placed at zero angle of attack in a stream having a velocity U_∞ and a temperature t_∞ (see Fig. 7-4). The complete boundary-layer equations and boundary conditions which govern the u, v, and t distributions are

$$u \frac{\partial u}{\partial x} + v \frac{\partial u}{\partial y} = \nu \frac{\partial^2 u}{\partial y^2} \qquad (6\text{-}20)$$

$$\frac{\partial u}{\partial x} + \frac{\partial v}{\partial y} = 0 \qquad (6\text{-}21)$$

$$u \frac{\partial t}{\partial x} + v \frac{\partial t}{\partial y} = \alpha \frac{\partial^2 t}{\partial y^2} \tag{7-7}$$

at $y = 0$ $u = 0$ $v = 0$ $t = t_o$

as $y \rightarrow \infty$ $u \rightarrow U_\infty$ $t \rightarrow t_\infty$

Replacing u in Eq. (6-20) and t in Eq. (7-7) by their "normalized" equivalents defined below, we obtain Eqs. (7-11) and (7-12), with the generalized

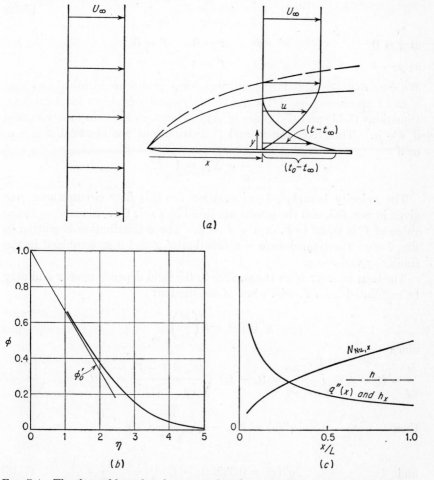

FIG. 7-4. The thermal boundary layer on a flat plate. (a) Flat plate at zero incidence. (b) Temperature distribution for $N_{\mathrm{Pr}} = 1.0$. (c) Distributions of heat-transfer quantities.

boundary conditions shown:

$$u' = \frac{u}{U_\infty}$$

$$t' = 1 - \phi = 1 - \frac{t - t_\infty}{t_o - t_\infty} = \frac{t_o - t}{t_o - t_\infty} \tag{7-10}$$

$$u\frac{\partial u'}{\partial x} + v\frac{\partial u'}{\partial y} = \nu\frac{\partial^2 u'}{\partial y^2} \tag{7-11}$$

$$u\frac{\partial t'}{\partial x} + v\frac{\partial t'}{\partial y} = \alpha\frac{\partial^2 t'}{\partial y^2} \tag{7-12}$$

at $y = 0$ $u' = 0$ $v = 0$ $t' = 0$

as $y \to \infty$ $u' \to 1$ $t' \to 1$

We note that the boundary conditions for u' and t' are identical and that u' and t' appear in Eqs. (7-11) and (7-12), respectively, in an identical way. Equations (7-11) and (7-12) are of similar form; in fact, they are identical if $\nu = \alpha$. Therefore, the u' and t' distributions are identical if $\nu = \alpha$, or if

$$\frac{\nu}{\alpha} = N_{\text{Pr}} = 1$$

The velocity boundary-layer solution for this flow circumstance was given in Sec. 6-5, and the results are listed in Table 6-1. Since $u' = t'$, the value of f' is equal to t', or $1 - f' = \phi$. The ϕ distribution is plotted in Fig. 7-4b. The temperature is a function of x and y as combined in the similarity variable η.

The heat transfer from the surface to the fluid depends upon x and may be calculated from Fourier's law of conduction:

$$q''(x) = -k\left(\frac{\partial t}{\partial y}\right)_{y=0}$$

Since

$$\frac{\partial t}{\partial y} = (t_o - t_\infty)\sqrt{\frac{U_\infty}{\nu x}}\frac{\partial\phi}{\partial\eta} = (t_o - t_\infty)\sqrt{\frac{U_\infty}{\nu x}}\frac{d(1 - f')}{d\eta} = -(t_o - t_\infty)\sqrt{\frac{U_\infty}{\nu x}}f''$$

then

$$q''(x) = k(t_o - t_\infty)\sqrt{\frac{U_\infty}{\nu x}}f''(0)$$

and

$$q''(x) = 0.332k(t_o - t_\infty)\sqrt{\frac{U_\infty}{\nu x}} \tag{7-13}$$

The heat flux decreases as the boundary-layer thickness increases.

It is customary to express heat-transfer characteristics in terms of a "surface coefficient" (or heat-transfer coefficient) h, defined as the heat-transfer rate per unit area (that is, heat flux) divided by the temperature difference causing the heat transfer. Since, as in this case, the flux is often variable over the surface, even for a uniform temperature difference, the surface coefficient h varies over the surface. Therefore, one may speak of local values h_x or of average values h. The local value is found by dividing Eq. (7-13) by $(t_o - t_\infty)$:

$$h_x = \frac{q''(x)}{t_o - t_\infty} = 0.332k \sqrt{\frac{U_\infty}{\nu x}} \tag{7-14}$$

Multiplying through by x/k, a dimensionless combination is formed on the left-hand side which is called the Nusselt number. The variables on the right combine to form a boundary-layer Reynolds number.

$$\frac{h_x x}{k} = N_{\mathrm{Nu},x} = 0.332 \sqrt{\frac{U_\infty x}{\nu}} = 0.332 \sqrt{N_{\mathrm{Re},x}} \tag{7-15}$$

The local flux, surface coefficient, and Nusselt number distributions are sketched in Fig. 7-4c.

The average surface coefficient h may be found from Eq. (7-14) or from the relation between h and the total heat-transfer rate per unit plate width; that is,

$$q = hL(t_o - t_\infty) \tag{7-16}$$

q is found by integrating Eq. (7-13).

$$q = \int_0^L q''(x)\, dx = 0.332k(t_o - t_\infty) \sqrt{\frac{U_\infty}{\nu}} \int_0^L \frac{dx}{\sqrt{x}} = 0.664k(t_o - t_\infty) \sqrt{\frac{U_\infty L}{\nu}}$$

Therefore,
$$h = 0.664 \frac{k}{L} \sqrt{\frac{U_\infty L}{\nu}}$$

or
$$\frac{hL}{k} = N_{\mathrm{Nu}} = 0.664 \sqrt{N_{\mathrm{Re}}} \tag{7-17}$$

where N_{Re} is the plate Reynolds number.

Flat Plate, Other Prandtl Numbers. Equations (7-15) and (7-17) summarize the heat-transfer behavior for a laminar boundary layer on a flat plate for a fluid Prandtl number of 1.0. The analysis for Prandtl numbers other than 1.0 proceeds from Eqs. (6-20), (6-21), and (7-7) by reducing them to ordinary differential equations through the use of a stream function ψ and a similarity variable η. This is the same technique as used in Sec. 6-5 for the velocity solution. Employing the same definition of ψ and a somewhat modified η, Eqs. (6-20), (6-21), and (7-7) become

$$ff'' + 2f''' = 0 \tag{6-28}$$

$$\phi'' + N_{\mathrm{Pr}}f\phi' = 0 \tag{7-18}$$

$$\eta = \frac{y}{2}\sqrt{\frac{U_\infty}{\nu x}}$$

at $\eta = 0$ $f = 0$ $f' = 0$ $\phi = 1$

as $n \to \infty$ $f' \to 1$ $\phi \to 0$

No exact, explicit solution is known for Eq. (6-28). Therefore, Eq. (7-18) may be solved only approximately. Pohlhausen (1921) presented an integral relation for the temperature distribution $\phi(\eta)$ as a function of the Prandtl number:

$$\phi(\eta) = 1 - \frac{\displaystyle\int_0^\eta \exp\left[-N_{\mathrm{Pr}}\int_0^\eta f(\eta)\,d\eta\right]d\eta}{\displaystyle\int_0^\infty \exp\left[-N_{\mathrm{Pr}}\int_0^\eta f(\eta)\,d\eta\right]d\eta} \tag{7-19}$$

Evaluation of $\phi(\eta,N_{\mathrm{Pr}})$ requires that $f(\eta)$ be introduced as a function of η. Note that f does not depend upon N_{Pr}.

Pohlhausen (1921) integrated Eq. (7-19) for several Prandtl numbers in the range 0.6 to 15. Eckert and Drewitz (1940) carried out the integration for the wider Prandtl number range 0.6 to 1000. These temperature distributions are reproduced in Fig. 7-5.

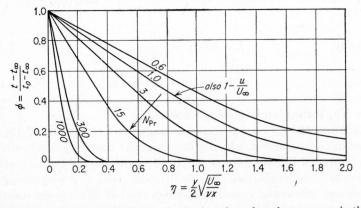

FIG. 7-5. Temperature distribution in the laminar boundary layer on an isothermal flat plate. [*From Schlichting* (1955).]

Recalling the similarity of the velocity and temperature distributions for $N_{Pr} = 1.0$, the velocity distribution curve is noted in Fig. 7-5. The Prandtl number effect is evident. A high Prandtl number, meaning low conductivity and/or high viscosity, results in the velocity boundary layer being thicker than the thermal boundary layer. The velocity disturbance extends farther out into the stream. For low Prandtl numbers, the reverse is true. In fact, for very low Prandtl numbers the velocity boundary layer is so thin, compared with the thermal boundary layer, that it may be ignored in solving the temperature equation for the heat-transfer characteristics. Such an analysis has been carried out for several shapes for liquid metals by Grosh and Cess (1958). Sparrow and Gregg (1957) discussed the effect of such an assumption for the flat-plate case.

Heat-transfer behavior is calculated from the temperature gradient at the surface, that is, ϕ_0'. This gradient depends upon the Prandtl number in a complicated way [see Eq. (7-19)]. However, the calculations by Pohlhausen have shown that the gradient is closely approximated, in the Prandtl number range 0.6 to 15, by

$$\phi_0' = -0.332\sqrt[3]{N_{Pr}} \tag{7-20}$$

The local flux and surface coefficient are, therefore,

$$q''(x) = 0.332k(t_o - t_\infty)\sqrt{\frac{U_\infty}{\nu x}}\sqrt[3]{N_{Pr}} \tag{7-21}$$

$$\frac{h_x x}{k} = N_{Nu,x} = 0.332\sqrt{N_{Re,x}}\sqrt[3]{N_{Pr}} \tag{7-22}$$

The average surface coefficient is determined as before by determining the total heat-transfer rate by integration. The resulting value is

$$\frac{hL}{k} = N_{Nu} = 0.664\sqrt{N_{Re}}\sqrt[3]{N_{Pr}} \tag{7-23}$$

Solutions for incompressible flow have been obtained for various other geometries and temperature conditions as well as for the isothermal flat plate. For example, Squire (1938) determined the heat-transfer characteristics for stagnation-point flow for flow normal to an isothermal cylinder. Chapman and Rubesin (1949) treated the flat-plate case for which the surface temperature varies with x. Fage and Falkner (1931) had shown that similarity variables exist for wedge flows, and Levy (1952) presented solutions of the boundary-layer equations for various wedge angles for heat-transfer temperature differences which vary as a power of the distance from the stagnation point. These are a few of the many solutions obtained from the boundary-layer equations. Many problems have also been solved by the application of an integral method similar to that discussed in Sec. 6-9 for analyzing flow.

Example 7-1. Water at 50°F flows at a velocity of 3 fps over a flat plate 1 ft long placed at zero incidence. The plate is maintained at 70°F. We shall find the surface coefficient at the midpoint of the plate and the total heat-transfer rate from one side. The properties of water at the average of the two temperatures are used.

The plate Reynolds number was found in Example 6-2 to be 248,000. The thermal conductivity and Prandtl number of water at 60°F are $k = 0.341$ Btu/hr ft °F and $N_{Pr} = 7.98$.

$$\frac{h_x x}{k} = 0.332\sqrt{N_{Re,x}}\ \sqrt[3]{N_{Pr}} = 0.332\sqrt{\frac{248,000}{2}}\ \sqrt[3]{7.98} = 330$$

$$h_x = 225 \text{ Btu/hr ft}^2 \text{ °F}$$

$$N_{Nu} = 0.664\sqrt{248,000}\ \sqrt[3]{7.98} = 934$$

$$h = 318 \text{ Btu/hr ft}^2 \text{ °F}$$

$$q = hA(t_o - t_\infty) = 318 \times 1 \times 20 = 6360 \text{ Btu/hr}$$

Mass Diffusion. In the preceding section the boundary-layer equations for the temperature and concentration distributions, Eqs. (7-7) and (7-9), are developed. The equations and boundary conditions are shown to be of identical form when the temperature and concentration variables are chosen as

$$\phi = \frac{t - t_\infty}{t_o - t_\infty} \quad \text{and} \quad C' = \frac{C - C_\infty}{C_o - C_\infty}$$

For $\alpha = D$, that is, a Lewis number of 1, the equations are identical, and the ϕ and C' distributions are the same for any laminar convection circumstance to which Eqs. (7-7) and (7-9) apply, with similar boundary conditions. This is the basis upon which the similarity between the convections of heat and mass rests. As a result of this similarity, convection characteristics may be measured in either a heat- or a mass-transfer circumstance and the results may be applied to either kind of convection. Such procedures have been widely used in the study of convection. However, similarity has been demonstrated herein only for circumstances in which Eqs. (7-7) and (7-9) are a valid description of heat and mass diffusion.

Earlier in this section it is shown that, for a Prandtl number of 1.0, the velocity and temperature distributions $(1 - \phi)$ are also identical for similar boundary conditions for the two distributions. Therefore, if the Lewis and Prandtl numbers (and, as a result, also the Schmidt number) are 1.0, the velocity, $(1 - \phi)$, and $(1 - C')$ distributions are identical for similar boundary conditions. Heat- and mass-convection information may be obtained directly from velocity solutions. However, the velocity distribution to which the temperature and concentration distributions are similar is the one which actually results in the presence of mass diffusion.

The diffusion of mass away from (or to) a surface results in an effective normal velocity component v_C at the surface, that is, at $y = 0$. Therefore, the usual boundary condition of $v = 0$ at $y = 0$, employed to solve most boundary-layer problems, must often be modified. The condition of a zero normal component applies with sufficient accuracy only if the diffusion rate at the surface results in a value of v_C which is negligible compared with the other velocities in the flow field.

Under conditions in which v_C is negligible, the distributions shown in Figs. 6-8 and 7-5 may be applied to mass diffusion from (or to) a flat plate. The distribution of u/U_∞ in Fig. 6-8 is also the distribution of $(1 - C')$ for diffusion with a Schmidt number of 1.0 for any Prandtl number. The distributions of ϕ in Fig. 7-5 are the distributions of C' for diffusion with a Lewis number of 1.0 for any Schmidt number (or Prandtl number). The mass-convection transport equation is developed below for diffusion with a Lewis number of 1.0 for a flat plate.

Mass-convection characteristics are often expressed in terms of a convection or surface coefficient H defined in a manner similar to the heat-convection coefficient h. The local flux of the diffusing species at the surface is set equal to H_x times the over-all concentration difference. The flux is then expressed in terms of the concentration gradient at the surface. This, in turn, is equal to the known temperature gradient, for a Lewis number of 1.0.

$$m''(x) = H_x(C_o - C_\infty) = -D\left(\frac{\partial C}{\partial y}\right)_{y=0} = 0.332\,D(C_o - C_\infty)\sqrt{\frac{U_\infty}{\nu x}}\ \sqrt[3]{N_{\mathrm{Pr}}}$$

$$(7\text{-}24)$$

since

$$\left(\frac{\partial C}{\partial y}\right)_{y=0} = (C_o - C_\infty)\sqrt{\frac{U_\infty}{\nu x}}\left(\frac{dC'}{d\eta}\right)_0 = (C_o - C_\infty)\sqrt{\frac{U_\infty}{\nu x}}\,\phi_0'$$

and
$$\phi_0' = -0.332\sqrt[3]{N_{\mathrm{Pr}}}\qquad(7\text{-}20)$$

The local and average mass-diffusion Nusselt numbers may be written

$$\frac{H_x x}{D} = 0.332\sqrt{N_{\mathrm{Re},x}}\,\sqrt[3]{N_{\mathrm{Pr}}} = 0.332\sqrt{N_{\mathrm{Re},x}}\,\sqrt[3]{N_{\mathrm{Sc}}}\qquad(7\text{-}25)$$

$$\frac{HL}{D} = 0.664\sqrt{N_{\mathrm{Re}}}\,\sqrt[3]{N_{\mathrm{Sc}}}\qquad(7\text{-}26)$$

Comparing these results with Eqs. (7-22) and (7-23), we see that the thermal- and mass-diffusion Nusselt numbers are equal, for a Lewis number of 1.0.

Hartnett and Eckert (1957) summarized the results for the laminar boundary-layer, flat-plate case for conditions under which the effective normal velocity component at the surface, v_C, may be appreciable. This change in the velocity boundary conditions adds another parameter to the analysis. Similar solutions of the velocity equations exist when v_C is inversely proportional to $\sqrt{x}$. Results are presented for Prandtl numbers of 0.7 and 1.0 for a Lewis number of 1.0.

Example 7-2. Air at 14.7 psia and 60°F having a relative humidity of 40 per cent flows at a velocity of 10 fps over a 1-ft-long porous flat plate. The exposed surface of the plate is kept wet by forcing water through the plate at a rate equal to the evaporation rate. The plate is maintained at 50°F by adding or removing heat as required. Assume that the water-air mixture at the interface is saturated at 50°F. We shall compute the rate of evaporation of water, the heat-transfer rate, and the rate of heat supply to (or removal from) the plate. The following properties are given for air and for water vapor–air diffusion:

$$\nu = 0.56 \text{ ft}^2/\text{hr} \qquad \alpha = 0.79 \text{ ft}^2/\text{hr} \qquad D = 0.85 \text{ ft}^2/\text{hr} \qquad k = 0.014 \text{ Btu/hr ft °F}$$

$$\rho_a = 0.076 \text{ lb/ft}^3 \qquad N_{Pr} = \frac{\nu}{\alpha} = 0.71 \qquad N_{Sc} = \frac{\nu}{D} = 0.66 \qquad N_{Le} = \frac{\alpha}{D} = 0.93$$

The average heat-convection coefficient and heat-transfer rate are found:

$$\sqrt{N_{Re}} = \sqrt{\frac{10 \times 3600}{0.56}} = \sqrt{64,000} = 254$$

$$h = 0.664 \frac{k}{L} \sqrt{N_{Re}} \sqrt[3]{N_{Pr}} = 2.1$$

$$q = 2.1 \times 1 \times (60 - 50) = 21 \text{ Btu/hr to the plate}$$

A psychrometric diagram for air–water vapor mixtures yields the following surface and free-stream specific humidities and concentrations:

$$C_o = 54 \text{ grains/lb air} = 0.59 \times 10^{-3} \text{ lb/ft}^3$$

$$C_\infty = 30 \text{ grains/lb air} = 0.33 \times 10^{-3} \text{ lb/ft}^3$$

Assuming that $N_{Le} = 0.93$ is sufficiently close to 1.0 that Eq. (7-26) applies,

$$H = 0.664 \frac{D}{L} \sqrt{N_{Re}} \sqrt[3]{N_{Sc}} = 124 \text{ fph}$$

$$m'' = HL(C_o - C_\infty) = 124 \times 0.26 \times 10^{-3} = 0.0322 \text{ lb/hr}$$

The heat required to vaporize water at this rate is

$$q_v = 0.0322 \times 1065.6 = 34.3 \text{ Btu/hr}$$

This exceeds the heat transfer, and heat must be supplied to the plate at a rate of

$$q_s = 34.3 - 21 = 13.3 \text{ Btu/hr}$$

7-5. SIMILARITY THEORIES FOR THE TURBULENT TRANSFER OF MOMENTUM, HEAT, AND MASS

The similarity of the transport equations, which relate the diffusion rates of momentum, heat, and mass to the gradients of velocity, temperature, and concentration through the viscosity, thermal-conductivity, and mass-diffusion coefficients, has led to the development of many theories of transport rates. Reynolds in 1874 suggested that velocity, temperature, and concentration distributions should be of similar form. In the preceding section the utility and limitations of similarity are shown for laminar flow.

In Sec. 6-6 the three diffusion equations are written for turbulent flow. Just as for laminar transport, these relations are all of the same form. The present section presents several of the theories which exploit this similarity for turbulent flow.

Prandtl (1910) pointed out that the velocity and temperature differential equations are identical if the molecular diffusivities of momentum and heat are equal. This led to a relation between heat transfer and pressure gradient for flow in a tube. Therefore, heat transfer could be calculated from friction loss. The result, however, applies only for a Prandtl number of 1.0.

G. I. Taylor (1916) developed a more general result, based upon a postulated nature of the turbulent flow process, which attempted to account for the effect of Prandtl numbers different from 1.0. A relation between heat transfer and friction loss resulted. However, this relation contains an additional parameter of the turbulent velocity distribution whose value is uncertain.

Following the accumulation of experimental information concerning turbulent velocity distributions, the predictions of the Prandtl mixing-length theory were substantiated. This led to a clearer understanding of the exact form of the velocity distribution, and a universal velocity distribution was presented by von Kármán (1939) which is a relatively good fit of the data. This distribution is discussed in Sec. 6-7. This detailed knowledge of the turbulent velocity distribution makes it possible to use the turbulent transport equations (6-45) to (6-47) to determine temperature and concentration distributions from the velocity distribution. Since the shear-stress distribution is linear across the tube for developed flow, τ is known in terms of τ_o. The velocity gradient may be found from the velocity distribution, and, therefore, the turbulent diffusivity of momentum is known. Since momentum, heat, and mass are all convected about the turbulent flow field by eddies, it is reasonable to assume that the three eddy (or turbulent) diffusivities are equal at each point in the flow field. This similarity of turbulent transport is the sense in which the term "similarity" is used in this section.

The assumed equality of the momentum- and heat-transfer eddy diffusivities permitted von Kármán (1939) to develop a heat-transfer equation which predicts the Prandtl number effect for developed turbulent flow in a smooth tube with considerable accuracy. This analysis is presented below.

The Reynolds Analogy. Before this analysis is presented, however, the simple result of assuming complete similarity of momentum and heat transfer, called the "Reynolds analogy," will be derived. The two general transport equations are

$$\frac{\tau}{\rho} = (\nu + \epsilon_M)\frac{du}{dy} \tag{6-45}$$

and
$$\frac{q''}{\rho c_p} = (\alpha + \epsilon_H)\frac{dt}{dy} = (\alpha + \epsilon_H)\frac{d\theta}{dy} \tag{6-46}$$

If $\nu + \epsilon_M = \alpha + \epsilon_H$,
$$\frac{du}{d\theta} = \left(\frac{\tau}{\rho}\right)\left(\frac{\rho c_p}{q''}\right)$$

Assuming that the variation of q'' (with y) is also linear,

$$\frac{du}{d\theta} = \left(\frac{\tau_o}{\rho}\right)\left(1 - \frac{y}{R}\right)\left(\frac{\rho c_p}{q_o''}\right)\frac{1}{1 - y/R} = \left(\frac{\tau_o}{\rho}\right)\left(\frac{\rho c_p}{q_o''}\right) = \text{constant} \tag{7-27a}$$

This result shows that the velocity and temperature distributions are of identical shape. Therefore, the average velocity V is found at the same distance from the wall, y_m, as the average temperature excess θ_m. Equation (7-27a) is integrated from the wall to y_m (see Fig. 7-6).

$$du = \left(\frac{\tau_o}{\rho}\right)\left(\frac{\rho c_p}{q_o''}\right) d\theta \tag{7-27b}$$

at $y = 0$ $u = 0$ $\theta = 0$

at $y = y_m$ $u = V$ $\theta = \theta_m$

$$V = \left(\frac{\tau_o}{\rho}\right)\left(\frac{\rho c_p}{q_o''}\right)\theta_m$$

The heat-convection coefficient h is defined as the wall heat flux q_o'' divided by the difference between the wall and average fluid temperature, that is, θ_m. The wall shear stress τ_o may be replaced by the friction factor f and dynamic pressure, Eqs. (6-48) and (6-53a). The result is

$$\frac{h}{\rho c_p V} = N_{St} = \frac{f}{8} \tag{7-28}$$

where N_{St} is the Stanton number and f is a function of the Reynolds number. The Stanton number is the Nusselt number divided by the product of the Reynolds and Prandtl numbers.

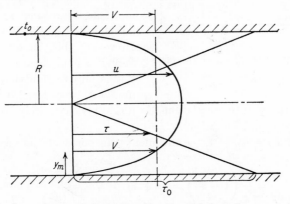

FIG. 7-6.   Turbulent flow in a circular tube.

The von Kármán Analogy. The results of the Reynolds analogy are essentially in agreement with experimental data for fluids having Prandtl numbers near 1.0. This is to be expected. For $N_{Pr} = 1.0$, $\nu = \alpha$. If $\epsilon_M = \epsilon_H$, then $\nu + \epsilon_M = \alpha + \epsilon_H$.

The von Kármán analysis assumes only that $\epsilon_M = \epsilon_H$. The distribution of ϵ_M is calculated from Eq. (6-45) and from the universal velocity distribution, $u^+ = f(y^+)$.

$$\frac{\tau}{\rho} = \frac{\tau_o}{\rho}\left(1 - \frac{y}{R}\right) = (\nu + \epsilon_M)\frac{du}{dy} = \frac{u^{*2}}{\nu}(\nu + \epsilon_M)\frac{du^+}{dy^+}$$

$$= \frac{\tau_o}{\rho}\left(1 + \frac{\epsilon_M}{\nu}\right)f'(y^+)$$

and

$$\frac{\epsilon_M}{\nu} = \frac{1 - y/R}{f'(y^+)} - 1 \tag{7-29a}$$

or

$$\frac{\epsilon_M}{\nu} \approx \frac{1}{f'(y^+)} - 1 \tag{7-29b}$$

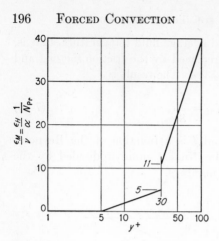

FIG. 7-7. The distribution of turbulent diffusivity.

The ratio of eddy and molecular diffusivity is plotted in Fig. 7-7. Turbulent diffusivity is zero in the laminar sublayer, is of the same order as the molecular diffusivity in the buffer region, and is much greater than the molecular diffusivity in the turbulent core. An important conclusion, employed in the subsequent analysis, is that the molecular transport of heat may be neglected in the turbulent core. However, this is strictly correct only if α is of the order of ν or less, that is, only for fluids having Prandtl numbers of order 1.0 or greater. Therefore, the resulting equations do not apply accurately to fluids having very low Prandtl numbers.

Assuming $\epsilon_M = \epsilon_H = \epsilon$, the turbulent transport equations are written as

$$\frac{\tau}{\rho} = \frac{\tau_o}{\rho}\left(1 - \frac{y}{R}\right) = (\nu + \epsilon)\frac{du}{dy} = \frac{\nu(1 - y/R)}{f'(y^+)}\frac{du}{dy}$$

or

$$\frac{\tau_o}{\rho} = \frac{\nu}{f'(y^+)}\frac{du}{dy} \tag{7-30}$$

$$\frac{q_o''}{\rho c_p} \approx \nu\left[\frac{\alpha}{\nu} - 1 + \frac{1}{f'(y^+)}\right]\frac{d\theta}{dy} \tag{7-31}$$

These are rewritten as differential relations between u and θ and y^+:

$$du = \sqrt{\frac{\tau_o}{\rho}}f'(y^+)\,dy^+ \tag{7-32}$$

$$d\theta \approx \left(\frac{q_o''}{\rho c_p}\right)\sqrt{\frac{\rho}{\tau_o}}\frac{dy^+}{\frac{1}{N_{\mathrm{Pr}}} - 1 + \frac{1}{f(y^+)}} \tag{7-33}$$

These relations are integrated from $y^+ = 0$, where u and θ are zero, to

$y^+ = 30$, where $u = u_{30}$ and $\theta = \theta_{30}$. In this region α/ν must be retained in Eq. (7-33) to account for molecular diffusion.

$$u_{30} = \sqrt{\frac{\tau_o}{\rho}} \int_0^{30} f'(y^+)\, dy^+ = \sqrt{\frac{\tau_o}{\rho}} f(30) = \sqrt{\frac{\tau_o}{\rho}} K \qquad (7\text{-}34a)$$

$$\theta_{30} = \left(\frac{q_o''}{\rho c_p}\right) \sqrt{\frac{\rho}{\tau_o}} \int_0^{30} \frac{dy^+}{\dfrac{1}{N_{Pr}} - 1 + \dfrac{1}{f(y^+)}} = \left(\frac{q_o''}{\rho c_p}\right) \sqrt{\frac{\rho}{\tau_o}} M(N_{Pr}) \qquad (7\text{-}34b)$$

Integration is next carried out from $y^+ = 30$, neglecting the molecular diffusion of heat. Equation (7-27b) therefore applies, and the velocity and temperature distributions are similar in the turbulent core. Since the turbulent core occupies a large fraction of the whole cross section, the average values of u and θ are assumed to be found at the same value of y. Therefore,

$$\int_{u_{30}}^{V} du = V - u_{30} = \left(\frac{\tau_o}{\rho}\right)\left(\frac{\rho c_p}{q_o''}\right)\int_{\theta_{30}}^{\theta_m} d\theta = \left(\frac{\tau_o}{\rho}\right)\left(\frac{\rho c_p}{q_o''}\right)(\theta_m - \theta_{30}) \qquad (7\text{-}34c)$$

u_{30} and θ_{30} are eliminated between Eqs. (7-34a, b, c), and the value of τ_o is introduced through the use of Eqs. (6-48) and (6-53a):

$$N_{St} = \frac{f/8}{1 + \sqrt{\dfrac{f}{8}}\dfrac{M(N_{Pr}) - K}{V}}$$

$$= \frac{f/8}{1 + 5\sqrt{f/8}\{N_{Pr} - 1 + \ln[1 + \tfrac{5}{6}(N_{Pr} - 1)]\}} \qquad (7\text{-}35)$$

The values of M and K are determined from the velocity distribution. The friction factor may be determined from an equation or from the Moody diagram, Fig. 6-13. If the relation of Blasius, valid to $N_{Re} = 10^5$, is used to eliminate the friction factor, the expression becomes

$$f = 0.3164(N_{Re})^{-\frac{1}{4}} \qquad (7\text{-}36)$$

$$N_{Nu} = \frac{0.0396 N_{Re}^{\frac{3}{4}} N_{Pr}}{1 + (0.99/\sqrt[8]{N_{Re}})\{N_{Pr} - 1 + \ln[1 + \tfrac{5}{6}(N_{Pr} - 1)]\}} \qquad (7\text{-}37)$$

The result of the von Kármán analysis, Eq. (7-35), is plotted in Fig. 7-8 for various values of the Prandtl number. The friction factors were taken from Fig. 6-13.

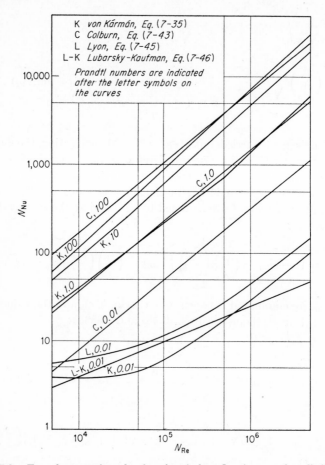

FIG. 7-8. Forced convection; developed turbulent flow in smooth-walled tubes.

The Universal Temperature Distribution. An additional result of the assumption of similarity (that is, $\epsilon_M = \epsilon_H$) is that the temperature distribution in the passage may be determined from the velocity distribution, for various Prandtl numbers. Equation (7-33) may be integrated, retaining the Prandtl number over the whole cross section. The result, for a flow Reynolds number of 10,000, is plotted in Fig. 7-9 for Prandtl numbers of 0.01, 1, and 100. The distribution for $N_{Pr} = 1$ is also the velocity distribution. These curves show the relative magnitudes of the molecular and eddy heat-transfer effects. For a high Prandtl number fluid, molecular transport is negligible in the core. However, the large temperature gradient in the core for a low Prandtl number fluid indicates substantial molecular transport.

Similarity Applied to Boundary-layer Processes. Since the universal velocity distribution also applies with reasonable accuracy to turbulent

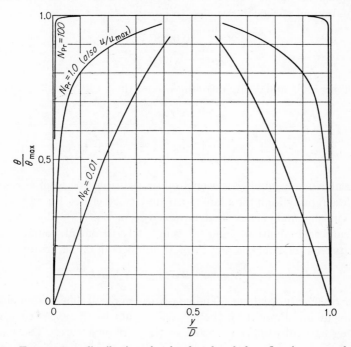

FIG. 7-9. Temperature distributions for developed turbulent flow in a smooth-walled tube. $N_{Re} = 10{,}000$.

boundary layers, the similarity theory may be applied as above to calculate the heat transfer from an isothermal flat plate. At a particular location, a distance x from the leading edge, Eqs. (7-32) and (7-33) are integrated from $y^+ = 0$ to $y^+ = 30$ to give Eqs. (7-34a) and (b). The next interval of integration is from $y^+ = 30$ out to a point in the undisturbed stream where $u = U_\infty$ and $\theta = (t_\infty - t_o)$:

$$U_\infty - u_{30} = \left(\frac{\tau_o}{\rho}\right)\left(\frac{\rho c_p}{q_o''}\right)[(t_\infty - t_o) - \theta_{30}] \qquad (7\text{-}34d)$$

u_{30} and θ_{30} are eliminated and the result rearranged. Note that h_x is based upon the maximum temperature difference.

$$\frac{q_o''(x)}{t_o - t_\infty} = h_x = \frac{\left(\dfrac{\rho c_p}{U_\infty}\right)\left(\dfrac{\tau_o}{\rho}\right)}{1 + \sqrt{\dfrac{\tau_o}{\rho}\dfrac{M - K}{U_\infty}}}$$

The dependence of the wall shear stress τ_o upon x may be determined from Eqs. (6-68) and (6-69), in Sec. 6-9, to be

$$\frac{\tau_o}{\rho} = \frac{0.0288 U_\infty{}^2}{\sqrt[5]{N_{\mathrm{Re},x}}} \tag{7-38}$$

The values of M and N are introduced, and the local Nusselt number is

$$N_{\mathrm{Nu},x} = \frac{h_x x}{k} = \frac{0.0288 N_{\mathrm{Re},x}^{0.8} N_{\mathrm{Pr}}}{1 + \dfrac{0.85}{\sqrt[10]{N_{\mathrm{Re},x}}}\{N_{\mathrm{Pr}} - 1 + \ln\left[1 + \tfrac{5}{6}(N_{\mathrm{Pr}} - 1)\right]\}} \tag{7-39}$$

The local Nusselt number is seen to decrease from the leading edge, but much less rapidly than for a laminar boundary layer [see Eq. (7-22)]. The plate Nusselt number may be determined from Eq. (7-39) by integration.

An empirical equation, valid for completely turbulent boundary layers on flat plates, for fluids having Prandtl numbers of 0.7 or greater, is

$$N_{\mathrm{Nu}} = 0.037 N_{\mathrm{Re}}{}^{0.8} N_{\mathrm{Pr}}^{\frac{1}{3}} \tag{7-40}$$

Other Similarity Analyses. The von Kármán result differs from observed behavior at low Prandtl numbers. This would be the expected result of assuming α small compared with ϵ in the turbulent core. The resulting equation is also inadequate at very high Prandtl numbers. A number of more sophisticated analyses have been carried out—for example, by Martinelli (1947), Deissler (1955), and Seban and Shimazaki (1951). Deissler assumed the equality of turbulent diffusivities and based the calculation of the velocity, temperature, and concentration distributions upon a derived distribution of ϵ across the stream. Heat- and mass-transfer relations are presented which are in good agreement with experimental data over Prandtl and Schmidt number intervals from 0.5 to 3000. However, a number of recent studies suggest that the initial assumption, $\epsilon_M = \epsilon_H$, may require considerable modification before an adequate theory of wide applicability results.

Similarity in Mass Diffusion. The similarity ideas used for the analysis of heat transfer may be applied to mass transfer as well. This is done below for tube flow in a manner exactly analogous to the foregoing analysis for heat transfer. The value of ϵ_C in Eq. (6-47) is assumed equal to ϵ_M, which in turn is known from the velocity distribution [see Eqs. (7-29)].

$$m'' = (D + \epsilon) \frac{dC}{dy} \tag{6-47}$$

$$m_o'' \approx \nu \left(\frac{D}{\nu} + \frac{\epsilon}{\nu} \right) \frac{dC}{dy} \approx \sqrt{\frac{\tau_o}{\rho}} \left[\frac{1}{N_{Sc}} - 1 + \frac{1}{f'(y^+)} \right] \frac{dC}{dy^+}$$

$$dC \approx m_o'' \sqrt{\frac{\rho}{\tau_o}} \frac{dy^+}{\dfrac{1}{N_{Sc}} - 1 + \dfrac{1}{f'(y^+)}}$$

Comparing this with Eq. (7-33), we see that C, m_o'', and N_{Sc} replace θ, q_o'', and N_{Pr}. Therefore, an equation exactly analogous to (7-35) results, except that the Stanton number is

$$N_{St} = \frac{H}{\rho c V} \qquad \text{where } H = \frac{m_o''}{C_m - C_o}$$

That is,

$$N_{St} = \frac{f/8}{1 + \sqrt{\dfrac{f}{8}} \dfrac{M(N_{Sc}) - K}{V}} \tag{7-41}$$

where $M(N_{Sc})$ is of the same form as $M(N_{Pr})$.

7-6. HEAT-TRANSFER CORRELATIONS FOR FLOW IN PASSAGES

The preceding sections of this chapter present the differential equations which govern heat and mass transfer for forced convection in a fluid having uniform properties ρ, μ, k, and D. The laminar boundary-layer method of analysis is demonstrated, and the similarity theory of turbulent transfer is applied. However, much of the information available concerning heat- and mass-transfer behavior has been determined by experimentation, and engineering design often proceeds from such information. Present techniques of analysis are often inadequate or impractical for many circumstances—for example, for regions of separated flow, for complicated geometries, and for cases wherein the transport properties are temperature-dependent in a complicated way.

The present section considers developed laminar and turbulent flow inside circular and noncircular passages. The effect of inlet sections in which the flow is undeveloped is considered. The effects of transport-property temperature dependence are discussed. The subsequent section presents transport information for the surfaces of objects which are immersed in a fluid stream.

Developed Turbulent Flow in Tubes. Since turbulent flow in circular tubes arises in many types of heat-exchange equipment, this type of transfer process has been studied in detail. Many expressions have been presented in attempts to summarize quantitatively the various influences to which such processes are subject. The convection coefficient, combined into a Nusselt number, depends upon the flow Reynolds number, the tube wall roughness, the fluid Prandtl number, any density variations due to pressure drop and temperature change, transport-property variations due to temperature differences, and the relative length of tube, that is, the length divided by the diameter.

For developed turbulent flow, that is, in long tubes (or far from the tube inlet), the following equation, essentially that presented by Dittus and Boelter (1930), has been widely used for relatively small heat-transfer temperature differences for fluids having Prandtl numbers between 0.6 and 100. This equation applies to smooth-walled tubes.

$$N_{\mathrm{Nu}} = \frac{hD}{k_m} = 0.023 \left(\frac{DV}{\nu_m}\right)^{0.8} \left(\frac{c_p \mu}{k}\right)_m^{n} \tag{7-42}$$

where $n = 0.4$ for heating and $n = 0.3$ for cooling. The properties are to be evaluated at the average fluid temperature t_m at the section.

In an attempt to correlate more closely heat-transfer behavior for fluids whose properties are temperature-dependent, Colburn (1933) suggested, in effect, that an exponent of $\frac{1}{3}$ be used for the Prandtl number and that several of the fluid properties be evaluated at a "film" temperature defined as the average of t_m and the wall temperature t_w. The equation is rearranged in terms of the Stanton number:

$$\left(\frac{h}{\rho V c_p}\right)_m \left(\frac{c_p \mu}{k}\right)_f^{\frac{2}{3}} = 0.023 \left(\frac{DV}{\nu_f}\right)^{-0.2} \tag{7-43}$$

The Colburn equation is plotted in Fig. 7-8 for Prandtl numbers of 0.01, 1 and 100.

The Colburn relation is inadequate for large temperature differences for fluids whose properties are sharply temperature-dependent. One of the principal effects of the radial temperature gradient is to distort the velocity distribution through a temperature influence upon viscosity. This affects the transport processes. Higher viscosity at the wall thickens the low-velocity layer and inhibits heat transfer. Lower viscosity thins the low-velocity layer and enhances heat transfer. Since for gases, generally, viscosity increases with temperature and, for liquids, viscosity decreases with temperature, the effect of viscosity gradients in heating is to decrease the transfer rate for gases and to increase the transfer rate for fluids. For cooling, the reverse effects result. Sieder and Tate (1936) attempted to correlate this effect in various heat-transfer equations by multiplying such equations by the ratio of the viscosities at t_m and t_w raised to a power of 0.14. The result for developed turbulent flow is

$$\frac{hD}{k_m} = 0.023 \left(\frac{DV}{\nu_m}\right)^{0.8} \left(\frac{c_p \mu}{k}\right)_m^{\frac{1}{3}} \left(\frac{\mu_m}{\mu_w}\right)^{0.14} \tag{7-44}$$

This equation is intended to apply also to fluids having high Prandtl numbers with moderate heat-transfer temperature differences. Kreith and Summerfield (1950) suggested modifying the viscosity-ratio exponent to 0.10.

Example 7-3. Water at 80°F is to be heated to 100°F in a 1-in.-ID smooth-walled tube whose inside surface temperature is to be maintained at 110°F. The average velocity is 5 fps. We shall compare the surface coefficients obtained from the various correlating equations and find the necessary tube length.

The average water temperature and film temperature are found in order to determine the properties and Reynolds and Prandtl numbers:

$$t_m = \frac{80 + 100}{2} = 90°F \qquad t_f = \frac{90 + 110}{2} = 100°F$$

$$\mu_m = 1.85 \qquad \mu_w = 1.48 \qquad \rho_m = 62.12$$

$$k_m = 0.358 \qquad (N_{Pr})_m = 5.15 \qquad (N_{Pr})_f = 4.55$$

$$(N_{Re})_m = \frac{5 \times 3600 \times 62.12 \times 1}{1.85 \times 12} = 50,400 \qquad (N_{Re})_f = 63,000$$

From the Dittus-Boelter relation,

$$\frac{hD}{k_m} = 0.023(50,400)^{0.8}(5.15)^{0.4} = 256$$

The Colburn relation is rearranged to give

$$\frac{hD}{k_m} = 0.023(N_{Re})_f^{-0.2}(N_{Re})_m(N_{Pr})_f^{-\frac{2}{3}} = 230$$

The Sieder-Tate form gives

$$\frac{hD}{k_m} = 0.023(50,400)^{0.8}(5.15)^{\frac{1}{3}} \left(\frac{1.85}{1.48}\right)^{0.14} = 237$$

The maximum difference in these estimates is 11 per cent. The necessary tube length is found by equating the rate of heat gain by the water to the total convection rate at the wall:

$$q = mc_p \, \Delta t = \rho \frac{V \pi D^2}{4} c_p \, \Delta t = hA \, \Delta t_l = h\pi DL \, \Delta t_l$$

$$\frac{hD}{k_m} = 237 \qquad h = 237 \times 0.358 \times 12 = 1020$$

The proper mean temperature difference is given by Eq. (1-12):

$$\Delta t_l = \frac{(110 - 80) - (110 - 100)}{\ln\left[(110 - 80)/(110 - 100)\right]} = \frac{30 - 10}{\ln 3} = 18.2°F$$

$$L = \frac{\rho V D c_p \, \Delta t}{4h \, \Delta t_l} = 25.4 \text{ ft}$$

The foregoing correlations, Eqs. (7-42) to (7-44), are only moderately successful attempts to relate the Nusselt, Reynolds, and Prandtl numbers. These relatively simple relations apply well to fluids having Prandtl numbers in the vicinity of 1.0. However, they do not accurately describe the Prandtl number effect for high Prandtl number fluids and do not properly relate either the Reynolds or Prandtl numbers for fluids having low Prandtl numbers. This may be seen in Fig. 7-8, where the Colburn equation is compared with the result of von Kármán's similarity theory. As a result of these inadequacies of the conventional correlation equations, special forms have been developed for fluids having Prandtl numbers substantially different from 1.0.

Several relations have been presented for fluids of low Prandtl number. These fluids are the liquid metals, such as mercury, sodium, lead, and bismuth, which are used in various process and power-production applications. The following equation of Lyon (1951) is based upon a similarity analysis and was compared with the limited amount of data available for liquid-metal heat transfer at that time:

$$\frac{hD}{k} = 5.0 + 0.025(N_{Re}N_{Pr})^{0.8} = 5.0 + 0.025(N_{Pe})^{0.8} \qquad (7\text{-}45)$$

where the product $N_{Re}N_{Pr}$ is called the Peclet number.

As the result of a thorough review of liquid-metal heat-transfer data, Lubarsky and Kaufman (1956) suggest the following relation as a closer correlation of behavior in the Peclet number range from 100 to 10,000:

$$\frac{hD}{k} = 0.625(N_{Pe})^{0.4} \qquad (7\text{-}46)$$

Equations (7-45) and (7-46) are plotted in Fig. 7-8 for $N_{Pr} = 0.01$ and may be compared with the results of the similarity theory.

For high Prandtl number fluids such as oils, heavy hydrocarbons, and sugar solutions, Eqs. (7-42) to (7-44) are not accurate. The Reynolds and Prandtl number dependencies, found by experiment, are stronger than indicated by the 0.8 and $\frac{1}{3}$ exponents in those equations. Friend and Metzner (1958) present a correlating equation for turbulent flow in tubes based upon the form predicted by Reichardt (1957). The correlating equation fits the data of Friend and Metzner, and those of other investigators as well, in the Prandtl number range from 1 to 500. These data were primarily in the low Reynolds number range commonly encountered in practice for such viscous fluids.

$$N_{Nu} = \frac{(f/8)N_{Re}N_{Pr}}{1.20 + 11.8\sqrt{f/8}(N_{Pr} - 1)N_{Pr}^{-\frac{1}{3}}} \tag{7-47}$$

This relation applies for heat transfer at low temperature differences, that is, for essentially uniform properties. Properties are evaluated at the average fluid temperature. For use in a case of substantial viscosity variation, Friend and Metzner recommend multiplying Eq. (7-47) by a Sieder-Tate type of correction factor.

Equation (7-47) was also compared with mass-transfer data for turbulent flow in tubes. The data extended up to Schmidt numbers of 3000, and the equation is sufficiently accurate to justify its use for mass diffusion also. The Prandtl number is replaced by the Schmidt number. This correspondence between heat and mass transfer is another demonstration of the close relationship between the turbulent diffusion of heat and mass.

The Effects of Wall Roughness. The foregoing relations apply to smooth-walled tubes. Wall roughness, which increases pressure loss (see Fig. 6-13) by promoting momentum transfer, also increases heat transfer. Cope (1941) investigated heat transfer in tubes whose inside surfaces were roughened by a knurling process. Tests carried out in the Reynolds number range 2000 to 60,000 showed a marked increase in heat transfer. The proportional increase in friction loss was greater, however. Sams (1952) studied the effect of roughness with tubes having square threads cut on the inside surface and obtained a correlation for heat-transfer behavior with such roughness elements. Nunner (1956) carried out extensive tests on tubes whose inside surfaces were roughened by attaching various types of rings. It was found that the Nusselt number for the roughened tube is a function of the flow Reynolds number and of the ratio of the actual friction factor and the friction factor for smooth-tube flow at the same Reynolds number. That is, the fractional increase in heat transfer is dependent simply upon the fractional increase in friction loss.

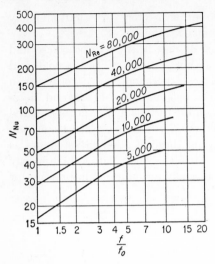

FIG. 7-10. Relation between heat transfer and flow loss. [*From Nunner* (1956).]

This relationship is shown in Fig. 7-10 for various Reynolds numbers. These results agree with the findings of Cope, in that the roughness increases friction loss more than heat transfer.

Inlet Sections. Heat-transfer relations for developed temperature and velocity distributions do not apply in the entrance regions of tubes or after any change to a wall condition which is inconsistent with the existing developed profiles. If, at the entrance of a tube, the velocity and temperature distributions are uniform across the passage, the large velocity and temperature gradients found at the wall result in high friction loss and high heat transfer. As the boundary layers thicken, the transport rates decrease. If the flow condition results in turbulent flow, transition occurs, and the velocity and temperature distributions adjust to the developed forms. Such an inlet-section development is sketched in Fig. 7-11a, and a typical variation of the Nusselt number is shown in Fig. 7-11b. The minimum value of N_{Nu} results from a thickening of the laminar boundary layer. Transition causes the large subsequent increase. The asymptotic value is rapidly approached thereafter.

The variation of heat-transfer characteristics in inlets or in sections of undeveloped flow has been studied analytically and experimentally for many types of inlet conditions. The analysis by Lazko in 1921 for various entry conditions is summarized in Jakob (1949). Boelter, Young, and Iverson (1948) experimented with various inlet geometries. Deissler (1955) analyzed entry-section heat transfer on the basis of the similarity theory. Aladyev (1954) reported tests with water and initially undeveloped temperature and velocity profiles. These studies, and many others as well, suggest that the local Nusselt number has closely approached its asymptotic value at $x/D = 20$. That is, the "starting length" is $20D$. For tubes having $L/D > 60$, the equations for developed flow may be used for the whole tube with sufficient accuracy. McAdams (1954) suggests the following design relation for shorter tubes with sharp-edged entries for flow Reynolds numbers greater than 10^4 and fluid Prandtl numbers between 0.7 and 120:

$$\frac{hD}{k_m} = 0.023 \left(\frac{DV}{\nu_m}\right)^{0.8} \left(\frac{c_p\mu}{k}\right)^{\frac{1}{3}}_m \left(\frac{\mu_m}{\mu_w}\right)^{0.14} \left[1 + \left(\frac{D}{L}\right)^{0.7}\right] \quad (7\text{-}48)$$

where h is based upon the logarithmic temperature difference discussed in Sec. 1-4 and the properties are based upon the average of the inlet and outlet average fluid temperatures.

Laminar Flow in Tubes. Since laminar fluid flow is susceptible to analysis, many laminar heat-transfer circumstances have been analyzed in detail. The early analysis of the circular-tube case by Graetz, in 1885, is summarized in Jakob (1949). This analysis applies for a developed velocity profile (parabolic) at the tube inlet and an isothermal tube wall. A subsequent analysis by Leveque (1928) extended the range of the results. Sellars, Tribus, and Klein (1956) evaluated the constants in the Graetz solution and extended the analysis to other wall temperature conditions. Kays (1955) obtained a numerical solution for an isothermal tube wall and for a constant wall heat flux with both the velocity and temperature fields

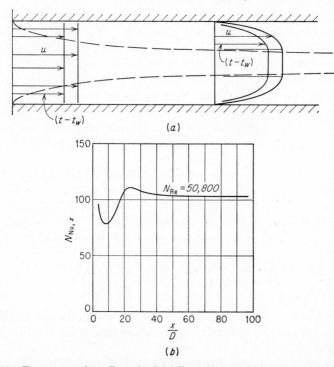

FIG. 7-11. Entrance-region effects for initially uniform velocity and temperature profiles. (*a*) Development of velocity and temperature profiles. (*b*) Variation of the local Nusselt number. (*From W. Linke and H. Kunze* (1953).]

initially uniform (undeveloped). These results apply for a Prandtl number of 0.7 and are in close agreement with experimental results for heat transfer to air.

Sieder and Tate (1936) suggested the following relation as a correlation of heat transfer in laminar flow:

$$\frac{hD}{k_m} = 1.86 \left(\frac{DV}{\nu_m}\right)^{\frac{1}{3}} \left(\frac{c_p\mu}{k}\right)^{\frac{1}{3}}_m \left(\frac{D}{L}\right)^{\frac{1}{3}} \left(\frac{\mu_m}{\mu_s}\right)^{0.14} \qquad (7\text{-}49)$$

where h is based upon the average of the inlet and outlet temperature differences and the properties are evaluated at the average fluid temperature. This relation is in close agreement with the Graetz and Leveque results for

$$\left(\frac{DV}{\nu}\right)\left(\frac{c_p\mu}{k}\right)\left(\frac{D}{L}\right) > 10$$

This last condition excludes extremely long tubes, for which a logarithmic temperature difference must be used to define h.

Noncircular Passages. Heat transfer for turbulent flow in noncircular passages has been studied for many geometries. For square, rectangular, and other shapes which are not drastically different from circular tubes, the foregoing relations may be used if the diameter D is replaced by the equivalent diameter D_e. The equivalent diameter is defined as four times the flow cross section divided by the flow perimeter upon which wall shear acts. For such passages the velocity and temperature distributions may be assumed to be developed within a distance of $x/D = 30$ from the entrance. Passages of complicated shape or with high-aspect-ratio cross sections require special relations.

Annuli, formed of concentric cylinders of diameters D_1 and D_2, are often encountered in heat-exchanger design, and many relations have been proposed to correlate the heat-transfer data. No single relation is satisfactory for all fluids, flow conditions, and geometries D_2/D_1. An expression which correlates data for Reynolds numbers above 10^4, based upon $D_e = D_2 - D_1$, is

$$\frac{hD_e}{k_m} = 0.023 \left(\frac{D_eV}{\nu_m}\right)^{0.8} \left(\frac{c_p\mu}{k}\right)^{\frac{1}{3}}_m \left(\frac{\mu_m}{\mu_w}\right)^{0.14} \qquad (7\text{-}50)$$

where h is based upon the logarithmic temperature difference and applies to both surfaces of the annulus. The starting length for annuli is of the order of $15D_e$.

The foregoing discussion of experimental correlations is by no means an exhaustive consideration of the large amount of such information which has been accumulated for various flow conditions and geometries. This section provides merely a summary of some of the principal results. For a more detailed guide to the literature, the reader is referred to Jakob (1949), McAdams (1954), and Knudsen and Katz (1958).

7-7. HEAT-TRANSFER CORRELATIONS FOR FLOW OVER SURFACES

The present section considers convection from surfaces immersed in a fluid stream. As discussed in Chap. 6, the flow process may be very complicated. The flow may be separated over a large portion of the surface. The stream may be laminar or turbulent, and the level and nature of the stream turbulence may affect separation, heat transfer, etc. In this section the transport characteristics of various types of geometries are discussed, and various other effects are considered.

For immersed objects generally, as for a flat plate as seen in Sec. 7-4, the convection coefficient varies over the surface. This results from changes in boundary-layer thickness, from flow separation, and from other effects as well. Local coefficients have been measured under various conditions. The Nusselt number distributions shown in Fig. 7-12 for a circular cylinder, subjected to a constant heat-flux surface condition, were reported by Giedt (1949). The numbers on the curves indicate the flow Reynolds number.

These curves show that the convection coefficient decreases from the stagnation point as the boundary layer thickens. For Reynolds numbers which do not result in boundary-layer transition, a minimum value of N_{Nu} occurs near the separation point, and relatively low heat-transfer coefficients are found in the separated region. For higher Reynolds numbers the distribution rises to another maximum on the back half of the cylinder. This high coefficient is thought to be the result of a local transition from a laminar to a turbulent boundary layer. The turbulent boundary layer resists separation, remaining attached up to perhaps 140°. Similar measurements have been made for other shapes. For example, for cylinders in banks, see Thomson et al. (1951), and for all elliptical cylinders, see Drake et al. (1953).

Most of the convection information, however, is in the form of average values of the Nusselt number for the whole surface. The average heat-convection coefficient for an isothermal surface is defined as the total heat-transfer rate divided by the product of the total area and the difference between the surface and remote stream temperature t_∞. For a given geometry this Nusselt number depends upon the flow Reynolds number, the fluid Prandtl number, any compressibility effects in the fluid, and perhaps also upon the nature of the turbulence in the stream. The present section considers only circumstances in which compressibility effects are negligible.

Flow Normal to Cylinders.   Many measurements have been made under various conditions for the flow of air and other fluids normal to cylinders of circular and other cross sections.   Results for a wide range of the Reynolds number in air are shown in Fig. 7-13.   The correlating curve may be fitted piecewise by an equation of the following form:

$$N_{\text{Nu}} = \frac{hD}{k_f} = B\left(\frac{DU_\infty}{\nu_f}\right)^n = B(N_{\text{Re}})^n \tag{7-51}$$

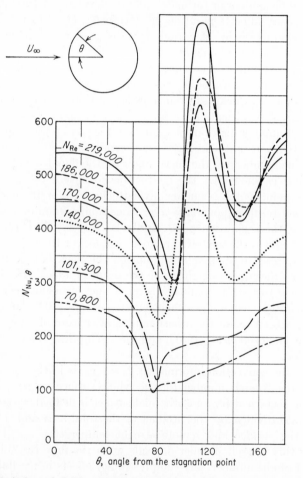

FIG. 7-12.   Variation of the local Nusselt number on the surface of a long cylinder normal to the flow.   [*From Giedt* (1949).]

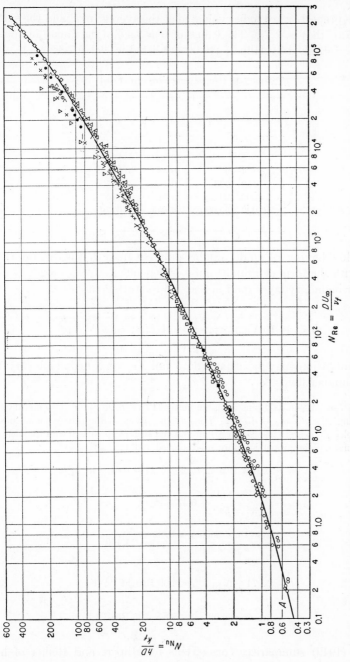

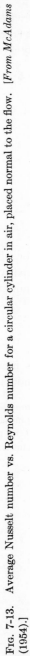

FIG. 7-13. Average Nusselt number vs. Reynolds number for a circular cylinder in air, placed normal to the flow. [*From McAdams* (1954).]

211

where the properties are to be evaluated at the average of t_∞ and the surface temperature, that is, at t_f. The values of B and n and the ranges of applicability as established by Hilpert (1933) are listed in Table 7-1.

TABLE 7-1. CONSTANTS FOR EQ. (7-51)

Range of N_{Re}	n	B
1–4	0.330	0.891
4–40	0.385	0.821
40–4000	0.466	0.615
4000–40,000	0.618	0.174
40,000–250,000	0.805	0.0239

For a fluid having a Prandtl number different from that of air, Eq. (7-51) is used with the form of Prandtl number dependence found in Sec. 7-4 for a laminar boundary layer (and in Sec. 7-6 for turbulent flow).

$$N_{Nu} = B(N_{Re})^n \frac{\sqrt[3]{N_{Pr}}}{\sqrt[3]{0.71}} = 1.12 B(N_{Re})^n \sqrt[3]{N_{Pr}} \tag{7-52}$$

This modification may be expected to fail for very high and very low Prandtl number fluids.

Example 7-4. A 2-in.-OD pipe is placed normal to a stream of air at standard conditions moving at a velocity of 15 fps. The outside surface of the tube is maintained at 140°F by electric heaters inside. We shall find the surface coefficient and the heat loss per unit length. The properties of air are found at 100°F.

$$k_f = 0.0157 \text{ Btu/hr ft °F} \qquad \mu_f = 0.0459 \text{ lb/hr ft}$$

$$\rho_f = \frac{14.7 \times 144}{53.34 \times 540} = 0.0735 \text{ lb/ft}^3$$

$$(N_{Re})_f = \frac{2 \times 15 \times 3600 \times 0.0735}{12 \times 0.0459} = 14,400$$

$$h = 0.174 \frac{k}{D} N_{Re}^{0.618} = 6.09 \text{ Btu/hr ft}^2 \text{ °F}$$

$$\frac{q}{L} = hA \, \Delta t = 6.09 \frac{2\pi}{12} \times 80 = 255 \text{ Btu/hr ft}$$

Jakob (1949) summarizes correlations by Hilpert and Reiher of heat transfer from noncircular cylinders to air. An equation of the form of

(7-51) is used. Table 7-2 indicates values of n and B for several shapes. The Reynolds number is based upon the cylinder width, perpendicular to the direction of flow.

TABLE 7-2. CONSTANTS FOR EQ. (7-51)

Configuration	Range of N_{Re}	n	B
→ ◇	5,000–100,000	0.588	0.222
→ □	5,000–100,000	0.675	0.092
→ ⬡	5,000–100,000	0.638	0.138
→ ◯	5,000–19,500	0.638	0.144
	19,500–100,000	0.782	0.0347
→ |	4,000–15,000	0.731	0.205

Spheres. Numerous experimental and analytical studies have been made for heat and mass transfer from the surface of a sphere. Equations similar to (7-51) and (7-52) have been used. An equation which correlates data in the Reynolds number range 1 to 70,000 is

$$N_{Nu} = 2.0 + 0.60(N_{Re})^{\frac{1}{2}}(N_{Pr})^{\frac{1}{3}} \tag{7-53}$$

where the properties are based upon t_f. For mass diffusion the same equation applies, with the Prandtl number replaced by the Schmidt number. This equation is not expected to be accurate for fluids having extreme Prandtl or Schmidt numbers. The 2.0 appearing in Eq. (7-53) applies in a completely stagnant stream.

Banks of Cylinders. Since many heat exchangers are designed in the form of banks of tubes, many experimental studies have considered the heat-transfer and flow-loss characteristics of tube banks in various geometric arrangements. The principal geometric variables are tube diameter, tube spacing between centers normal and parallel to the flow direction (S_n and S_p), number of rows, and arrangement of tubes—in-line (in the flow direction) or staggered. The spacing variables are restated as ratios to the tube diameter, that is, S_n/D and S_p/D.

The fluid-property and flow parameters are the Prandtl number and the Reynolds number. The Reynolds number is based upon tube diameter and upon the average fluid velocity across the minimum-flow area in the bank. The heat-transfer behavior, in terms of the Nusselt number, is expressed in conventional form as follows:

$$N_{Nu} = 1.12C \left(\frac{DV_{max}}{\nu} \right)^n (N_{Pr})^{\frac{1}{3}} \tag{7-54}$$

where the values of C and n depend only upon geometry, for a narrow Reynolds number range. The properties are evaluated at a temperature halfway between that of the tube wall and the stream. The convection coefficient is the average for the bank. This expression should be valid for fluids having moderate Prandtl numbers.

Grimison (1937) presented a correlation of the test results available at that time in air for the Reynolds number range 2000 to 40,000 and for banks of 10 rows or greater. The correlation is in the form of values of C and n for Eq. (7-54) for various geometric arrangements. This information is presented in Table 7-3. Grimison has also presented a correlation of flow-loss behavior which is not reproduced here.

The heat-transfer coefficients for banks having fewer than 10 rows are greater. An account of a recent series of measurements and their correlation was presented by Jones and Monroe (1958) and by Gram, Mackey, and Monroe (1958).

Effects of Stream Turbulence. The foregoing convection correlations for various arrangements, shapes, etc., do not include any allowance for the effect of the turbulence in the free stream upon the convection rate from

TABLE 7-3. GRIMISON'S CORRELATION FOR HEAT TRANSFER FOR TUBE BANKS OF 10 ROWS OR MORE

Arrangement	S_p/D	S_n/D							
		1.25		1.5		2.0		3.0	
		C	n	C	n	C	n	C	n
In-line	1.25	0.348	0.592	0.275	0.608	0.100	0.704	0.0633	0.752
	1.5	0.367	0.586	0.250	0.620	0.101	0.702	0.0678	0.744
	2.0	0.418	0.570	0.299	0.602	0.229	0.632	0.198	0.648
	3.0	0.290	0.601	0.357	0.584	0.374	0.581	0.286	0.608
Staggered	0.6	...	...	...	...	...	...	0.213	0.636
	0.9	...	...	...	...	0.446	0.571	0.401	0.581
	1.0	...	...	0.497	0.558				
	1.125	...	...	...	...	0.478	0.565	0.518	0.560
	1.25	0.518	0.556	0.505	0.554	0.519	0.556	0.522	0.562
	1.5	0.451	0.568	0.460	0.562	0.452	0.568	0.488	0.568
	2.0	0.404	0.572	0.416	0.568	0.482	0.556	0.449	0.570
	3.0	0.310	0.592	0.356	0.580	0.440	0.562	0.421	0.574

the surface. These correlations may be assumed to predict behavior for uniform streams of relatively low turbulence, since these are the conditions in which most measurements were made. High free-stream turbulence, characterized perhaps by intensity and scale, would be expected to have an effect upon the transport processes.

As a result of the increased understanding of turbulence and of the development of equipment which accurately measures the characteristics of turbulent flow fields, numerous experimental investigations have recently been made concerning such effects. The cases of a circular cylinder normal to the flow and of a sphere have been studied for a wide range of intensity and scale of free-stream turbulence. Comings et al. (1948) measured heat and mass transfer, in a Reynolds number range from 400 to 20,000, with various turbulence intensities. Maisel and Sherwood (1950a and b) studied mass diffusion (e.g., water vapor into air) for plates, disks, cylinders, and spheres in the Reynolds number range 1000 to 13,000. Giedt (1951) investigated the range 70,000 to 220,000 for a cylinder with two different levels of stream turbulence intensity, estimated at 1 and 4 per cent. Kestin and Maeder (1957) report an investigation of heat transfer from a cylinder in the Reynolds number range 125,000 to 310,000 with turbulence intensities up to 2.7 per cent. Sato and Sage (1958) present the results of heat-transfer studies from spheres for Reynolds numbers between 900 and 7200 for intensities up to 14 per cent.

In all these measurements, convection increased with increasing intensity of turbulence. The scale of turbulence appears relatively unimportant. For lower Reynolds number flow, the percentage increases in Nusselt number were relatively small even for high intensities. Sato and Sage show a 1 per cent increase for an intensity of 6 per cent at $N_{Re} = 2000$ and a 4 per cent increase at $N_{Re} = 8000$. For Reynolds numbers above 140,000, Kestin and Maeder found large increases in N_{Nu}, even at small turbulence intensities.

The experimental results, taken as a whole, are somewhat contradictory. However, the trends mentioned above seem reliable. Turbulence apparently has only a small effect upon the transport process in the attached laminar boundary layer. However, at higher Reynolds numbers, free-stream turbulence may cause boundary-layer transition before separation. Transition results in a considerable increase in the local transfer rate (see Fig. 7-12) and delays the separation point. The effect of free-stream intensity upon transport in the separated region is not clear. No quantitative relations for the effects of turbulence are available at the present time.

7-8. CONVECTION WITH APPRECIABLE VISCOUS DISSIPATION OF ENERGY

In Sec. 7-4 several solutions of the incompressible boundary-layer equation for the temperature distribution are presented. The heat-transfer equations (7-15) and (7-17) result for the isothermal flat plate.

The energy equation upon which these results are based is Eq. (7-3), derived in Sec. 7-2 by writing a balance of the energy-conduction rate and the time rate of change of energy storage. However, even for an incompres-

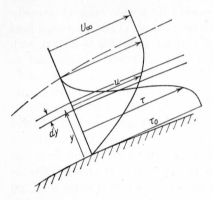

FIG. 7-14. Velocity and shear-stress distributions in a laminar boundary layer.

sible fluid, there is another possible energy contribution to the mass ($\rho\,dx\,dy\,dz$). The various viscous stresses shown in Fig. 6-3 act upon surfaces which are in motion and, as a result, energy crosses the six cube faces. The resultant of the viscous stresses $\mathbf{F}_s$ acting upon the element moving at velocity $\mathbf{V}$ amounts to a power input $\mathbf{F}_s \cdot \mathbf{V}$, which affects the kinetic, potential, and flow energy of the fluid element. However, the net power input across the six faces is always larger than $\mathbf{F}_s \cdot \mathbf{V}$, and the difference is the amount of viscous energy input which is dissipated within the mass ($\rho\,dx\,dy\,dz$). In many processes this "viscous-dissipation" effect is not negligible and must be included in the energy equation. The energy equation for an incompressible fluid, including these effects, is

$$\rho c_p \frac{Dt}{D\tau} = k\nabla^2 t + \mu\phi \tag{7-55}$$

where ϕ, the "dissipation function," is developed below for laminar boundary-layer flow.

Consider the thin layer of fluid, of thickness dy, moving in a laminar boundary layer (see Fig. 7-14). The fluid beyond this layer exerts a shear stress upon its outer surface in the direction of flow. This layer in turn exerts a force in the direction of flow upon the fluid nearer the plate. The shear stress τ acts upon a surface moving at a velocity u to produce an energy-transfer rate of $u\tau$ per unit of layer area. Therefore, the rate of net energy input to the layer by viscous forces, per unit area, is the difference in the rate of energy input at the upper surface and the rate of energy output at the lower surface, that is,

$$\frac{\partial}{\partial y}(u\tau)\,dy$$

The power absorbed in changing kinetic, potential, and flow energy is the velocity u times the net force on the layer:

$$u\,\frac{\partial \tau}{\partial y}\,dy$$

The difference between the two quantities is the rate of energy dissipation in the layer:

$$\frac{\partial}{\partial y}(u\tau)\,dy - u\,\frac{\partial \tau}{\partial y}\,dy = \tau\,\frac{\partial u}{\partial y}\,dy = \mu\left(\frac{\partial u}{\partial y}\right)^2 dy$$

The energy-dissipation rate per unit volume of fluid is, therefore,[*]

$$\mu\left(\frac{\partial u}{\partial y}\right)^2$$

This is seen to be invariably positive; that is, viscosity invariably causes a dissipation of energy. This effect amounts to the presence of a distributed source of energy in the fluid.

The dissipation term is added to the laminar boundary-layer energy equation for an incompressible fluid, Eq. (7-7):

$$\rho c_p\left(u\,\frac{\partial t}{\partial x} + v\,\frac{\partial t}{\partial y}\right) = k\,\frac{\partial^2 t}{\partial y^2} + \mu\left(\frac{\partial u}{\partial y}\right)^2 \tag{7-56}$$

The force balance and continuity equations (6-22) and (6-23) [or (6-20) and (6-21) for the flat plate] are unchanged.

The effect of viscous dissipation upon the temperature distribution is relatively small for many of the low-velocity processes encountered in practice. However, in processes involving a dynamic temperature which is comparable to the imposed heat-transfer temperature difference, the effects of viscous dissipation may not be ignored. This is shown below for flow between parallel plates. Boundary-layer theory has been used to analyze the effects of viscous dissipation for both compressible and incompressible flow. The present section considers an incompressible-flow case which demonstrates many of the important additional features which

---

[*] The same result is obtained by applying boundary-layer simplifying assumptions to the general dissipation function.

appreciable viscous dissipation introduces into heat-transfer analysis. This case is the flat plate at zero angle of incidence.

Flow between Stationary Plates. The velocity distribution for developed laminar flow between stationary parallel plates is one of the special cases of the general Couette flow analyzed in Sec. 6-3. The velocity distribution is given by Eq. (6-10), with $N = 0$, and is plotted in Fig. 6-4b. The differential equation governing the velocity distribution is

$$\mu \frac{\partial^2 u}{\partial y^2} = \mu \frac{d^2 u}{dy^2} = \frac{dp}{dx}$$

at $y = \pm R$ $u = 0$

We shall find the temperature distribution which results from retaining the viscous-dissipation effect in the energy equation, applying the conditions that both plates are at t_o and assuming that the temperature distribution is developed, that is, $\partial t/\partial x = 0$. The coordinate system is shown in Fig. 7-15. The boundary-layer energy equation (7-56) applies in this case, with $v = 0$:

$$0 = k \frac{\partial^2 t}{\partial y^2} + \mu \left(\frac{\partial u}{\partial y}\right)^2 = k \frac{d^2 t}{dy^2} + \mu \left(\frac{du}{dy}\right)^2$$

at $y = \pm R$ $t = t_o$

The gradient of u in the y direction is found from the velocity differential equation. Note that $\partial u/\partial y = 0$ at $y = 0$.

$$\frac{du}{dy} = \frac{y}{\mu}\left(\frac{dp}{dx}\right)$$

The differential equation for temperature is integrated and the boundary conditions introduced:

$$\frac{d^2 t}{dy^2} = -\frac{\mu}{k}\left(\frac{du}{dy}\right)^2 = -\frac{y^2}{\mu k}\left(\frac{dp}{dx}\right)^2$$

$$t = -\frac{y^4}{12\mu k}\left(\frac{dp}{dx}\right)^2 + C_1 y + C_2$$

$$C_1 = 0 \qquad C_2 = \frac{R^4}{12\mu k}\left(\frac{dp}{dx}\right)^2 + t_o$$

$$t - t_o = \frac{R^4}{12\mu k}\left(\frac{dp}{dx}\right)^2 \left(1 - \frac{y^4}{R^4}\right) \tag{7-57}$$

Introducing the relation between pressure gradient and maximum velocity, from Sec. 6-3, we have

$$t - t_o = \frac{u_m^2 \mu}{3k} \left(1 - \frac{y^4}{R^4} \right) \tag{7-58}$$

The temperature distribution is seen to be a fourth-degree parabola, symmetric about $y = 0$. Such a distribution is plotted in Fig. 7-15. The maximum temperature is at the center. As an indication of the magnitude of this effect for low velocities, the maximum temperature is 0.042°F greater

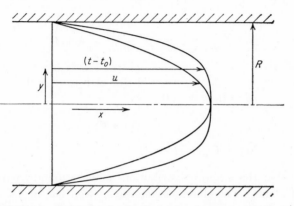

FIG. 7-15. Viscous dissipation for developed flow between extensive flat plates.

than the wall temperature for water at 60°F flowing through a passage at an average velocity of 10 fps. The effect increases rapidly with u_m. The maximum temperature difference may be shown to be merely dependent upon the dynamic temperature and the fluid Prandtl number. V is the average velocity.

$$t_m - t_o = \frac{8}{3} N_{\text{Pr}} \frac{V^2}{2g_o c_p J} = \frac{8}{3} N_{\text{Pr}} t_d \tag{7-59}$$

Viscous-dissipation Effects in a Boundary Layer. The preceding case demonstrates the temperature effects which result from viscous dissipation in a passage. The remainder of this section is devoted to a discussion of the effects of dissipation in the laminar boundary layer on a flat plate placed in a uniform stream (U_∞, t_∞).

The no-slip requirement at the fluid-solid interface results in fluid shear, which in turn results in a nonuniform temperature field, even if the plate temperature is t_∞. In order to demonstrate such effects, two cases are considered: (1) the plate surface adiabatic, that is, $\partial t / \partial y = 0$; and (2) the plate surface maintained at an arbitrary temperature t_o, different from t_∞. The adiabatic case approximates, for example, an insulated wall, an isolated model, or a plate used as a thermometer. The boundary-layer equations and boundary conditions for the two cases are written as follows:

$$u \frac{\partial u}{\partial x} + v \frac{\partial u}{\partial y} = \nu \frac{\partial^2 u}{\partial y^2} \tag{6-20}$$

$$\frac{\partial u}{\partial x} + \frac{\partial v}{\partial y} = 0 \tag{6-21}$$

$$u \frac{\partial t}{\partial x} + v \frac{\partial t}{\partial y} = \alpha \frac{\partial^2 t}{\partial y^2} + \frac{\nu}{c_p} \left(\frac{\partial u}{\partial y} \right)^2 \tag{7-56}$$

at $y = 0$ $u = 0$ $v = 0$ $\left\{ \begin{array}{l} \text{for case 1, } \dfrac{\partial t}{\partial y} = 0 \\[2ex] \text{for case 2, } t = t_o \end{array} \right.$

as $y \rightarrow \infty$ $u \rightarrow U_\infty$ $t \rightarrow t_\infty$

We note that the u and v distributions may be found from Eqs. (6-20) and (6-21) alone. Therefore, viscous dissipation has no effect upon the velocity distribution for an incompressible fluid, and the distributions found in Sec. 6-5 apply as they did in the heat-transfer case considered in Sec. 7-4. The additional term in the energy equation complicates the temperature solution, however. Employing the similarity variable η,

$$\eta = \frac{y}{2} \sqrt{\frac{U_\infty}{\nu x}}$$

the energy equation is rewritten

$$\frac{d^2 t}{d\eta^2} + N_{\mathrm{Pr}} f \frac{dt}{d\eta} + \frac{N_{\mathrm{Pr}}}{2} \frac{U_\infty{}^2}{2c_p} f''^2 = 0 \tag{7-60}$$

We shall consider case 1, the adiabatic plate, first. The dynamic temperature appears in the coefficient of the last term of Eq. (7-60). Therefore, generalizing the temperature as follows results in a simpler form of Eq. (7-60). The boundary conditions are also rewritten.

$$T = \frac{t - t_\infty}{U_\infty{}^2 / 2c_p} = \frac{t - t_\infty}{t_d} \tag{7-61}$$

$$T'' + N_{\text{Pr}}fT' + \frac{N_{\text{Pr}}}{2}f''^2 = 0 \tag{7-62}$$

at $\eta = 0$ $T' = 0$ for case 1

as $\eta \to \infty$ $T \to 0$

A solution of this problem was given by Pohlhausen (1921) for Prandtl numbers from 0.6 to 15. Eckert and Drewitz (1940) carried out the calculation for a range of Prandtl numbers from 0.6 to 1000. The results are

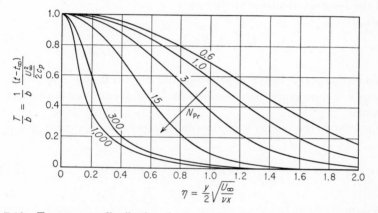

Fig. 7-16. Temperature distributions in the laminar boundary layer on an adiabatic flat plate. [*From Schlichting* (1955).]

plotted in Fig. 7-16, where the ordinate is T divided by b, which is a function of the Prandtl number.

We see that the temperature everywhere in the boundary layer is greater than t_∞. The energy dissipated in the boundary layer is conducted out to the undisturbed stream; note the temperature gradient. The temperature curves have zero slope at $\eta = 0$, thus satisfying the adiabatic-surface condition. The adiabatic-plate temperature t_a, which is equal to the fluid temperature at $\eta = 0$, may be found in terms of b and the dynamic temperature. Since, at $\eta = 0$, $T/b = 1$,

$$t_a - t_\infty = bt_d = b\frac{U_\infty{}^2}{2g_oc_pJ}$$

where g_o and J have been introduced as conversion factors for units. t_a is called the "recovery temperature," and the ratio of $(t_a - t_\infty)$ and t_d is called the recovery factor.   Therefore, the recovery factor is merely b.

$$b = \frac{t_a - t_\infty}{U_\infty{}^2/2g_0 c_p J} \tag{7-63}$$

The recovery factor is plotted in Fig. 7-17 versus N_{Pr}.   The straight line of slope $\frac{1}{2}$ closely approximates the curves for Prandtl numbers near 1.0.   Therefore,

$$b \approx \sqrt{N_{\mathrm{Pr}}} \tag{7-64}$$

and the recovery temperature becomes

$$t_a - t_\infty = \sqrt{N_{\mathrm{Pr}}}\, t_d = \sqrt{N_{\mathrm{Pr}}}\, \frac{U_\infty{}^2}{2g_0 c_p J} \tag{7-65}$$

Since the recovery factor may be greater than 1.0 (for $N_{\mathrm{Pr}} > 1.0$), the recovery temperature may exceed the stagnation temperature of the stream.

For case 2, the energy equation and temperature boundary conditions are

$$\frac{d^2 t}{d\eta^2} + N_{\mathrm{Pr}} f \frac{dt}{d\eta} + \frac{N_{\mathrm{Pr}}}{2} t_d f''^2 = 0 \tag{7-60}$$

at $y = 0$ $t = t_o$

as $y \to \infty$ $t \to t_\infty$

It is shown below that the solution of this problem is merely a combination of the solution of case 1 and the solution of the zero-dissipation case in

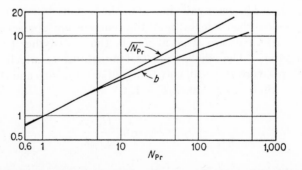

FIG. 7-17. The recovery factor for a flat plate as a function of the Prandtl number. [*Adapted from Eckert and Drewitz* (1940).]

Sec. 7-4. The temperature distribution $(t - t_\infty)$ is written as a combination of two temperature distributions: T [Eq. (7-61)] and ϕ [defined above Eq. (7-5), in Sec. 7-3]:

$$t - t_\infty = Tt_d + \phi(t_o - t_a) \tag{7-66}$$

This is seen to satisfy the boundary conditions for case 2:

at $\eta = 0$ $\qquad T = \dfrac{t_a^{\ *} - t_\infty}{t_d}$ $\quad$ and $\quad \phi = 1$

as $\eta \to \infty$ $\qquad T \to 0$ $\qquad$ and $\qquad \phi \to 0$

We must determine whether Eq. (7-66) satisfies the differential equation (7-60). Substituting and rearranging, we have

$$t_d \left(\frac{d^2 T}{d\eta^2} + N_{\mathrm{Pr}}f \frac{dT}{d\eta} + \frac{N_{\mathrm{Pr}}}{2} f''^2 \right) + (t_o - t_a) \left(\frac{d^2 \phi}{d\eta^2} + N_{\mathrm{Pr}}f \frac{d\phi}{d\eta} \right) \overset{?}{=} 0$$

The differential equation is satisfied, for example, if both of the quantities in the large parentheses are zero. The first quantity is merely the differential equation for T, Eq. (7-62), which is zero. The second quantity is the differential equation for ϕ, Eq. (7-18), which is also zero. Therefore, $(t - t_\infty)$ in Eq. (7-66) satisfies the conditions for case 2, where T is the solution of case 1, Fig. 7-16, and ϕ is the zero-viscous-dissipation solution, Fig. 7-5. This solution, Eq. (7-66), is rewritten in generalized form, denoting the variables upon which the various quantities depend:

$$\frac{t - t_\infty}{t_o - t_\infty} = \frac{N_{\mathrm{Ec}}}{2} b(N_{\mathrm{Pr}}) \left[\frac{T(\eta, N_{\mathrm{Pr}})}{b} \right] + \left[1 - \frac{N_{\mathrm{Ec}}}{2} b(N_{\mathrm{Pr}}) \right] \phi(\eta, N_{\mathrm{Pr}}) \tag{7-67}$$

where N_{Ec} means the Eckert number, which is defined as two times the ratio of the dynamic temperature t_d and the heat-transfer temperature difference $(t_o - t_\infty)$; that is,

$$N_{\mathrm{Ec}} = 2 \frac{t_d}{t_o - t_\infty} = \frac{U_\infty^2}{g_o J c_p (t_o - t_\infty)} \tag{7-68}$$

Solutions may be obtained for various Prandtl numbers by combining the results shown in Figs. 7-16 and 7-5 according to Eq. (7-67). The additional parameter $b N_{\mathrm{Ec}}$ is present, and, for each Prandtl number, a series of curves results for various values of $b N_{\mathrm{Ec}}$. The result is shown in

Fig. 7-18 for $N_{\mathrm{Pr}} = 0.7$. We note that, for $bN_{\mathrm{Ec}} = 2$, $t_o = t_a$, which is the adiabatic-plate solution. For $bN_{\mathrm{Ec}} = 0$, viscous dissipation is negligible, and the solution in Fig. 7-5 results. The negative values of bN_{Ec} result for $t_o < t_\infty$.

$$bN_{\mathrm{Ec}} = 2\,\frac{t_a - t_\infty}{t_o - t_\infty} \tag{7-69}$$

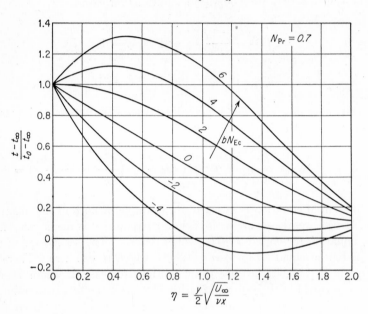

FIG. 7-18. Temperature distribution in the laminar boundary layer on a flat plate; appreciable viscous dissipation. [*From Schlichting* (1955).]

Heat-transfer Relations. The temperature distributions which apply for $bN_{\mathrm{Ec}} > 2$ show a very important characteristic. The slope of the temperature distribution at the plate surface, $\eta = 0$, is positive, and, therefore, heat flows from the boundary layer to the plate even though $t_o > t_\infty$. The maximum temperature is found in the boundary layer. This reversal of heat flow is due to viscous dissipation.

This effect of viscous dissipation requires a modification of the equation relating the heat flux, the surface coefficient, and the temperature difference. The conventional equation written below is inadequate:

$$q''(x) = h_x(t_o - t_\infty)$$

For a given positive value of $(t_o - t_\infty)$, an increasing velocity decreases heat flow and even reverses the direction of flow. This would require a negative value of h. However, if the heat-transfer temperature difference is taken as the plate temperature minus the "effective" temperature of the stream, the difficulty disappears. The proper choice of effective temperature may be seen to be the temperature level attained by an adiabatic plate placed in the stream, that is, t_a for the flow condition

$$q''(x) = h_x^*(t_o - t_a) \tag{7-70}$$

If, for a given flow condition, $bN_{\text{Ec}} = 2$, then $t_o = t_a$ and $q''(x)$ is zero. For $bN_{\text{Ec}} > 2$, $t_a > t_o$, and for $bN_{\text{Ec}} < 2$, $t_a < t_o$. Therefore, h_x^* is always positive.

The relation for h_x^* is determined from the temperature solution:

$$q''(x) = -k\left(\frac{\partial t}{\partial y}\right)_0 = -k\sqrt{\frac{U_\infty}{\nu x}}\left[\frac{d(t - t_\infty)}{d\eta}\right]_0$$

$$= -k(t_o - t_\infty)\sqrt{\frac{U_\infty}{\nu x}}\left[\frac{d}{d\eta}\left(\frac{t - t_\infty}{t_o - t_\infty}\right)\right]_0$$

From Eqs. (7-67) and (7-69),

$$\left[\frac{d}{d\eta}\left(\frac{t - t_\infty}{t_o - t_\infty}\right)\right]_0 = \frac{N_{\text{Ec}}}{2}\left(\frac{dT}{d\eta}\right)_0 + \left(1 - \frac{bN_{\text{Ec}}}{2}\right)\left(\frac{d\phi}{d\eta}\right)_0$$

$$= \left(1 - \frac{bN_{\text{Ec}}}{2}\right)\phi_0' = \frac{t_o - t_a}{t_o - t_\infty}\phi_0'$$

Therefore, $q''(x) = h_x^*(t_o - t_a) = -k\phi_0'\sqrt{\frac{U_\infty}{\nu x}}(t_o - t_a)$

and $h_x^* = -k\phi_0'\sqrt{\frac{U_\infty}{\nu x}}$

The local surface coefficient is written in terms of a Nusselt number:

$$\frac{h_x^* x}{k} = N_{\text{Nu},x}^* = -\phi_0'\sqrt{\frac{U_\infty x}{\nu}} = -\phi_0'\sqrt{N_{\text{Re},x}}$$

For a range of Prandtl number around 1.0, ϕ_0' is given by Eq. (7-20). The heat-transfer relations are then

$$N_{\text{Nu},x}^* = 0.332\sqrt{N_{\text{Re},x}}\sqrt[3]{N_{\text{Pr}}} \tag{7-71}$$

$$N_{\text{Nu}}^* = 0.664\sqrt{N_{\text{Re}}}\sqrt[3]{N_{\text{Pr}}} \tag{7-72}$$

The resulting heat-transfer equations are identical in form to those found in the absence of viscous dissipation, in Sec. 7-4. The only difference is that t_a, the "effective" stream temperature, is used in place of t_∞ in the definition of the surface coefficient. In fact, one may consider the analysis of the present section as a general treatment which includes the case of Sec. 7-4, because for low velocities, that is, negligible viscous dissipation, $t_a \rightarrow t_\infty$. Under this condition the definitions of h and h^* become identical.

Example 7-5. In the test section of a wind tunnel, air at 70°F and 1.0 psia flows at a velocity of 800 fps over a model of a thin wing having a chord of 4 in. The model is treated as a flat plate, and the effects of compressibility are ignored. We shall compute the model equilibrium temperature if its supports are adiabatic. We shall then determine the amount of heat which must be supplied by electric heaters in the model if its surface temperature is to be maintained at 130°F. The properties of air at 100°F will be used.

$$\rho = \frac{1 \times 144}{53.34 \times 560} = 0.00483 \text{ lb/ft}^3 \qquad \mu = 0.0459 \text{ lb/hr ft} \qquad k = 0.0157 \text{ Btu/hr ft °F}$$

$$N_{Pr} = 0.706 \qquad c_p = 0.24 \text{ Btu/lb °F}$$

The adiabatic temperature is found from the dynamic temperature and recovery factor:

$$t_d = \frac{U_\infty{}^2}{2g_oJc_p} = \frac{800^2}{2g_o \times 778 \times 0.24} = 53.3°$$

$$b = \sqrt{N_{Pr}} = 0.84$$

$$t_a - t_\infty = bt_d = 44.8°F \qquad t_a = 114.8°F$$

The average convection coefficient is found from Eq. (7-72):

$$\sqrt{N_{Re}} = \sqrt{\frac{800 \times 3600 \times 4 \times 0.00483}{12 \times 0.0459}} = \sqrt{101{,}000} = 318$$

$$\sqrt[3]{N_{Pr}} = 0.89$$

$$h^* = 0.664 \frac{k}{L} \sqrt{N_{Re,L}} \sqrt[3]{N_{Pr}} = 8.84 \text{ Btu/hr ft}^2 \text{ °F}$$

$$q = 2h^*L(t_o - t_a) = \frac{8.84 \times 2 \times 4(130 - 114.8)}{12} = 89.6 \text{ Btu/hr ft}$$

If viscous dissipation had been neglected, the calculated heat transfer would have been

$$q = 2hL(t_o - t_\infty) = \frac{8.84 \times 2 \times 4(130 - 70)}{12} = 354 \text{ Btu/hr ft}$$

or four times larger.

The Recovery Factor. One of the principal results of the foregoing analysis is the prediction that the laminar recovery factor for a flat plate is $\sqrt{N_{Pr}}$. The recovery factor is an important quantity in thermometry for high-velocity streams. Eckert and Weise (1942) report measurements for air which support the analytical result for boundary-layer Reynolds numbers up to 5×10^5. For turbulent boundary layers, the recovery factor is expected to be $\sqrt[3]{N_{\mathrm{Pr}}}$. This result is found in air for locations on flat plates beyond the transition region. However, for various other geometries this simple result does not apply.

The desirability of referring the convection coefficient to the adiabatic temperature has been studied experimentally. For example, McAdams, Nicolai, and Keenan (1946) made measurements with air flowing at high subsonic velocities in a steam-heated smooth-walled tube. These tests substantiated the procedure of basing the convection coefficient upon t_a.

7-9. CONVECTION WITH VARIABLE PROPERTIES

The forced-convection analysis and correlations discussed in the preceding sections of this chapter apply for processes in which the density (and other properties) vary relatively little over the flow field. Although some of these results apply in circumstances in which substantial variations occur, for many cases the inclusion of such effects complicates analysis and correlation efforts.

Many processes of practical interest involve flow fields in which the density, viscosity, thermal conductivity, and specific heat vary over a considerable range. Gases and vapors at high velocities invariably exhibit compressibility effects. At very high velocities the temperature field resulting from compression and viscous dissipation alone is sufficient to cause important gradients in transport and other fluid properties. At extreme velocities the resulting temperatures cause chemical effects such as dissociation.

As a result of the need for design information for high-velocity vehicles, many circumstances have been analyzed, and many experimental studies have been carried out. In the present section the relevant boundary-layer equations are presented, and several methods of correlating friction loss and heat transfer are considered.

Convection analysis proceeds from the differential equations which relate the distributions of velocity, pressure, and temperature in the flow field. The Navier-Stokes and continuity equations apply in their compressible forms. The energy equation (7-3), derived in Sec. 7-2, is inapplicable, however. This relation does not allow for the effects of viscous dissipation or for the energy flows resulting from compression. The general form of the energy equation for variable properties is obtained by writing an energy balance for a mass $(\rho \, dx \, dy \, dz)$. The energy additions due to conduction and stresses are set equal to the rate of change of internal and kinetic energy. The resulting expression is

$$\rho \frac{De}{D\tau} + p \operatorname{div} \mathbf{V} = \frac{\partial}{\partial x}\left(k\frac{\partial t}{\partial x}\right) + \frac{\partial}{\partial y}\left(k\frac{\partial t}{\partial y}\right) + \frac{\partial}{\partial z}\left(k\frac{\partial t}{\partial z}\right) + \mu\phi \qquad (7\text{-}73a)$$

where $D/D\tau$ is the particle derivative, ϕ is the general dissipation function, and e is the internal energy per unit mass. For an ideal gas this equation may be reduced to

$$\rho c_p \frac{DT}{D\tau} = \frac{Dp}{D\tau} + \frac{\partial}{\partial x}\left(k\frac{\partial t}{\partial x}\right) + \frac{\partial}{\partial y}\left(k\frac{\partial t}{\partial y}\right) + \frac{\partial}{\partial z}\left(k\frac{\partial t}{\partial z}\right) + \mu\phi \qquad (7\text{-}73b)$$

The energy equation and the general Navier-Stokes equations may be reduced to the boundary-layer forms by the usual methods. The two-dimensional steady-state forms for an ideal gas are

$$\rho\left(u\frac{\partial u}{\partial x} + v\frac{\partial u}{\partial y}\right) = -\frac{dp}{dx} + \frac{\partial}{\partial y}\left(\mu\frac{\partial u}{\partial y}\right) \qquad (7\text{-}74)$$

$$\frac{\partial(\rho u)}{\partial x} + \frac{\partial(\rho v)}{\partial y} = 0 \qquad (7\text{-}75)$$

$$\rho c_p\left(u\frac{\partial t}{\partial x} + v\frac{\partial t}{\partial y}\right) = u\frac{dp}{dx} + \frac{\partial}{\partial y}\left(k\frac{\partial t}{\partial y}\right) + \mu\left(\frac{\partial u}{\partial y}\right)^2 \qquad (7\text{-}76)$$

The boundary-layer equations may be applied to a particular case by specifying the boundary conditions and the dependence of μ and k upon temperature. A number of special techniques have been developed for simplifying these relations, and solutions have been obtained for many cases. The flat-plate problem has been solved for a wide range of conditions. Various other cases, for which similarity variables exist, have also been analyzed.

For the flat plate it has been shown that the effects of viscous dissipation are essentially the same as for incompressible flow, and the temperature of an adiabatic plate is calculated in the same way. For an ideal gas this is

$$t_a = t_\infty + \sqrt{N_{\mathrm{Pr}}}\,\frac{U_\infty{}^2}{2g_o c_p J} = t_\infty\left(1 + \sqrt{N_{\mathrm{Pr}}}\,\frac{\gamma-1}{2}M_\infty{}^2\right) \qquad (7\text{-}77)$$

where the temperatures are absolute, γ is the specific-heat ratio, and M_∞, the Mach number, is the stream velocity divided by the sonic velocity in the free stream. The direction of heat flow for an isothermal surface at t_o

results from the relative magnitude of $(t_o - t_\infty)$ and $\sqrt{N_{Pr}}\, t_d$. For

$$\frac{t_o - t_\infty}{t_\infty} > \frac{t_a - t_\infty}{t_\infty} = \sqrt{N_{Pr}}\, \frac{\gamma - 1}{2} M_\infty{}^2$$

heat flows from the surface to the gas.

The convection coefficient is based upon adiabatic temperature, as for the incompressible case. The complications arising from a large variation of c_p or Prandtl number may be avoided by restating the problem in terms of enthalpy instead of temperature.

The effects of the variations of density and transport properties may be included in an approximate way by evaluating the properties at a properly chosen reference temperature t_r. The following estimate has been recommended by Eckert (1956):

$$t_r = t_\infty + \frac{t_o - t_\infty}{2} + 0.22(t_a - t_\infty) \tag{7-78}$$

With properties evaluated in this way, the relations for the frictional drag and heat transfer for incompressible flow, Eqs. (6-30) and (7-22) [or (6-32) and (7-23)], are applicable to the flat-plate, laminar boundary-layer case with variable properties.

The transport rates for turbulent boundary-layer processes with large property variations are not well established. However, various design procedures have been suggested, based upon experimental information in air. Summaries are given by Eckert (1956) and Monaghan (1958). For an isothermal plate, and relatively small variations in c_p and N_{Pr}, it appears that a procedure analogous to that recommended for laminar boundary layers is reasonably accurate. Properties are evaluated at the temperature given by Eq. (7-78). The surface coefficient is based upon the recovery temperature calculated from Eq. (7-77), introducing a recovery factor of $\sqrt[3]{N_{Pr}}$ instead of $\sqrt{N_{Pr}}$. The friction-loss and heat-transfer relations for turbulent, incompressible flow, Eqs. (6-70) and (7-40), are then used.

7-10. SIMILARITY IN FORCED-CONVECTION PROCESSES

For many complicated physical circumstances engineering design information has been obtained primarily from experimentation. The complexity of the problem must be reduced to a minimum for the greatest economy in carrying out experiments, in correlating the results, and in using this information for design. This is done by reducing to a minimum the number of independent variables which must be considered. For example, for the flow of a fluid over a cylinder, the average surface coefficient depends upon the following quantities:

$$h = f(D,\rho,\mu,k,c_p) \tag{7-79}$$

It would appear that the establishment of a correlating equation in this case would require the determination of the independent effects of the five variables D, ρ, μ, k, and c_p upon h. However, we have seen that both the analytic solutions and the experimental correlations are simpler than this. When h is expressed as a Nusselt number, only two independent variables, N_{Re} and N_{Pr}, are necessary. Considerable simplification is evidently possible by properly grouping the variables. Several methods of analysis have been developed for combining variables.

Dimensional analysis proceeds from Buckingham's π theorem and is a purely formal method of combining a group of dimensional variables. This method is carried out without any consideration of the physical nature of the process in question and, in general, yields several sets of dimensionless quantities. The method attaches no physical significance to the results, and the selection of the proper set of results must be based upon other considerations.

Another method has come into use which avoids some of the ambiguities of dimensional analysis. This method, sometimes called "differential similarity," is based upon physical reasoning. It is particularly suited to processes for which the relevant differential equations, although known, are too difficult to solve. This method groups the variables for a given kind of process by determining the conditions under which different examples of a given type of process are "similar." The physical significance of the various dimensionless groups is apparent, and the conditions under which various groups may be ignored are suggested.

In the present section, the method of differential similarity is applied to forced convection. The effects of viscous dissipation are included. However, the transport properties are assumed uniform. The effects of compressibility are included for processes in which only moderate density changes occur.

There are five differential equations. However, for brevity, only one Navier-Stokes equation is written:

$$\rho \frac{Du}{D\tau} = -\frac{\partial p}{\partial x} + \mu \left(\nabla^2 u + \frac{1}{3} \frac{\partial}{\partial x} \operatorname{div} \mathbf{V} \right)$$

$$\frac{\partial(\rho u)}{\partial x} + \frac{\partial(\rho v)}{\partial y} + \frac{\partial(\rho w)}{\partial z} = 0$$

$$\rho c_p \frac{Dt}{D\tau} = \frac{Dp}{D\tau} + k\nabla^2 t + \mu\phi$$

Consider, for example, the flow of a uniform fluid stream $(U_\infty, t_\infty, \rho_\infty)$ over a surface at t_o. The boundary conditions are

$t = t_o,$ $\qquad u = v = w = 0$ $\qquad$ over the surface, say, for $f(x,y,z) = 0$

$t \to t_\infty,$ $\qquad \mathbf{V} \to \mathbf{U}_\infty$ $\qquad\qquad$ away from the surface

The method is applied by generalizing the variables and finding the conditions under which the generalized temperature distribution is independent of the conditions of a specific problem. The dependent and independent variables are generalized as follows:

$$X = \frac{x}{L} \qquad Y = \frac{y}{L} \qquad Z = \frac{z}{L} \qquad T = \frac{t - t_\infty}{t_o - t_\infty} \qquad P = \frac{p - p_\infty}{\rho U_\infty{}^2/2}$$

$$U = \frac{u}{U_\infty} \qquad V = \frac{v}{U_\infty} \qquad W = \frac{w}{U_\infty} \qquad \mathbf{V'} = \frac{\mathbf{V}}{U_\infty} \qquad \phi' = \frac{L^2}{U_\infty{}^2}\phi$$

$$\nabla'^2 = L^2\nabla^2$$

where L is some significant length of the surface in question. Introducing these new variables, the statement of the problem becomes

$$U\frac{\partial U}{\partial X} + V\frac{\partial U}{\partial Y} + W\frac{\partial U}{\partial Z} = -\frac{1}{2}\frac{\partial P}{\partial X} + \frac{\mu}{\rho U_\infty L}\left[\nabla'^2 U + \frac{1}{3}\frac{\partial}{\partial X}\operatorname{div}(\mathbf{V'})\right]$$

$$\tag{7-80}$$

$$\frac{\partial U}{\partial X} + \frac{\partial V}{\partial Y} + \frac{\partial W}{\partial Z} = 0 \tag{7-81}$$

$$U\frac{\partial T}{\partial X} + V\frac{\partial T}{\partial Y} + W\frac{\partial T}{\partial Z} = \frac{U_\infty{}^2}{c_p(t_o - t_\infty)}\left(U\frac{\partial P}{\partial X} + V\frac{\partial P}{\partial Y} + W\frac{\partial P}{\partial Z}\right)$$

$$+ \frac{k}{\rho U_\infty L c_p}\nabla'^2 T + \frac{\mu U_\infty \phi'}{\rho c_p L(t_o - t_\infty)} \tag{7-82}$$

$T = 1,$ $\qquad U = V = W = 0$ $\qquad$ over the surface, for $F(X,Y,Z) = 0$

$T \to 0,$ $\qquad \mathbf{V'} \to 1$ $\qquad\qquad$ away from the surface

where each equation has been written with its simplest coefficients. The effect of density in the continuity equation has been neglected.

The solutions of the above generalized equations are U, V, W, P, and T as functions of (X,Y,Z). These solutions (their form, etc.) depend upon the constant coefficients in the differential equations (7-80) to (7-82). We note, however, that the boundary conditions depend only upon the geometry, since $F(X,Y,Z)$ depends only upon the shape, and not upon the size, of the object. Therefore, the temperature distribution, for example, depends only upon the geometry and upon the four coefficients in the differential equations. These coefficients are written below and converted to more familiar forms:

$$\frac{\mu}{\rho U_\infty L} = \frac{1}{N_{\mathrm{Re}}}$$

$$\frac{k}{\rho U_\infty L c_p} = \left(\frac{\mu}{\rho U_\infty L}\right)\left(\frac{k}{c_p \mu}\right) = \frac{1}{N_{\mathrm{Re}}\, N_{\mathrm{Pr}}} = \frac{1}{N_{\mathrm{Pe}}}$$

$$\frac{U_\infty{}^2}{c_p(t_o - t_\infty)} = N_{\mathrm{Ec}}$$

$$\frac{\mu U_\infty}{\rho c_p L(t_o - t_\infty)} = \left(\frac{\mu}{\rho U_\infty L}\right)\left(\frac{U_\infty{}^2}{c_p(t_o - t_\infty)}\right) = \frac{N_{\mathrm{Ec}}}{N_{\mathrm{Re}}}$$

The values of the four coefficients are fixed by the values of the three parameters N_{Re}, N_{Pr}, and N_{Ec}. The Reynolds number arises as the ratio of viscous forces and momentum. The product $N_{\mathrm{Re}}N_{\mathrm{Pr}}$ is the ratio of the conduction and convection of energy. The Eckert number relates the magnitudes of the compressibility and viscous-dissipation effects to the convection of energy.

The dependence of the generalized temperature upon geometry, N_{Re}, N_{Pr}, and N_{Ec} is related to heat transfer by generalizing the definition of the average surface coefficient:

$$h^* = \frac{\displaystyle\int_A q'' \, dA}{A(t_o - t_a)} = \frac{\dfrac{1}{A}\displaystyle\int_A k\left(-\dfrac{\partial t}{\partial n}\right)_0 dA}{(t_o - t_a)} = \frac{\overline{k\left(-\dfrac{\partial t}{\partial n}\right)_0}}{(t_o - t_a)}$$

$$= \frac{k(t_o - t_\infty)}{L(t_o - t_a)}\overline{\left(-\frac{\partial T}{\partial N}\right)_0}$$

where A denotes the surface area of the object, n is the normal direction at the surface, and $N = n/L$. The average value of the derivative depends only upon N_{Re}, N_{Pr}, and N_{Ec} for any given geometry. Therefore,

$$\frac{h^* L}{k} = N_{\mathrm{Nu}}^* = \frac{t_o - t_\infty}{t_o - t_a} f_1(N_{\mathrm{Re}}, N_{\mathrm{Pr}}, N_{\mathrm{Ec}}) = f_2(N_{\mathrm{Re}}, N_{\mathrm{Pr}}, N_{\mathrm{Ec}}) \qquad (7\text{-}83)$$

For processes in which viscous dissipation and compressibility are negligible, the result is

$$\frac{hL}{k} = N_{Nu} = f_3(N_{Re}, N_{Pr}) \tag{7-84}$$

The result of the similarity analysis is, then, that Eq. (7-79) is actually of the simpler form, Eq. (7-83) or (7-84). Therefore, if we were attempting to correlate heat-transfer behavior for a particular geometry, we would convert the experimental results to N_{Nu}, N_{Re}, N_{Pr}, and N_{Ec} and attempt to determine the relation between this smaller number of variables.

The method of differential similarity was used extensively by Nusselt and is discussed in Jakob (1949) and Schlichting (1955). An interesting application of this procedure was made by Ostrach (1958) for convection with body forces.

7-11. NONCONTINUUM EFFECTS

The consideration of fluid flow and heat transfer thus far in Chaps. 6 and 7 has been based upon a particular physical model of fluid behavior. This model amounts to assuming that a body of fluid, consisting of many discrete particles, may be looked upon as a continuous "smear" of material in local equilibrium. This point of view, called the "continuum" assumption, is a very reasonable model for circumstances in which the relative density of the particles is very large, that is, when the average spacing of the particles or molecules is very small compared with the physical distances which are important in the process.

Flow which satisfies the requirements for the continuum assumption is analyzed from a relatively simple point of view. At any arbitrary point (x,y,z) in the fluid field, we may assign properties ρ, t, p, etc., with the assurance that there are enough particles in the vicinity of the point so that collisions are sufficiently frequent to yield conditions approaching local equilibrium. As a result, at solid-fluid interfaces we may assume zero relative velocity and the equality of the temperatures of the fluid and solid. The reason for this is that, for very small particle spacing, a particle experiences many collisions while in a particular location and, therefore, comes into equilibrium with its local surroundings, which in this case are the wall.

For a number of flow and heat-transfer processes of importance, either the fluid density or the relevant physical scale of the circumstance is sufficiently small so that the distance between collisions is of the order of the physical scale. In such a circumstance the continuum point of view is inadequate. Missiles and satellites operate at altitudes at which the mean free path of air molecules is very large. At the other extreme, a small physical scale, we have the hot-wire anemometer, a velocity-measuring device, whose operation depends upon the heat-transfer characteristics of very fine wires. Under many important flow conditions the molecular mean free path is of the order of the wire diameter.

It is necessary, therefore, to divide flow processes into regimes on the basis of the ratio of the molecular mean free path and the significant physical scale of the process. This type of ratio is called the Knudsen number. Continuum flow results for small values of this number. For large values of this ratio, molecular collisions occur primarily at the surface and at large distances from the surface, in the undisturbed stream. The resulting transport is by the free motion of the molecules between the surface and the remote fluid. This regime is called "free-molecule." Between the extremes of the continuum and free-molecule regimes is a range of transition between these two types of processes. The conditions under which the continuum model of flow first fails is called the "slip-flow" regime, because it may be analyzed by assigning temperature and velocity "slip" at fluid-solid interfaces. Slip flow changes to free-molecule flow through a transition regime.

For the boundary-layer type of flow the continuum point of view remains valid until the molecular mean free path λ becomes appreciable compared with the boundary-layer thickness δ. This ratio may be written as

$$\frac{\lambda}{\delta} \propto \frac{\lambda}{\sqrt{\mu L / \rho U_\infty}} = \frac{\rho \lambda U_\infty / \mu}{\sqrt{N_{Re}}} \propto \frac{U_\infty / a}{\sqrt{N_{Re}}} = \frac{M}{\sqrt{N_{Re}}} = N_{Kn}$$

where a is the sonic velocity. The observed limit of continuum boundary-layer flow is

$$N_{Kn} = \frac{M}{\sqrt{N_{Re}}} < 0.01 \qquad (7\text{-}85)$$

For low Reynolds number flow the boundary-layer treatment is not applicable, and the relevant physical scale becomes the size of the object, L. The Knudsen number limit is still taken as 0.01.

$$\frac{\lambda}{L} \propto \frac{M}{N_{Re}} = N_{Kn} < 0.01 \qquad (7\text{-}86)$$

The conditions for which slip-flow analysis is accurate extend from continuum conditions to approximately

$$N_{Kn} = \frac{M}{\sqrt{N_{Re}}} = 0.1 \qquad (7\text{-}87)$$

Free-molecule transport is found for Knudsen numbers above approximately 10:

$$N_{Kn} = \frac{M}{N_{Re}} > 10 \qquad (7\text{-}88)$$

Transition occurs between the slip-flow and free-molecule regimes. The boundaries between regimes are plotted in Fig. 7-19. The regimes appear as the spaces between. The Mach-Reynolds number ranges for various important applications are shown.

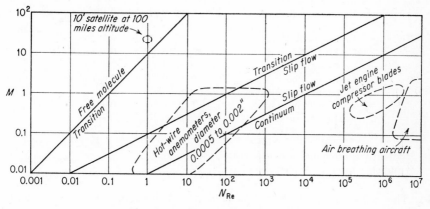

FIG. 7-19. Flow regimes for gases.

The departure from continuum flow conditions reduces friction loss and heat transfer below the amounts predicted by continuum theories or by correlations of data taken under continuum conditions. A considerable amount of analysis and experimental study has been devoted to slip-flow and free-molecule conditions. The surface-gas interaction for noncontinuum conditions is characterized by thermal-accommodation and momentum (or reflection) coefficients.

The thermal-accommodation coefficient α at a point on a surface is defined as follows:

$$\alpha = \frac{e_i'' - e_r''}{e_i'' - e_o''} \qquad (7\text{-}89)$$

where e_i'' is the molecular energy flux incident upon the surface, e_r'' is the energy flux of the molecules as they are actually reflected from the surface, and e_o'' is the energy flux that would have resulted if the molecules had been reflected in equilibrium at the wall temperature t_o. If the molecules make no accommodation to the wall, $\alpha = 0$, and if they accommodate completely, $\alpha = 1$ (as under continuum conditions, i.e., for multiple collisions at the surface). Accommodation coefficients for air on typical surfaces are listed in Table 7-4. The values are seen to be near 1.0 and are relatively independent of the surface condition.

TABLE 7-4. THERMAL-ACCOMMODATION COEFFICIENTS FOR AIR *

Surface description	α	Emissivity
Flat black lacquer on bronze...	0.88–0.89	0.932
Bronze, polished............	0.91–0.94	0.103
Bronze, machined...........	0.89–0.93	0.110
Bronze, etched †............	0.93–0.95	0.192
Cast iron, polished..........	0.87–0.93	0.184
Cast iron, machined.........	0.87–0.88	0.391
Cast iron, etched †..........	0.89–0.96	0.697
Aluminum, polished.........	0.87–0.95	0.221
Aluminum, machined........	0.95–0.97	0.091
Aluminum, etched †.........	0.89–0.97	0.775

* From Wiedmann and Trumpler (1946).
† Surface removal with nitric acid.

The reflection coefficient f is similarly defined in terms of incident, reflected, and equilibrium momenta. The typical values listed in Table 7-5 are seen to be near 1.0.

TABLE 7-5. REFLECTION COEFFICIENTS *

Gas and surface	f
Air on fresh shellac.................	0.79
Air or CO_2 on brass or old shellac......	1.00
Air on oil.........................	0.895
CO_2 on oil........................	0.92
H_2 on oil.........................	0.93
Air on glass......................	0.89
He on oil.........................	0.87

* From Millikan (1923).

Free-molecule Flow. For free-molecule processes the transport rates are calculated directly from considerations of molecular motion, and the methods of the kinetic theory of gases are used. For example, the net heat-transfer rate is the difference between the translational, rotational, and vibrational energy content of the incident and reflected molecules. The incident molecules are at the known free-stream conditions and are reflected according to the accommodation coefficient. The techniques are generally simpler than the continuum flow analysis for the same geometry.

The heat-transfer characteristics for a surface at temperature t_o, and the surface temperature for an adiabatic surface, t_a, are conveniently written in terms of a modified Stanton number and a modified recovery factor as follows:

$$N'_{St} = \frac{h^*}{\rho U_\infty c_p} \frac{\gamma}{\alpha(\gamma + 1)} = N^*_{St} \frac{\gamma}{\alpha(\gamma + 1)} \tag{7-90}$$

$$b' = \frac{t_a - t_\infty}{U_\infty^2/2g_o c_p J} \frac{\gamma + 1}{\gamma} = b \frac{\gamma + 1}{\gamma} \tag{7-91}$$

where the average heat-transfer coefficient h^* is defined in terms of the recovery temperature t_a, and γ is the specific-heat ratio. The modified Stanton number and recovery factor depend upon geometry and upon the ratio of U_∞ to the most probable velocity of the molecules with respect to the gas. This quantity, called the molecular-speed ratio, is denoted by S and may be written in terms of the Mach number M:

$$S = \frac{U_\infty}{\sqrt{2RT_\infty}} = \sqrt{\frac{\gamma}{2}} M \tag{7-92}$$

where $\sqrt{2RT_\infty}$ is the most probable molecular velocity.

The case of a plate at an angle of attack θ was treated by Stalder and Jukoff (1948). The results, written in terms of N'_{St} and b', are

$$N'_{St} = \frac{1}{4\sqrt{\pi} S} [e^{-(S \sin \theta)} + \sqrt{\pi} (S \sin \theta) \text{ erf } (S \sin \theta)] \tag{7-93}$$

$$b' = \frac{1}{S^2} \left[2S^2 + 1 - \frac{1}{1 + \sqrt{\pi} (S \sin \theta) \text{ erf } (S \sin \theta) e^{(S \sin \theta)^2}} \right] \tag{7-94}$$

where the error function (erf) is plotted in Fig. 3-3. Similar relations have been derived for the front and back surfaces of spheres [Sauer (1951)] and for long cylinders normal to the flow [Stalder et al. (1951)]. These various results are plotted in Figs. 7-20 and 7-21 from the collected information published by Oppenheim (1953).

Since the lowest value of b' in Fig. 7-21 is 2 and since γ must be greater than 1.0, the recovery factor b is invariably greater than 1.0. Such effects have been measured in wind tunnels.

Slip Flow. The analysis of slip flow often employs modified continuum differential equations and applies velocity-slip and temperature-jump boundary conditions at the fluid-solid interface. The velocity slip is

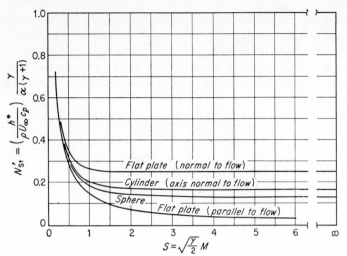

FIG. 7-20. Modified Stanton number for free-molecule flow. [*Plotted from information tabulated by Oppenheim* (1953).]

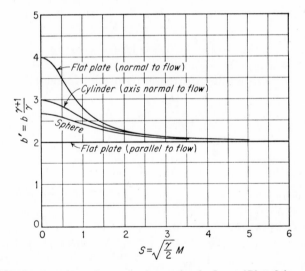

FIG. 7-21. Modified recovery factor for free-molecule flow. [*Plotted from information tabulated by Oppenheim* (1953).]

characterized by a reflection coefficient and the temperature jump by an accommodation coefficient. These two quantities depend upon the nature of the surface and upon the materials involved. A flat-plate solution for gases is discussed by Eckert (1959). For an accommodation coefficient of 0.8 and a specific-heat ratio of 1.4, the coefficient of drag and Stanton number are given by the following relations:

$$C_D M = \frac{2.67}{X_1^2} \left(e^{X_1^2} \operatorname{erfc} X_1 - 1 + \frac{2}{\sqrt{\pi}} X_1 \right) \tag{7-95}$$

$$N_{St} M = \frac{0.38}{X_2^2} \left(e^{X_2^2} \operatorname{erfc} X_2 - 1 + \frac{2}{\sqrt{\pi}} X_2 \right) \tag{7-96}$$

where $\qquad X_1 = \frac{2}{3} \frac{\sqrt{N_{Re}}}{M} \qquad$ and $\qquad X_2 = \sqrt{\frac{6.9}{N_{Pr}}} \frac{\sqrt{N_{Re}}}{M}$

and erfc $X = 1 - \operatorname{erf} X$. The erf X is plotted in Fig. 3-3.

Example 7-6. Steel wires of 0.005 in. diameter are to be used to support a model in the test section of a low-density supersonic wind tunnel. For test-section conditions of 0.072 psfa, $-100°F$, and a velocity of 3500 fps, we shall calculate the temperature of the wires, assuming them to be adiabatic, and then calculate the expected temperature, allowing for heat loss by radiation.

The Knudsen number is found:

$$M = \frac{3500}{\sqrt{\gamma g_o R T_\infty}} = 3.77 \qquad \rho = 3.5 \times 10^{-6} \text{ lb/ft}^3$$

$$N_{Re} = \frac{0.005 \times 3500 \times 3600 \times 3.5 \times 10^{-6}}{12 \times 0.0319} = 0.575$$

$$N_{Kn} = \frac{M}{N_{Re}} = 6.56 \qquad \text{essentially free-molecule flow}$$

The molecular-speed ratio is found, and the modified recovery factor and Stanton number are determined assuming the wires to be normal to the flow:

$$S' = \sqrt{\frac{1.4}{2}} M = 3.15 \qquad N'_{St} = 0.16 \qquad \text{and} \qquad b' = 2.0$$

The recovery temperature is found:

$$t_a - t_\infty = b' \left(\frac{\gamma}{\gamma + 1} \right) \frac{U_\infty^2}{2 g_o c_p J} = \frac{2.0 \times 1.4 \times 1020}{2.4} = 1190°F$$

$$t_a = 1090°F$$

This is an unrealistic estimate of the wire temperature, since the radiation loss would be appreciable. Equating the convection gain and radiation loss (assuming negligible radiation gain from the tunnel walls), we have

$$h^*A(t_a - t_o) = \epsilon\sigma A T_o^4$$

h^* is introduced from Eq. (7-90), and values of α and ϵ are taken as 0.88 and 0.66, respectively.

$$\rho U_\infty c_p(t_a - t_o) \frac{\alpha(\gamma + 1)}{\gamma} N'_{\text{St}} = \epsilon\sigma T_o^4$$

$$\frac{t_a - t_o}{[(t_o + 460)/100]^4} = 0.0443$$

A value of $t_o = 577°F$ satisfies this relation approximately. This temperature, resulting from a balance of convection and radiation, is sometimes called the radiation-equilibrium temperature.

Compressibility, Dissipation, and Noncontinuum Effects. In Secs. 7-6 and 7-7, heat-transfer correlations for flow at relatively low velocities are discussed. Sections 7-8 and 7-9 deal with the modifications that must be made in the basic definitions in order to treat viscous-dissipation and property-variation effects. In the present section, noncontinuum considerations are introduced. These various considerations have shown that, for a given geometry and flow arrangement, the Nusselt number is a function of the Reynolds, Prandtl, Mach, and Knudsen numbers. In addition, the convection coefficient is, in general, to be based upon the difference between the surface and adiabatic stream temperatures, and the fluid properties are to be chosen at suitable reference temperatures.

The present discussion considers a correlation which treats the whole range of flow circumstances for a particular geometry. This case is the long, isothermal cylinder normal to the flow. Baldwin et al. (1960) have shown that it is possible to correlate much of the experimental data and the principal analytical results for this case on a single plot (see Fig. 7-22). The Nusselt, Reynolds, and Mach numbers are defined as follows:

$$N_{\text{Nu}}^* = \frac{h^*D}{k_s} \tag{7-97}$$

$$N_{\text{Re}} = \frac{\rho_\infty U_\infty D}{\mu_s} \tag{7-98}$$

$$M = \frac{U_\infty}{a_s} \tag{7-99}$$

where the subscripts ∞ and s indicate free-stream static and stagnation conditions, respectively. The convection coefficient h^* is based upon $(t_o - t_a)$, where t_o is the surface temperature and t_a is the adiabatic-surface

temperature for the flow condition—for example, for continuum flow, from
Eq. (7-63), and for free-molecule flow, from Eq. (7-91) and Fig. 7-21.

The correlation appears as contours of constant Mach number. The
contour $M \approx 0$ is based upon the low-velocity, continuum correlation
shown in Fig. 7-13. Other contours converge to this curve at higher
Reynolds numbers [continuum flow; see Eq. (7-85)], indicating that the

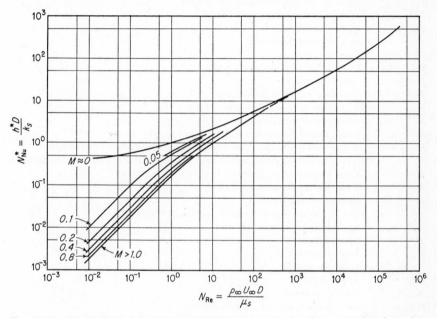

FIG. 7-22. Correlation of forced-convection heat transfer for flow normal to long, isothermal cylinders. [*From Baldwin et al.* (1960).]

definitions of Eqs. (7-97) to (7-99) are an adequate allowance for compressibility and viscous dissipation. The divergence at low Reynolds numbers
is due to noncontinuum effects. In the very low range, free-molecule flow
occurs, and the behavior shown in Fig. 7-20 (for the cylinder) results in the
curves' approaching a slope of 1.0. The small variation at higher Mach
numbers in the free-molecule region is a result of the rapid approach to the
asymptote of the curve for the cylinder in Fig. 7-20. Figure 7-22 shows
that noncontinuum effects considerably reduce the heat-transfer rate.

Baldwin et al. have shown that this correlation is also valid for subsonic
flow over long, yawed cylinders. If ϕ is the angle between U_∞ and the
cylinder axis, the velocity in both the Reynolds and Mach numbers is taken
as the component of U_∞ normal to the cylinder, that is, $U_\infty \sin \phi$. This
treatment is expected to be valid for values of ϕ as small as 20°.

NOTATION

b	recovery factor
b'	modified recovery factor, defined in Eq. (7-91)
c	specific heat
c_p	specific heat at constant pressure, per unit mass
C	concentration of a molecular species
C'	ratio of two concentration differences
D	chemical diffusivity
D_e	equivalent diameter
e''	flux of molecular energy
f	friction factor
f_o	friction factor of a smooth pipe
f or $f(\eta)$	stream function
f or $f(y^+)$	universal velocity distribution
g_o	a conversion factor for units of force
h	convection coefficient
h_x	local convection coefficient
h^*	convection coefficient, based upon "adiabatic-surface" temperature
h_x^*	local convection coefficient, based upon "adiabatic-surface" temperature
H	mass-convection coefficient
H_x	local mass-convection coefficient
k	thermal conductivity
m''	rate of diffusion of a chemical species, per unit area
m_o''	mass-diffusion rate at the wall
M	Mach number
N_{Ec}	Eckert number
N_{Kn}	Knudsen number
N_{Le}	Lewis number
N_{Nu}	Nusselt number
$N_{\text{Nu},x}$	local boundary-layer Nusselt number
N_{Nu}^*	Nusselt number, based upon "adiabatic-surface" temperature
$N_{\text{Nu},x}^*$	local boundary-layer Nusselt number, based upon "adiabatic-surface" temperature
N_{Pe}	Peclet number
N_{Pr}	Prandtl number
N_{Re}	Reynolds number
$N_{\text{Re},x}$	local boundary-layer Reynolds number
N_{Sc}	Schmidt number
N_{St}	Stanton number
N_{St}^*	Stanton number, based upon "adiabatic-surface" temperature
N_{St}'	modified Stanton number, defined in Eq. (7-90)
p	pressure
q''	heat flux
q_o''	heat flux at the wall
S	molecular-speed ratio
t	temperature, °F or °C
t_a	"adiabatic-surface" temperature
t_d	dynamic temperature
T	generalized temperature, Eq. (7-61)

u	component of velocity in the x direction
u^*	"friction velocity"
u^+	generalized velocity
U	velocity
v	component of velocity in the y direction
w	component of velocity in the z direction
y^+	generalized distance from the wall
α	thermal diffusivity
α	thermal-accommodation coefficient
γ	specific-heat ratio
δ	thickness of the velocity boundary layer
δ_C	thickness of the concentration boundary layer
δ_t	thickness of the temperature boundary layer
ϵ	eddy diffusivity
ϵ_C	eddy diffusivity of a chemical species
ϵ_H	eddy diffusivity of thermal energy
ϵ_M	eddy diffusivity of momentum
η	similarity variable
θ	temperature excess
θ	angle of attack
θ_m	average temperature excess
λ	molecular mean free path
μ	absolute (or dynamic) viscosity
ν	kinematic viscosity
ρ	density of mass
τ	time
τ	shear stress
τ_0	shear stress at the wall
ϕ	ratio of two temperature excesses
ϕ	dissipation function

REFERENCES

Aladyev, I. T.: *NACA Tech. Mem.* 1356, 1954.

Baldwin, L. V., V. A. Sandborn, and J. C. Laurence: *Trans. ASME*, ser. C, vol. 82, p. 77, 1960.

Boelter, L. M. K., G. Young, and H. W. Iverson: *NACA Tech. Note* 1451, 1948.

Chapman, D., and N. W. Rubesin: *J. Aeronaut. Sci.*, vol. 16, p. 547, 1949.

Colburn, A. P.: *Trans. AIChE*, vol. 21, p. 174, 1933.

Comings, E. W., J. T. Clapp, and J. F. Taylor: *Ind. Eng. Chem.*, vol. 40, p. 1076, 1948.

Cope, W. F.: *Proc. Inst. Mech. Engrs. (London)*, vol. 145, p. 99, 1941.

Deissler, R. G.: *NACA Rept.* 1210, 1955.

Dittus, F. W., and L. M. K. Boelter: *Univ. Calif. (Berkeley) Publs. Eng.*, vol. 2, p. 443, 1930.

Drake, R. M., Jr., R. A. Seban, D. L. Doughty, and S. Levy: *Trans. ASME*, vol. 75, p. 1291, 1953.

Eckert, E.: *Trans. ASME*, vol. 78, p. 1273, 1956.

——— and R. M. Drake, Jr.: "Heat and Mass Transfer," 2d ed., McGraw-Hill Book Company, Inc., New York, 1959.

Eckert, E., and O. Drewitz: *Forsch. Gebiete Ingenieurw.*, vol. 7, p. 116, 1940: translated and reprinted as *NACA Tech. Mem.* 1045, 1943.

———— and H. Weise: *Forsch. Gebiete Ingenieurw.*, vol. 13, p. 246, 1942.

Fage, A., and V. M. Falkner: *Brit. Aeronaut. Research Comm. Rept. and Mem.* 1408, 1931.

Friend, W. L., and A. B. Metzner: *AIChE Journal*, vol. 4, p. 393, 1958.

Giedt, W. H.: *Trans. ASME*, vol. 71, p. 375, 1949.

————: *J. Aeronaut. Sci.*, vol. 18, p. 725, 1951.

Gram, A. V., C. O. Mackey, and E. S. Monroe, Jr.: *Trans. ASME*, vol. 80, p. 25, 1958.

Grimison, E. D.: *Trans. ASME*, vol. 59, p. 583, 1937.

Grosh, R. J., and R. D. Cess: *Trans. ASME*, vol. 80, p. 667, 1958.

Hartnett, J. P., and E. Eckert: *Trans. ASME*, vol. 79, p. 247, 1957.

Hilpert, R.: *Forsch. Gebiete Ingenieurw.*, vol. 4, p. 215, 1933.

Jakob, M.: "Heat Transfer," vol. 1, John Wiley & Sons, Inc., New York, 1949.

Jones, C. E., and E. S. Monroe, Jr.: *Trans. ASME*, vol. 80, p. 18, 1958.

Kays, W. M.: *Trans. ASME*, vol. 77, p. 1265, 1955.

Kestin, J., and P. F. Maeder: *NACA Tech. Note* 4018, 1957.

Knudsen, J. G., and D. L. Katz: "Fluid Dynamics and Heat Transfer," McGraw-Hill Book Company, Inc., New York, 1958.

Kreith, F., and M. Summerfield: *Trans. ASME*, vol. 72, p. 869, 1950.

Leveque, J.: *Ann. mines*, ser. 12, vol. 13, pp. 201, 305, 381, 1928.

Levy, S.: *J. Aeronaut. Sci.*, vol. 19, p. 341, 1952.

Linke, W., and H. Kunze: *Allgem. Warmetech.*, vol. 4, p. 73, 1953.

Lubarsky, B., and S. J. Kaufman: *NACA Rept.* 1270, 1956.

Lyon, R. N.: *Chem. Eng. Progr.*, vol. 47, p. 75, 1951.

McAdams, W. H.: "Heat Transmission," 3d ed., McGraw-Hill Book Company, Inc., New York, 1954.

————, L. A. Nicolai, and J. H. Keenan: *Trans. AIChE*, vol. 42, p. 907, 1946.

Maisel, D. S., and T. K. Sherwood: *Chem. Eng. Progr.*, vol. 46, p. 131, 1950a.

———— and ————: *Chem. Eng. Progr.*, vol. 46, p. 172, 1950b.

Martinelli, R. C.: *Trans. ASME*, vol. 69, p. 947, 1947.

Millikan, R. A.: *Phys. Rev.*, vol. 21, p. 217, 1923.

Monaghan, R. J.: *Aeronaut. Research Council Tech. Rept., Rept. and Mem.* 3033, 1958.

Nunner, W.: *VDI-Forschungsheft* 455, 1956.

Oppenheim, A. K.: *J. Aeronaut. Sci.*, vol. 20, p. 49, 1953.

Ostrach, S.: "Symposium on Boundary Layer Research," H. Görtler (ed.), Springer-Verlag, Berlin, 1958.

Pohlhausen, E.: *Z. angew. Math. Mech.*, vol. 1, p. 115, 1921.

Prandtl, L.: *Z. Physik*, vol. 11, p. 1072, 1910.

Reichardt, H.: translated in *NACA Tech. Mem.* 1408, 1957.

Sams, E. W.: *NACA Research Mem.* E52D17, 1952.

Sato, K., and B. H. Sage: *Trans. ASME*, vol. 80, p. 1380, 1958.

Sauer, F. M.: *J. Aeronaut. Sci.*, vol. 18, p. 353, 1951.

Schaaf, S. A., and P. L. Chambre: "High Speed Aerodynamics and Jet Propulsion," pt. H, vol. III, Princeton University Press, Princeton, N.J., 1958.

Schlichting, H.: "Boundary Layer Theory," McGraw-Hill Book Company, Inc., New York, 1955.

Seban, R. A., and T. T. Shimazaki: *Trans. ASME*, vol. 73, p. 803, 1951.

Sellars, J. R., M. Tribus, and J. S. Klein: *Trans. ASME*, vol. 78, p. 441, 1956.

Sieder, E. N., and G. E. Tate: *Ind. Eng. Chem.*, vol. 28, p. 1429, 1936.

Sparrow, E. M., and J. L. Gregg: *J. Aeronaut. Sci.*, vol. 24, p. 852, 1957.

Squire, H. B.: "Modern Developments in Fluid Dynamics," S. Goldstein (ed.), Oxford University Press, New York, 1938.

Stalder, J. R., G. Goodwin, and M. O. Creager: *NACA Rept.* 1032, 1951.

—— and D. Jukoff: *J. Aeronaut. Sci.*, vol. 15, p. 381, 1948.

Taylor, G. I.: *Brit. Aeronaut. Comm. Rept. and Mem.* 272, p. 423, 1916.

Thomson, A. S. T., A. W. Scott, A. McK. Laird, and H. S. Holden: "General Discussion on Heat Transfer," IME and ASME, 1951.

von Kármán, T.: *Trans. ASME*, vol. 61, p. 705, 1939.

Wiedmann, M. L., and P. R. Trumpler: *Trans. ASME*, vol. 68, p. 57, 1946.

PROBLEMS

1. Estimate the orders of magnitude of the thicknesses of the velocity and temperature boundary layers for laminar flow of air and for water at standard conditions over a zero-angle-of-incidence flat plate 6 in. long at a velocity of 10 fps.

2. For conditions of 14.7 psia and 60°F, determine the momentum and thermal diffusivities and the Prandtl number for water, air, mercury, light oil, alcohol, and oxygen.

3. For laminar boundary layers, compare the velocity and temperature boundary-layer thicknesses for mercury, air, water, and light oil.

4. A fluid having a Prandtl number of 1.0 and a temperature of 80°F flows over a flat plate maintained at 100°F.

  a. For a laminar boundary layer, plot the temperature distribution versus y/δ.

  b. Calculate the temperature at the midpoint of the velocity boundary layer.

  c. Plot the heat flux in the y direction in the boundary layer (divided by q'' at $y = 0$) versus y/δ.

5. Employing the definitions of η and ψ of Sec. 6-5, reduce the boundary-layer equation for the temperature distribution, Eq. (7-7), to the ordinary differential equation (7-18).

6. Air at standard conditions flows at a velocity of 20 fps over a flat plate 9 in. long maintained at 100°F. The plate is 18 in. wide.

  a. Compute the surface coefficient and local heat flux at $x = 3$, 6, and 9 in.

  b. Find the average Nusselt number and the average surface coefficient.

  c. Calculate the total heat-transfer rate for one side of the plate.

7a. For a laminar boundary layer on a flat plate, develop an expression for the Stanton number N_{St} (defined as $N_{Nu}/N_{Re}N_{Pr}$).

  b. Prove that the ratio of the coefficient of drag and the Stanton number depends only upon the Prandtl number and suggest the physical basis of this result.

8a. Compare the Nusselt numbers, surface coefficients, and heat-transfer rates for air and water, both at 14.7 psia and 60°F, flowing over a 6-in.-long flat plate at 80°F at a Reynolds number of 10^5.

  b. For each fluid, calculate the free-stream velocity necessary to result in a Reynolds number of 10^5.

9. For the diffusion circumstance stated in Example 7-2, find the relation between the local evaporation rate on the plate surface and the distance x from the leading edge. Calculate the evaporation rate at $x = L/2$.

10. For the air and flow conditions given in Example 7-2, find the plate temperature which would result in a balance of heat transfer and latent heat supply required by evaporation. That is, find the temperature that the plate would assume if no additional heating or cooling were provided. Use the transport properties given in Example 7-2.

11a. Estimate the velocity at which rain droplets of $\frac{1}{4}$ in. diameter fall through an atmosphere at 14.7 psia and 60°F with a relative humidity of 60 per cent. Assume that weight and drag are equal and that the droplet is a sphere.

b. If the heat-convection Nusselt number is 20, estimate the temperature of the droplet and the fraction of droplet mass lost per second. Assume a Lewis number of 1.0 and similarity of heat and mass transfer. Use the diffusion coefficient given in Example 7-2.

12. Derive mass-transport equation (7-41) from the concentration differential equation which precedes it, proving that $M(N_{Sc})$ is of the same form as $M(N_{Pr})$.

13. If $\epsilon_M = \epsilon_H = \epsilon_C$ in a tube, determine the conditions under which the velocity, temperature, and concentration distributions are completely similar.

14a. Employing the universal velocity distribution of von Kármán and assuming $\epsilon_M = \epsilon_H$, develop a universal temperature distribution, that is, θ as a function of y^+.

b. Write the result as θ/θ_m, where θ_m is the maximum value of θ.

15. Water at 100°F flows through a smooth 1-in.-ID tube, whose inside surface is maintained at 120°F, at a rate of 1 cfm. Determine the surface coefficient and heat-transfer rate per unit tube length from the Reynolds analogy and from the von Kármán analogy. Use properties at the average of the surface and fluid temperatures. Comment on the physical reasons for the difference in the two calculated convection coefficients.

16. Water at 140°F flows at a velocity of 3.0 fps through a long, smooth 2-in.-ID pipe whose wall temperature is maintained at 120°F.

a. Find the surface coefficient from the von Kármán analogy.

b. Compare the magnitude of the molecular and eddy diffusivities for momentum at a distance of 0.10 in. from the pipe wall.

17. For the conditions of Prob. 16, find the surface coefficient and the necessary total tube length if the water is to be cooled to 130°F.

18. For the conditions of Prob. 15, find the surface coefficient and heat flux at the wall from the Colburn and from the Sieder-Tate relations.

19a. Air at 30 psia is to be heated from 60 to 120°F in smooth-walled tubes of $\frac{3}{4}$ in. ID whose inside walls are maintained at 140°F. Find the required tube length for an average air velocity of 30 fps.

b. How much different would the calculated tube length be if the "average temperature difference" were used in relating h to the heat-transfer rate?

20. Superheated steam at 2000 psia and 800°F enters superheater tubes of 1.25 in. ID at a velocity of 50 fps. If the inside surface of the tube is at 1000°F, find the length of tubing necessary to raise the steam temperature to 920°F.

21. Mercury is to be heated from 100 to 150°C in smooth tubes of $\frac{1}{2}$ in. ID whose inside surface temperature is 160°C. The mercury velocity will be 10 fps.

a. Calculate the surface coefficient from the von Kármán analogy and from the Lyon and Lubarsky-Kaufman equations.

b. Find the necessary tube length, using the Lubarsky-Kaufman result.

22. A sodium-potassium alloy (78 per cent K) is to be circulated through $\frac{1}{2}$-in.-ID tubes in a reactor core for cooling. The liquid-metal inlet temperature and velocity are to be 600°F and 30 fps. If the tubes are 2 ft long and have an inside surface temperature of 700°F, find the coolant temperature rise and the energy gain per pound of liquid metal.

23. Water at 80°F flows at a velocity of 6 fps through a 1-in. nominal standard-weight commercial steel pipe whose surface is maintained at 100°F. Find the surface coefficient for a smooth-walled pipe of this size and for the roughness which characterizes such a pipe.

24. Water at 60°F is to be heated in an exchanger made up of $\frac{1}{2}$-in.-ID tubes 1 ft long. The tube entries are sharp-edged. For an average water velocity of 3 fps, calculate the water temperature rise for one pass through the tubes for a tube wall temperature of 150°F.

25. A heat exchanger is to be designed to cool lubricating oil from 140 to 110°F. The oil will flow through the tubes at a velocity of 3 fps, and the tube surface temperature will be 90°F. Calculate the required tube length for a tube diameter of $\frac{1}{4}$ in. The properties of oil are as follows:

t, °F	ρ, lb/ft³	k, Btu/hr ft °F	μ, cp	c_p, Btu/lb °F
100	54	0.082	20.3	0.40
120	54	0.081	12.0	0.42
140	54	0.080	5.7	0.44

26. The coolant passages in a reactor core are 5 in. long and are to have a rectangular cross section of $\frac{3}{4}$ by 1 in. The walls of the passages are to be at 700°F.

a. If the coolant is nitrogen gas at 8 atmospheres which enters at 500°F, what velocity in the passages will result in a nitrogen discharge temperature of 600°F?

b. If the passage walls are assumed to have a roughness equivalent to that of commercial steel pipes, what velocity is required?

27. For developed turbulent flow in a tube, develop the relation between the required length L, divided by the tube diameter D, necessary to effect a fluid temperature change of Δt. This will be in terms of flow and heat-transfer parameters. Use the Colburn equation for Prandtl numbers near 1.0 and the Lubarsky-Kaufman equation for liquid metals.

28a. Develop an expression for the ratio of the heat-transfer rates to air for a long cylinder of diameter D and a long strip of width L, of equal surface area per unit span. The cylinder is placed normal to the flow, and the strip is placed at zero angle of attack, with its axis normal to the flow.

b. Plot this ratio for the Reynolds number range 10^2 to 2×10^5 on semilog paper. Discuss the trend.

c. Compare the trend of this ratio with that for flow loss, developed in Sec. 6-8.

29a. Compare the heat transfer from a long strip of width L placed normal and parallel to a stream of air for the Reynolds number range 5000 to 15,000.

b. Repeat part *a* for flow loss, that is, drag.

c. Explain why the analogy between momentum and heat transfer apparently does not hold in this case.

30. The outside surface of a long tube of 6 in. diameter is maintained at 220°F by steam inside. Air at 20 psia and 90°F flows across the tube at 40 fps. Find the surface coefficient and heat-transfer rate per foot of length.

31. A fine wire, of diameter D, is positioned across a flow passage to determine flow velocity from heat-transfer characteristics. Current is passed through the wire to heat it. This energy (Q Btu/ft) is dissipated to the flowing fluid by convection. The resistance of the wire is determined from electrical measurements, and the temperature is known from the resistance.

a. Develop an expression for the velocity in terms of the temperature difference, the Hilpert correlating constants, etc., for fluids of arbitrary Prandtl number.

b. Find the velocity of air at standard conditions if a 0.005-in. wire attains a temperature of 160°F while dissipating 40 Btu/hr ft.

32. Water at 100°F flows at a velocity of 10 fps over a steam-heated tube of 1 in. diameter. If the outside surface of the tube is at 180°F, find the convection coefficient and the heat transfer per unit length of tube.

33. For a Reynolds number of 15,000, compare the heat-transfer rates for the geometries shown in Table 7-2 with the rate for a cylinder of the same surface area per foot of length.

34. Metal spheres of $\frac{1}{8}$ in. diameter at a temperature of 200°F are dropped into a pool of water at 60°F for cooling, after a machining process. If the spheres settle at a velocity of 3 fps, calculate the surface coefficient and the initial rate of heat transfer.

35. A heat exchanger is to consist of 300 tubes 6 ft long and 1 in. in OD. The tubes are to be arranged in 15 rows, with normal and parallel spacing of 2 in. For a tube surface temperature of 200°F and air at 14.7 psia and 120°F flowing to the bank, normal to the tubes, at a velocity of 20 fps, compare the average surface coefficients and total heat-transfer rates for in-line and staggered arrangements.

36. Derive Eq. (7-59) from the velocity- and temperature-distribution expressions for developed laminar flow between two plates.

37. Oil is forced through a long passage $\frac{1}{2}$ in. high between two plates at a rate of 0.3 cfs/ft of passage width. The plates are at 60°F. For developed velocity and temperature conditions, find the pressure gradient and plot the temperature and velocity distributions. The properties of the oil are

$$\rho = 54 \text{ lb/ft}^3 \qquad \mu = 100 \text{ lb/hr ft} \qquad k = 0.08 \text{ Btu/hr ft °F}$$

$$c_p = 0.40 \text{ Btu/lb °F}$$

38. A supporting strut in a large conduit through which water at 60°F flows at a velocity of 20 fps may be idealized as a flat plate 2 in. long at zero angle of attack. If the strut is adiabatic, find its temperature.

39. A 3-in.-long piece of thin-walled tubing of 6 in. diameter is placed in a stream of air at 80°F with a velocity parallel to the axis of the tubing. (Neglect compressibility effects.)

a. For air-stream velocities of 100 and 1000 fps, estimate the temperature of the tubing material, assuming that the heat losses by radiation and by conduction along supports are negligible.

b. For an air velocity of 100 fps, find the tubing temperature necessary to dissipate 8.0 Btu/hr from the tubing to the air.

40. A flat-plate model 2 in. long is placed at zero angle of attack in a wind tunnel having static conditions in the test section maintained at 2.5 psia and 60°F.

a. Neglecting compressibility effects, plot the stagnation and surface temperature (if the plate is adiabatic) for wind-tunnel velocities in the range 100 to 600 fps.

b. If the model surface temperature is to be maintained at 75°F (by internal heating or cooling, as required), plot the heat-transfer rate for the velocity range in part *a*.

c. For a plate temperature of 70°F and an air velocity of 530 fps, plot the boundary-layer temperature distribution.

41. For the test-section static conditions of Prob. 40, a model 8 in. long, and a velocity of 800 fps, assume that boundary-layer transition occurs halfway along the plate. If the plate is locally adiabatic, estimate the surface temperatures for the front and rear halves.

42. A journal bearing consists of a shaft of 6 in. diameter in a sleeve of 6.012 in. diameter lubricated with oil having the properties listed below:

$$\mu = 100 \text{ lb/hr ft} \qquad c_p = 0.48 \text{ Btu/lb °F} \qquad \frac{\nu}{\alpha} = 1000 \qquad \rho = 54 \text{ lb/ft}^3$$

a. Derive the expression relating oil temperature to location in the film for a film of uniform thickness when the shaft speed is N, in rpm. Assume the shaft and sleeve to be at 60°F.

b. If the oil temperature is not to exceed 250°F at any point, find the maximum rotational speed that may be used.

43. Air at 60°F and 3 psia flows at a velocity of 550 fps over a 2-in.-long flat plate, placed at zero incidence. Assuming constant fluid properties and incompressible laminar flow, find the direction and magnitude of heat flow for each of the following plate surface temperatures: (*a*) 75°F, (*b*) 50°F. Sketch the boundary-layer temperature and velocity profiles for both cases, against a common scale.

44. A model of a very thin wing section of 1-in. chord is to be tested in a wind tunnel at zero angle of attack and at a Mach number of 4.0. The static conditions in the test section will be 400°R and 1.0 psia.

a. Estimate the equilibrium temperature the model surface will reach, assuming it to be adiabatic. (Neglect radiation effects.)

b. If the model surface is to be maintained at an equilibrium temperature of 800°R, find which way heat flows and at what rate.

45. Air at a velocity and temperature of 1000 fps and −60°F flows from a nozzle and in a laminar manner over the flat wall of a wind tunnel. The test-section pressure is 0.05 atmosphere. Assume that there is no boundary layer at the end of the nozzle but that one builds up on the flat wall.

a. What are the stagnation and adiabatic wall temperatures?

b. At 0.3 ft along the wall from the nozzle, find the maximum temperature and the direction and magnitude of heat flow for wall temperatures of −25 and 40°F.

46. The guidance vanes of a small rocket may be approximated by flat plates of 8-in. chord.

a. For flight at a Mach number of 3 at an altitude where the atmospheric conditions are 4.8 psia and −40°F, find the equilibrium temperature of the vanes if they are adiabatic. (Neglect radiation effects.)

b. If the vanes are to be kept at 900°F, find the direction and rate of heat transfer per foot of span. (Neglect radiation effects.)

47. By the methods of differential similarity, find the dimensionless moduli upon which θ_m/θ_i depends for any group of geometrically similar objects, initially at t_i, suddenly immersed in a bath at t_e. The average surface coefficient is taken as h. θ_m is the average temperature excess in the object material, and θ_i is the initial temperature excess. Repeat for the case of a uniformly distributed energy generation at a rate q''' in the solid material.

48*a.* Apply differential similarity to the laminar flow of an incompressible fluid in long passages of rectangular cross section. Determine the simplest grouping of variables which will relate the pressure loss to length, velocity, etc.

b. Prove that the coefficients of drag and lift for an object immersed in a stream are a function of Reynolds number.

c. What restriction is there on the choice of an area in the definition of C_D in part *b*?

49*a.* From Fig. 7-20 compare the free-molecule and laminar continuum Stanton numbers for air on a flat plate at zero angle of incidence.

b. For free-molecule flow, prove, from Fig. 7-21, that the recovery factor is always greater than 1.0.

50a. For the flow of air at 14.7 psia and 60°F at a Mach number of 1.0 normal to a fine wire, find the minimum diameter for continuum flow and the maximum diameter for free-molecule flow.

b. A wire of a diameter which just produces free-molecule flow for air at 50 μ of mercury pressure and 60°F is maintained at 300°F by passing an electric current through the wire. Find the rate of heat loss in watts per foot of wire length. The air velocity is 600 fps. Assume an α of 0.9.

51. A very thin model of a wing (assumed equivalent to a flat plate) having a chord of 1.2 in. is to be tested in a shock-driven wind tunnel at a Mach number of 10. The test-section static conditions are $p = 10^{-3}$ atmosphere, $T = 400°R$, and $\rho = 0.975 \times 10^{-4}$ lb/ft³. We shall consider a test at zero angle of attack and assume shockless flow.

a. Find the relevant Knudsen number for this flow circumstance.

b. Calculate the drag force per foot of span.

c. For a model temperature of 80°F, find the direction and magnitude of the heat transfer, assuming that the surface coefficient is based upon recovery temperature.

$$\mu = 10^{-5} \text{ lb/sec ft} \qquad N_{\text{Pr}} = 0.72$$

52. A spherical satellite of 2 ft diameter with a polished aluminum surface orbits at 100 miles altitude at a velocity of 26,400 fps. The properties of the atmosphere at this altitude may be taken as air with

$$\rho = 5.07 \times 10^{-11} \text{ lb/ft}^3 \qquad t = 480°F \qquad a = 920 \text{ fps}$$

$$\mu = 9 \times 10^{-6} \text{ lb/sec ft} \qquad p = 3.0 \times 10^{-6} \text{ psfa} \qquad \lambda = 270 \text{ ft}$$

a. Determine the regime of flow for these conditions.

b. Determine the equilibrium temperature of the satellite if it is otherwise adiabatic.

c. Repeat part b, accounting for radiation losses, an internal energy-generation rate of 50 watts, and a gain from solar effects of 90 Btu/hr. (Neglect other radiation gains from the surroundings.)

53. For the model and wind-tunnel conditions given in Prob. 44, find the model temperature if the energy gain by convection is exactly balanced by the radiation loss. The test-section walls are at 100°F. The model and test-section wall emissivities are 0.40.

54. Estimate the temperature of the guidance vanes of Prob. 46, allowing for radiation to surroundings at an "effective" temperature of 300°R. The vanes are otherwise adiabatic and have a surface emissivity of 0.30.

CHAPTER 8

Convection with Body Forces

8-1. THE EFFECTS OF BODY FORCES

Convection is the term applied to transfer processes whose rate is directly influenced by relative fluid motion. If the fluid motion arises as a result of the transport process, the process is called natural convection. This interconnection (or coupling) between transfer and fluid motion causes natural-convection processes to be more difficult to analyze than similar forced-convection arrangements.

Many circumstances give rise to natural convection. Heat transfer results in temperature differences, and since for virtually all conditions the density of a fluid is temperature-dependent, density differences arise. In a gravitational field such density differences are the cause of buoyancy forces which result in relative fluid motion. Density differences in a rotating body of fluid also produce relative motion.

Mass diffusion may cause density differences which, because of gravitation or acceleration, will result in relative motion. Such density effects result, for example, in the counterdiffusion of two chemical species of different molecular weights. Water vapor diffusing in air results in natural convection.

Many studies have been made of natural convection. The present chapter considers both analytical treatments and empirical correlations. The governing equations are presented and solutions discussed for several cases. Correlations for various geometries are considered. Combined natural- and forced-convection processes are considered.

8-2. GOVERNING EQUATIONS FOR NATURAL CONVECTION

The differential equations for the velocity, temperature, and concentration distributions apply equally well for natural convection within the limits of the conditions upon which they are based. The body force in the force

251

balance is taken equal to the buoyancy effect, relative to the fluid a large distance from the convection region (see Fig. 8-1). If, at point x, y, z, the density is ρ in a large body of fluid at density ρ_∞, the difference between the buoyant force and the weight in a gravitational field of local strength g is

$$g(\rho_\infty - \rho)$$

per unit volume. This force is written in the M, L, T system of dimensions. This is the force which causes fluid motion. If the x axis is taken parallel

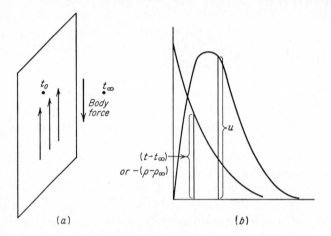

FIG. 8-1. Convection with a body force. (a) Surface at t_o in a fluid at t_∞. (b) Resulting temperature and velocity distributions.

to the lines of force of the gravitational field, with the positive direction chosen in such a way as to make the net force always positive, the net body force in the x direction is

$$X = g(\rho_\infty - \rho)$$

Introducing the coefficient of thermal expansion,

$$\beta = \rho \left[\frac{\partial (1/\rho)}{\partial t} \right]_p \tag{8-1}$$

we have approximately

$$X = g\beta\rho(t - t_\infty) \tag{8-2}$$

The body forces Y and Z are zero. These results may be substituted into the Navier-Stokes equations. If buoyancy is due to other effects—for example, rotation or acceleration of the fluid—the forces are written in terms of the acceleration effects of the motion.

All natural-convection processes involve changes in density and, in principle, must be described by the general equations. However, for many processes of practical importance, involving both gases and liquids, the density changes are sufficiently small so that their effect upon continuity, upon energy, and upon the viscous-force terms may be ignored. Large temperature differences produce large density differences in gases, however, and treatments which neglect these effects are applicable to processes involving relatively small temperature differences.

The analytical treatments of the present chapter admit density differences only in their effect in producing body forces, except in the energy equation where c_p is used. That is, energy conducted into an element of mass contributes to enthalpy. The relevant equations for a two-dimensional steady, laminar process are, therefore,

$$u \frac{\partial u}{\partial x} + v \frac{\partial u}{\partial y} = -\frac{1}{\rho} \frac{\partial p}{\partial x} + \frac{\mu}{\rho} \left(\frac{\partial^2 u}{\partial x^2} + \frac{\partial^2 u}{\partial y^2} \right) + g\beta(t - t_\infty) \qquad (8\text{-}3)$$

$$u \frac{\partial v}{\partial x} + v \frac{\partial v}{\partial y} = -\frac{1}{\rho} \frac{\partial p}{\partial y} + \frac{\mu}{\rho} \left(\frac{\partial^2 v}{\partial x^2} + \frac{\partial^2 v}{\partial y^2} \right) \qquad (8\text{-}4)$$

$$\frac{\partial u}{\partial x} + \frac{\partial v}{\partial y} = 0 \qquad (8\text{-}5)$$

$$u \frac{\partial t}{\partial x} + v \frac{\partial t}{\partial y} = \frac{k}{\rho c_p} \left(\frac{\partial^2 t}{\partial x^2} + \frac{\partial^2 t}{\partial y^2} \right) + \frac{\mu}{\rho c_p} \phi \qquad (8\text{-}6)$$

No general solution is known for this system of equations. Just as in analyzing fluid flow and forced convection, the complete equations are too complicated. Therefore, analysis in natural convection is based upon simplified forms which are sufficiently accurate for particular circumstances. For example, many interesting problems may be treated by boundary-layer methods.

Schmidt and Beckmann (1930) made detailed temperature and velocity measurements in natural-convection layers of air adjacent to a vertical flat plate, and from these distributions it was evident that the general equations may be considerably simplified, to boundary-layer forms. The analysis of Ostrach (1953) indicates the conditions under which the general equations are sufficiently accurate and the range of validity of boundary-layer forms.

For flat surfaces arranged with the body force parallel to the surface, with relatively small temperature differences and with constant fluid transport properties, the boundary-layer equations may be shown to be

$$u \frac{\partial u}{\partial x} + v \frac{\partial u}{\partial y} = \frac{\mu}{\rho} \frac{\partial^2 u}{\partial y^2} + g\beta(t - t_\infty) \tag{8-7}$$

$$\frac{\partial u}{\partial x} + \frac{\partial v}{\partial y} = 0 \tag{8-5}$$

$$u \frac{\partial t}{\partial x} + v \frac{\partial t}{\partial y} = \frac{k}{\rho c_p} \frac{\partial^2 t}{\partial y^2} + \frac{\mu}{\rho c_p} \left(\frac{\partial u}{\partial y} \right)^2 \tag{8-8}$$

For curved surfaces, similar equations apply. For cylinders with the body force parallel to the axis, boundary-layer equations are written in cylindrical coordinates. Boundary-layer solutions are discussed in Sec. 8-4.

8-3. SIMILARITY IN NATURAL-CONVECTION PROCESSES

The technique of differential similarity, applied in Sec. 7-10 for forced convection, may be applied to the natural-convection equations. By such analysis the proper combinations of the variables are determined, and the dimensionless parameters peculiar to natural convection are found. The analysis also indicates the physical significance of the various parameters and suggests the conditions under which they are important.

The relevant equations for a steady, laminar process, (8-3) to (8-6), are generalized for a surface, having a significant length L, at temperature t_o, placed in a fluid at rest at t_∞. In this case there is no imposed velocity level U_∞. Therefore, the velocity components u and v must be generalized in a different way from that used in the forced-convection case. A generalizing velocity must be chosen which has physical significance and which will yield the simplest result.

Velocity arises in the convection layer owing to the body force $g\beta(t_o - t_\infty)$, per unit mass. This force acts through a distance related to L. The resulting kinetic energy is proportional to the product $g\beta(t_o - t_\infty)L$. The velocity level in the convection layer is then proportional to

$$U_c = \sqrt{g\beta L(t_o - t_\infty)} = \sqrt{g\beta L \, \Delta t}$$

Therefore, the velocities are generalized by dividing them by this quantity. The generalized variables are

$$X = \frac{x}{L} \qquad Y = \frac{y}{L} \qquad T = \frac{t - t_\infty}{t_o - t_\infty} \qquad P = \frac{p - p_\infty}{\rho U_c^2 / 2}$$

$$U = \frac{u}{\sqrt{g\beta L \, \Delta t}} \qquad V = \frac{v}{\sqrt{g\beta L \, \Delta t}} \qquad \phi' = \frac{L^2}{U_c^2} \phi \qquad \nabla'^2 = L^2 \nabla^2$$

Introducing these new variables into Eqs. (8-3) to (8-6) and rearranging, we have

$$U \frac{\partial U}{\partial X} + V \frac{\partial U}{\partial Y} = -\frac{1}{2} \frac{\partial P}{\partial X} + \frac{\mu}{\rho U_c L} \nabla'^2 U + T$$

$$U \frac{\partial V}{\partial X} + V \frac{\partial V}{\partial Y} = -\frac{1}{2} \frac{\partial P}{\partial Y} + \frac{\mu}{\rho U_c L} \nabla'^2 V$$

$$\frac{\partial U}{\partial X} + \frac{\partial V}{\partial Y} = 0$$

$$U \frac{\partial T}{\partial X} + V \frac{\partial T}{\partial Y} = \left(\frac{k}{c_p \mu}\right)\left(\frac{\mu}{\rho U_c L}\right) \nabla'^2 T + \left(\frac{\mu}{\rho U_c L}\right)\left(\frac{U_c^2}{c_p \, \Delta t}\right) \phi'$$

The boundary conditions are

$T = 1, \quad U = V = 0 \qquad$ over the surface, i.e., for $F(X,Y) = 0$

$T \to 1, \quad \mathbf{V} \to 0 \qquad$ away from the surface

From the equations and boundary conditions we see that the distribution of T depends upon geometry and upon the three dimensionless coefficients of the differential equations. The coefficients are rewritten below:

$$\frac{\mu}{\rho U_c L} = \sqrt{\frac{\nu^2}{g\beta L^3 \, \Delta t}} = \frac{1}{\sqrt{N_{\mathrm{Gr}}}} \tag{8-9}$$

$$\left(\frac{k}{c_p \mu}\right)\left(\frac{\mu}{\rho U_c L}\right) = \frac{1}{N_{\mathrm{Pr}}} \frac{1}{\sqrt{N_{\mathrm{Gr}}}}$$

$$\left(\frac{\mu}{\rho U_c L}\right)\left(\frac{U_c^2}{c_p \, \Delta t}\right) = \frac{g\beta L/c_p}{\sqrt{N_{\mathrm{Gr}}}} \tag{8-10}$$

where N_{Gr} is the Grashof number and arises in the force balance as the ratio of viscous forces and momentum. The Grashof number is seen to be proportional to the square of a convection-layer Reynolds number. This interpretation of the Grashof number is important in connection with turbulence in natural-convection layers. The Prandtl number also appears. An additional dimensionless quantity, $g\beta L/c_p$, arises because of viscous-dissipation effects. Dissipation effects are important, therefore, if g, β, or L is large and/or c_p is small.

The heat-transfer rate is related to the temperature distribution through the definition of the surface coefficient:

$$h = \frac{\displaystyle\int_A q'' \, dA}{A(t_o - t_\infty)} = \frac{\dfrac{1}{A}\displaystyle\int_A k\left(-\dfrac{\partial t}{\partial n}\right)_0 dA}{t_o - t_\infty} = \frac{k}{L}\overline{\left(-\frac{\partial T}{\partial N}\right)_0}$$

where A is the surface area and n is the direction normal to the surface. Since T depends only upon geometry and upon N_{Gr}, N_{Pr}, and $g\beta L/c_p$, the average of the normal derivative depends only upon these quantities. Therefore, for a given geometry we have

$$\frac{hL}{k} = N_{Nu} = f\left(N_{Gr}, N_{Pr}, \frac{g\beta L}{c_p}\right) \qquad (8\text{-}11)$$

If viscous-dissipation effects are negligible, the result is

$$N_{Nu} = f(N_{Gr}, N_{Pr}) \qquad (8\text{-}12)$$

For flat surfaces the analytical results and empirical correlations have this form. Empirical correlations for other shapes are also of the form of Eq. (8-12).

8-4. ANALYSIS OF LAMINAR NATURAL CONVECTION

Experimental and analytical considerations of natural convection were carried out very early in the study of heat transfer. From early measurements it was evident that the heat-transfer rate from a surface depended upon the temperature difference to a higher power than the first. This indicated that the surface coefficient depends not merely upon geometry and fluid properties but also upon the driving force, the temperature difference.

Lorenz, in 1881, presented an analysis for a vertical surface at uniform temperature in an extensive fluid at rest. This analysis is based upon the assumption that the flow in the convection layers is primarily parallel to the surface. A force balance which included the effects of buoyancy, weight, and fluid shear resulted in an expression for the thickness of the convection layer. By considering this layer to be a slab, across which heat is conducted, an expression for the surface coefficient was found. The average convection coefficient, combined in the Nusselt number, was found to be

$$\frac{hL}{k} = 0.548 \sqrt[4]{\frac{gc_p\rho^2\beta(t_o - t_\infty)L^3}{\mu k}} = 0.548 \sqrt[4]{aL^3(t_o - t_\infty)} \qquad (8\text{-}13)$$

where the quantity a denotes a combination of fluid properties. This equation may be rearranged to

$$N_{Nu} = 0.548\sqrt[4]{N_{Gr}N_{Pr}} = 0.548\sqrt[4]{N_{Ra}} \qquad (8\text{-}14)$$

where N_{Ra} is called the Rayleigh number. This very simple result is of the form of the result of the similarity argument, Eq. (8-12).

Isothermal Flat Plates. Since the Lorenz analysis is based upon a number of questionable simplifications and since the result does not accurately predict the Prandtl number effect, the natural-convection process has been analyzed starting from the differential equations. The boundary-layer equations are obtained from the general differential equations and are justified by the measurements of Schmidt and Beckmann (1930). These equations have been solved for many different natural-convection circumstances. Pohlhausen determined the proper similarity variable for the boundary-layer equations and solved them for a Prandtl number

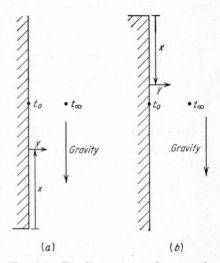

Fig. 8-2. Coordinate system for natural-convection analysis. (a) $t_o > t_\infty$. (b) $t_o < t_\infty$.

of 0.733. Solutions were subsequently obtained by others for different Prandtl numbers.

Pohlhausen reduced the boundary-layer equations (8-7), (8-5), and (8-8) for negligible viscous dissipation to two ordinary differential equations by introducing a stream function $\psi(x,y)$ and a similarity variable η. The variable η is different from that used for forced convection because of the buoyancy term in Eq. (8-7). The coordinate system is shown in Fig. 8-2.

$$\phi = \frac{t - t_\infty}{t_o - t_\infty}$$

$$u = \frac{\partial \psi}{\partial y} \qquad v = -\frac{\partial \psi}{\partial x}$$

$$\eta = \frac{y}{x}\sqrt[4]{\frac{N_{Gr,x}}{4}} \qquad (8\text{-}15)$$

where $N_{Gr,x}$ is the local Grashof number:

$$N_{Gr,x} = \frac{g\beta x^3(t_o - t_\infty)}{\nu^2} \tag{8-16}$$

The stream function $\psi(x,y)$ is written in terms of a function of η, that is, $f(\eta)$:

$$f(\eta) = \frac{\psi(x,y)}{4\nu\sqrt[4]{N_{Gr,x}/4}}$$

The x-direction velocity component may be written in terms of f as

$$u = \frac{\partial\psi}{\partial y} = 4\nu\sqrt[4]{\frac{N_{Gr,x}}{4}}\frac{\partial f(\eta)}{\partial y} = \frac{2\nu}{x}\sqrt[2]{N_{Gr,x}}\,f' \tag{8-17}$$

These relations are introduced into Eqs. (8-7), (8-5), and (8-8) by methods similar to those discussed in Sec. 6-5 to yield the following ordinary differential equations and boundary conditions:

$$f''' + 3ff'' - 2f'^2 + \phi = 0 \tag{8-18}$$

$$\phi'' + 3N_{Pr}f\phi' = 0 \tag{8-19}$$

at $\eta = 0$ $f = 0$ $f' = 0$ $\phi = 1$

as $\eta \to \infty$ $f' \to 0$ $\phi \to 0$

The Prandtl number appears as a parameter in these relations. Therefore, a separate solution must be obtained for each value. In addition to the Pohlhausen solution, Schuh, in 1948, solved these equations for Prandtl numbers of 10, 100, and 1000. These results are reported in Schlichting (1955).

Ostrach (1953), starting from the complete equations for variable properties, determined the conditions under which Eqs. (8-18) and (8-19) are an adequate description of the physical process. These equations were then solved for Prandtl numbers of 0.01, 0.72, 0.733, 1, 2, 10, 100, and 1000. The resulting temperature and velocity distributions are shown in Figs. 8-3 and 8-4 in terms of ϕ and f'. The curves show a strong Prandtl number effect. The Prandtl number affects the shape of the curves and the relative thickness of the thermal and velocity boundary layers. One cannot say, however, that for low Prandtl numbers the fluid velocity layer is of negligible relative thickness, as in the forced-convection case. For natural convection the velocity and temperature fields are coupled, and the thicknesses are connected by buoyancy and fluid shear effects.

The local heat flux at the solid-fluid interface may be calculated from the slopes of the temperature distributions at $\eta = 0$, that is, from ϕ_0'. This quantity is a function of the Prandtl number.

$$q''(x) = -k \left(\frac{\partial t}{\partial y}\right)_0 = k \frac{t_o - t_\infty}{x} \sqrt[4]{\frac{N_{\mathrm{Gr},x}}{4}} (-\phi_0')$$

The flux, therefore, decreases inversely with the fourth root of x. The local convection coefficient and Nusselt number are

$$h_x = (-\phi_0') \frac{k}{x} \sqrt[4]{\frac{N_{\mathrm{Gr},x}}{4}} \qquad (8\text{-}20)$$

or

$$N_{\mathrm{Nu},x} = \frac{-\phi_0'}{\sqrt{2}} \sqrt[4]{N_{\mathrm{Gr},x}} = F(N_{\mathrm{Pr}}) \sqrt[4]{N_{\mathrm{Gr},x}} \qquad (8\text{-}21)$$

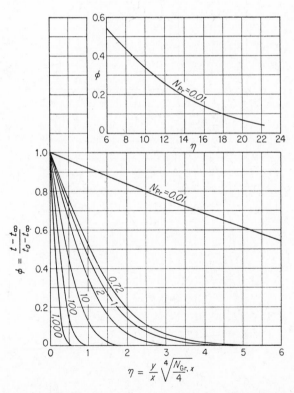

FIG. 8-3. Temperature distributions for natural convection on a vertical, isothermal plate for laminar boundary-layer flow conditions. [*From Ostrach* (1953).]

The average surface coefficient for a plate of height L may be found by integrating Eq. (8-20) over the range of x from 0 to L (noting that ϕ_0' is independent of x). The result for the fourth-root distribution in x is

$$h = \frac{1}{L}\int_0^L h_x\,dx = \frac{1}{L}\int_0^L h_L\left(\frac{L}{x}\right)^{\frac{1}{4}}dx = \frac{h_L\sqrt[4]{L}}{L}\int_0^L \frac{dx}{\sqrt[4]{x}} = \tfrac{4}{3}h_L \quad (8\text{-}22)$$

Therefore, $$\frac{hL}{k} = N_{\mathrm{Nu}} = \tfrac{4}{3}N_{\mathrm{Nu},L} = \tfrac{4}{3}F(N_{\mathrm{Pr}})\sqrt[4]{N_{\mathrm{Gr}}} \quad (8\text{-}23)$$

where $$N_{\mathrm{Gr}} = \frac{g\beta L^3(t_o - t_\infty)}{\nu^2} \quad (8\text{-}24)$$

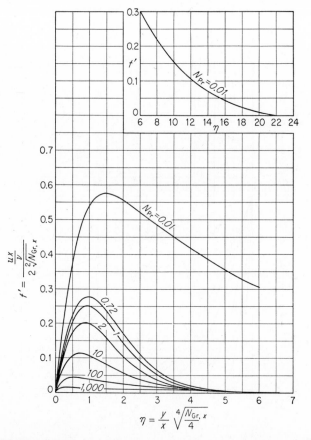

FIG. 8-4. Velocity distributions for natural convection on a vertical, isothermal plate for laminar boundary-layer flow conditions. [*From Ostrach* (1953).]

That is, the Nusselt number, based upon the average coefficient, depends only upon the Prandtl number and upon the "plate" Grashof number.

The Prandtl number function in Eq. (8-21) is plotted in Fig. 8-5, and $\frac{4}{3}F(N_{Pr})$ in Eq. (8-23) is listed in Table 8-1 from the results of Ostrach.

Table 8-1. Comparison of the Isothermal and Uniform-flux Cases

N_{Pr}	$\frac{4}{3}F(N_{Pr})$	$F_1(N_{Pr})$	$F_2(N_{Pr})$
0.01	0.0765		
0.1	. . .	0.237	0.224
0.72	0.475		
1	0.535	0.573	0.543
2	0.675		
10	1.10	1.17	1.11
100	2.06	2.18	2.07
1000	3.74		

The Lorenz equation, (8-14), may be written in terms of local values by the result in Eq. (8-22):

$$N_{Nu,x} = \tfrac{3}{4} \times 0.548\sqrt[4]{N_{Gr,x}}\sqrt[4]{N_{Pr}} = 0.411\sqrt[4]{N_{Gr,x}}\sqrt[4]{N_{Pr}} \quad (8\text{-}25)$$

This is plotted in Fig. 8-5. The Prandtl number trend of the Lorenz equation is not in agreement with the boundary-layer results.

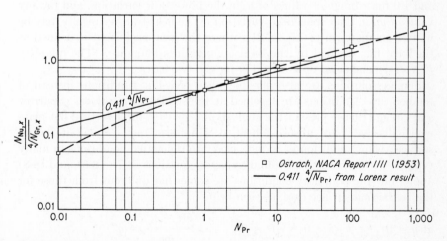

Fig. 8-5. Heat-transfer characteristics for laminar natural convection from an isothermal, vertical plate.

Example 8-1. A heating element of a water heater may be idealized as a 4- by 4-in. vertical plate. If the plate temperature is 80°F and the water temperature is 60°F, find the amount of heat transferred, from the results of the boundary-layer theory. Properties are taken at 70°F.

$$a = 238 \times 10^6 \text{ ft}^{-3} \text{ °F}^{-1} \qquad N_{Pr} = 6.81 \qquad k = 0.347 \text{ Btu/hr ft °F}$$

$$N_{Ra} = 238 \times 10^6 \times \tfrac{20}{3} \times 3 \times 3 = 176.2 \times 10^6$$

$$N_{Gr} = \frac{N_{Ra}}{N_{Pr}} = 25.9 \times 10^6$$

From Fig. 8-5 for $N_{Pr} = 6.81$, $F(N_{Pr}) = 0.74$. From Eq. (8-23),

$$N_{Nu} = \tfrac{4}{3} \times 0.74 \sqrt[4]{N_{Gr}} = 70.3$$

$$h = 70.3 \frac{k}{L} = 73.2 \text{ Btu/hr ft}^2 \text{ °F}$$

$$q = hA(t_o - t_\infty) = 73.2 \times 2 \times \tfrac{20}{3} \times 3 = 325 \text{ Btu/hr, or } 0.095 \text{ kw}$$

Other Surface Conditions for Flat Plates. Vertical plates with other wall temperature conditions have been analyzed by boundary-layer methods. Similarity variables exist for surface temperature distributions of

$$t_o - t_\infty = N x^n$$

and

$$t_o - t_\infty = M e^{mx}$$

where n, m, N, and M are constants.

Sparrow and Gregg (1958a) present solutions for Prandtl numbers of 0.7 and 1.0 for a range of values of n, in the power-law variation, and for any value of m, in the exponential variation. The heat-transfer results may be written in the form of Eq. (8-21), where the local coefficient is defined as the local flux divided by the local temperature difference. The quantity $F(N_{Pr})$ depends also upon n and m for the two cases.

Similar solutions are also possible when heat-flux conditions instead of temperature conditions are specified at the solid-fluid interface. Sparrow and Gregg (1956a) present the analysis and solution for a vertical flat plate which dissipates (or absorbs) heat at a uniform rate q'' over its entire surface. This condition is, in fact, closer to the actual conditions in many types of exchangers. The boundary-layer equations (8-7), (8-5), and (8-8) apply, but the boundary conditions are somewhat different from those for the isothermal surface case, as seen below:

at $y = 0$ $\qquad f = 0 \qquad f' = 0 \qquad -k \dfrac{\partial(t - t_\infty)}{\partial y} = q''$

as $y \to \infty$ $\qquad f' \to 0 \qquad t - t_\infty \to 0$

The temperature variable, generalized stream function, and similarity variable must be defined differently to result in similarity conditions for these boundary conditions:

$$\phi = \frac{t_\infty - t}{q''x/k} \sqrt[5]{\frac{g\beta x^4 q''}{5k\nu^2}} = \frac{t_\infty - t}{q''x/k} \sqrt[5]{\frac{N'_{Gr,x}}{5}} \tag{8-26}$$

$$\eta = \frac{y}{x} \sqrt[5]{\frac{N'_{Gr,x}}{5}} \tag{8-27}$$

$$f(\eta) = \frac{\psi(x,y)}{5\nu \sqrt[5]{N'_{Gr,x}/5}} \tag{8-28}$$

where N'_{Gr} indicates a modified Grashof number in which $q''x/k$ replaces $(t_o - t_\infty)$ for the isothermal case. The resulting differential equations and boundary conditions are

$$f''' - 3f'^2 + 4ff'' - \phi = 0$$

$$\phi'' + N_{Pr}(4\phi'f - \phi f') = 0$$

at $\eta = 0$ $\qquad\qquad f = 0 \qquad f' = 0 \qquad \phi' = 1$

as $\eta \rightarrow \infty$ $\qquad\qquad f' \rightarrow 0 \qquad \phi \rightarrow 0$

The solutions of these equations were determined for Prandtl numbers of 0.1, 1, 10, and 100. The temperature difference between the surface and the distant fluid $(t_o - t_\infty)$ varies with x as indicated in Eq. (8-26).

$$t_o - t_\infty = \frac{q''x}{k} \frac{-\phi_0}{\sqrt[5]{N'_{Gr,x}/5}} \tag{8-29}$$

The average temperature difference for a plate of height L may be found by integration to be

$$\overline{t_o - t_\infty} = \frac{5}{6} \frac{q''L}{k} \frac{-\phi_0}{\sqrt[5]{N'_{Gr}/5}} \tag{8-30}$$

The convection coefficient based upon $\overline{t_o - t_\infty}$ is combined in a Nusselt number to give

$$\frac{hL}{k} = \frac{q''L/k}{\overline{t_o - t_\infty}} = \frac{6}{5(-\phi_0)} \sqrt[5]{\frac{N'_{Gr}}{5}} \tag{8-31a}$$

The modified Grashof number N'_{Gr} may be converted into a conventional Grashof number, defined in Eq. (8-24), where $(\overline{t_o - t_\infty})$ is used as the temperature difference. The result is

$$\frac{hL}{k} = \left[\frac{6}{5\sqrt[5]{5}(-\phi_0)}\right]^{\frac{5}{4}} \sqrt[4]{N_{Gr}}$$

$$N_{Nu} = F_1(N_{Pr})\sqrt[4]{N_{Gr}} \tag{8-31b}$$

The isothermal solution of Ostrach, Eq. (8-23), is compared with the uniform-flux solution, Eq. (8-31b), in Table 8-1. The results for these two different cases are seen to be in close agreement. Basing the surface coefficient and Grashof number upon the temperature difference at $x = L/2$ results in a different coefficient $F_2(N_{Pr})$ in Eq. (8-31b). These values are also listed in the last column in Table 8-1 and are seen to be in even closer agreement with the isothermal case. This suggests that a single heat-transfer relation may apply accurately for a number of different cases.

Vertical Cylinders. The foregoing flat-plate solutions apply also to vertical cylinders of various sections as long as the radius of curvature of the surface is large compared with the thickness of the convection layer. If this condition is not met, the curvature affects convection and, for circular cylinders, the equations in cylindrical coordinates apply. However, the boundary-layer equations in cylindrical coordinates do not reduce to simple form for the typical boundary conditions of interest. Sparrow and Gregg (1956b) present an approximate solution for relatively short cylinders for $N_{Pr} = 0.72$ and 1.0.

Millsaps and Pohlhausen (1956 and 1958) show that a similarity variable exists for the vertical-cylinder boundary-layer equations when the temperature difference varies linearly from zero at the leading edge. The resulting equations are solved numerically for Prandtl numbers of 0.733, 1, 10, and 100. The results may be accurately approximated by

$$\frac{hD}{k} = 1.058\sqrt[4]{N'_{Gr}} \sqrt[4]{\frac{N_{Pr}^2}{4 + 7N_{Pr}}} \tag{8-32}$$

The local surface coefficient is uniform over the surface. The modified Grashof number N'_{Gr} is defined in terms of the surface temperature gradient.

$$N'_{Gr} = \frac{g\beta D^4}{\nu^2}\left(\frac{dt}{dx}\right)_0 \tag{8-33}$$

This solution applies for laminar boundary-layer flow.

Variable Fluid Properties. The solutions discussed in the preceding paragraphs are based upon the assumption that the fluid properties are uniform, except for density. Most fluids, however, have properties which are temperature-dependent. Therefore, for processes involving large temperature differences the equations may be in serious error. Some study has been given to this problem, and Sparrow and Gregg (1958b) have shown that, for the property variations common to gases, the properties other than β should be evaluated at the following reference temperature for vertical isothermal plates with laminar boundary layers:

$$t_r = t_o - 0.38(t_o - t_\infty) \qquad (8\text{-}34)$$

β should be taken as $1/T_\infty$. This procedure has been shown to be adequate over the range

$$0.5 < \frac{t_o}{t_\infty} < 3.0$$

where the temperatures are absolute. For mercury, the same procedure may be used except that all properties are evaluated at the reference temperature given in Eq. (8-34). For both types of fluids this reference temperature is a better choice than the "film" temperature.

Many other natural-convection problems have been solved by use of the boundary-layer equations and by integral methods, applied to thermal boundary layers.

8-5. CORRELATIONS OF NATURAL CONVECTION

Natural-convection processes have been studied experimentally for many different geometries under widely varying conditions. In this section observed behavior is discussed, and empirical correlations are presented for a number of cases. Heat transfer from horizontal cylinders and plates and from vertical surfaces to extensive bodies of fluid is considered. Several cases of convection to enclosed and partially enclosed bodies of fluid are discussed.

The analytical methods discussed in the preceding sections have been supported by experimentally determined convection behavior. However, the laminar boundary-layer point of view has certain limitations. Consider, for example, the data obtained by Saunders (1936) for natural convection from vertical plates to air. These data are plotted in Fig. 8-6 as the Nusselt number vs. the Rayleigh number. The result of the Lorenz analysis, Eq. (8-14), and of the boundary-layer theory, Eq. (8-23), is that the correlation N_{Nu} versus N_{Gr} (or N_{Ra} for a given fluid) should be a straight line of 0.25 slope on ln-ln coordinates. The data in Fig. 8-6 show this to be true for only a restricted range of N_{Ra}, from perhaps 10^4 to 10^9.

The deviation from the boundary-layer result in the range of Grashof numbers below 10^4 results because the boundary-layer point of view is no

longer sufficiently accurate in this range. For such conditions the boundary-layer thickness is too great, relative to the size of the object, for the
boundary-layer approximations to be valid. The deviation at high values
of the Grashof number occurs because the flow in the convection layers
becomes so vigorous that transition to turbulence occurs. In Sec. 8-3 the
connection between N_{Gr} and a convection-layer Reynolds number was

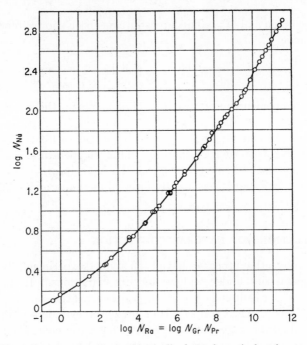

FIG. 8-6. Natural convection from electrically heated vertical strips to air. [*From Saunders* (1936).]

shown, and we recall from Chap. 6 that the Reynolds number is the criterion
for transition to turbulence. Observations of Eckert and Soehngen (1951)
in interferometric studies of natural convection have shown that transition
begins in air on a vertical plate at a local Grashof number of approximately
4×10^8.

Interference photographs show many interesting aspects of a natural-
convection process. A composite photograph, obtained by Eckert and
Soehngen for a vertical plate in air, is shown in Fig. 8-7. Isotherms show
as the alternate light and dark lines. The numbers are distances from the
lower edge of the plate, in inches. Conditions for which these pictures were
made resulted in a local Grashof number on the upper part of the plate

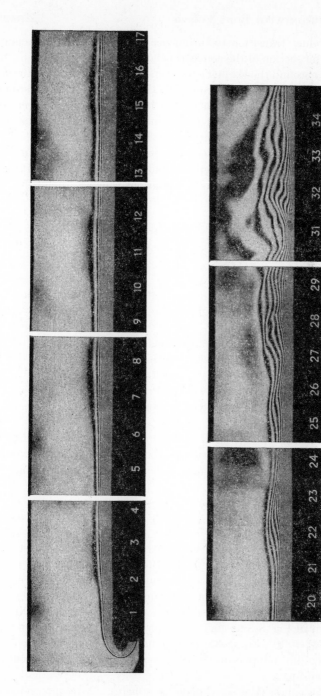
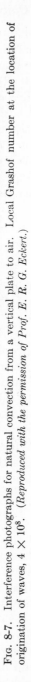

FIG. 8-7. Interference photographs for natural convection from a vertical plate to air. Local Grashof number at the location of origination of waves, 4×10^8. (*Reproduced with the permission of Prof. E. R. G. Eckert.*)

sufficient to produce transition to turbulence. The disturbances begin as waves in the outer section of the convection layer.

The isotherms around the leading edge of the plate show that the thermal layer extends ahead of the plate. Since the thermal layer is thinnest here, the local coefficient is a maximum at the leading edge. However, the coefficient is not extremely large at this point, compared with the rest of the surface, as suggested by boundary layer-theory [see Eq. (8-20)].

Vertical Plates. The heat-transfer behavior shown in Fig. 8-6 applies for vertical plates and large-diameter cylinders in fluids whose Prandtl numbers are not far different from 1.0. Equations which fit such behavior, with their ranges of application, are

$$N_{\mathrm{Nu}} = 0.59 \sqrt[4]{N_{\mathrm{Ra}}} \qquad 10^4 < N_{\mathrm{Ra}} < 10^9 \qquad (8\text{-}35)$$

$$N_{\mathrm{Nu}} = 0.13 \sqrt[4]{N_{\mathrm{Ra}}} \qquad 10^9 < N_{\mathrm{Ra}} \qquad (8\text{-}36)$$

where fluid properties are to be determined at the "film" temperature and the significant dimension is the height of the plate or the diameter of the cylinder.

The empirical relation for the laminar range, Eq. (8-35), is about 15 per cent above the results of the analytic solution. This is probably due to rate-increasing disturbances usually present in actual equipment. For Prandtl numbers far different from 1.0, the Prandtl number effect found in Sec. 8-4, Table 8-1, may be employed to correct Eq. (8-35) for laminar convection layers.

Eckert and Jackson (1951) used an approximate integral method of analysis for natural convection with a turbulent boundary layer for vertical, isothermal plates. The result, applicable to the whole surface for Grashof numbers greater than 10^{10}, is

$$N_{\mathrm{Nu}} = 0.0246(N_{\mathrm{Gr}})^{\frac{2}{5}} N_{\mathrm{Pr}}^{\frac{7}{15}} (1 + 0.494 N_{\mathrm{Pr}}^{\frac{2}{3}})^{-\frac{2}{5}} \qquad (8\text{-}37)$$

This relation correlates the data well and is expected to be a better estimate of the Prandtl number effect than Eq. (8-36).

Horizontal Cylinders and Spheres. Long horizontal cylinders have been studied for many sizes and fluids for a wide range of temperature difference. A number of correlations have been suggested. One of these, due to Nusselt (1929), is shown in Fig. 8-8 as curve *N*. For the laminar boundary-layer range, above $N_{\mathrm{Ra}} = 10^4$, Eq. (8-35) may be used with a coefficient of 0.52. Properties at the film temperature are to be used, and the diameter is the significant dimension.

A number of studies have been made for spheres. A recent review by

Yuge (1959) suggests the following correlation for Grashof numbers between 1 and 100,000.

$$N_{Nu} = 2 + 0.45 \sqrt[4]{N_{Gr}} \, \sqrt[3]{N_{Pr}} \tag{8-38}$$

This is expected to apply for Prandtl numbers in the vicinity of 1.0. Properties at the film temperature are to be used.

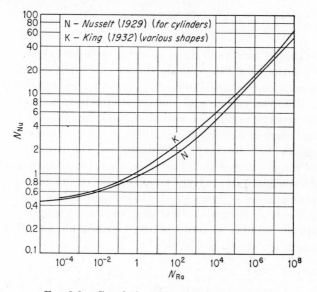

FIG. 8-8.   Correlations for natural convection.

Miscellaneous Shapes.   King (1932) correlated data taken in various fluids for shapes such as plates, spheres, cylinders, and blocks. The recommended relation is curve K in Fig. 8-8. For the range of N_{Ra} between 10^4 and 10^9, Eq. (8-35) may be used with a constant of 0.60. The characteristic length of an object is found as

$$\frac{1}{L} = \frac{1}{L_h} + \frac{1}{L_v} \tag{8-39}$$

where L_h and L_v are the significant horizontal and vertical dimensions. This relation may be used as an estimate for various geometries when more specific information is not available.

Vertical Cylinders.   For vertical cylinders of small diameter, or for vertical wires, the convection layer may be a substantial fraction of the diameter. In such a circumstance the curvature of the surface has an

important effect upon the transport process. The approximate results of
Sparrow and Gregg (1956b) for Prandtl numbers of 0.72 and 1.0, discussed
in Sec. 8-4, indicate the conditions under which this curvature becomes
important. For example, the vertical-flat-plate solution for heat transfer
is within 5 per cent of the vertical-cylinder solution for

$$\frac{D}{L} \geq \frac{35}{\sqrt[4]{N_{\mathrm{Gr}}}} \qquad (8\text{-}40)$$

where the Grashof number is based upon the cylinder height.

Several solutions for the vertical-cylinder case were mentioned in Sec.
8-4. Because of mathematical difficulties, few complete solutions have been
obtained. However, various experimental studies have been made. Eigenson (1940) reports results for cylinders, and Mueller (1942) gives results for fine wires in air. Elenbaas (1948) developed a transport theory
which suggests that, for very small diameters, the Nusselt number is a
function of the product of the Grashof number, based upon diameter, and
the diameter-height ratio. Kyte et al. (1953) report measurements for
wires in various gases. Hama et al. (1958a and 1958b) report measurements in air and an integral-method analysis which suggests a correlation
for the Nusselt number in terms of the Grashof number–D/L product.
Various results are shown in Fig. 8-9.

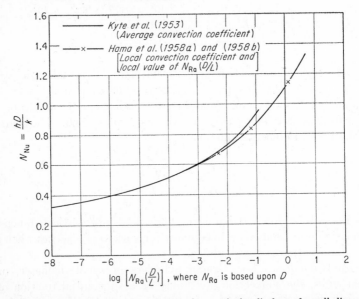

FIG. 8-9. Natural-convection correlations for vertical cylinders of small diameter.

Example 8-2. A 0.05-in.-diameter wire 4 in. long having a surface temperature of 60°F is placed vertically in air at 40°F and 14.7 psia. We shall find the heat-transfer rate. Properties at 50°F will be used.

$$a = 1.94 \times 10^6 \text{ ft}^{-3} \text{ °F}^{-1} \qquad k = 0.0143 \text{ Btu/hr ft °F} \qquad N_{Pr} = 0.712$$

The Grashof number based upon height is

$$\frac{aL^3(t_o - t_\infty)}{N_{Pr}} = \frac{1.94 \times 10^6 \times 20}{27 \times 0.712} = 2.02 \times 10^6$$

$$\frac{D}{L} = \frac{0.05}{4} = 0.0125 \qquad \text{and} \qquad \frac{35}{\sqrt[4]{N_{Gr}}} = 0.9$$

Since a large error would result from the use of vertical-plate results [see Eq. (8-40)], the Kyte results in Fig. 8-9 will be used:

$$N_{Ra}\frac{D}{L} = aD^3(t_o - t_\infty)\frac{D}{L} = 0.0349 \qquad \log 0.0349 = -1.457$$

$$N_{Nu} = \frac{hD}{k} = 0.83 \qquad h = 0.83 \times \frac{0.0143 \times 12}{0.05} = 2.85 \text{ Btu/hr ft}^2 \text{ °F}$$

$$q = hA(t_o - t_\infty) = \frac{2.85 \times \pi \times 0.05 \times 4 \times 20}{144} = 0.249 \text{ Btu/hr}$$

The vertical-plate convection coefficient is

$$N_{Nu} = \frac{hL}{k} = 0.59\sqrt[4]{1.44 \times 10^6 \times 0.72} = 18.8$$

$$h = \frac{18.8 \times 0.0143}{4/12} = 0.807 \text{ Btu/hr ft}^2 \text{ °F}$$

which is 28 per cent of the proper value.

Horizontal and Inclined Plates. For square plates, placed horizontally, Fishenden and Saunders (1950) suggest equations of the form of Eqs. (8-35) and (8-36). The length of an edge is taken as the significant length. For heated surfaces facing upward (or cooled surfaces facing downward) the relations are

$$N_{Nu} = 0.54\sqrt[4]{N_{Ra}} \qquad 10^5 < N_{Ra} < 10^8 \tag{8-41}$$

$$N_{Nu} = 0.14\sqrt[3]{N_{Ra}} \qquad 10^8 < N_{Ra} < 3 \times 10^{10} \tag{8-42}$$

For the other case, heated surfaces facing downward (or cooled surfaces facing upward), the following relation is recommended by McAdams (1954):

$$N_{Nu} = 0.27\sqrt[4]{N_{Ra}} \qquad 3 \times 10^5 < N_{Ra} < 3 \times 10^{10} \tag{8-43}$$

Tests on inclined plates were carried out by Rich (1953). The principal effect, for small inclinations from the vertical, appears to be the reduction of the body force parallel to the plate due to inclination. If the gravitational acceleration g in the Grashof number is replaced by $g \cos \theta$, where θ is the angle of inclination with respect to the vertical, the equations for vertical plates correlate the experimental results within 10 per cent, for small angles.

Enclosed Fluid Layers. Natural-convection effects in a body of fluid enclosed by surfaces of nonuniform temperature have been studied analytically and experimentally. Two cases frequently encountered are horizontal and vertical air spaces formed by two plates at different temperatures, t_{o_1} and t_{o_2}. A surface coefficient is defined as follows:

$$q'' = h(t_{o_1} - t_{o_2})$$

For horizontal air spaces there are two different cases. If the upper plate is at the higher temperature no convection effects will arise, except possibly at the edges, and heat transfer will be entirely by conduction. The convection coefficient h is merely k/s, where s is the distance between the enclosing surfaces. Therefore, the Nusselt number is 1.0:

$$\frac{h}{k/s} = N_{Nu} = 1.0 \tag{8-44}$$

If the lower plate is warmer, an unstable condition results. Lighter layers of fluid are overlain by denser layers. For a Grashof number, based upon s, less than perhaps 1700, no motion results, and the simple conduction rate pertains. For greater values, natural-convection effects arise. Jakob (1949) correlates the data of various investigators as follows:

$$N_{Nu} = 0.195 \sqrt[4]{N_{Gr}} \qquad 10^4 < N_{Gr} < 4 \times 10^5 \tag{8-45}$$

$$N_{Nu} = 0.068 \sqrt[3]{N_{Gr}} \qquad 4 \times 10^5 < N_{Gr} \tag{8-46}$$

The lower range corresponds to an ordered, cellular convection process and the upper range to a disordered, turbulent one. The above correlation shows that the layer thickness is the only feature of the geometry which affects heat transfer and that this effect disappears for the upper range.

Globe and Dropkin (1959) made heat-transfer measurements for horizontal spaces filled with mercury, water, and silicone oils. A Prandtl number range from 0.02 to 8750 resulted. Measurements were made in essentially the Rayleigh number range 3×10^5 to 7×10^9. The following relation correlates the test results with reasonable accuracy:

$$N_{Nu} = 0.069 \sqrt[3]{N_{Gr}} \, N_{Pr}^{0.407} \tag{8-47}$$

Properties are to be evaluated at the average of the two surface temperatures.

In vertical air spaces the effects of geometry are more complicated than for horizontal layers. The thickness s and the height H of the space are both important. Jakob (1949) has summarized the results of several investigators. For a Grashof number, based upon s, less than 2000, the process is simple conduction, and Eq. (8-44) applies. For higher values of the Grashof number, the ratio H/s is important. Two ranges result, and the correlating equations are

$$N_{Nu} = 0.18 \sqrt[4]{N_{Gr}} \left(\frac{H}{s}\right)^{-\frac{1}{9}} \qquad 2 \times 10^4 < N_{Gr} < 2 \times 10^5 \quad (8\text{-}48)$$

$$N_{Nu} = 0.065 \sqrt[3]{N_{Gr}} \left(\frac{H}{s}\right)^{-\frac{1}{9}} \qquad 2 \times 10^5 < N_{Gr} < 11 \times 10^6 \quad (8\text{-}49)$$

These results are expected to apply for $H/s > 3$. For thicker vertical layers the convection coefficients typical of isolated vertical plates apply approximately for each surface.

8-6. COMBINED FORCED AND NATURAL CONVECTION

Chapter 7 considers forced convection, and the preceding sections of this chapter consider natural convection. The present section considers combined processes. In any heat-transfer circumstance, density differences arise and, in the presence of a force field, natural-convection effects result. If, in a forced-convection circumstance, the forces and the momentum-transport rates are very large, the effects of natural-convection tendencies may be negligible. On the other hand, if buoyancy forces are of greater relative magnitude, forced-convection effects may be ignored. However, in many practical circumstances the two effects may be of comparable order. The present section considers the circumstances in which such conditions arise and discusses some of the studies of the resulting combined-convection problems.

An indication of the relative magnitudes of the natural- and forced-convection effects may be obtained from the differential equations. Consider a uniform stream (U_∞, t_∞) flowing laminarly over an object at t_o. We shall consider the case wherein U_∞ and the buoyancy effect are parallel—for example, flow in the vertical direction. Taking the flow direction as x, the Navier-Stokes equation for uniform properties (other than the temperature effect upon density, which is assumed to be small) is

$$u\frac{\partial u}{\partial x} + v\frac{\partial u}{\partial y} + w\frac{\partial u}{\partial z} = -\frac{1}{\rho}\frac{\partial p}{\partial x} + \frac{\mu}{\rho}\nabla^2 u + g\beta(t - t_\infty) \qquad (8\text{-}50)$$

This equation is generalized by introducing the following substitutions (see Sec. 7-10):

$$X = \frac{x}{L} \qquad Y = \frac{y}{L} \qquad Z = \frac{z}{L} \qquad T = \frac{t - t_\infty}{t_o - t_\infty} \qquad P = \frac{p - p_\infty}{U_\infty^2/2g_0}$$

$$u' = \frac{u}{U_\infty} \qquad v' = \frac{v}{U_\infty} \qquad w' = \frac{w}{U_\infty} \qquad \nabla'^2 = L^2\nabla^2$$

Equation (8-50) becomes

$$u' \frac{\partial u'}{\partial X} + v' \frac{\partial u'}{\partial Y} + w' \frac{\partial u'}{\partial Z}$$

$$= -\frac{1}{2}\frac{\partial P}{\partial X} + \frac{\mu}{\rho U_\infty L}\nabla'^2 u' + \left[\frac{g\beta L^3(t_o - t_\infty)}{\nu^2}\right]\left(\frac{\nu^2}{U_\infty^2 L^2}\right)T \quad (8\text{-}51)$$

The portion of the flow field which controls heat transfer and drag is that near the surface. In this region, $\partial u'/\partial X$ and u' are both of order 1.0 (see Sec. 6-4). Therefore, the left-hand side of Eq. (8-51) is of order 1.0. Since momentum transport and viscous forces are of the same order, the viscous-force term is also of order 1.0. Since T is of order 1.0, the buoyancy term will be of importance in establishing the velocity distribution, upon which the temperature distribution depends, if the coefficient of T is of order 1.0, that is, if

$$\left[\frac{g\beta L^3(t_o - t_\infty)}{\nu^2}\right]\left(\frac{\nu^2}{U_\infty^2 L^2}\right) = \frac{N_{Gr}}{N_{Re}^2} = O(1)$$

or

$$N_{Gr} = O(N_{Re}^2) \qquad\qquad\qquad (8\text{-}52)$$

We should expect buoyancy effects to appear first in forced convection for a considerably smaller magnitude of the buoyancy term. In a qualitative way the ratio N_{Gr}/N_{Re}^2 is an indication of the relative effect of buoyancy upon forced convection.

By a similar argument for a natural-convection process subject to forced convection, an estimate of the relative magnitude of the forced-convection effect upon the velocity distribution is

$$\frac{N_{Re}}{\sqrt{N_{Gr}}}$$

Small values of this ratio result in small forced-convection effects. The two effects are again comparable for the condition given in Eq. (8-52).

For forced convection on a vertical, isothermal plate in the laminar boundary-layer regime, Sparrow and Gregg (1959a) determined the conditions under which buoyancy effects would appreciably change the drag and the heat-transfer rate. The analysis considered Prandtl numbers of 0.01, 1.0, and 10. The parameter N_{Gr}/N_{Re}^2 is an indication of the relative effect of natural convection upon forced-convection transfer [as indicated in the analysis which resulted in Eq. (8-52)]. For forced convection the

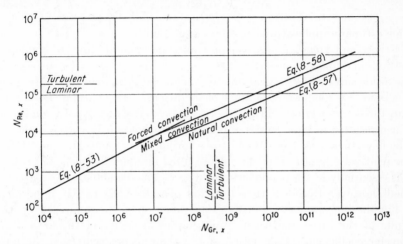

FIG. 8-10. Regimes of convection for flow and buoyancy effects parallel; boundary-layer processes.

effects of buoyancy upon the local heat-convection coefficient will be less than 10 per cent if

$$|N_{Gr,x}| \leq 0.150(N_{Re,x})^2 \tag{8-53}$$

where the Reynolds and Grashof numbers are both based upon the distance from the leading edge of the plate. The limit of Eq. (8-53) is plotted in Fig. 8-10 in the relatively low ranges of $N_{Re,x}$ and $N_{Gr,x}$ for which laminar flow results. Above the curve, essentially forced convection results. Immediately below the curve are conditions for which both effects are important. The laminar limits are also shown in the diagram for both forced and natural convection.

The effect of natural convection upon the average heat-transfer coefficient will be less than 5 per cent for

$$|N_{Gr}| \leq 0.225 N_{Re}^2 \tag{8-54}$$

The total drag force will be affected less than 5 per cent if

$$|N_{Gr}| \leq 0.30 N_{Re}^2 \tag{8-55}$$

where the Reynolds and Grashof numbers are both based upon the plate length in the direction of flow. These estimates apply for buoyancy effects either opposed to, or in the direction of, flow.

For forced convection on a horizontal isothermal plate, Mori (1960) has shown that the effects of natural convection upon the local convection coefficient are less than 10 per cent if

$$|N_{\mathrm{Gr},x}| \leq 0.083(N_{\mathrm{Re},x})^{2.5} \tag{8-56}$$

This estimate applies to both sides of the plate.

Eckert and Diaguila (1954) report an experimental study of combined natural- and forced-convection effects in air. The heat-transfer surface was the inside surface of a vertical tube 10 ft high of $23\frac{1}{4}$ in. diameter. Measurements were made for a wide range of conditions. Pure natural convection, pure forced convection, and mixed convection were studied under conditions which resulted in large values of both the Grashof and Reynolds numbers. The flow, therefore, was thought to be turbulent for almost all tests. Since the relatively small L/D of the tube resulted in undeveloped flow, the flow was essentially of the boundary-layer type. The diameter was sufficiently small, however, that deviations from flat-plate behavior may be important.

For the buoyancy effect in the same direction as the imposed flow, the limits of the three regimes were established in terms of the local heat-transfer coefficient. A deviation of less than 10 per cent from the pure natural-convection behavior was found for

$$|N_{\mathrm{Gr},x}| \geq 0.007(N_{\mathrm{Re},x})^{2.5} \tag{8-57}$$

A deviation of less than 10 per cent from the pure forced-convection behavior was found for

$$|N_{\mathrm{Gr},x}| \leq 0.0016(N_{\mathrm{Re},x})^{2.5} \tag{8-58}$$

The region between these two limits is mixed convection. The two limits are plotted in Fig. 8-10 for the range in which the data were taken.

Acrivos (1958) employed an integral method to analyze combined laminar convection from a vertical, isothermal plate. Prandtl numbers of 0.73, 10, and 100 were considered. The results show that heat transfer is increased by buoyancy effects in the direction of flow and decreased when the effect is opposed to the flow. If the adverse buoyancy effect is sufficiently strong, the flow may be reversed near the surface. The results of this analysis confirm Eq. (8-53) as the condition under which natural convection has little effect upon local heat transfer. Forced convection has negligible effect in natural convection if

$$\frac{N_{\mathrm{Gr},x}}{(N_{\mathrm{Re},x})^2} > 10 \qquad \text{for } N_{\mathrm{Pr}} = 0.73 \text{ and } 10 \qquad (8\text{-}59a)$$

and
$$\frac{N_{\mathrm{Gr},x}}{(N_{\mathrm{Re},x})^2} > 100 \qquad \text{for } N_{\mathrm{Pr}} = 100 \qquad (8\text{-}59b)$$

Example 8-3. For a vertical, isothermal plate 1 ft high in air at 60°F and 14.7 psia we shall determine, for flow in the vertical direction, what free-stream velocity will result in important forced-convection effects for a plate temperature of 100°F. We shall then calculate the maximum plate temperature for which natural-convection effects are negligible for a vertical velocity of 6 fps.

Properties at 80°F will be used throughout.

$$a = 1.53 \times 10^6 \qquad N_{\mathrm{Pr}} = 0.708 \qquad \mu = 0.0446 \text{ lb/hr ft} \qquad \rho = 0.0735 \text{ lb/ft}^3$$

For a plate temperature of 100°F,

$$N_{\mathrm{Gr}} = \frac{aL^3 \, \Delta t}{N_{\mathrm{Pr}}} = \frac{1.53 \times 10^6 \times 40}{0.708} = 8.65 \times 10^7$$

From Eq. (8-59a), forced convection is certainly negligible if

$$N_{\mathrm{Re}}^2 < \frac{N_{\mathrm{Gr}}}{10}$$

that is, if
$$N_{\mathrm{Re}} < 2940 \qquad \text{or} \qquad U_\infty < 0.5 \text{ fps}$$

The plate temperature for negligible natural convection for $U_\infty = 6$ fps is found from Eq. (8-54):

$$N_{\mathrm{Re}} = 35{,}800$$

$$N_{\mathrm{Gr}} \leq 0.225 N_{\mathrm{Re}}^2 = 2.88 \times 10^8$$

$$\Delta t < \frac{2.88 \times 10^8}{a} = 189°$$

or
$$t_o < 60 + 189 = 249°\text{F}$$

Sparrow et al. (1959b) obtained a solution for combined convection for several special conditions under which similarity variables exist. Isothermal and constant-flux surface conditions result in similarity variables for included wedge angles of 120 and 135°, respectively. This analysis ignores the effect of the component of buoyancy normal to the surface.

Solutions are given for the range of $N_{\mathrm{Gr}}/N_{\mathrm{Re}}^2$ from 0 to 100 for buoyancy effects in the direction of flow and from 0 to 1.1544 for the buoyancy effects opposed to flow. These results apply for a Prandtl number of 0.7 and are an indication of the nature of combined transfer.

Yuge (1959) reported studies of combined convection from a sphere in air for the Reynolds and Grashof number ranges of 3.5 to 144,000 and 1 to 100,000, respectively. Horizontal and vertical (up and down) flow direc-

tions were investigated. Mixed-convection behavior was similar for flow
and buoyancy effects at 90° and in the same direction. For flow and buoyancy effects opposed, a minimum heat-transfer rate occurred as the Reynolds number increased (for a given Grashof number). The two different

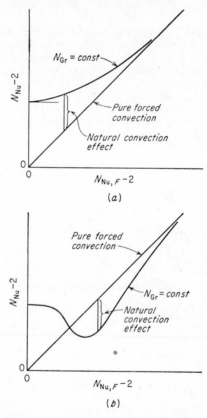

FIG. 8-11.   Combined convection characteristics.   (a) Parallel and crossflow.   (b)
Counterflow.

characteristics are shown in Fig. 8-11a and b. The actual Nusselt number
is plotted vs. the forced-convection Nusselt number $N_{\text{Nu},F}$ at the flow
Reynolds number. If this is done for a given Grashof number, a curve
results. The effects of natural convection are clearly shown.

Collis and Williams (1959) determined the importance of combined convection for heat transfer from horizontal wires. A criterion is established
for negligible natural-convection effects.

The effects of buoyancy upon laminar forced convection in pipes has been
studied analytically. The effects of buoyancy in vertical pipes may be large.

Martinelli and Boelter (1942) present a relation for this case. This result was subsequently substantiated by comparing it with experimental data. Morton (1959) considers the case of the horizontal tube. The Nusselt number is increased by the secondary flow resulting from buoyancy. The increase depends upon the $N_{Ra}N_{Re}$ product squared.

NOTATION

c_p	specific heat at constant pressure, per unit mass
f or $f(\eta)$	stream function in terms of η
g	local gravitational acceleration
g_o	a conversion factor for units of force
k	thermal conductivity
N_{Gr}	Grashof number
N'_{Gr}	modified Grashof number, based upon flux or gradient
$N_{Gr,x}$	local Grashof number
$N'_{Gr,x}$	local modified Grashof number, based upon flux
N_{Nu}	Nusselt number
$N_{Nu,x}$	local boundary-layer Nusselt number
N_{Pr}	Prandtl number
N_{Ra}	Rayleigh number, product of the Grashof and Prandtl numbers
N_{Re}	Reynolds number
$N_{Re,x}$	local boundary-layer Reynolds number
p	pressure
q''	heat flux
t	temperature, °F or °C
u	component of velocity in the x direction
U	velocity
v	component of velocity in the y direction
w	component of velocity in the z direction
β	thermal-expansion coefficient
η	similarity variable
μ	absolute viscosity
ρ	density of mass
ϕ	ratio of temperature excesses
ϕ	dissipation function
ϕ	generalized temperature, Eq. (8-26)
ψ	stream function in terms of x and y

REFERENCES

Acrivos, A.: *AIChE Journal*, vol. 4, p. 285, 1958.
Collis, D. C., and M. J. Williams: *J. Fluid Mech.*, vol. 6, p. 357, 1959.
Eckert, E., and A. J. Diaguila: *Trans. ASME*, vol. 76, p. 496, 1954.
——— and T. W. Jackson: *NACA Rept.* 1015, 1951.
——— and E. Soehngen: "General Discussion on Heat Transfer," IME and ASME, 1951.
Eigenson, L. S.: *Compt. rend. acad. sci. U.R.S.S.*, vol. 26, p. 440, 1940.
Elenbaas, W.: *J. Appl. Phys.*, vol. 19, p. 1148, 1948.

Fishenden, M., and O. A. Saunders: "Heat Transfer," Oxford University Press, New York, 1950.

Globe, S., and D. Dropkin: *Trans. ASME*, ser. C, vol. 81, p. 24, 1959.

Hama, F. R., and J. Christiaens: *Univ. Maryland Tech. Note* BN-138, May, 1958b.

—— and J. V. Recesso: *Univ. Maryland Tech. Note* BN-116, January, 1958a.

Jakob, M.: "Heat Transfer," vol. I, John Wiley & Sons, Inc., New York, 1949.

King, W. J.: *Mech. Eng.*, vol. 54, p. 347, 1932.

Kyte, J. R., A. J. Madden, and E. L. Piret: *Chem. Eng. Progr.*, vol. 49, no. 2, p. 653, 1953.

McAdams, W. H.: "Heat Transmission," 3d ed., McGraw-Hill Book Company, Inc., New York, 1954.

Martinelli, R. C., and L. M. K. Boelter: *Univ. Calif. (Berkeley) Publs. Eng.*, vol. 5, p. 23, 1942.

Millsaps, K., and K. Pohlhausen: *J. Aeronaut. Sci.*, vol. 23, p. 381, 1956.

—— and ——: *J. Aeronaut. Sci.*, vol. 25, p. 357, 1958.

Mori, Y.: *ASME Paper* 60-WA-220, 1960.

Morton, B. R.: *Quart. J. Mech. Appl. Math.*, vol. 12, p. 410, 1959.

Mueller, A. C.: *Trans. AIChE*, vol. 38, p. 613, 1942.

Nusselt, W.: *Z. VDI*, vol. 73, p. 1475, 1929.

Ostrach, S.: *NACA Rept.* 1111, 1953.

Rich, B. R.: *Trans. ASME*, vol. 75, p. 489, 1953.

Saunders, O. A.: *Proc. Roy. Soc. (London)*, ser. A, vol. 157, p. 278, 1936.

Schlichting, H.: "Boundary Layer Theory," McGraw-Hill Book Company, Inc., New York, 1955.

Schmidt, E., and W. Beckmann: *Tech. Mech. u. Thermodynam.*, vol. 1, pp. 341, 391, 1930.

Sparrow, E. M., R. Eichhorn, and J. L. Gregg: *Phys. Fluids*, vol. 2, p. 319, 1959b.

—— and J. L. Gregg: *Trans. ASME*, vol. 78, p. 435, 1956a.

—— and ——: *Trans. ASME*, vol. 78, p. 1823, 1956b.

—— and ——: *Trans. ASME*, vol. 80, p. 379, 1958a.

—— and ——: *Trans. ASME*, vol. 80, p. 879, 1958b.

—— and ——: *Trans. ASME*, ser. E, vol. 81, p. 133, 1959a.

Yuge, T.: *ASME Paper* 59-A-123, 1959.

PROBLEMS

1a. A cylinder of radius R and length L having a temperature t_o is placed vertically in a stagnant fluid at t_∞. For steady-state, laminar heat transfer, write the complete differential equations and boundary conditions in cylindrical coordinates for this circumstance, neglecting viscous-dissipation effects.

b. Write the equations which apply if a boundary-layer treatment is permissible.

2. For the general problem in part *a* of the preceding problem, carry out a differential similarity analysis and determine the quantities upon which the Nusselt number depends.

3. Discuss the conditions (fluids, states, fields, etc.) for which the viscous-dissipation number $(g\beta L/c_p)$ would be large. Relate a large value of $(g\beta L/c_p)$ to the nature of the resulting convection layers. How is the heat-transfer rate affected?

4. For an ideal gas, that is, $p = \rho RT$, prove that the thermal-expansion coefficient β is equal to the reciprocal of the absolute temperature.

5. Employing the similarity variable and stream-function definitions of Pohlhausen, develop Eqs. (8-18) and (8-19) (with the relevant boundary conditions) from Eqs. (8-7), (8-5), and (8-8) for an isothermal, vertical flat plate.

6. A 10-in.-high, 1-ft-wide plate at 80°F is placed vertically in oxygen at 60°F and 10 psia. Using average properties for oxygen:

a. Find the plate Grashof number.

b. Determine the heat-transfer rate from the Lorenz and Ostrach results.

c. Compute the location and value of the maximum x component of velocity in the boundary layer. What is the temperature at this point?

7. A 4-in.-diameter cylinder 6 ft long having a surface temperature of 1100°F is placed vertically in air at 100°F and 14.7 psia.

a. Find the convection heat-transfer rate using properties evaluated at a "film" temperature.

b. Find the heat-transfer rate estimating properties at the reference temperature recommended by Sparrow and Gregg.

8a. For the uniform flux case for a vertical plate of height L show from Eq. (8-29) that the average temperature difference is as given in Eq. (8-30).

b. Convert the modified Grashof number to the ordinary Grashof number and show that Eq. (8-31b) follows from Eq. (8-31a).

c. Find the relation between $(t_o - t_\infty)$ and the value of $(t_o - t_\infty)$ at $x = L/2$.

9a. A plate 6 ft high and 1 ft wide is placed in air at standard conditions. For a uniform surface flux of 40 Btu/hr ft^2, find the maximum, minimum, and average plate temperatures.

b. Employing the average plate temperature found in part *a*, find the heat-transfer rate from the Ostrach results and compare this with the given heat-transfer rate.

10. A vertical cylinder 6 in. long and $\frac{1}{2}$ in. in diameter is surrounded by water at 60°F. The surface temperature of the cylinder varies from 60°F at the bottom to 100°F at the top. Find the heat-transfer rate.

11a. For a vertical plate 2 ft high in air at 60°F and 14.7 psia, estimate the plate temperature which would result in transition at the upper edge.

b. For a vertical plate and a temperature difference of 10°F, find the minimum height which results in boundary-layer type of flow.

c. For both cases, find the average convection coefficient.

12. A cylinder 3 in. in diameter and 6 in. high, having a surface temperature of 120°F, is placed vertically in water at 60°F. Find the average surface coefficient and the heat-transfer rate.

13. For the circumstance given in Prob. 6, find the heat-transfer rate from the empirical correlation and from the analytical result.

14. A vertical pipe of 1 ft OD and 5 ft long passes through a tank which contains air at 30 psia and 60°F. The outside surface of the pipe is at 80°F. Find the average surface coefficient and heat-transfer rate.

15. Find the heat-transfer rate in the circumstance given in the preceding problem if the pipe is horizontal instead of vertical.

16. A small heating plate, 1 ft by 3 in., is installed in the vertical wall of a water heater which contains water at 140°F. If the heating rate is to be 1.0 kw, what plate temperature must be maintained? The 1-ft dimension is vertical.

17. A steam pipe, 6 in. nominal (standard weight), passes through a factory space maintained at 70°F. If the pipe is uninsulated and has an outside surface temperature of 220°F, find the rate of energy loss by natural convection per foot of pipe length.

18. For a 4- by 4-in. plate at 100°F placed in air at 14.7 psia and 60°F, compare the average surface coefficients and heat-transfer rates from each side of the plate for the following three orientations: (*a*) vertical, (*b*) horizontal, (*c*) inclined at 30° with respect to the vertical.

19. Compare the heat-transfer rates for a 0.003-in.-diameter wire at 100°F placed horizontally and vertically in N_2 at 14.7 psia and 60°F. The wire is 1 in. long. For a vertical arrangement use the results of Kyte et al.

20. Two large horizontal plates, 2 by 2 ft, having surface temperatures of 100 and 60°F are separated by an air space 1 in. thick. A strip around the edges encloses the air space. Find the Nusselt number and total heat-transfer rate for (*a*) the warmer plate above, (*b*) the warmer plate below.

21. For condition *b* in the preceding problem:

a. What thickness of air space would result in the suppression of convection? Find the heat-transfer rate for this condition.

b. What thickness would result in a turbulent convection process?

22. A horizontal layer of water 2 in. thick is enclosed by two plates, the lower being at 140°F and the upper one at 100°F. Find the surface coefficient and the heat-transfer rate per unit area.

23. If the plates discussed in Prob. 20 are placed vertically, find the Nusselt number and the total heat-transfer rate.

24. A vertical air space 3 in. thick, 15 in. wide, and 2 ft high is bounded by surfaces at 50 and 30°F. Compare the convection heat-transfer rate per unit area with that which would result if the space were subdivided by placing a thin metal foil vertically in the middle of the space. Make the same comparison for two metal foils equally spaced.

25. Air at 80°F and 14.7 psia flows vertically over a flat plate 4 ft high at a velocity of 30 fps. For what plate temperature levels will natural-convection effects be small?

26. For the circumstance given in Prob. 6, find the maximum permissible imposed vertical velocity of the gas for forced-convection effects to be unimportant.

27. For the heat-transfer process discussed in Prob. 12, find the maximum vertical velocity for negligible forced-convection effects.

28. For a horizontal cylinder and flow of air in the horizontal direction normal to the cylinder, sketch the Nusselt-Reynolds number relationship for Grashof numbers of 10^4, 10^5, 10^6, 10^7, and 10^8. Show the pure natural- and forced-convection asymptotes and assume that the curves are of a form similar to those for spheres in Fig. 8-11*a*.

29. If the plate and flow direction in Prob. 6, Chap. 7, are vertical, determine whether or not the natural-convection effects are negligible.

CHAPTER 9

Heat Transfer with Liquid Vaporization

9-1. CHANGE-OF-PHASE HEAT-TRANSFER PROCESSES

The various heat-transfer processes in which changes of phase occur are quite different in nature from the heat-transfer processes taking place in single-phase regions, such as in the convection and conduction processes previously discussed. In the latter types of processes the energy transfer is sometimes quite complicated, but at base a conduction process governs the rate of transfer. Conduction also occurs with phase change and may even govern the rate of transfer in some circumstances. However, in general, the mechanism whereby the substance changes phase, either from liquid to vapor or from vapor to liquid, is of considerable importance in determining the rate. As a result of this complication, one would expect that the rates of transfer and the nature of the variation of the rates of transfer with, for example, temperature difference and velocity might be quite different from those for conduction and convection processes. In addition, theories concerning the way in which phase-change processes occur generally must take into account the basic features of both conduction and phase change.

Experimentally determined rates in phase-change processes are generally different in both magnitude and nature of variation from those for convection processes. The rates of energy transfer are, under most conditions, much higher for a given Δt. Further, various basically different processes might occur under apparently slightly differing conditions. The result is that the theories are not general but are developed for each kind of transfer process.

The present chapter considers vaporization processes, their nature, experimentally determined rates, correlations of these rates, and theories, with the resulting rate predictions. The subsequent chapter presents the same type of information for condensation processes.

Vaporization may occur in two distinctly different ways. For example, a pool of liquid which is heated from below may be vaporized by two different processes. If the rate of heat addition is low, vapor will be formed at the free surface. With higher rates of energy input, surface vaporization may still occur but, in addition, bubbles will be formed at the heating surface and may either increase or decrease in size while rising through the liquid. The second type of process is called boiling or ebullition and is the most important in practice. Surface vaporization is an important effect only for relatively small rates of heat flow.

Boiling processes occur under widely differing conditions. The result has been the development of general classification systems under which most processes may be grouped. Although no single classification system or group of descriptive names enjoys universal acceptance, the one following seems reasonable and is widely used. There are two general features by which processes may be distinguished. The first is the nature and state of the liquid being boiled. It may be either a pure substance or a solution of several substances. The state of the bulk of the liquid may be either subcooled, that is, at a temperature less than the saturation temperature corresponding to the existing pressure level, or essentially saturated, that is, at a temperature approximately equal to the saturation temperature. Therefore, the liquid is either a pure substance or a mixture undergoing saturated or subcooled boiling. The second distinguishing feature is the relation between the liquid and the heating and other surfaces enclosing it. The boiling liquid may be standing in a pool with the heating surface being a plate, tube, or wire in contact with the liquid—for example, a pan of water being heated on a stove or a hot piece of metal being quenched in a tank of water. This is called pool boiling. On the other hand, the liquid may be actively flowing over a heated surface or through a heated passage— for example, water flowing through the tubes in a modern steam generator. The term applied here is convection boiling. As an example of the use of this terminology, the quenching referred to above produces the pool boiling of a subcooled, pure substance; the modern steam generator produces the convection boiling of a saturated, pure substance.

Certain additional terminology is necessary but will be introduced in connection with the discussion of the differences which it distinguishes. The foregoing classifications are natural and reasonable, and the rates of heat transfer and the nature of the process change considerably from one class to another. As a result, most theories of mechanism or correlations of data apply to only one type of process. The major part of the present chapter is devoted to the pool vaporization of pure substances, because this type of process has been studied most intensively. The last section of the chapter briefly considers subcooled pool and convection boiling.

9-2. NATURE OF VAPORIZATION PHENOMENA

The simplest kind of vaporization process, pool vaporization of a saturated, pure substance, will be considered in detail. This is desirable because a large number of the important features of vaporization processes are encountered in this case and because this process is not complicated by such secondary effects as subsequent condensation or vapor formation arising from flow-induced pressure differences, that is, from cavitation.

Flux vs. Temperature Difference in Pool Boiling. The data shown in Fig. 9-1 were obtained by Farber and Scorah (1948) for water boiling at atmospheric pressure on a submerged, electrically heated Chromel C wire. The wire was horizontal and was 6 in. long and 0.040 in. in diameter. One curve is a plot of the heat flux per unit area of the wire vs. the difference between the temperature of the surface of the wire and the temperature of the liquid. The other curve, of the surface coefficient h, is merely q'' divided by Δt.

It is evident from the nature of the q'' curve that there are several rates of q'' variation. The various rate regions are separated by the letters a, b,

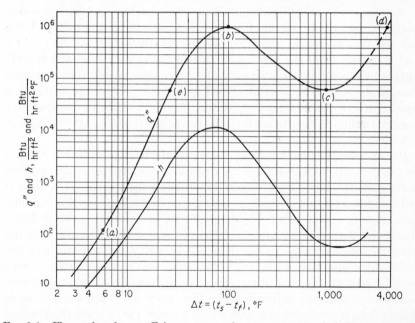

FIG. 9-1. Flux and surface coefficient versus Δt for water at 14.7 psia boiling on a 0.040-in.-diameter horizontal Chromel C wire. [*From data presented by Farber and Scorah* (1948).]

and c on the curve. The value of q'' increases slowly with Δt up to a, then increases very rapidly to a maximum at b. Between b and c, the value of q'' actually decreases with increasing Δt; beyond c, it again increases slowly, then rapidly. The behavior of q'' versus Δt suggests that there are several different processes by which vaporization occurs, even for a single substance. Visual observation indicates that such is the case. In the region up to point a, no boiling would be observed; the liquid would be slightly superheated and at an essentially constant temperature throughout, except immediately below the free surface and very near the heating surface. Vaporization occurs at the free surface, and energy is transferred from the heating surface to the liquid by a free-convection process. From a to b, the process is quite different and is called nucleate boiling. Small bubbles are formed at favored points, or "nuclei," on the heating surface; they grow, are finally displaced from the surface by buoyant forces, and rise into the liquid above. The liquid is also superheated, and the bubbles usually grow while rising through it. In the liquid one sees many rising streams of bubbles, each bubble of a stream arising from a common point on the heating surface. The value of q'' increases rapidly in this region as more surface locations become origins of bubble streams. This process, as well as those subsequently described, involves bubbles and is, therefore, boiling vaporization. As the Δt is increased and point b is approached, the flux and rate of bubble formation become very large. Since the transfer rate is greater from the heating surface to liquid than from the heating surface to vapor, this large rate of bubble formation means that more and more of the surface is being blanketed by bubbles. Therefore, a region is reached where the increased blanketing begins to offset the tendency of higher Δt values to give higher flux; the two effects balance at the peak q'' at point b.

For Δt values beyond b, a large fraction of the heating surface is covered by vapor at any instant of time. A vapor film extends over a large portion of the surface. Large quantities of vapor occasionally break off, and their place is taken by liquid which evaporates explosively against the hot surface. A very violent process is observed until, at some temperature difference above that at b, a relatively stable, permanent film is formed over the whole heating surface. Under these conditions, vapor is formed at the liquid-vapor interface of the film. The latent heat of vaporization is supplied by heat crossing the vapor film from the heating surface by convection, conduction, and radiation. The film builds up locally until a large bubble detaches. Increasing Δt tends to increase the average thickness of the vapor film and thereby to reduce the flux. This, perhaps, accounts for the falling portion of the curve. However, in this region, the Δt is becoming large enough for the resulting radiation transfer to become important relative to the conduction and convection transfer rate. In fact, under many conditions, the heating surface is red at the Δt for which the minimum is found. The effect of the increasing radiation transfer is to overcome the decreasing trend and to cause q'' to increase for increasing Δt. The rate of increase becomes quite high, since the rate of radiation transfer is essentially proportional to the fourth power of the absolute surface temperature.

At this juncture, it is necessary to point out that the b-to-c portion of the curve is not usually obtained with electric heaters and that the characteristics discussed above for the region b to c were first observed on the surfaces of steam-heated tubes. The reason for the difficulty with electric heaters is that the rate of energy generation inside the heaters is somewhat independent of the temperature of the heater material. A voltage is imposed, and a current results which generates energy in the heater material. If the heater temperature is to remain constant, energy must be flowing to the vaporizing fluid at the same rate. Now consider the situation for an electric heater when the process has proceeded from a to b owing to an increase in the voltage across the heater resistance. If there is a further increase in voltage, giving a higher generation rate, the surface temperature will tend to rise, but the surface temperature rise produces a boiling process which cannot absorb heat as rapidly as at b. As a result, the difference between the generation rate and the dissipation rate will lead to a further increase in heater temperature and, therefore, in Δt, thus further decreasing the dissipation rate. Since the flux at b is very high, the rate of heater temperature rise will be very great. No balance between the generation and dissipation rates is possible until point d is reached. For many fluids, the temperature at d is above the melting point of most heater materials, and melting, called "burnout," occurs before d is reached. The possibility of burnout is a serious concern in certain practical processes in which energy-generation rates are relatively independent of material temperatures.

If the heater surface does not melt, the region above d may be observed by further increasing the voltage, and the region from d to c may be observed by decreasing the voltage from d. After c has been reached, a further decrease of voltage will usually give the process from e down. An increase in voltage at c will again generally give points along c to d.

The process indicated by b to c of the boiling curve may be more easily observed when the heater is a tube with steam condensing inside to supply the heat. High Δt values may be obtained merely by increasing the condensation pressure of the steam. As the peak q'' is passed, the rate of steam condensation adjusts to balance the rate of energy dissipation to the boiling liquid. Therefore, the whole vaporization range, up to the highest Δt obtainable for the available steam condition, may be observed.

Liquid Superheat. An important and common feature of pool-boiling processes is that the liquid is invariably somewhat superheated. For water the superheat is essentially uniform throughout the pool. The amount of superheat depends upon the pressure, the condition of the surface, and the kind of boiling process. For example, the superheat is around $\frac{1}{2}$°F for water at 1 atmosphere on a typical surface. Of course, much higher liquid superheat is found immediately adjacent to the heating surface.

The presence of superheat introduces some complication in the meaning of Δt. The value of Δt based upon the liquid temperature would be somewhat less than the Δt based upon the saturation temperature. However, since the difference between the two Δt values is small, it is often ignored. Data are usually, but not always, presented in the form of q'' versus the difference between the surface and liquid temperatures.

Liquid superheat is also present in convection vaporization processes. Numerous temperature measurements, summarized in Jakob (1949), indicate that in the convection region the temperature is relatively uniform throughout the pool and that the drop in temperature from the superheat to the saturation value occurs in a relatively thin layer on the surface. This and certain other observations suggest that convection vaporization processes are relatively simple, at least from the standpoint of predicting or estimating transfer rates. The isothermal condition of the main body of the pool suggests that the transfer process from the heating surface is primarily by free convection into a well-mixed isothermal fluid region. The energy then passes into the surface layer, causing vaporization. Since the amount of liquid superheat is small, the values of surface coefficients may be estimated as those applying for a free-convection process between a surface and a surrounding fluid at the saturation temperature corresponding to the vapor pressure. Such convection processes are discussed in Chap. 8.

Effects of Gases and Surface Condition. The effect of the condition of the liquid regarding dissolved gases and of the condition of the heating surface with reference to absorbed gases, roughness, and liquid wettability is unimportant in some types of vaporization processes and very important in others. For convection vaporization processes little effect is found; the transfer rate is dependent mainly upon geometry, temperature difference, and fluid properties. Dissolved gases have an effect if they tend to come out of solution because of increased temperature, in that they blanket the heating surface somewhat. For film boiling, the transfer rate is mainly dependent upon the radiation and convection processes across the vapor film and is not therefore influenced in a major way by such features as geometry, dissolved gases, and wettability.

Nucleate-boiling processes, on the other hand, have been found to give widely varying rates of transfer, depending upon initially dissolved gases. In addition, the rates of transfer depend upon numerous other imperfectly understood effects. For example, the crystal structure and chemical nature of the heating surface and the liquid surface tension have been found to be important under some circumstances. Jakob (1949) summarizes various investigations concerning the effects of heating-surface conditions, such as oxidation and roughness, upon the q''-versus-Δt curve for the nucleate-boiling process. Very large effects are reported, and surface roughness apparently increases the heat-transfer rate by considerably more than would be indicated by taking into account the increased heating surface due to roughening a smooth surface. Considerable decreases of q'' at all Δt values have been observed with time for a given heating surface and quantity of liquid.

Effects of Curvature, Cavities, and Nuclei. An important factor in the explanation of surface effects in the process of nucleate boiling is the following physical consideration. Lord Kelvin demonstrated that the equilibrium vapor pressure for a liquid at a given temperature depends upon the curvature of the surface separating the liquid and vapor regions. The vapor pressure for a flat surface is taken as a reference at each temperature, and the vapor pressure above a concave surface is shown to be less, and above a convex surface greater, than the reference value. The magnitude of the difference in equilibrium vapor pressure above a flat and a concave liquid surface is inversely proportional to the radius of curvature of the concave surface. Since bubbles have concave surfaces, only this case will be discussed further.

The application of these considerations to nucleate-boiling processes provides a plausible partial explanation for liquid superheat and for the effect of dissolved gases and surface irregularities on the rate of heat transfer. Consider the conditions necessary for the stability of a detached bubble in the pool. The pressure level above the approximately flat surface of the pool is the reference saturation pressure for the temperature of the vapor above the pool. Neglecting hydrostatic effects, the pressure throughout the pool is the same as above it. Therefore, the pressure of the vapor in the bubble must be slightly greater than the reference value, to prevent its collapse due to the action of liquid surface tension on the bubble boundary. But, because of the concave liquid surface, the equilibrium vapor pressure in the bubble is less than the standard value if the temperature of the liquid is the same as that of the vapor above the pool surface. Therefore, the bubble will exist and grow only if the liquid is superheated enough to result in a vapor pressure in the bubble somewhat greater than that in the space above the pool. These considerations indicate that smaller bubbles require a larger amount of superheat. The effect of hydrostatic pressure is to increase further the amount of superheat necessary for stable bubbles.

The effect of the presence of surface nuclei or cavities upon the rate of energy transfer, that is, upon the rate of bubble formation, is described in a similar manner. In the absence of roughness, of foreign particles, or of bubbles of dissolved gas coming out of solution, the vapor bubbles must form initially at very small size. For the stability of very small bubbles, very high superheats are necessary. The presence of nuclei or cavities reduces the necessary superheat by increasing the radius at which bubbles may be formed. An increase in the number and size of these bubble-formation centers promotes the transfer process and increases the q'' for a given Δt. This trend does not continue indefinitely, however; a rate of transfer is reached beyond which an increase in the number of surface irregularities seems to have little further effect. Many surfaces of practical importance apparently possess at least this minimum amount of roughness.

Another feature of the relation between the heating surface and the vaporizing liquid which has an important effect upon the transfer rate is the tendency of the liquid to wet the surface. It is evident that most of the energy of vaporization is transferred from the surface to the liquid and that vaporization occurs mainly at the bubble liquid surface; that is, the energy is first transferred from the surface to the liquid. This explanation of the process is consistent with the observation that an increased tendency of the liquid to wet the heating surface will produce a larger q'' at a given Δt. It is clear from consideration of convection processes that the flux at a point covered by liquid will be higher than at a point covered by vapor. Wetting agents added to water, such as detergents, increase the transfer rate. Surface coatings, such as mineral oil and chrome plating, reduce the transfer rate by reducing the wetting tendency, by covering surface irregularities, and by adding resistance to heat transfer.

Effects of Other Variables on Flux. The curve of q'' versus Δt presented in Fig. 9-1 was determined for a horizontal wire. Numerous experimental investigations have indicated that the same kinds of vaporization processes occur on, and that the same form of q'' curve applies to, various heating-surface arrangements, such as horizontal and vertical plates, wires, and tubes. The value of the peak q'' and the Δt at which it is found are approximately the same for various arrangements and tube diameters. However, the diameter of the horizontal cylinder has been found to affect the level of the curve in the convection-vaporization and film-boiling ranges. The effect is a lower q'' for a given Δt for larger diameters. The equations used for the prediction of transfer rates have this same characteristic; see, for example, the natural-convection equation for moderate values of

$N_{Gr}N_{Pr}$. The effect of diameter on q'' is evidently not so great in the nucleate range.

Higher rates of transfer may, under certain conditions, be obtained by inducing a liquid velocity across the heating surface. Several investigations indicate that higher rates may be expected for convection vaporization processes. This result would be predicted by the equations for the natural- and forced-convection processes on a cylinder. No considerable velocity

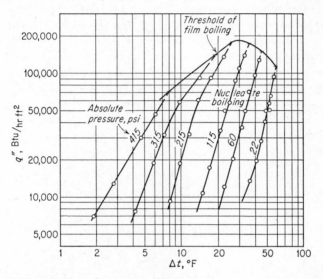

FIG. 9-2. Nucleate boiling of n-pentane (90 per cent pure) on a horizontal chrome-plated disk. [*From Cichelli and Bonilla* (1945).]

effect was found in the region of vigorous nucleate boiling. If velocities high enough to produce cavitation were used, the transfer rates decreased.

Although most investigations have concerned themselves with single heating surfaces, some data have been presented for banks of tubes. The indication is that the rate is decreased when the surfaces are arranged sufficiently close to cause a damping of liquid currents in convection vaporization. Similarly, for nucleate boiling, lower rates may be expected if upper surfaces are arranged in such a way that they are blanketed by the vapor formed on lower surfaces. If the separation of the various heating surfaces is large, no effect is expected.

For a given substance and heating-surface arrangement the magnitude of q'' for a given Δt depends upon the pressure level and, therefore, upon the temperature level at which the vaporization process occurs. The transfer rates for both the convection and the film-boiling processes are predicted with fair accuracy from equations developed by consideration of simple conduction, convection, and radiation processes. Therefore, the effect of pressure upon convection and film-boiling transfer rates can be looked upon as a result merely of the temperature dependence of the liquid and vapor properties which are important in the conduction, convection, and radiation processes. The effect of the temperature of the liquid is indicated by its effect upon the properties entering the equations.

For nucleate boiling, however, no generally satisfactory theory exists, and the large effect of pressure cannot be reliably predicted. Many investigators have published data taken at various pressure levels for many technically important pure substances and solutions. The typical results are summarized qualitatively as follows. For a given substance, higher pressure results in higher values of q'' at a given Δt. The Δt at which convection vaporization is supplanted by nucleate boiling decreases with increasing pressure. The peak q'' increases with pressure to a maximum and then decreases. The Δt at the peak q'' decreases with increasing pressure. Typical examples of behavior in this range are shown in Figs. 9-2 and 9-3.

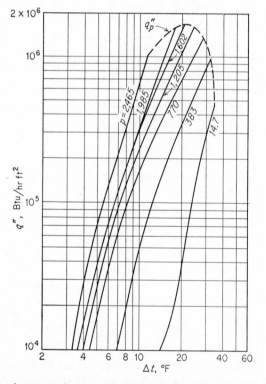

FIG. 9-3. Effect of pressure for water boiling on a horizontal 0.024-in. platinum wire. [*From McAdams* (1954).]

9-3. CORRELATIONS FOR SATURATED-LIQUID VAPORIZATION

Numerous data indicate that the conventional convection equations predict convection vaporization transfer rates with sufficient accuracy in the limited range of Δt for which a convection process is found. Vaporization transfer information is often presented in the form of q'' as a function of Δt. The empirical equations for laminar and turbulent natural convection are shown below converted to this form.

$$q'' = 0.59 \frac{k}{L} \Delta t (N_{Gr} N_{Pr})^{\frac{1}{4}} \tag{9-1}$$

$$q'' = 0.13 \frac{k}{L} \Delta t (N_{Gr} N_{Pr})^{\frac{1}{3}} \tag{9-2}$$

Since N_{Gr} contains Δt to the first power, the value of q'' varies with Δt to the 5/4 and 4/3, respectively. No general method is available for the prediction of the Δt at which the convection equations are no longer applicable. Jakob (1949) has indicated that the transition occurs at somewhat above $N_{Gr} N_{Pr} = 10^9$ for several experiments with water and carbon tetrachloride on vertical and horizontal surfaces. However, the upper limit of convection does not correspond in general to a fixed value of $N_{Gr} N_{Pr}$.

Nucleate Boiling. At higher temperature differences nucleate boiling is encountered, and the value of q'' for a given substance and pressure level varies over a wide range. The value of q'' varies sharply with Δt; for most data it varies with Δt to the third to fifth power up to the region of peak flux. As a result, the surface coefficient h varies with Δt to the second to fourth power. A considerable amount of data has been collected concerning the relation between q'' and Δt in the nucleate range for a large number of important substances over wide ranges of pressure. Several examples of such data from the work of Cichelli and Bonilla (1945) and Addoms (1948) are shown in Figs. 9-2 and 9-3. The effect of pressure on q'' for pure substances and even for solutions is generally as shown in the figures; q'' at a given Δt increases with pressure and, therefore, also with temperature.

The data obtained in numerous early investigations were summarized in the form

$$q'' = C \Delta t^n \tag{9-3}$$

where values of C and n were given for a particular substance and pressure level. An example of such an expression is quoted in Jakob (1949) for water boiling on a horizontal surface at atmospheric pressure. The value of C is 0.168 and of n is 4.0 when q'' and Δt are expressed in the usual units of Btu/ft^2 hr and degrees Fahrenheit.

Many attempts have been made to arrive at a general method of relating q'' and Δt, or q'' and h, which would be applicable to at least a group of substances. Several efforts have begun with a grouping of the variables believed to be relevant into dimensionless ratios by the technique of dimensional analysis. Then the nature of the relation between these dimensionless groups was sought by an analysis of the available data. Certain other investigations were based upon a theory of the nature of the nucleate-boiling process. By this means certain additional variables were shown to be important, and relations between the variables have been studied. As a result of such efforts a number of relations have been presented which involve an empirical quantity which is different for different surface-liquid combinations and must be evaluated from experiment. For examples of such results, see Jakob (1949) and Rohsenow (1952). However, these correlations are not sufficiently accurate to be of general use. Certain empirical equations have been presented which correlate reasonably well the data for a particular group of substances at particular pressures. However, the value of such empirical relations is not great, because the limits of their applicability cannot be predicted and because such relations do not account for the effect of pressure upon q''.

Film Boiling. The nucleate-boiling region ends at the critical value of temperature difference Δt_c, where the peak flux q_p'' is found. No general relation is available for the range of Δt immediately beyond Δt_c, and relatively little information has been presented for this range. However, for the region beyond the minimum, where the film is very stable and where radiation becomes important, numerous measurements have been made. An example of such data is shown in Fig. 9-1 in region c-d.

A theory has been developed by Bromley (1950) for a stable-film process. This theory assumes a transfer by conduction and radiation to the liquid-vapor interface. The film coefficient for conduction on horizontal tubes, in the absence of radiation, is

$$h_{co} = C \left[\frac{ g h_{fv} k^3 v \rho_v (\rho_L - \rho_v) }{ D \mu_v \, \Delta t } \right]^{\frac{1}{4}} \tag{9-4}$$

The physical properties of the vapor are to be evaluated at the average film temperature, and h_{fv} is the difference between the enthalpy of the fluid and the vapor at the average vapor-film temperature. Since radiation does occur, the vapor film is thicker than that predicted from conduction alone. The true coefficient h_c is related to h_{co} and to the total coefficient h as follows:

$$h_c = h_{co} \left(\frac{h_{co}}{h}\right)^{\frac{1}{3}}$$ (9-5)

Therefore the total coefficient may be written as

$$h = h_c + h_r = h_{co} \left(\frac{h_{co}}{h}\right)^{\frac{1}{3}} + h_r$$ (9-6)

where h_r is the radiation coefficient defined in Sec. 5-6. This expression is solved by successive approximations for h after values of h_{co} and h_r have

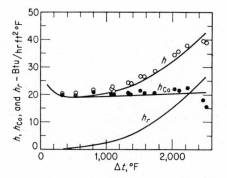

Fig. 9-4. Film boiling of liquid nitrogen on an electrically heated carbon tube of 0.35 in. diameter. [From Bromley (1950).]

been computed for the process in question. However, in the lower Δt range, where h_r is less than h_{co}, Eq. (9-6) may be replaced by the following relation. Equation (9-6) and (9-7) agree within 5 per cent under these conditions.

$$h = h_{co} + \tfrac{3}{4} h_r$$ (9-7)

The above theory and correlation have been compared with film-boiling data obtained at atmospheric pressure for a number of substances, including benzene, carbon tetrachloride, water, n-pentane, and nitrogen on carbon tubes of various diameters. The experiments were carried out over a wide range of Δt; values up to 2500°F were encountered. Figure 9-4, taken from Bromley (1950), shows values of h obtained from experiment and values of h_{co} calculated from Eq. (9-6), using h and values of h_r calculated from radiation considerations. The curve of h_{co} is calculated from Eq. (9-4), with $C = 0.62$, and the curve of h is drawn according to Eq. (9-6) from computed values of h_{co} and h_r. Actual coefficients agree closely with computed ones for a choice of $C = 0.62$ in Eq. (9-4). However, data for very small diameter wires (0.004 to 0.024 in.) indicate values of h considerably above those given by the foregoing equations [see McAdams et al. (1948)].

Example 9-1. As a demonstration of the use of the results of the analysis of stable-film-boiling transfer rates discussed above, let us compute the transfer rate for water at atmospheric-pressure boiling on an electrically heated 0.040-in.-diameter horizontal wire at a Δt of 1500°F. This result may be compared with the rate measured by Farber and Scorah (1948) and presented in Fig. 9-1.

For water at 212°F and steam at $212 + 750 = 962$°F, the properties in usual units are

$h_{fv} = 1513.8 - 180.07 = 1333.7$ Btu/lb

$k_v = 0.0337$ Btu/hr ft °F $\rho_v = 0.0173$ lb/ft^3

$\mu_v = 0.066$ lb/hr ft $\rho_L = 59.8$ lb/ft^3

$$h_{co} = 0.62 \left[\frac{4.17 \times 10^8 \times 1333.7 \times (0.0337)^3 \times 0.0173 \times 59.8}{(0.040/12) \times 0.066 \times 1500} \right]^{\frac{1}{4}} = 56 \text{ Btu/hr ft}^2 \text{ °F}$$

Equation (5-39) may be used for h_r if the reflectivity of the liquid surface is taken as zero. ϵ_1 is taken as 1.0.

$T_f = 460 + 212 = 672$°R $T_1 = 2172$°R

$$h_r = \frac{\sigma \epsilon_1 (T_1{}^4 - T_f{}^4)}{T_1 - T_f} = \frac{0.1713 \times 1.0[(21.72)^4 - (6.72)^4]}{2172 - 672} = 25.1 \text{ Btu/hr ft}^2 \text{ °F}$$

From Eq. (9-7) the value of h may be found:

$$h = 56 + \tfrac{3}{4} \times 25.1 = 74.8 \text{ Btu/hr ft}^2 \text{ °F}$$

Therefore, $q'' = h \, \Delta t = 74.8 \times 1500 = 112{,}000$ Btu/hr ft^2

The value from Fig. 9-1 at $\Delta t = 1500$°F is 100,000 Btu/hr ft^2.

9-4. PEAK-FLUX CORRELATIONS

Information concerning the magnitude of the peak flux q_p'' and the temperature difference at which it occurs, Δt_c, is of value for the design of heat exchangers in which boiling processes occur. Often a minimum area and size of heat exchanger will result from a design which will operate near or at the peak-flux point. A considerable amount of data has been collected concerning the values of q_p'' and Δt_c for many substances of technical interest. For some of these substances, values of q_p'' and Δt_c have been determined over a wide range of pressures between zero and the critical pressure p_c. A selection of typical peak-flux information is contained in Table 9-1.

Several efforts have been made to determine a general method whereby peak-flux values and the associated temperature differences can be pre-

Table 9-1. Observed Peak Heat-transfer Rates for Various Liquids,
Pool-boiling on Submerged Heaters

Liquid	Pressure, psia	Liquid temperature, °F	Peak flux q_p'', Btu/hr ft^2	Critical temperature difference Δt_c, °F	Heater surface and condition	Reference
Water	14.7	212	993,000	99.9	0.040-in.-diameter	a
	64.7	297	906,000	39.5	horizontal Chromel	a
	114.7	337	1,590,000	12.8	C wire	a
	14.7	212	210,000	42	0.004-in.-diameter clean platinum wire	b
	14.7	212	380,000	42	0.008-, 0.016-, and 0.024-in.-diameter clean platinum wire	b
Propane, comm. grade	555	196.8	36,200	6.1		c
Ethyl alcohol	14.7	172.6	192,500	53.2	Clean surface; horizontal plate, electroplated with 0.002-in. chromium, polished	c
	375	379.3	350,000	22.6		c
	657	432.2	261,000	10.0		c
n-Pentane, 90+% pure	170	272.2	191,100	42.9		c
	457	375.5	42,000	5.3		c
n-Heptane, 70+% pure	14.7	...	109,000	...		c
	50	...	157,000	...		c
	215	...	205,000	...	Dirty surface; horizontal plate, electroplated with 0.002-in. chromium, polished	c
Benzene, c.p. grade	14.7	...	139,000	...		c
	355	...	269,000	...		c
	667	...	57,000	...		c

[a] Farber and Scorah (1948).
[b] McAdams et al. (1948).
[c] Cichelli and Bonilla (1945).

dicted for various substances and pressure levels. Cichelli and Bonilla (1945) found, for many pure substances and mixtures, that q_p'' increased with pressure until the pressure level reached about one-third of the critical pressure. The q_p'' decreased toward zero with a further increase in pressure. Further, at any given reduced pressure p/p_c, the value of the peak flux divided by the critical pressure, q_p''/p_c, was about the same for a number of organic substances, including ethanol, propane, benzene, and n-pentane. It was concluded, therefore, that q_p''/p_c would depend only upon p/p_c. The resulting relation is shown in Fig. 9-5. This correlation is also approximately valid for many other pure substances and mixtures. The value of Δt_c was noted to be dependent more upon the reduced pressure at which the process occurs than upon the substance. This approximately valid relation is shown as the dashed curve in Fig. 9-5. The Δt_c decreases from a high value at small reduced pressures toward zero at the critical pressure. Some deviations from the Cichelli and Bonilla correlation have been reported. For example, from Kazakova (1951) and from the previous discussions in this chapter it is clear that, even for a given substance and pressure, q_p'' depends somewhat upon such independent factors as the nature and material of the heating surface. However, the relations shown in the figure are still valuable when exact, specific information is lacking.

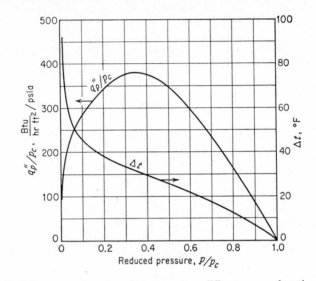

FIG. 9-5. Peak heat-transfer rate and temperature difference as a function of reduced pressure. [*Adapted from information contained in Cichelli and Bonilla* (1945).]

Another method of relating peak flux to pressure and other physical properties is cited in McAdams (1954). In this approach $q''_p/h_{fg}\rho_v(g\alpha)^{\frac{1}{3}}$ was plotted against $(p_L - \rho_v)/\rho_v$, where α is the thermal diffusivity of the liquid. Numerous experimental points for water, n-propane, n-pentane, n-heptane, benzene, and ethanol lay close to a single smooth curve.

Zuber (1958) presents a theory for peak flux based upon the condition for intolerable interference between ascending vapor and descending liquid. The following relation is in close agreement with the data of a number of investigators:

$$q_p'' = \frac{\pi}{24} h_{fg}\rho_v \left[\frac{\sigma g(\rho_L - \rho_v)}{\rho_v^2}\right]^{\frac{1}{4}} \left(\frac{\rho_L + \rho_v}{\rho_L}\right)^{\frac{1}{2}} \tag{9-8}$$

A suggested relation for the minimum flux in the region of transition to film boiling is

$$q_m'' = \frac{\pi}{24} h_{fg} \rho_v \left[\frac{\sigma g (\rho_L - \rho_v)}{(\rho_L + \rho_v)^2} \right]^{\frac{1}{4}} \tag{9-9}$$

where σ in Eqs. (9-8) and (9-9) is the liquid surface tension.

The foregoing correlations of peak flux indicate the means whereby a high heat flux may be obtained in heat-exchanger design. Large values of h_{fg}, ρ_v, g, and σ are desirable. Water has a very high value of h_{fg}. For any fluid, high pressures result in a large vapor density ρ_v. The acceleration g has an effect upon buoyancy. More effective liquid-vapor separation results from acceleration induced by flow or from accelerating the heat exchanger. Such an effect was studied by Siegel and Usiskin (1959) by taking motion pictures of a freely falling boiler. In the absence of gravity the bubbles remained in the vicinity of the heater, and the heat-transfer process was seriously impeded.

9-5. SURFACE BOILING IN SUBCOOLED LIQUIDS

In certain circumstances a boiling process is encountered in heating a liquid whose temperature is below the saturation temperature corresponding to the pressure level, that is, a subcooled liquid. Such a process may be expected on the portions of a heating surface which are at a temperature somewhat higher than the saturation temperature corresponding to the local pressure. This condition often occurs in heating slightly subcooled liquids or in heating liquids at a rapid rate, as by quenching a hot piece of metal. In the surface boiling of subcooled liquids, bubbles are formed at the surface, as in the nucleate and film processes previously discussed. However, as the bubbles rise into the cool liquid, because of their buoyancy, they tend to condense.

In processes in which such subcooled boiling is found, the heat-transfer rates are higher, often much higher, than the rate which would be expected for a convection process in the same circumstances. This is true whether the process is natural or forced convection. Usually the rate of transfer and the surface coefficient are even higher than those which would be found for a nucleate-boiling process of the saturated liquid under similar conditions. Transfer rates upward of 10^6 Btu/hr ft^2 have often been measured at moderate temperature differences—for example, 150°F. Gambill and Greene (1958) measured the heat flux for the subcooled boiling of water flowing in a helical manner in an electrically heated tube. High accelerations were obtained at high rotative velocities. Extremely large burnout fluxes were obtained. In one test, at 850 psia, a flux of 54.8×10^6 Btu/hr ft^2 was measured. The magnitude of this flux may be appreciated by comparing it with the radiant flux at the "surface" of the sun, which is of the order of 20×10^6 Btu/hr ft^2.

The kinds of boiling processes found for subcooled boiling are similar to those discussed for saturated liquids. At small Δt values, the surface is in contact with both liquid and vapor, and a nucleate process is found. A peak flux is encountered beyond which a vapor film blankets the surface.

The extraordinarily high flux obtained in subcooled liquid boiling evidently cannot be explained satisfactorily as simple convection in conjunction with an added mechanism for the transfer of energy from the region of the tube to the body of the liquid, that is, by the travel of vapor

TABLE 9-2. OBSERVED HEAT-TRANSFER RATES FOR THE SUBCOOLED BOILING OF WATER FLOWING OVER HEATED SURFACES

Veloc-ity,* fps	Pres-sure, psia	Temperatures, °F					Flux q'', Btu/hr ft^2	Heater surface and condition	Refer-ence
		Satu-ration	Aver-age heater surface	Liquid in	Liquid out	Sur-face minus satu-ration			
6.2	16	216	271	80	132	55	595,000		a
6.7	16	216	276	81	170	60	1,115,000		a
12.3	24.6	239	281	77	113	42	840,000		a
12.3	24.6	239	289	77	125	50	1,160,000		a
12.2	24.6	239	294	77	140	55	1,440,000	Water flowing upward in an electrically	a
12.3	63	296	315	77	113	21	840,000	heated stainless-steel	a
12.3	63	296	333	77	125	37	1,100,000	tube 0.587 in. in ID	a
12.4	63	296	342	77	139	46	1,440,000	and 17.6 in. long	a
6.9	110	334.8	347.8	81	126	13	580,000		a
6.9	110	334.8	355.3	81	144	20.5	825,000		a
6.9	110	334.8	360.8	81	165	26	1,090,000		a
6.6	168	367.5	388.5	81	169	21	1,080,000		a
6.6	202	382.5	401.5	81	168	19	1,080,000		a
4.0	30	250.3	291.6	200.3	...	41.3	480,000	Water flowing upward	b
4.0	30	250.3	297.7	200.3	...	47.4	730,000	in an annulus over a clean, electrically	b
4.0	30	250.3	305.1	200.3	...	54.8	1,090,000	heated stainless-steel	b
12.0	30	250.3	283.9	200.3	...	33.6	295,000	tube 0.25 in. in diam-eter; outside surface	b
12.0	30	250.3	290.0	200.3	...	39.7	510,000	of annulus formed by	b
12.0	30	250.3	297.0	200.3	...	46.7	830,000	various glass tubes 0.43 to 0.77 in. in ID	b

* For reference a, computed by dividing w/A by the density of the liquid at inlet.

[a] Kreith and Summerfield (1949).

[b] McAdams et al. (1949); temperature data are in slightly different form, converted to correspond with the form of the table.

bubbles which condense. Analysis of the number and size of bubbles indicates that this is not a large enough effect. The important effect is thought to be the disturbance of the liquid boundary layer on the heater due to the formation of bubbles at the liquid-heater interface.

There have been many recent contributions to the understanding of sub-cooled boiling. Data and correlations for transfer rates in forced flow over cylinders, inside circular and noncircular tubes, and in annuli have been presented. In addition, a considerable amount of information has been gathered concerning the burnout conditions for the flow of saturated and subcooled liquids inside vertical and horizontal tubes. These more specialized subjects are not discussed further here. A collection of subcooled-boiling heat-flux data is presented in Table 9-2.

NOTATION

g	local gravitational acceleration
h	total heat-transfer coefficient
h_c	"true" conduction coefficient
h_r	radiation surface coefficient
h_{co}	conduction coefficient
h_{fg}	latent heat of vaporization
h_{fv}	difference in enthalpy of liquid, and of vapor at the average film temperature
k	thermal conductivity
N_{Gr}	Grashof number
N_{Pr}	Prandtl number
p	pressure
q''	heat flux
t	temperature, °F or °C
v	specific volume
μ	absolute viscosity
ρ	density of mass
σ	liquid surface tension

REFERENCES

Addoms, J. N.: 1948: reported in McAdams, p. 382, 1954.

Bromley, L. A.: *Chem. Eng. Progr.*, vol. 46, p. 221, 1950.

Cichelli, M. T., and C. F. Bonilla: *Trans. AIChE*, vol. 41, p. 755, 1945.

Farber, E. A., and R. L. Scorah: *Trans. ASME*, vol. 70, p. 369, 1948.

Gambill, W. R., and N. D. Greene: *Chem. Eng. Progr.*, vol. 54, no. 10, p. 68, 1958.

Jakob, M.: "Heat Transfer," vol. 1, John Wiley & Sons, Inc., New York, 1949.

Kazakova, E. A.: Maximum Heat Transfer to Boiling Water at High Pressures: reported in *Engrs. Dig.*, vol. 12, p. 81, 1951.

Kreith, F., and M. Summerfield: *Trans. ASME*, vol. 71, p. 805, 1949.

McAdams, W. H.: "Heat Transmission," 3d ed., McGraw-Hill Book Company, Inc., New York, 1954.

McAdams, W. H., et al.: *Chem. Eng. Progr.*, vol. 44, p. 639, 1948.
———— et al.: *Ind. Eng. Chem.*, vol. 41, p. 1945, 1949.
Rohsenow, W. M.: *Trans. ASME*, vol. 74, p. 969, 1952.
Siegel, R., and C. Usiskin: *Trans. ASME*, ser. C, vol. 81, p. 230, 1959.
Zuber, N.: *Trans. ASME*, vol. 80, p. 711, 1958.

PROBLEMS

1. Construct a plot of flux vs. temperature difference for the convection vaporization of water at atmospheric pressure. Heat is supplied from an electrically heated horizontal tube $\frac{1}{4}$ in. in diameter.

2. Plot q'' versus Δt for Δt values from 1 to 10°F for the convection vaporization of water at 1, 2, 5, and 10 atmospheres with a horizontal heating tube $\frac{1}{4}$ in. in diameter.

3. Repeat Prob. 1 for saturated water at 1 atmosphere for heating-tube diameters of 0.05, 0.10, 0.5, and 1.0 in.

4. Consider the pool vaporization of water at atmospheric pressure on the surface of a vertical, electrically heated plate of 6 in. diameter. Plot q'' versus Δt from 1 to 40°F, assuming convection vaporization in the lower part and nucleate boiling in the higher part of the Δt range. At what Δt and value of $N_{Gr}N_{Pr}$ is the same rate found?

5. Estimate the rate of heat transfer per unit area and unit length for the vaporization of saturated water at 25.0 psia by an electrically heated horizontal cylinder 0.5 in. in diameter. The surface temperature of the cylinder is to be 2000°F. The cylinder surface may be assumed black.

6. For benzene, n-pentane, carbon tetrachloride, and water, estimate the peak flux and critical temperature difference for pool boiling on a flat surface at 1 and 20 atmospheres pressure.

7. A small shell-and-tube heat exchanger is to be designed for the vaporization of 12,700 lb/hr of propane at 143 psia. The tubes are to be horizontal, and hot water will be circulated through them in a parallel arrangement. There will be 10 tubes, 0.760 in. ID and 0.840 in. OD, arranged randomly, not in vertical tiers.

For saturated propane at 143 psia,

$$\rho_L = 30.70 \qquad \rho_v = 1.30 \qquad t = 80°F \qquad h_{fg} = 146$$

The critical temperature and pressure of propane are 206°F and 619 psia.

a. What temperature level of the outside surface of the tubes would result in the minimum exchanger length? Estimate this length.

b. For the length computed in part *a*, a heat flux of 150,000 Btu/ft² based upon outside surface, and an outside surface temperature of 110°F, determine the Reynolds number required on the water side for a mean temperature difference from water to inside surface of 60°F. Compute the amount of water required per hour.

c. For the rate of flow found in part *b*, estimate the pressure loss through the tubes of the exchanger.

8. For the saturated pool boiling of water on a small horizontal plate, plot the peak flux for nucleate boiling vs. absolute pressure for the range 1.5 to 100 psia. The surface tension of water is

$$\sigma = 5.3 \times 10^{-3}(1 - 0.0025t)$$

where σ is in pounds per foot and t is in degrees centigrade.

CHAPTER 10

Heat Transfer with Vapor Condensation

10-1. CONDENSATION PROCESSES

A vapor in contact with a surface at a temperature lower than the saturation temperature corresponding to the vapor pressure will condense. The condensate thus formed will be somewhat subcooled by contact with the cooled surface, and more vapor will condense on the exposed surface and upon the previously formed condensate. There are two distinctly different kinds of condensation processes, and the type found in any particular instance depends primarily upon the behavior of the condensate on the cooled surface. If the condensate tends to wet the surface and thereby forms a liquid film, the process is called film condensation. If the condensate does not tend to wet the surface, but instead collects in growing droplets on the cooled surface, the process is called dropwise condensation. Both types of condensation process are common, and in many circumstances both types may be encountered in a single piece of apparatus.

In a dropwise-condensation process only a part of the surface is covered with condensate. The droplets grow, break away, and then run down the surface, knocking off other droplets as they go. The result of the good contact between vapor and the cooling surface and of the extended-surface effect due to the droplets is that very high transfer rates are found in the dropwise processes. Fluxes of the order of 250,000 Btu/hr ft² have often been obtained, and at quite low temperature differences. However, if the condensate forms a film over the cooling surface, the process is quite different. Any new condensate formed joins the liquid film, which is being drained by gravity. The heat transferred to the cooling surface must come to this face through the liquid film by conduction and convection from the opposite face, which is in contact with the vapor. This conduction-convection process may greatly impede the over-all transfer process, depending upon the thickness and turbulence of the liquid film. Therefore, one would expect lower transfer rates for film condensation than for dropwise condensation, and experimentally determined rates show that this is the case.

Since dropwise condensation is a much more effective transfer process, considerable study and experiment have been devoted to attempts to determine the mechanism of the process and the conditions under which it will occur. Many attempts have been made to discover or perfect "promoters" which, when added to the vapor or applied to the surface, will ensure dropwise condensation. These matters are further discussed in Sec. 10-7.

10-2. THE THEORY OF LAMINAR FILM CONDENSATION

Most condensation processes encountered in actual equipment are filmwise or mixed in character. Therefore, a study of film condensation takes on a special importance, because a developed, complete, laminar film will give the lowest flux one would have to contend with in designing equipment. Almost any departure from a simple film process will give a higher flux at a given Δt.

The physical nature of the laminar film-condensation process is well understood. Nusselt described the process in 1916 and analyzed condensation processes occurring under several different geometric and vapor velocity conditions. Many of the predictions of Nusselt's results are in good agreement with experiment.

The theory of the behavior of the liquid film is as follows. In steady state the film of condensate flows down the surface in laminar motion under the influence of gravity. The increase in mass flow between successive locations is due to the vapor condensed on the film surface between. Since the liquid film is in good thermal contact with the cooling surface, the inside film face has the temperature of the cooling surface, t_o. All resistance to heat flow is assumed to be in the liquid film and, therefore, the liquid-vapor interface temperature is taken equal to the saturation temperature of the vapor, t_v. Since the flow is laminar, the transfer process is one of conduction through the film. We observe at this point that, since the film thickness varies from point to point, the flux, and therefore the surface coefficient, will vary over the cooling surface. Another observation concerning such a film is that surface-tension effects are not important if the cooled surface is of appreciable size. These assumptions, along with certain other special ones, are sufficient for the development of expressions for the local surface coefficients for various types of surfaces, such as plates and horizontal cylinders.

In subsequent sections, two relatively simple cases are considered: the inclined (or vertical) plate and the horizontal cylinder. The heat-transfer characteristics are determined by the simplified methods of analysis developed by Nusselt. Then the results of recent boundary-layer analyses are given.

10-3. LAMINAR FILM CONDENSATION ON FLAT PLATES AND HORIZONTAL CYLINDERS

Consider a flat plate of length L whose exposed face is at a uniform temperature t_o and which is inclined at an angle ϕ with the horizontal, as shown in Fig. 10-1. Let Y be the condensate-film thickness at distance x along the plate from the upper edge. The analysis will be carried out for a small layer of fluid, dx thick, perpendicular to the plate, as shown in Fig. 10-1, and of unit width across the plate. The subsection of this layer from y to Y will be considered in the balance of forces. Vapor condenses upon the exposed surface, and heat is conducted from this surface through the film to the plate. The local film coefficient h_x will be k/Y if a linear temperature distribution is assumed. The mass rate of flow in the film, $\dot{M}$, increases with x by the amount of the vapor condensed upon the surface. The mass-flow rate at $x = 0$ is zero. The balance of forces on the layer from y to Y must consider the component of the gravity force parallel to the plate on a mass of $\rho(Y - y)\, dx$, that is, $\rho(g/g_o)(Y - y)\, dx \sin \phi$. A partially balancing force is present as a result of the difference in pressure between the upper and lower faces of the element due to the hydrostatic effect in the surrounding vapor. The magnitude of this force is $\rho_v(g/g_o)$ $(Y - y) \sin \phi\, dx$. The other force is the shear force due to the velocity gradient du/dy, where u is the velocity parallel to the plate at x and at a

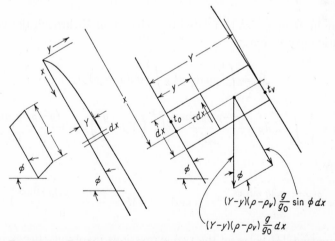

FIG. 10-1.   Condensation upon the upper face of an inclined plate.

distance of y from the plate surface. For laminar flow this shear force is $\tau\, dx = \dfrac{\mu}{g_o}\dfrac{du}{dy}\, dx$, where τ is the viscous shear stress, force per unit area. The Nusselt analysis neglects acceleration. Therefore, the sum of the forces parallel to the plate must be zero:

$$\rho\,\frac{g}{g_o}\,(Y - y)\, dx \sin \phi = \rho_v\,\frac{g}{g_o}\,(Y - y) \sin \phi\, dx + \frac{\mu}{g_o}\frac{du}{dy}\, dx$$

or

$$du = \frac{(\rho - \rho_v)g}{\mu}\,(Y - y) \sin \phi\, dy$$

Integrating this from $y = 0$, $u = 0$ to y where $u = u$, we have

$$u = \frac{(\rho - \rho_v)g \sin \phi}{\mu}\left(Yy - \frac{y^2}{2}\right)$$

The above expression shows that the velocity distribution is parabolic. Now the amount of heat transferred between $x - dx/2$ and $x + dx/2$, that is, dq, is approximately $(k/Y)\, dx\,(t_v - t_o)$, and this is closely equal to the rate of vapor condensation on the film-vapor interface between $x - dx/2$ and $x + dx/2$ times the latent heat of vaporization, h_{fg}. But the rate of condensation on the surface is equal to the difference in mass-flow rate at $x - dx/2$ and $x + dx/2$, that is, $d\dot{M}$. Therefore,

$$dq = \frac{k}{Y}\, dx\,(t_v - t_o) = h_{fg}\, d\dot{M} \qquad \text{or} \qquad d\dot{M} = \frac{k(t_v - t_o)}{Y h_{fg}}\, dx$$

A change in $\dot{M}$ may also be related to a change in Y through the velocity-distribution expression:

$$\dot{M} = \int_0^Y \rho u\, dy = \rho \int_0^Y u\, dy = \rho Y u_{av}$$

$$u_{av} = V = \frac{1}{Y}\int_0^Y u\, dy = \frac{(\rho - \rho_v)g \sin \phi}{\mu Y}\int_0^Y \left(Yy - \frac{y^2}{2}\right) dy = \frac{(\rho - \rho_v)g \sin \phi\, Y^2}{3\mu}$$

Therefore,

$$\dot{M} = \frac{\rho(\rho - \rho_v)g \sin \phi}{3\mu}\, Y^3 \qquad \text{and} \qquad d\dot{M} = \frac{\rho(\rho - \rho_v)g \sin \phi}{\mu}\, Y^2\, dY$$

By eliminating $d\dot{M}$ between the two expressions involving this quantity, a differential relation between Y and x is obtained:

$$dM = \frac{k\, dx(t_v - t_o)}{Yh_{fg}} = \frac{\rho(\rho - \rho_v)g\sin\phi}{\mu} Y^2\, dY$$

and
$$Y^3\, dY = \frac{k\mu(t_v - t_o)}{\rho(\rho - \rho_v)gh_{fg}\sin\phi}\, dx$$

Integrating from $x = 0$ where $Y = 0$ to (x,Y) to obtain a relation between x and Y, we have

$$\frac{Y^4}{4} = \frac{k\mu(t_v - t_o)}{\rho(\rho - \rho_v)gh_{fg}\sin\phi}\, x \quad \text{or} \quad Y = \left[\frac{4k\mu(t_v - t_o)x}{\rho(\rho - \rho_v)gh_{fg}\sin\phi}\right]^{\frac{1}{4}} \quad (10\text{-}1)$$

The Nusselt analysis assumes a linear variation of temperature through the liquid layer, from t_v to t_o. Therefore, the value of the local surface coefficient h_x is

$$h_x = \frac{k}{Y} = \left[\frac{\rho(\rho - \rho_v)k^3 gh_{fg}\sin\phi}{4\mu(t_v - t_o)}\right]^{\frac{1}{4}} \left(\frac{1}{x}\right)^{\frac{1}{4}} \quad (10\text{-}2a)$$

Written in terms of a local Nusselt number, this becomes

$$\frac{h_x x}{k} = N_{\text{Nu},x} = \left[\frac{(\rho - \rho_v)gc_p x^3 \sin\phi}{4\nu k}\right]^{\frac{1}{4}} \left[\frac{h_{fg}}{c_p(t_v - t_o)}\right]^{\frac{1}{4}} \quad (10\text{-}2b)$$

For a plate of length L, the value of h_x is averaged to give h, the average surface coefficient for the plate:

$$h = \frac{1}{L}\int_0^L h_x\, dx = \frac{1}{L}\int_0^L h_L \left(\frac{L}{x}\right)^{\frac{1}{4}} dx = \tfrac{4}{3}h_L$$

$$h = 0.943 \left[\frac{\rho(\rho - \rho_v)k^3 gh_{fg}\sin\phi}{L\mu(t_v - t_o)}\right]^{\frac{1}{4}} \quad (10\text{-}3a)$$

or
$$N_{\text{Nu}} = \frac{hL}{k} = 0.943 \left[\frac{(\rho - \rho_v)gc_p L^3 \sin\phi}{\nu k}\right]^{\frac{1}{4}} \left[\frac{h_{fg}}{c_p(t_v - t_o)}\right]^{\frac{1}{4}} \quad (10\text{-}3b)$$

The fluid properties k, ρ, and μ appearing in Eqs. (10-2) and (10-3) apply to the film and are, therefore, the properties of the liquid. If the properties

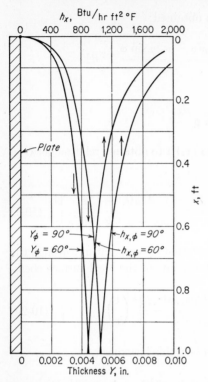

FIG. 10-2. Local surface coefficient and film thickness for the laminar film condensation of steam on a plate.

vary across the film because of the temperature gradient, an average value should be used.

Although the foregoing analysis was proposed specifically for the upper side of a flat plate, certain other cases are included as well. Condensation on the lower side of an inclined plate is similar when the inclination is small or when the film is sufficiently thin. The development is also valid for the inside and outside surfaces of vertical tubes if the tubes are large in diameter, compared with the film thickness. These results cannot be extended to inclined tubes, however. In such cases the film flow would not be parallel to the axis of the tube, and the effective angle of inclination would vary with x.

The variation of film thickness and the effect of its variation upon the local surface coefficient are plotted in Fig. 10-2. The thickness of the film and h_x are plotted perpendicular to the plate for a 1-ft-high plate at a surface temperature of 188°F for values of ϕ of 30 and 90°. The values are for steam condensing at 1 atmosphere pressure.

Example 10-1. Consider saturated steam at 7.5 psia condensing in a filmwise manner on a vertical plate 1 ft high whose surface is maintained at 160°F. Compute the average surface coefficient and minimum local coefficient predicted by the Nusselt theory. Calculate the heat-transfer rate per foot of plate width.

The average coefficient is given by Eq. (10-3a). The following property information is used:

$$t_v = 180°F \qquad\qquad k = 0.386 \text{ Btu/hr ft } °F$$

$$h_{fg} = 990.2 \text{ Btu/lb} \qquad\qquad \mu = 0.900 \text{ lb/hr ft}$$

$$\rho = 60.8 \text{ lb/ft}^3 \qquad\qquad g = 4.17 \times 10^8 \text{ ft/hr}^2$$

$$\sin \phi = 1 \qquad\qquad t_v - t_o = 180 - 160 = 20°F$$

$$h = 0.943 \left[\frac{(60.8)^2 \times (0.386)^3 \times 4.17 \times 10^8 \times 990.2 \times 1}{1 \times 0.900 \times 20} \right]^{\frac{1}{4}}$$

$$= 0.943(4.87 \times 10^{12})^{\frac{1}{4}} = 1400 \text{ Btu/hr ft}^2 \ °F$$

The local value is given by Eqs. (10-2), and h_x is a minimum when x, or Y, is a maximum. The largest value of x is at L, or 1 ft.

$$h_{min} = \left[\frac{k^3\rho(\rho - \rho_v)gh_{fg}\sin\phi}{4L\mu(t_v - t_o)}\right]^{\frac{1}{4}} = 1050 \text{ Btu/hr ft}^2 \text{ °F}$$

This is seen to be three-fourths of the value of h. The rate of heat transfer to the plate per foot of width is

$$q = hA\ \Delta t = 1400 \times 1 \times (180 - 160) = 28{,}000 \text{ Btu/hr ft}$$

Horizontal Cylinders. The procedure for condensation on the outside of a single horizontal cylinder is somewhat more complicated and is merely

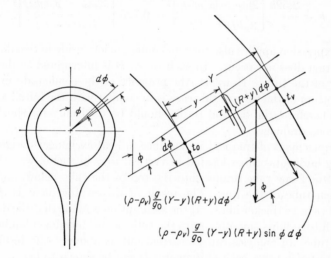

FIG. 10-3.   Condensation on the outside surface of a horizontal tube.

outlined here. The general equations and final results are given. Consider the circumstance shown in Fig. 10-3. The thickness Y is exaggerated for clarity. A balance of forces parallel to the surface yields

$$(\rho - \rho_v)\frac{g}{g_o}(Y - y)(R + y)\sin\phi\,d\phi = \frac{\mu}{g_o}\frac{du}{dr}(R + y)\,d\phi$$

and

$$du = \frac{(\rho - \rho_v)g(Y - y)\sin\phi}{\mu}\,dy$$

From this expression, u as a function of Y, y, and ϕ (and u_{av} as a function of Y and ϕ) may be found as before:

$$u = \frac{(\rho - \rho_v)g \sin \phi}{\mu}\left(Yy - \frac{y^2}{2}\right) \tag{10-4}$$

$$u_{av} = \frac{(\rho - \rho_v)g \sin \phi Y^2}{3\mu} \tag{10-5}$$

An energy balance upon the element of the film yields a differential relation between Y and ϕ. The integration of this relation and the determination of the local heat-transfer coefficient are discussed in Jakob (1949). The average coefficient for the tube is found to be

$$h = \frac{2.52k}{\pi}\left[\frac{2\rho(\rho - \rho_v)gh_{fg}}{3\mu kD(t_v - t_o)}\right]^{\frac{1}{4}} = 0.725\left[\frac{k^3\rho(\rho - \rho_v)gh_{fg}}{D\mu(t_v - t_o)}\right]^{\frac{1}{4}} \tag{10-6}$$

This expression applies also for film condensation inside horizontal tubes if separation does not occur. In such cases, D is interpreted as the inside diameter of the tube. However, the presence of the condensate in a pool at the bottom of the tube in this case is in conflict with the initial assumptions. Therefore, the derived result should be used only for short tubes having good drainage.

An arrangement of frequent importance in heat-exchanger design is one involving horizontal tubes located in vertical tiers in such a way that the condensate of one tube drains onto the top of the tube below, and so on down each tube of the tier. The result of this arrangement is that the lower tubes have thicker films. If the assumption is made that the drainage from each tube flows smoothly onto the tube below, forming a laminar film on that tube, an analysis can be carried out as above. The result for a vertical tier of n tubes each of diameter D can be shown to be

$$h = 0.725\left[\frac{k^3\rho(\rho - \rho_v)gh_{fg}}{nD\mu(t_v - t_o)}\right]^{\frac{1}{4}} \tag{10-7}$$

The value of h from this equation is the average surface coefficient for the n tubes. We note that h for four tubes is 70.7 per cent of that for a single tube of the same diameter under similar conditions.

Additional cases were considered by Nusselt in the original presentation of this theory of filmwise-condensation processes. The case of condensation on the inside surface of vertical tubes was analyzed for appreciable vapor velocities both up and down inside the tube. Since the liquid film is slow-moving, a significant vapor velocity produces a shear stress at the vapor-liquid interface. This shear stress will be upward for upflow and downward for downflow. This shear stress is evaluated from Eqs. (6-48) and (6-53a) by assuming that the velocity of the vapor-liquid interface is so small compared with the vapor velocity that it may be taken equal to zero. Therefore, the V in Eq. (6-53a) may be taken as the vapor velocity. The primary equations are quite complicated in these circumstances, and numerical solutions were obtained. This case is discussed further in Sec. 10-5.

The Film Reynolds Number. The foregoing expressions for average film coefficients for the three general cases considered, that is, Eqs. (10-3), (10-6), and (10-7), are in a convenient form for use as presented. However, in order to consider these equations from the point of view of a fluid flow process in the liquid film, it is convenient to transform them to a form which contains only dimensionless quantities. One of the desirable dimensionless quantities is the film Reynolds number, which is analogous to the Reynolds number defined for noncircular passages or open channels. The Reynolds number of the film at any location, in terms of the average film velocity V, is

$$N'_{\text{Re},f} = \frac{D_e V \rho}{\mu} = \frac{4 r_h V \rho}{\mu} = \frac{4 A V \rho}{P \mu}$$

where A is the area of flow, that is, $Y \times 1$ per unit width, and P is the shear perimeter, that is, 1 ft per unit width. Therefore,

$$N'_{\text{Re},f} = \frac{4 Y V \rho}{\mu} = \frac{4 \dot{M}}{\mu} \tag{10-8}$$

where $\dot{M}$ is the time rate of liquid flow in the film per unit width of surface, normal to the flow, at x on a flat plate or vertical tube or at ϕ on a horizontal tube. $N'_{\text{Re},f}$ is a local Reynolds number and increases down the surface.

The general form of Eqs. (10-3), (10-6), and (10-7) is

$$h = C \left[\frac{k^3 \rho (\rho - \rho_v) g h_{fg}}{\mu (t_v - t_o)} \left(\frac{\sin \phi}{Hn} \right) \right]^{\frac{1}{4}} \tag{10-9}$$

where, for example, H is the vertical dimension and $\sin \phi$ is not present for horizontal tubes.

Another relation among h, $(t_v - t_o)$, and the dimension of the surface may be obtained. Let us denote by Γ the mass rate of condensate flow at the lower edge of the surface per unit width of the surface. That is, $\Gamma = \dot{M}$ at the bottom of the surface. The heat-transfer area per unit width of surface is called A/W. The quantity A/W is equal to L for plates and vertical tubes. Now the rate of heat transfer indicated by h must equal the rate of energy released by condensation as indicated by Γ.

$$h \frac{A}{W} (t_v - t_o) = \Gamma h_{fg} \tag{10-10}$$

The value of A/W for vertical or inclined surfaces is $L \times 1 = L$, and for horizontal tubes it is $n\pi D$, or πD for a single tube. This interpretation for horizontal tubes means that Γ is the total rate of drainage off the bottom of the tube and therefore the sum of the rates of flow in the two films, one on each side of the tube. Eliminating $(t_v - t_o)$ from Eqs. (10-9) and (10-10), we have

$$h = C \left[\left(\frac{k^3 \rho (\rho - \rho_v) g h_{fg}}{\mu} \right) \left(\frac{\sin \phi}{Hn} \right) \left(\frac{h_m (A/W)}{\Gamma h_{fg}} \right) \right]^{\frac{1}{4}}$$

Upon dividing through by $h^{\frac{1}{4}}$, arranging a Reynolds number on the right, and raising each side to the $\frac{4}{3}$ power, we have

$$h^{\frac{3}{4}} = C \left[\left(\frac{k^3 \rho (\rho - \rho_v) g}{\mu^2} \right) \left(\frac{4(A/W) \sin \phi}{Hn} \right) \left(\frac{\mu}{4\Gamma} \right) \right]^{\frac{1}{4}}$$

$$h = C^{\frac{4}{3}} \left[\frac{k^3 \rho (\rho - \rho_v) g}{\mu^2} \right]^{\frac{1}{3}} \left[\frac{4(A/W) \sin \phi}{Hn} \right]^{\frac{1}{3}} \left(\frac{4\Gamma}{\mu} \right)^{-\frac{1}{3}}$$

The quantity $h[\mu^2/k^3 \rho (\rho - \rho_v) g]^{\frac{1}{3}}$ is dimensionless and is called the condensation number, and $4\Gamma/\mu$, the film Reynolds number, is the value of $N'_{Re,f}$ at the bottom of the surface. Therefore,

$$N_{Co} = C^{\frac{4}{3}} \left[\frac{4(A/W) \sin \phi}{Hn} \right]^{\frac{1}{3}} (N_{Re,f})^{-\frac{1}{3}}$$

Substituting in the values for A/W, C, and H which apply to vertical or inclined plates, we have

$$N_{Co} = 1.47 (\sin \phi)^{\frac{1}{3}} (N_{Re,f})^{-\frac{1}{3}} \tag{10-11}$$

For single or multiple horizontal tubes the result is

$$N_{Co} = 1.51 (N_{Re,f})^{-\frac{1}{3}} \tag{10-12}$$

These forms are often convenient because of the importance of the magnitude of the film Reynolds number in determining the heat-transfer rate in actual condensation processes.

Example 10-2. Saturated steam at 25 psia is to condense in a filmwise manner on the 200°F outside surface of a single 2-in.-diameter horizontal tube. Predict the rate of heat transfer per foot of length, the condensation number, and the film Reynolds number at the bottom of the tube.

From Eq. (10-7), the value of h may be found:

$$t_v = 240°F \qquad\qquad k = 0.394 \text{ Btu/hr ft °F}$$

$$h_{fg} = 952.1 \text{ Btu/lb} \qquad\qquad \mu = 0.655 \text{ lb/hr ft}$$

$$\rho = 59.63 \text{ lb/ft}^3 \qquad\qquad t_v - t_o = 240 - 200 = 40°F$$

$$h = 0.725 \left[\frac{k^3 \rho (\rho - \rho_v) g h_{fg}}{D\mu(t_v - t_o)} \right]^{\frac{1}{4}} = 1540 \text{ Btu/hr ft}^2 \text{ °F}$$

$$\frac{q}{L} = h\frac{A}{L}\Delta t = h\pi D(t_v - t_o) = \frac{1540 \times \pi \times 2 \times 40}{12} = 32{,}200 \text{ Btu/hr ft}$$

The value of N_{Co} may be found from h and the known properties; the $N_{Re,f}$ may be found from Eq. (10-12). An alternative approach, and the one followed here, is to find Γ from the known heat-transfer rate. Then $N_{Re,f}$ is found, and N_{Co} is computed from Eq. (10-12).

We note that

$$\frac{q}{L} = \Gamma h_{fg} \qquad \text{or} \qquad \Gamma = 33.8 \text{ lb/hr ft}$$

$$N_{Re,f} = \frac{4\Gamma}{\mu} = 206$$

$$N_{Co} = 1.51 \times 206^{-\frac{1}{3}} = 0.256$$

10-4. IMPROVED ANALYSES OF FILM CONDENSATION

The analysis discussed in the preceding section is based upon a number of assumptions which are questionable for many condensation processes of practical interest. Acceleration effects in the liquid film are ignored. The surface coefficient is evaluated by assuming a linear temperature distribution in the film. No allowance is made for the energy effect of liquid subcooling.

Bromley (1952) carried out an analysis similar to that of Sec. 10-3 without the assumption of a linear temperature distribution. An equation similar to (10-3) resulted. Rohsenow (1956) presented a similar analysis which dispensed with some of the approximations of Bromley's treatment. The results are identical with those of the Nusselt theory, Eqs. (10-2), (10-3), (10-6), and (10-7), except that h_{fg} in those relations is replaced by $h_{fg} + 0.68c_p(t_v - t_o)$, where c_p is the specific heat of the liquid. The correction $0.68c_p(t_v - t_o)$ is not negligible for some condensation processes. The resulting equation, written in terms of the local Nusselt number, is

$$N_{\text{Nu},x} = \left[\frac{(\rho - \rho_v)gc_p x^3}{4\nu k} \right]^{\frac{1}{4}} \left[0.68 + \frac{h_{fg}}{c_p(t_v - t_o)} \right]^{\frac{1}{4}} \tag{10-13}$$

Sparrow and Gregg (1959a and 1959b) applied the boundary-layer method of analysis to film condensation on isothermal vertical plates and horizontal cylinders. These analyses were carried out without any of the three assumptions listed in the first paragraph of this section. Solutions were obtained for the condensate Prandtl number range from 0.003 to 100. The analysis of the flat-plate case is discussed below.

The usual boundary-layer equations are written for the laminar condensate film on a vertical plate. The body force which appears in the force-balance equation is the liquid weight minus the vapor buoyancy effect. The coordinate system of Fig. 10-1 is employed. The boundary conditions result from no slip at the solid-liquid interface and from zero shear stress at the liquid-vapor interface. The equations and boundary conditions are written below:

$$\rho \left(u \frac{\partial u}{\partial x} + v \frac{\partial u}{\partial y} \right) = \mu \frac{\partial^2 u}{\partial y^2} + g(\rho - \rho_v) \tag{10-14}$$

$$\frac{\partial u}{\partial x} + \frac{\partial v}{\partial y} = 0 \tag{10-15}$$

$$\rho c_p \left(u \frac{\partial t}{\partial x} + v \frac{\partial t}{\partial y} \right) = k \frac{\partial^2 t}{\partial y^2} \tag{10-16}$$

at $y = 0$ $u = 0$ $v = 0$ $t = t_o$

at $y = Y$ $\dfrac{\partial u}{\partial y} = 0$ $t = t_v$

The equations are similar to those of natural convection but do not involve a coupling of the u and t distributions. The outer boundary condition is also different.

A stream function and similarity variable are introduced to reduce Eqs. (10-14) to (10-16) to ordinary differential equations. The results are given below:

$$\eta = \left[\frac{gc_p(\rho - \rho_v)}{4\nu k} \right]^{\frac{1}{4}} \frac{y}{\sqrt[4]{x}} = b \frac{y}{\sqrt[4]{x}} \tag{10-17}$$

$$F(\eta) = \frac{\psi}{\sqrt[4]{x^3}} \frac{1}{4\alpha b}$$

$$\phi(\eta) = \frac{t - t_v}{t_o - t_v}$$

(10-18)

$$F''' + \frac{1}{N_{\text{Pr}}} (3F''F - 2F'^2) + 1 = 0$$

(10-19)

$$\phi'' + 3F\phi' = 0$$

(10-20)

at $\eta = 0$ \qquad $F = 0$ \qquad $F' = 0$ \qquad $\phi = 1$

at $\eta = \eta_Y = \dfrac{bY}{\sqrt[4]{x}}$ \qquad $F'' = 0$ \qquad $\phi = 0$

The solution of Eqs. (10-19) and (10-20) depends upon the two parameters N_{Pr} and η_Y. The Prandtl number, which did not appear in the Nusselt analysis, is present here because of the allowance for liquid acceleration. The parameter η_Y depends upon the Prandtl number and upon the relative importance of liquid subcooling, as indicated by the quantity $c_p(t_v - t_o)/h_{fg}$. The heat-transfer results may be written in the following form:

$$\frac{N_{\text{Nu},x}}{\left[\dfrac{(\rho - \rho_v)gc_px^3}{4k\nu}\right]^{\frac{1}{4}} \left[\dfrac{h_{fg}}{c_p(t_v - t_o)}\right]^{\frac{1}{4}}} = f_1 \left[N_{\text{Pr}}, \frac{c_p(t_v - t_o)}{h_{fg}}\right]$$

(10-21)

Equations (10-19) and (10-20) were solved numerically for various values of the Prandtl number and for $c_p(t_v - t_o)/h_{fg}$ between 0 and 2. For large Prandtl numbers (10 and 100) the acceleration effects are negligible, and the Sparrow and Gregg results are in close agreement with those of Rohsenow [Eq. (10-13)]. However, for smaller Prandtl numbers the differences are substantial. The Nusselt, Rohsenow, and Sparrow and Gregg results for vertical plates are compared in Fig. 10-4.

The Sparrow and Gregg heat-transfer results for the circular cylinder may be conveniently presented in the following form:

$$\frac{N_{\text{Nu}}}{0.733 \left[\dfrac{\rho gh_{fg}D^3}{k\nu(t_v - t_o)}\right]^{\frac{1}{4}}} = f_2 \left[N_{\text{Pr}}, \frac{c_p(t_v - t_o)}{h_{fg}}\right]$$

(10-22)

where the Nusselt number is based upon the average surface coefficient. The function f_2 is essentially identical to f_1 in Eq. (10-21). Therefore,

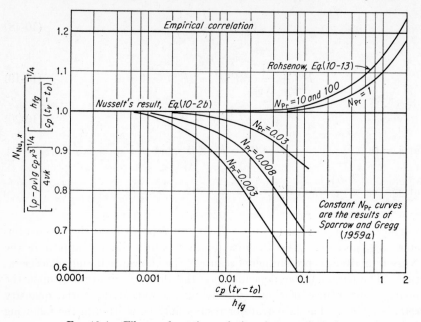

FIG. 10-4.   Film condensation; solutions for a vertical plate.

Fig. 10-4 may be used for horizontal cylinders as well when the ordinate is interpreted as the quantity on the left-hand side of Eq. (10-22).

Example 10-3.   We shall compare the local and average Nusselt numbers obtained from the Nusselt, Rohsenow, and Sparrow and Gregg analyses for saturated mercury vapor at 450°F condensing upon 1-ft-high vertical tubes of large diameter maintained at 350°F.   The relevant properties of mercury are

$$\mu = 1.01 \text{ cp} \qquad c_p = 0.0325 \text{ cal/g °C} \qquad k = 0.030 \text{ cal/sec cm °C}$$

$$h_{fg} = 127 \text{ Btu/lb}$$

$$N_{Pr} = \frac{0.0325 \times 1.01 \times 10^{-2}}{0.030} = 0.011$$

$$\frac{c_p(t_v - t_o)}{h_{fg}} = \frac{0.0325 \times 100}{127} = 0.0256$$

From Fig. 10-4 the local condensation parameter is 1.0 for the Nusselt and Rohsenow results and approximately 0.89 for the boundary-layer solution.   Therefore, the calculated local and average heat-transfer coefficients are 11 per cent less for the boundary-layer results.

10-5. CORRELATIONS OF EXPERIMENTAL RESULTS

The theories outlined in the preceding sections are in many respects satisfactory. Under certain conditions actual transfer rates and trends agree closely with those predicted from the theory, and the previously developed expressions may be used with confidence when smooth, low Reynolds number films are expected.

In many circumstances, however, actual transfer rates are substantially higher than predicted ones. These discrepancies arise mainly because the behavior of an actual film differs in certain respects from that assumed. In many actual processes mixed condensation occurs. Since dropwise processes give higher rates, higher average surface coefficients result. In addition, thinner films are found where film condensation occurs. Further, many actual films flow in a rippled manner. These ripples arise because of such disturbances as uneven, though small, vapor velocity or as a result of condensate drainage from higher surfaces. The effect of these ripples is to increase mixing in the film and to give a higher average surface coefficient because of local thinning of the film. The fact that the actual coefficients for vertical surfaces are very frequently higher than those predicted from Eq. (10-3a) has led to the suggestion by McAdams (1954) that the value of h in that equation be increased by 20 per cent. Equation (10-3a) is then written as

$$ h = 1.13 \left[\frac{k^3 \rho (\rho - \rho_v) g h_{fg}}{L \mu (t_v - t_o)} \right]^{\frac{1}{4}} \tag{10-23} $$

For vertical surfaces, Eq. (10-11) becomes

$$ N_{Co} = 1.88 (N_{Re,f})^{-\frac{1}{3}} \tag{10-24} $$

Film Turbulence. A more important deviation from the theory arises when the liquid film is thick enough for turbulent flow to arise. In a turbulent film, heat is transferred not only by conduction but also by eddy-diffusion processes. This second mechanism becomes very important in the turbulent film range, and in fact N_{Co} increases with increasing $N_{Re,f}$. In the laminar range, the trend is the opposite; note the negative exponent of $N_{Re,f}$ in Eq. (10-24). The film is typified by turbulent flow when the value of $N_{Re,f}$ exceeds about 1800. Therefore, for a value of $N_{Re,f} = 4\Gamma/\mu$, greater than 1800 for single film surfaces, such as vertical tubes and plates and inclined plates, a turbulent film may be expected on some portion of the surface. The rising trend may be seen in the right-hand portion of

Fig. 10-5. The line is the correlation of the data suggested by Kirkbride (1934). Its equation is

$$N_{Co} = 0.0076(N_{Re,f})^{0.4} \tag{10-25}$$

For horizontal tubes, turbulence will likewise be found at high values of $N'_{Re,f}$. A value of $N'_{Re,f}$ of 1800 would result in $N_{Re,f} = 3600$, because two films join at the bottom of the tube to give a total rate of flow of Γ. In most cases, however, $N_{Re,f}$ for single tubes is much less than 3600. For

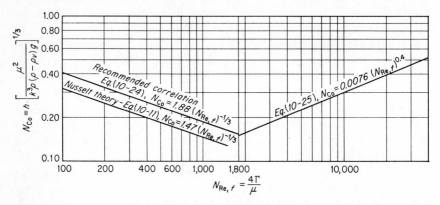

FIG. 10-5. Relations between the condensation and Reynolds numbers for vertical surfaces.

example, for atmospheric steam condensing on a single 2-in.-diameter tube with such an extreme temperature difference as $100°$, the value of $N_{Re,f}$ is 346. For a tier of tubes the Reynolds number may exceed 3600, and turbulence may result. For films involving turbulence, higher values of N_{Co} would be expected, and N_{Co} would increase with the Reynolds number.

The value of the Reynolds number for laminar films under various conditions and temperature differences may be derived by eliminating h from Eqs. (10-9) and (10-10). The result for vertical tubes and inclined plates is

$$N_{Re,f} = \frac{4\Gamma}{\mu} = 3.77 \left[\frac{k^3(t_v - t_o)^3 L^3 \rho(\rho - \rho_v)g \sin \phi}{\mu^5 h_{fg}{}^3} \right]^{\frac{1}{4}} \tag{10-26}$$

For horizontal tubes, we have

$$N_{Re,f} = \frac{4\Gamma}{\mu} = 9.11 \left[\frac{k^3(t_v - t_o)^3 n^3 D^3 \rho(\rho - \rho_v)g}{\mu^5 h_{fg}{}^3} \right]^{\frac{1}{4}} \tag{10-27}$$

Example 10-4. Given a vertical, 2-in.-OD tube whose outside surface is maintained at 140°F. Steam, saturated at 7.5 psia, is to condense in a filmwise manner on the outside surface. Predict the tube length which will produce turbulent film flow and estimate the average coefficient. Find the leaving film Reynolds number and average surface coefficient for a tube twice as long as the one for which turbulence first becomes important.

For $N_{Re,f} = 1800$, the values of N_{Co} and h may be found from Eq. (10-24):

$$N_{Co} = 1.88 \times 1800^{-\frac{1}{3}} = 0.155 = h\left(\frac{\mu^2}{k^3\rho^2 g}\right)^{\frac{1}{3}}$$

$$t_{av} = 160°F \quad \mu = 0.968 \text{ lb/hr ft} \quad \rho = 61.00 \text{ lb/ft}^3$$

$$k = 0.384 \text{ Btu/hr ft °F}$$

$$h = N_{Co}\left[\frac{k^3\rho(\rho - \rho_v)g}{\mu^2}\right]^{\frac{1}{3}} = 702 \text{ Btu/hr ft}^2 \text{ °F}$$

Now
$$\Gamma = \frac{1800\mu}{4} = \frac{hL\,\Delta t}{h_{fg}}$$

or
$$L = \frac{1800\mu h_{fg}}{4h\,\Delta t} = \frac{1800 \times 0.968 \times 990.2}{4 \times 702 \times 40} = 15.4 \text{ ft}$$

For the longer tube, 30.8 ft long, Eq. (10-25) is an estimate of the relation between h and Γ. One more relation may be written on an energy basis, as follows:

$$\Gamma h_{fg} = hL\,\Delta t$$

h may be eliminated from the two relations giving an equation in Γ:

$$\frac{\Gamma h_{fg}}{L\,\Delta t} = h = 0.0076\left[\frac{k^3\rho(\rho - \rho_v)g}{\mu^2}\right]^{\frac{1}{3}}\left(\frac{4\Gamma}{\mu}\right)^{0.4}$$

from which Γ is found as 1390 lb/hr ft.

$$N_{Re,f} = \frac{4 \times 1390}{0.968} = 5750$$

$$h = \frac{\Gamma h_{fg}}{L\,\Delta t} = \frac{1390 \times 990.2}{30.8 \times 40} = 1120 \text{ Btu/hr ft}^2 \text{ °F}$$

Effects of Vapor Velocity and Superheat. In preceding pages reference was made to results derived from the film theory by Nusselt for the case of an appreciable vapor velocity inside vertical tubes. Appreciable velocities introduce a shear stress at the vapor-liquid interface. The physical effect of upflow is to retard and thicken the liquid film, thereby reducing the average surface coefficient. Downflow thins the film and increases the coefficient. Jakob (1949) discusses the analytical solution and presents a comparison between the predicted and actual transfer rates over a range of velocity and $(t_v - t_o)$. The predictions are of the proper order of magnitude and have approximately the proper trends of change with velocity and $(t_v - t_o)$ but are in some cases considerably less than the observed rates. An example of the nature of the experimental results is the following empirical relation by Jakob (1936), which fits the data for saturated steam flowing into a 1.57-in.-ID tube 4 ft long at entrance velocities V_o between 30 and 260 fps. V_o is in feet per second and L is in feet.

$$h = \frac{1100 + 9.9V_o}{L^{\frac{1}{3}}} \qquad (10\text{-}28)$$

Another, more complicated condensation process arises when a super-heated vapor at temperature t contacts a surface at a temperature t_o less than the saturation temperature t_v corresponding to the pressure level. Condensation will still occur, but the presence of initial superheat introduces a complication into the analysis. The superheat of some of the vapor is removed by a convection process between the body of the vapor and the liquid film surface. The liquid film surface temperature may still be assumed to be approximately equal to the vapor saturation temperature t_v; a higher temperature would be inconsistent with the pressure level. The amount by which the film surface temperature is less than t_v depends upon how cold the surface is, as indicated by t_o. If $(t_v - t_o)$ is relatively small or if the convection process is vigorous, then the film surface temperature is close to t_v, and the previously presented equations would apply. Otherwise, a different and much more complicated approach from the theory is required.

Experimental results suggest that in most circumstances the effect of superheat may be ignored and that the equations for saturated vapors may be used for the prediction of surface coefficients with little error. It is necessary to emphasize that $(t_v - t_o)$ is still to be interpreted as the vapor saturation temperature minus the surface temperature and that the actual vapor temperature does not affect the calculations. Clearly, if t_o is greater than the vapor saturation temperature, no condensation occurs, and the process is merely desuperheating by convection.

10-6. INFLUENCE OF THE PRESENCE OF NONCONDENSABLE GASES

Greatly reduced rates of condensation have been observed when the condensable vapor is contaminated with even very small amounts of non-condensable gas. For example, for moderate temperature differences $(t_v - t_o)$, the surface coefficients obtained for pure and for contaminated vapor are in the ratio 2:1 or 3:1 with a contaminate concentration of as little as 1 per cent by volume. This large effect is present for both film- and dropwise-condensation processes. The effect of a change in contaminant concentration is large in the low-concentration range.

This effect is explained as follows. In the absence of noncondensable gases, the resistance to condensation is merely the resistance to the change of phase, that is, to the agglomeration of molecules into droplets or film. In a mixture with a noncondensable substance, another barrier is present. The vapor which is to condense must diffuse to the cooled surface through a layer of gas. That is, the noncondensable component is left at the surface, and the condensable vapor must diffuse from the main body of mixture to the region of the cold surface. The resistance to this diffusion process would be evidenced by a drop in the partial pressure of the condensable component across the region near the surface. For film condensation the result is that the temperature of the outside surface of the liquid film, t_v', would be lower than the bulk temperature of the mixture and less even than the saturation temperature corresponding to the vapor pressure of the condensable component in the bulk of the mixture. This is analogous to condensation at a lower pressure level. The local surface coefficient would be higher, because it is inversely proportional to the one-fourth power of the film Δt, that is, $h' \propto 1/(t_v' - t_o)^{\frac{1}{4}}$. However, q'' would be less because

$$q'' = h'(t_v' - t_o) \propto (t_v' - t_o)^{\frac{3}{4}}$$

Therefore, the local surface coefficient based upon $(t_v - t_o)$ would be less for any contamination because t_v' would always be less than t_v.

$$h = \frac{q''}{t_v - t_o} \propto \frac{(t_v' - t_o)^{\frac{3}{4}}}{t_v - t_o}$$

Since t_v' decreases with the amount of noncondensable gas, we should expect h to decrease also. Such a characteristic has been repeatedly observed.

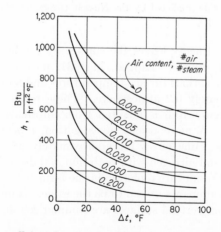

FIG. 10-6. Surface coefficient for air-contaminated steam at 2.85 psia condensing on a vertical surface. [*Adapted from Jakob* (1949).]

A theory for this type of condensation process is quite involved because a constant film-vapor interface temperature may not be assumed. The interface temperature would depend upon the thickness of the liquid film, and this thickness varies over the surface. The value of t_v' at a point would be the value which would result in an energy balance. Energy comes to the film surface by convection from the mixture and by diffusion of vapor

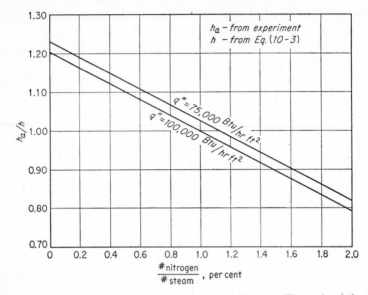

FIG. 10-7. The effect of the presence of noncondensable gas. The ratio of the actual coefficient h_a to the value predicted by the Nusselt theory for filmwise condensation. [*From Hampson* (1951).]

from the mixture. Energy leaves the surface by conduction through the film to the cooled surface. Langen, in 1931, measured heat fluxes on vertical surfaces for various surface temperatures and air concentrations in steam at approximately 0.2 atmosphere. These results are discussed in Jakob (1949). Figure 10-6 is adapted from information for a vertical surface 1 m high. A more recent investigation, reported by Hampson (1951), studied the same effect for approximately atmospheric-pressure mixtures of steam and nitrogen with both film and dropwise condensation. When the reported results are replotted in the form of Fig. 10-6, the nature of the effect of contaminants is seen to be the same. Hampson's results for film condensation on vertical surfaces are summarized in Fig. 10-7.

10-7. DROPWISE CONDENSATION

The process of dropwise condensation was referred to in Sec. 10-1 and was distinguished from film condensation by the relation between the condensate and the cooling surface. When dropwise condensation occurs, a considerable proportion of the cooling surface is bare. The condensate collects in many growing droplets, which presumably originate at surface nuclei. These droplets grow until detached by the force of gravity.

A considerable amount of attention has been devoted to the dropwise-condensation process because of its distinctive nature. Interest was also stimulated by the fact that, under a given vapor condition and cooling-surface temperature, a dropwise process will result in a heat flow which may be as much as ten or twenty times as great as that for a filmwise process. Therefore, if dropwise condensation could be promoted in a heat exchanger, a considerable reduction in size would be possible.

Dropwise condensation has been studied in considerable detail. The transfer rates and surface coefficients have been determined for various vapors, temperature levels, and temperature differences. The nature of the process, the surface and vapor conditions promoting it, and the size distribution of the droplets have been investigated experimentally. Finally, several theories of the process have been advanced. Most of the attention to date has been given to pure vapors or to vapors contaminated only by noncondensable gases or by substances intended to act as promoters of the dropwise process.

The theories offered to date give explanations of the process but are not sufficiently complete to permit a rational determination of the magnitudes of surface coefficients under various conditions.

The studies of the nature of the process and of the conditions and promoters which result in dropwise condensation have yielded numerous valuable generalizations. Drew, Nagle, and Smith (1935) summarize the conditions causing filmwise condensation by reporting that clean steam, whether or not it contains a noncondensable gas, will always condense on a clean surface in a filmwise manner. The same authors indicate that dropwise condensation will occur only on a surface which has been contaminated by a promoter which prevents the condensate from wetting the surface. The studies upon which these conclusions are based indicate that oleic acid, benzyl mercaptan, and certain fats and waxes, among many other substances, are effective promoters for various surfaces. Many promoters and surface combinations are effective for only limited periods of time, and Hampson (1951) summarizes the conditions which seem to control the length of the effective period.

Surface coefficients for dropwise condensation have been determined for condensing steam by numerous investigators. Shea and Krase (1940) reported that the surface coefficient varies with flux, that is, temperature difference, increasing to a maximum and then decreasing as higher condensation rates result in the increased blanketing of the surface with liquid. They also observed a large vapor velocity effect. For example, a velocity of the order of 20 fps results in a surface coefficient about twice as large as

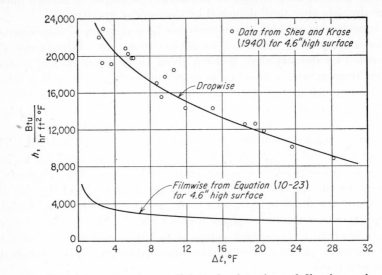

FIG. 10-8. Comparison of surface coefficients for dropwise and filmwise condensation of atmospheric steam at low velocity on a short vertical surface (L = 4.6 in.).

that found with small velocity under the same temperature conditions. The upper curve of Fig. 10-8, which is adapted from the data contained in Table IV of the above reference, is based upon the dropwise condensation of atmospheric-pressure steam at small velocity upon a vertical plate 4.6 in. high. Benzyl mercaptan was used as a promoter. These data compare reasonably well with those gathered by other investigators under similar conditions.

An appreciation of the relative magnitudes of the surface coefficients for dropwise- and filmwise-condensation processes for atmospheric steam may be obtained by comparing the two curves in Fig. 10-8. The lower curve, for the filmwise condensation of atmospheric steam on a 4.6-in.-high vertical surface, was computed from Eq. (10-23). The ratio of the coefficients varies, but is of the order of 6.0:1.0.

The effect of the presence of noncondensable gases in the condensing vapor is similar to that for filmwise processes. Data reported by Hampson

(1951) for various steam-nitrogen mixtures indicate that, at a given temperature difference, there is a sharp decrease in surface coefficient with increasing concentration of nitrogen. For a given concentration, the surface coefficient decreases with temperature difference. These trends are similar to those shown in Fig. 10-6 for the surface coefficient for filmwise condensation.

NOTATION

c_p	specific heat at constant pressure, per unit mass
D_e	equivalent diameter
F	generalized stream function
g	local gravitational acceleration
g_o	a conversion factor for units of force
h	surface coefficient
h_x	local surface coefficient
h_{fg}	latent heat of vaporization
k	thermal conductivity
$\dot{M}$	mass rate of condensate flow
N_{Co}	condensation number
N_{Nu}	Nusselt number
$N_{Nu,x}$	local Nusselt number
$N_{Re,f}$	film Reynolds number
$N'_{Re,f}$	local film Reynolds number
t	temperature
u	condensate velocity
V	average condensate velocity
Γ	the value of $\dot{M}$ at the bottom of the surface
η	similarity variable
μ	absolute viscosity
ν	kinematic viscosity
ρ	density of mass
ϕ	angle of inclination
ϕ	ratio of temperature excesses

REFERENCES

Bromley, L. A.: *Ind. Eng. Chem.*, vol. 44, p. 2966, 1952.
Drew, T. B., W. M. Nagle, and W. Q. Smith: *Trans. AIChE*, vol. 31, p. 605, 1935.
Hampson, H.: "General Discussion on Heat Transfer," IME and ASME, 1951.
Jakob, M.: *Mech. Eng.*, vol. 58, p. 729, 1936.
————: "Heat Transfer," vol. 1, John Wiley & Sons, Inc., New York, 1949.
Kirkbride, C. G.: *Trans. AIChE*, vol. 30, p. 170, 1934.
McAdams, W. H.: "Heat Transmission," 3d ed., McGraw-Hill Book Company, Inc., New York, 1954.
Rohsenow, W. H.: *Trans. ASME*, vol. 78, p. 1645, 1956.
Shea, F. J., Jr., and N. W. Krase: *Trans. AIChE*, vol. 36, p. 463, 1940.

Sparrow, E. M., and J. L. Gregg: *Trans. ASME*, ser. C, vol. 81, p. 13, 1959*a*.
——— and ———: *Trans. ASME*, ser. C, vol. 81, p. 291, 1959*b*.

PROBLEMS

1. A plate 2.0 ft high and inclined at 45° is maintained at 200°F. The plate is in contact with saturated steam at 25 psia. Estimate the theoretical average surface coefficient and the local coefficient at distances of 0.1 ft and 2.0 ft from the upper edge of the plate. Are these values valid for both the upper and lower plate surfaces? Discuss.

2. For the circumstance given in Prob. 1, find the theoretical film thickness and film-vapor interface velocity at a position halfway down the plate and at the lower edge.

3. A horizontal, 1.00-in.-OD tube is maintained at 80°F on its outside surface. It is surrounded by saturated steam at 1.7 psia. Find the theoretical average surface coefficient.

4. Consider a vertical tier consisting of 10 horizontal tubes of the size and temperature given in Prob. 3. The condensing vapor and its condition are also the same. Compare the ideal average surface coefficients of the top, second, third, and tenth tubes with the average surface coefficient of the whole tier, assuming that the film flow is laminar throughout.

5. For the tube and conditions given in Prob. 3, compare the value of the theoretical local surface coefficient at the top of the tube, that is, at $\phi = 0$, with the average coefficient of the tube.

6. The inside surface of a vertical, 1.5-in.-ID tube is maintained at 250°F. The tube is 3 ft long, and saturated steam at 50 psia is to be condensed inside. Estimate h, Γ, and the total heat-transfer rate for idealized filmwise condensation if the steam velocity is assumed small. If the steam flows downward through the tube at an appreciable velocity, would you expect a higher or lower h? Repeat the explanation for upflow.

7. For the tube of Prob. 6, with negligible vapor velocity, estimate the film Reynolds numbers halfway down the tube and at the bottom. Find the average surface coefficient if the tube is 14 ft long.

8. Sketch Fig. 10-4 on graph paper and show the regions relevant to the following engineering applications (assume that the heat-transfer Δt ranges between 10 and 40°F): (*a*) steam-power-plant condensers, (*b*) a mercury condenser in a nuclear power plant, (*c*) a Freon-12 condenser in an air-conditioning system.

9. For the circumstance given in Example 10-3, find the average surface coefficient and heat-transfer rate per unit tube area.

10. Find the tube OD necessary for the conditions stated in Prob. 3 to cause a turbulent film at the bottom of the tube.

11. A flat, vertical surface 3.0 ft high, with a surface temperature of 340°F, is to be in contact with saturated steam at 250 psia. Estimate the average surface coefficient.

12. For the tube and conditions given in Prob. 6, find the average surface coefficient for negligible velocity if the steam is at 320°F instead of at the saturated state at 50 psia.

13. For the tube and conditions given in Prob. 6, estimate and compare the average surface coefficients for negligible velocities and for downward flow at 60 fps.

14. A certain shell-and-tube heat exchanger consists of a bundle of 10-ft-long copper tubes of 0.402 in. ID and 0.500 in. OD. We wish to estimate the capacity of this exchanger to condense saturated steam at 5 psig when the outside tube wall temperature is maintained at 200°F by circulating cooling water through the tubes. The tubes are horizontal and are arranged in vertical tiers as follows: 2 tiers of 3 tubes, 2 of 7 tubes,

2 of 9 tubes, 4 of 11 tubes, and 3 of 13 tubes—a total of 121 tubes. Express the expected capacity in pounds of steam condensed per hour.

15. Solve the preceding problem if, instead of taking an outside tube surface temperature of 200°F, water at 180°F is assumed flowing through the tubes at an average velocity of 5.0 fps. The water circuits are in parallel; that is, a given quantity of water passes through only one tube. State any assumptions made in the solution.

16. Saturated steam at 5.0 psia condenses on the outside surface of a vertical, 2.0-in.-diameter tube whose surface is maintained at 140°F.

a. Compute the average theoretical surface coefficient and heat-transfer rate for a tube 2 ft long.

b. Find the length which will possibly produce a turbulent film and the average surface coefficient for this length.

17. A shell-and-tube heat exchanger contains 10 vertical 6-ft-long copper tubes of 0.605 in. ID and 0.675 in. OD. Saturated steam at 14.7 psia condenses in a filmwise manner on the outside surface, and water at an average temperature of 180°F is circulated through the tubes in parallel at a sufficient rate to keep the tube surface at 190°F.

a. Compute the theoretical average surface coefficient for the outside surface and the heat-transfer rate per unit area.

b. Compute the inside surface coefficient, the water velocity, the flow rate, and the temperature rise of the cooling water.

c. For the same vapor and surface temperature conditions, what length of tube would produce a turbulent film?

CHAPTER 11

Heat Transfer by Combined Mechanisms

11-1. COMBINED HEAT-TRANSFER PROCESSES

In the foregoing chapters the three fundamental modes of heat transfer—conduction, radiation, and convection—are considered individually and separately from one another, and the distinctive mechanisms of each process are delineated, described, and analyzed. By this method of approach the distinctive aspects of the various physical mechanisms entering into heat-energy-transfer processes are emphasized, and an effective understanding may be gained concerning the important variables and their effects under varying conditions. Almost all the successful attempts to establish theories which yield quantitative predictions of transfer rates proceed from the consideration of a single mechanism in isolation.

However, most of the actual processes whereby heat is transferred do not consist solely of processes which may be adequately described as being of only one mode. Usually one mode is of most importance, often even of overriding importance, but each of the modes may be involved in all parts or in different parts of the physical region in which the transfer process occurs. Many common examples of these more complicated processes come to mind. For example, the heat lost from the interior of a building through a wall to the outside arrives by convection and radiation at the inside face of the wall, is conducted through the various layers of building materials, passes across any air spaces by convection and radiation, and arrives at the outside face, where it is dissipated to the cold surroundings by convection and radiation. Heating a piece of metal in a heat-treating furnace presents a somewhat different type of example: heat is conducted to the object's bottom surface, which is in contact with the furnace floor, and heat arrives at its other surfaces by radiation and convection; the energy is distributed throughout the interior of the object by a conduction process. It may be seen that various mechanisms may operate in series and in parallel to produce an over-all transfer of energy from one region to another.

328

The analysis of processes in which various modes operate is generally somewhat complicated. The analysis may often be simplified by neglecting certain effects or by making judicious assumptions; the proper course depends upon the exact nature of the circumstances. However, the following simplifying assumption is almost always adopted and will be employed throughout this chapter. Various transfer mechanisms operating in parallel will be considered unconnected; that is, each mechanism will be assumed to operate independently and as though the others were not present. This condition is not met in certain circumstances. As an example, consider a surface receiving energy by radiation from surrounding surfaces and by convection from a fluid in contact with the surface. If the fluid is an active absorber of radiation, the convection and radiation processes may not be separated. The radiation absorbed by the fluid may cause buoyancy forces; these forces would affect the velocity distribution in the fluid film and therefore the surface coefficient for convection. However, in many circumstances such coupling effects are not found, and energy transfer by parallel processes may be superimposed, that is, simply added.

The primary purpose of the present chapter is to present certain concepts and standard techniques which are useful in analyzing processes involving combined mechanisms. In the course of this presentation many circumstances of practical importance are considered, and additional analysis and experimental information are introduced.

11-2. HEAT TRANSFER THROUGH COMPOSITE BARRIERS

Consider two regions containing fluids of different temperatures, t_i and t_o, separated by a barrier made up of layers of various solid materials, as shown in Fig. 11-1. The materials a, b, c, and d have thermal conductivities k_a, k_b, k_c, and k_d, and the layers are of thicknesses x_a, x_b, x_c, and x_d. These solid layers are assumed to be in perfect thermal contact; the presence of any gas layers would otherwise have to be accounted for by the method discussed in Sec. 11-4. The surface coefficients on the two faces are h_i and h_o. Heat will be transferred from region i to o for the temperature difference shown. The energy will pass by convection from the main body of fluid i to the left face of layer a, will pass by conduction through each layer in turn, and will eventually be delivered to fluid o by convection from the right face of layer d. A typical temperature distribution is shown for the case in which the thermal conductivities do not vary with temperature.

The rate of heat transfer from fluid i to fluid o depends upon h_i, h_o, t_i, t_o, x_a, x_b, x_c, x_d, k_a, k_b, k_c, and k_d. The expression relating heat-flow rate to these quantities may be derived for a steady-state process. The values of t_1, t_2, t_3, and t_4 result from the thicknesses, conductivities, etc., and need not appear in the final expression. For steady state, that is, for temperatures at all locations independent of time, it is clear that there are six resistances in series with an equal flux through each. Therefore, we may write

$$q''_{i\text{-}1} = h_i(t_i - t_1) \qquad q''_{3\text{-}4} = \frac{k_c}{x_c}(t_3 - t_4)$$

$$q''_{1\text{-}2} = \frac{k_a}{x_a}(t_1 - t_2) \qquad q''_{4\text{-}5} = \frac{k_d}{x_d}(t_4 - t_5)$$

$$q''_{2\text{-}3} = \frac{k_b}{x_b}(t_2 - t_3) \qquad q''_{5\text{-}o} = h_o(t_5 - t_o)$$

where $q''_{i\text{-}1} = q''_{2\text{-}3} = \cdots = q''$. Solving for the temperature differences, we have

$$t_i - t_1 = \frac{q''}{h_i} \qquad t_3 - t_4 = \frac{q''}{k_c/x_c}$$

$$t_1 - t_2 = \frac{q''}{k_a/x_a} \qquad t_4 - t_5 = \frac{q''}{k_d/x_d}$$

$$t_2 - t_3 = \frac{q''}{k_b/x_b} \qquad t_5 - t_o = \frac{q''}{h_o}$$

Adding the left- and right-hand sides of the equations, we have

$$(t_i - t_1) + (t_1 - t_2) + (t_2 - t_3) + (t_3 - t_4) + (t_4 - t_5) + (t_5 - t_o)$$

$$= t_i - t_o$$

$$= q''\left(\frac{1}{h_i} + \frac{1}{k_a/x_a} + \frac{1}{k_b/x_b} + \frac{1}{k_c/x_c} + \frac{1}{k_d/x_d} + \frac{1}{h_o}\right)$$

Therefore,

$$q'' = \frac{t_i - t_o}{\dfrac{1}{h_i} + \dfrac{1}{k_a/x_a} + \dfrac{1}{k_b/x_b} + \dfrac{1}{k_c/x_c} + \dfrac{1}{k_d/x_d} + \dfrac{1}{h_o}} = U_o(t_i - t_o)$$

The last part of this equation is a definition of the over-all coefficient of heat transmission, U_o. This quantity is called the over-all conductance. It is evident that

$$U_o = \frac{1}{\dfrac{1}{h_i} + \dfrac{1}{k_a/x_a} + \dfrac{1}{k_b/x_b} + \dfrac{1}{k_c/x_c} + \dfrac{1}{k_d/x_d} + \dfrac{1}{h_o}} \qquad (11\text{-}1)$$

and that the heat-transfer rate per unit area, q'', is in general given as

$$q'' = U_o(t_i - t_o) = U_o \, \Delta t_T \qquad (11\text{-}2)$$

If there are more or fewer layers than four, there will be more or fewer k/x quantities in the denominator of Eq. (11-1). The k/x quantities are called conductances. The reciprocal x/k is a resistance. If one of the layers is an air space, a term $2/h$ or $1/C$ will appear in the denominator, where h

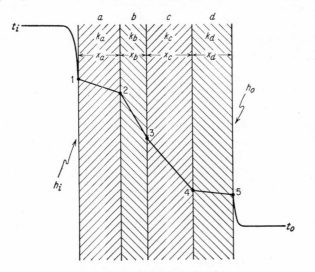

Fig. 11-1.   A composite barrier.

is the surface coefficient for each face if the space is sufficiently wide or C is the air-space conductance if the space is relatively thin. In discussing each of the six barriers in series, it was assumed that only one mode of heat transfer was important in each. However, if more than one mode is in operation, the same general expressions apply. For example, if both radiation and convection are important on the inside face, the flux $q''_{i\text{-}1}$ will be related to the temperature difference $(t_i - t_1)$ by the sum of the conductances h_c for convection and h_r for radiation (discussed in Sec. 5-6):

$$q''_{i\text{-}1} = (h_c + h_r)_i(t_i - t_1)$$

Therefore, h_i in Eq. (11-1) will be replaced by $(h_c + h_r)_i$. The same procedure applies to any layer; the quantity in the denominator of Eq. (11-1) for any layer is to be the reciprocal of the sum of the conductances.

A resistance method may be used instead to sum the effects of the various components of a barrier. The resistance of a conduction layer is x/k and of a surface process is $1/h$. Therefore, the total, or over-all, resistance R_o in the above case is

$$R_o = \frac{1}{h_i} + \frac{x_a}{k_a} + \frac{x_b}{k_b} + \frac{x_c}{k_c} + \frac{x_d}{k_d} + \frac{1}{h_o} \tag{11-3}$$

Now the flux q'' is related to the potential $(t_i - t_o)$ by

$$q'' = \frac{t_i - t_o}{R_o} \tag{11-4}$$

On comparing Eqs. (11-1) and (11-3), the following expected relation between the over-all resistance and the over-all coefficient is found:

$$U_o = \frac{1}{R_o}$$

Often one is interested in the temperatures at various locations within a barrier. The interface temperatures may be found by computing the temperature differences across the various elements of the barrier. In this calculation, it is more convenient to use resistances. If, for example, $(t_2 - t_3)$ is to be found, we note

$$q'' = \frac{k_b}{x_b}(t_2 - t_3) = \frac{t_2 - t_3}{R_b} \quad \text{and} \quad q'' = \frac{\Delta t_T}{R_o}$$

Therefore, $\qquad \dfrac{t_2 - t_3}{R_b} = \dfrac{\Delta t_T}{R_o} \quad \text{and} \quad t_2 - t_3 = \dfrac{R_b}{R_o}\Delta t_T$

This technique can be applied to any of the individual resistances; therefore, writing it in general terms for the jth element, we have

$$\Delta t_j = \frac{R_j}{R_o}\Delta t_T \tag{11-5}$$

If temperatures inside a layer are wanted, a linear interpolation between the faces may be used.

The foregoing results may be applied to any barrier to heat flow, no matter how complicated it may be, provided that the process occurs in steady state. If the thermal conductivities of the constituent materials depend upon temperature, the average value of the thermal conductivity in the layer is used. For large temperature differences and for materials whose conductivities change markedly with temperature, this requirement introduces an additional complication. Since the temperature distribution is not known at the outset, the average temperature or thermal conductivity must be assumed. These values then permit the calculation of the temperature distribution by Eq. (11-5). If the resulting average temperatures are considerably different from those assumed, new values of the conductivities are found. This process is repeated until a good check is obtained.

The preceding analysis applies strictly to one-dimensional flow only. The first step in the analysis requires that q'' for all the elements be the same. However, there are many other circumstances in which the above results may be applied with sufficient accuracy. Consider the case where the barrier is the wall of an enclosure whose width is very large compared with the thickness of the wall. The area normal to the direction of heat flow will be practically the same for all elements of the barrier, and one-dimensional heat flow may be assumed. Such an assumption is not justified in certain cases, and two such exceptions, the thick-walled cylindrical and spherical shells, are considered in detail in Sec. 11-3.

Example 11-1. Consider a large rectangular combustion chamber which is to supply combustion products to a furnace. The walls of the combustion chamber are to be 8 in. of common brick lined with an 8-in.-thick layer of magnesite brick. The combustion products are to be at 2470°F, and the radiation and convection coefficients on the inside surface are expected to be 3.1 and 2.9 Btu/hr ft^2 °F. The chamber is to be located in a building where the air and surrounding-surface temperatures will be 70°F. The radiation and convection coefficients on the outside surface are expected to be 1.3 and 2.1 Btu/hr ft^2 °F.

We wish to estimate the rate of heat loss through the wall per unit area, the maximum temperature to which the common brick will be subjected, and the outside surface temperature.

Thermal conductivities of common and magnesite brick are taken from Table A-3 as $k_b = 0.38$ and $k_m = 2.2$. The four resistances are

$$\frac{1}{(h_c + h_r)_i} = \frac{1}{3.1 + 2.9} = 0.1667 \qquad \frac{x_m}{k_m} = \frac{8}{12 \times 2.2} = 0.303$$

$$\frac{x_b}{k_b} = \frac{8}{12 \times 0.38} = 1.754 \qquad \frac{1}{(h_c + h_r)_o} = \frac{1}{2.1 + 1.3} = 0.294$$

$$R_o = 0.167 + 0.303 + 1.754 + 0.294 = 2.518$$

$$\Delta t_i = \frac{R_i}{R_o} \Delta t_T = \frac{0.167}{2.518} \times 2400 = 159°F$$

$$\Delta t_m = \frac{0.303}{2.518} \times 2400 = 289°F$$

$$\Delta t_b = \frac{1.754}{2.518} \times 2400 = 1672°F$$

$$\Delta t_o = \frac{0.294}{2.518} \times 2400 = 280°F$$

The interface temperatures are found as

$$t_i = 2311\,°\text{F} \qquad t_{mb} = 2022\,°\text{F} \qquad \text{and} \qquad t_o = 350\,°\text{F}$$

The maximum brick temperature is that at the inside face of the layer, $t_{mb} = 2022\,°\text{F}$. The outside face of the wall will be at $t_o = 350\,°\text{F}$. The heat loss per unit area may be found by using the total resistance computed above.

$$q'' = \frac{\Delta t_T}{R_o} = \frac{2400}{2.518} = 954 \text{ Btu/hr ft}^2$$

Or, the over-all coefficient may be computed as

$$U_o = \left(\frac{1}{3.1 + 2.9} + \frac{8}{12 \times 2.2} + \frac{8}{12 \times 0.38} + \frac{1}{2.1 + 1.3} \right)^{-1} = 0.397$$

and $\qquad q'' = U_o \, \Delta t_T = 0.397 \times 2400 = 954 \text{ Btu/hr ft}^2$

11-3. COMPOSITE CYLINDRICAL AND SPHERICAL BARRIERS

Expressions for the over-all coefficients of heat transmission for composite cylindrical and spherical barriers are derived by methods similar to that employed in Sec. 11-2 for composite walls. In that analysis the essential observation is that the heat flow per unit area, q'', is the same for all elements or layers of the wall. Each expression for q'' was solved for the temperature difference, and the differences were added. For the cylindrical case, it is the heat flow per unit length, q/L, which is the same for all layers. For the spherical barrier, the total heat flow q is the same for all layers.

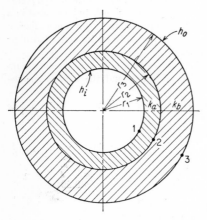

FIG. 11-2. A composite cylindrical or spherical barrier.

Composite Cylinder. As a general case of a composite cylinder, consider the arrangement shown in Fig. 11-2, with the two layers a and b and the surface coefficients h_i and h_o to the regions inside and outside the cylinder. The surface heat-flow rates per unit length of cylinder are given by

$$\frac{q_{i\text{-}1}}{L} = 2\pi r_1 h_i (t_i - t_1) \qquad \text{and} \qquad \frac{q_{3\text{-}o}}{L} = 2\pi r_3 h_o (t_3 - t_o)$$

For conduction through the solid shells a and b we have, from Eq. (2-12), in Sec. 2-3,

$$\frac{q_{1\text{-}2}}{L} = \frac{2\pi k_a(t_1 - t_2)}{\ln (r_2/r_1)} \quad \text{and} \quad \frac{q_{2\text{-}3}}{L} = \frac{2\pi k_b(t_2 - t_3)}{\ln (r_3/r_2)}$$

Solving each equation for the temperature difference, recalling that the sum is equal to $(t_i - t_o)$ and that all the q/L quantities are equal in steady state, we have

$$(t_i - t_1) + (t_1 - t_2) + (t_2 - t_3) + (t_3 - t_o) = (t_i - t_o)$$

$$= \frac{q}{L}\left[\frac{1}{2\pi r_1 h_i} + \frac{\ln (r_2/r_1)}{2\pi k_a} + \frac{\ln (r_3/r_2)}{2\pi k_b} + \frac{1}{2\pi r_3 h_o}\right]$$

Therefore, $$\frac{q}{L} = \frac{2\pi(t_i - t_o)}{\dfrac{1}{h_i r_1} + \dfrac{\ln (r_2/r_1)}{k_a} + \dfrac{\ln (r_3/r_2)}{k_b} + \dfrac{1}{h_o r_3}} = U_o(t_i - t_o)$$

The over-all transmission coefficient U_o is clearly given by

$$U_o = \frac{2\pi}{\dfrac{1}{h_i r_1} + \dfrac{\ln (r_2/r_1)}{k_a} + \dfrac{\ln (r_3/r_2)}{k_b} + \dfrac{1}{h_o r_3}} \tag{11-6}$$

The units of U_o are Btu/hr ft (length) °F in contrast with those of the over-all coefficient given by Eq. (11-1) for the one-dimensional case. An over-all resistance R_o may again be defined in

$$U_o = \frac{1}{R_o}$$

The temperature difference across the jth individual resistance is related to Δt_T by Eq. (11-5). The individual resistances are of a somewhat different form from those for the one-dimensional case. For example, the resistances for the a shell, R_a, and the resistance of the outside surface, R_o', are

$$R_a = \frac{\ln (r_2/r_1)}{2\pi k_a} \quad \text{and} \quad R_o' = \frac{1}{h_o 2\pi r_3}$$

Composite Sphere. The composite spherical barrier to heat flow is analyzed in a similar way. Figure 11-2 may also be considered to be the section of the spherical barrier made up of two solid layers, a and b, with fluids inside and out and surface coefficients h_i and h_o. The total heat-flow rates across the two surfaces are

$$q_{i\text{-}1} = h_i 4\pi r_1{}^2(t_i - t_1) \quad \text{and} \quad q_{3\text{-}o} = h_o 4\pi r_3{}^2(t_3 - t_o)$$

For conduction through the solid shells a and b, Eq. (2-14) yields

$$q_{1\text{-}2} = \frac{4\pi k_a(t_1 - t_2)}{1/r_1 - 1/r_2} \quad \text{and} \quad q_{2\text{-}3} = \frac{4\pi k_b(t_2 - t_3)}{1/r_2 - 1/r_3}$$

Solving again for the temperature differences, adding them, and recalling that $q_{i\text{-}1} = q_{1\text{-}2} = \cdots = q$, we have

$$q = \frac{4\pi(t_i - t_o)}{\dfrac{1}{h_1 r_1{}^2} + \dfrac{1/r_1 - 1/r_2}{k_a} + \dfrac{1/r_2 - 1/r_3}{k_b} + \dfrac{1}{h_o r_3{}^2}} = U_o(t_i - t_o)$$

The over-all coefficient U_o, which has the units Btu/hr $^\circ$F, is

$$U_o = \frac{4\pi}{\dfrac{1}{h_1 r_1{}^2} + \dfrac{1/r_1 - 1/r_2}{k_a} + \dfrac{1/r_2 - 1/r_3}{k_b} + \dfrac{1}{h_o r_3{}^2}} \qquad (11\text{-}7)$$

The over-all resistance may again be used, and the temperature distribution may be determined by the resistance method from Eq. (11-5). Individual resistances are easily determined. For example, for the a shell

$$R_a = \frac{1/r_1 - 1/r_2}{4\pi k_a}$$

For the cylindrical and spherical barriers, as for the wall, the numerical value of the thermal conductivity to be used in a conduction region is the average thermal conductivity of the region. For a large temperature gradient or for a substance whose thermal conductivity changes rapidly with temperature, this requirement may necessitate successive approximations as outlined in Sec. 11-2 for the flat surface.

Example 11-2. A long, 6-in. nominal standard steel pipe covered with a 3-in. layer of 85 per cent magnesia insulation transmits superheated steam at 500 psia and 600°F. The average steam velocity in the pipe is 60 fps. The pipe is located in a large space wherein the temperature is 80°F. The total outside surface coefficient may be taken as 3.5 Btu/hr ft² °F.

We wish to find the heat loss per unit length of pipe and to estimate the temperature levels on the inside surface of the pipe, at the pipe-magnesia interface, and at the outside surface of the insulation.

At estimated temperatures of 590 and 350°F for the steel and insulation the values of the thermal conductivities are 25.0 and 0.035 Btu/hr ft °F.

The inside surface coefficient may be computed from Eq. (7-43) at an average film temperature estimated as 600°F. The over-all coefficient may be found from Eq. (11-6), and it is used to compute q/L.

$$U_o = \frac{2\pi}{\dfrac{2 \times 12}{125 \times 6.065} + \dfrac{\ln (6.625/6.065)}{25} + \dfrac{\ln (9.625/6.625)}{0.035} + \dfrac{2 \times 12}{3.5 \times 9.625}}$$

$$= 0.549 \text{ Btu/hr ft °F}$$

$$\frac{q}{L} = U_o \, \Delta t_T = 0.549(600 - 80) = 286 \text{ Btu/hr ft}$$

The over-all and individual resistances are

$$R_o = \frac{1}{U_o} = 1.82 \qquad R_i = 0.005 \qquad R_{out} = 0.114$$

$$R_{steel} = 0.0005 \qquad R_{mag} = 1.70$$

The various Δt values are

$$\Delta t_i = \frac{0.005}{1.82} \times 420 = 1.2° \qquad \Delta t_{steel} = \frac{0.0005}{1.82} \times 420 = 0.10°$$

$$\Delta t_{mag} = \frac{1.70}{1.82} \times 420 = 392.4° \qquad \Delta t_{out} = \frac{0.114}{1.82} \times 420 = 26.3°$$

The inside pipe surface temperature t_1 is $600 - \Delta t_i = 598.8°F$. The pipe-magnesia interface is at $t_2 = t_1 - \Delta t_{steel} = 598.7°F$. Finally, the outside surface temperature t_3 is $\Delta t_{out} + 80 = 106.3°F$.

Thickness of Insulation. The results of the analysis of cylindrical conduction regions are used to determine the proper thickness of pipe insulation. Consider an insulated metal pipe or tube which conveys a high-temperature fluid. A question may arise concerning the proper thickness of insulation. Will the addition of more and more insulation to a bare pipe continually reduce the heat loss, or does the effect of increased outside area for convection and radiation offset the effect of the added insulation? The following analysis of this problem proceeds on the basis of simplifying assumptions which are justifiable in many practical circumstances. Assume that the inside surface temperature of the insulation is independent of its thickness. This is reasonable for thin-walled metal tubes and relatively high velocity liquid flow because in such cases the liquid film and wall temperature differences are very small compared with the difference through the insulation. A considerable further simplification is achieved by considering the total outside surface coefficient to be independent of the OD and, therefore, of insulation thickness. The reasonableness of this assumption depends somewhat upon the particular circumstances. The outside surface temperature decreases with increasing OD, and therefore the radiation component of the outside coefficient decreases. Further, an increase in diameter either decreases or leaves unchanged the convection coefficient, as far as the effect of temperature difference is concerned. However, the effect of the decreasing surface temperature upon the average film properties, and therefore upon the convection coefficient, depends primarily upon whether the surrounding fluid is a liquid or a gas. For a liquid, the coefficient would tend to increase; for a gas, it would tend to decrease with decreasing temperature, that is, increasing diameter. These effects are not, therefore, self-canceling, and caution is required in applying results which depend upon such assumptions.

The analysis is based upon the foregoing assumptions. Notation follows Fig. 11-2. Layer a is the pipe wall, and layer b is the insulation. The relative thickness of the layers in Fig. 11-2 are unrealistic for insulated pipes; layer a should be relatively much thinner. The assumptions amount to assuming t_2 and h_o constant as r_3 varies for given temperature levels t_i and t_o. Two expressions for q/L may be written, one for the insulation and the other for the outside surface:

$$\frac{q}{L} = \frac{2\pi k_b(t_2 - t_3)}{\ln(r_3/r_2)} \quad \text{and} \quad \frac{q}{L} = h_o 2\pi r_3(t_3 - t_o)$$

These two equations contain three variables: q/L, t_3, and r_3. t_3 may be eliminated, yielding one equation relating q/L and r_3. Solving both equations for t_3, we obtain

$$t_3 = t_2 - \frac{q}{L}\frac{\ln(r_3/r_2)}{2\pi k_b} \quad \text{and} \quad t_3 = \frac{q}{L}\frac{1}{h_o 2\pi r_3} + t_o$$

Equating the two expressions involving q/L and r_3 and solving for q/L, we find

$$\frac{q}{L} = \frac{t_2 - t_o}{1/h_o 2\pi r_3 + \ln(r_3/r_2)/2\pi k_b}$$

Note that the two terms in the denominator are merely the two resistances and that this expression could be written directly as the Δt divided by the sum of the resistances. The question now is, how does q/L vary with increasing r_3? Does it increase or decrease initially? Is there a value of r_3 which results in a minimum or maximum value of q/L? The equation is inspected for these characteristics by taking the derivative with respect to r_3, setting the results equal to zero to find the locations of any maximum or minimum values of q/L, and then discovering whether the extreme points, if any, are maxima or minima:

$$\frac{d}{dr_3}\left(\frac{q}{L}\right) = \frac{t_2 - t_o}{[1/h_o 2\pi r_3 + \ln (r_3/r_2)/2\pi k_b]^2}\left(\frac{1}{h_o 2\pi r_3{}^2} - \frac{1}{2\pi k_b r_3}\right)$$

$$\frac{1}{h_o 2\pi r_3{}^2} - \frac{1}{2\pi k_b r_3} = 0$$

and

$$r_3 = \frac{k_b}{h_o} \tag{11-8}$$

Only one extreme value is found, and it may be shown to be a maximum by demonstrating that the derivative is positive for $r_3 < k_b/h_o$ and negative for $r_3 > k_b/h_o$. This result indicates that the heat loss increases with the addition of insulation until $r_3 = k_b/h_o$.

The insulation thickness, expressed as a fraction of pipe radius, for maximum loss may be written as

$$\frac{r_3 - r_2}{r_2} = \frac{k_b}{h_o r_2} - 1 \tag{11-9}$$

From this relation it is clear that $(r_3 - r_2)$ is negative for $(k_b/h_o r_2) < 1.0$. That is, for $(k_b/h_o r_2) < 1.0$, the maximum does not occur, and any addition of insulation reduces heat loss. In this circumstance, the amount of insulation to be used would be limited by economic considerations. For the other case, of $(k_b/h_o r_2) > 1.0$, a maximum occurs. The thickness of the insulation should be well beyond that which produces the maximum and also beyond the thickness which would produce a loss equal to that of the bare pipe. For relatively good insulators, the first condition, that is, $(k_b/h_o r_2) < 1.0$, is met, and no maximum is found. For example, for 85 per cent magnesia and an outside surface coefficient typical for air, a pipe radius of less than 0.2 in. is necessary to make $(k_b/h_o r_2) > 1.0$ and to result, therefore, in a maximum.

Effects of Thermal Radiation. In the foregoing consideration of over-all transfer processes, total surface conductances are employed, that is, the sum of the radiation and convection coefficients. The following discussion considers the magnitude of the radiation coefficient, the accuracy of the simplified equation (5-40), and a comparison of the radiation and convection surface coefficients for a cylindrical surface in air. In the discussion a "black" surface will be assumed; many surfaces of practical importance are essentially black. Equation (5-40) is written for the outside surface of a cylinder as

$$h_r = 4\sigma T_{\mathrm{av}}{}^3 = 4\sigma \left(T_o + \frac{\Delta t}{2} \right)^3 \tag{11-10}$$

where T_o is the surrounding temperature and Δt is the temperature difference between the cylindrical surface and the air and surfaces surrounding
it.   The values of h_r from Eq. (11-10) and from the more accurate form,
Eq. (5-39) in Sec. 5-5, are plotted in Fig. 11-3 versus Δt for a surrounding
temperature of 70°F.   Also shown for comparison is h_c.

The curves in Fig. 11-3 show certain very significant characteristics.
The difference between Eq. (5-39) and its approximation is initially small
but becomes appreciable at higher Δt values.   The value of h_r is not zero
at zero Δt.   A comparison of the h_c and h_r values shows that radiation is a
more important effect than free convection in a fluid such as air, whose
low thermal conductivity results in a low convection coefficient h_c.   For
the low-Δt range the total conductance h increases in the same manner as
does h_c.   As the Δt becomes higher, the nature of the h_r variation dominates
h, and h_r is the major contribution to h.   These observations indicate that

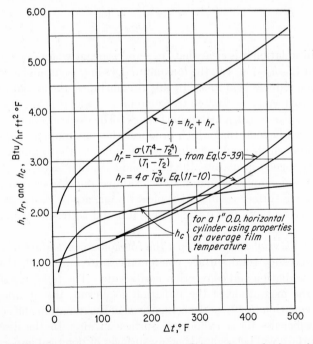

Fig. 11-3.   Radiation and convection surface coefficients from a horizontal cylinder in
air; surroundings at 70°F.

the radiation coefficient is very important for high-surface-temperature combined-mode transfers and that careful consideration must be given to an evaluation of its effect.

11-4. COMBINED CONDUCTANCES OF FLUID LAYERS AND SURFACES

In the foregoing chapters concerning conduction, convection, and radiation processes, sufficient information was presented to make possible the estimation of the thermal conductances, or resistances, of many of the types of elements which are found in heat-transfer barriers of practical importance. However, numerous elements are commonly encountered for which the foregoing techniques do not apply and for which special analytical or experimental treatment is required. Two important cases are briefly discussed here. The first is the combined process whereby heat is transferred between the two surfaces enclosing a thin layer of air. The second case, important in heating- and cooling-load calculations for buildings, is the transfer of heat between the weather surface of a building and its surroundings by radiation and by convection. The convection process is complicated in an enclosed-layer case by the dampening influence of the enclosing surfaces and in the second case by the necessity of considering various air velocities, due to wind, near the weather surface.

In both of the above circumstances, it is customary to refer to total conductances rather than to surface coefficients. The total conductance C is the sum of the conductances due to convection and radiation (and to conduction in the enclosed-air-layer case). The heat-transfer rate per unit area is then given by the product of the conductance and the temperature difference across the element:

$$q'' = C \, \Delta t \tag{11-11}$$

For an enclosed layer of air the radiation conductance h_r between the parallel enclosing surfaces may be simply derived if the area of the enclosure is large compared with the thickness of the layer. In this circumstance the enclosure consists merely of two parallel surfaces, and Eq. (5-24) applies. Note that A_1 and A_2 are equal. The conductance is found by dividing q by A and Δt.

$$h_r = \frac{\sigma(T_1^4 - T_2^4)}{(1/\epsilon_1 + 1/\epsilon_2 - 1)(T_1 - T_2)} \tag{11-12}$$

If $(T_1 - T_2) \ll T_1$, Eq. (11-12) may be simplified, as was Eq. (5-39):

$$h_r = \frac{4\sigma T_{\mathrm{av}}^3}{1/\epsilon_1 + 1/\epsilon_2 - 1} = \frac{4\epsilon_1 \epsilon_2 \sigma T_{\mathrm{av}}^3}{\epsilon_1 + \epsilon_2 - \epsilon_1 \epsilon_2} \tag{11-13}$$

The air-layer conductance due to conduction and convection, h_c, is discussed in Sec. 8-5; data and correlations for the horizontal and vertical cases are presented. The total layer conductance may be obtained by adding the appropriate value of h_c to the value of h_r from Eq. (11-13).

Air-layer conductances obtained by the foregoing method are somewhat in error for some applications. Consider a practical circumstance such as the air spaces formed by the studs in a typical frame-construction wall, that is, between the surface of the lath and the sheathing. The rough surfaces of the air space have an effect upon h_c, and since the stud spacing is relatively small compared with the thickness of the layer, Eq. (11-12) does not apply strictly. Further, the conductance through the stud is less than that of the air layer. For higher accuracy an average conductance may be computed. Such effects must be treated individually and with judgment as they arise in practical problems.

Example 11-3. As an example of a calculation of air-space conductance, consider the combustion-chamber wall discussed in Example 11-1 modified by the inclusion of an air space of an average thickness of 5 in. and a height of 30 in. between the 8-in. magnesite lining and the 8-in. outside brick. The air-space conductance, the over-all coefficient, and the rate of heat loss are to be found.

In order to compute the air-space conductance, the temperature of the two enclosing surfaces must be assumed. From the results of Example 11-1, values of 2030°F and 2010°F seem reasonable. The average is 2020°F. The lining and brick emissivities are assumed equal at 0.80.

The radiation conductance is

$$h_r = \frac{0.1713 \times 10^{-8}[(2030 + 460)^4 - (2010 + 460)^4]}{(1/0.8 + 1/0.8 - 1)(2030 - 2010)} = 69.7 \text{ Btu/hr ft}^2 \text{ °F}$$

From Eq. (8-48) the combined conduction and convection conductance is found:

$$h_c = 0.18 \frac{k}{L} \sqrt[4]{N_{Gr}} \left(\frac{H}{s}\right)^{-\frac{1}{9}} = \frac{0.18 \times 0.053 \times 12}{5} \sqrt[4]{43,500} \left(\frac{30}{5}\right)^{-\frac{1}{9}}$$

$$= 0.271 \text{ Btu/hr ft}^2 \text{ °F}$$

The layer conductance and resistance are, therefore,

$$C = 70 \text{ Btu/hr ft}^2 \text{ °F} \qquad R = \frac{1}{C} = 0.0143$$

Using the same thermal conductivities as before, the total resistance is computed:

$$R_o = 2.518 + 0.014 = 2.532$$

and

$$q'' = \frac{2400}{2.532} = 948 \text{ Btu/hr ft}^2$$

A comparison of this result with that computed in Example 11-1 shows that an air layer has little effect upon the over-all coefficient and heat-transfer rates at these temperature levels.

No information is presented in the chapters on convection concerning the convection surface coefficient for the outside surface of a wall subject to various wind velocities. No precise information concerning this effect is possible, because the convection process is strongly influenced by such diverse effects as the orientation of the building, the terrain, the relation

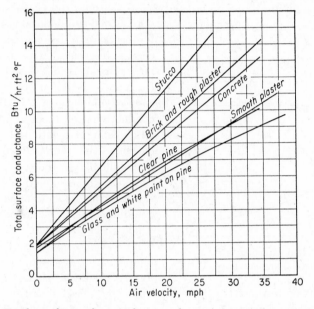

Fig. 11-4. Total weather surface conductance for various surfacing materials. [*From Rowley and Algren* (1937).]

of surrounding buildings, and the exact nature and condition of the surface. Further, because of similar complicating effects, it is not possible to present the radiation surface coefficient in a general way. However, some estimate of transfer rates must be made, and a considerable amount of study and experimentation has been devoted to determining values of total surface conductance which will be approximately correct for a wide range of practical circumstances. The value of conductance is presented as a function of surface material and wind velocity. Figure 11-4 is a graphical presentation of this relationship as reported by Rowley and Algren (1937). The ordinate is total conductance, that is, the sum of the convection and radiation surface coefficients. These values are often used in the absence of sufficient exact information to permit a more accurate analysis.

11-5. ANALYTIC SOLUTIONS IN SEVERAL COMBINED-MODE PROBLEMS

In this section the solutions of two idealized cases are considered in which combined transfer processes occur. Each case is significant because it corresponds to practical situations of importance.

The first circumstance to be analyzed is that of a rod of length L, cross-sectional area A, and perimeter P which has one end maintained at a fixed

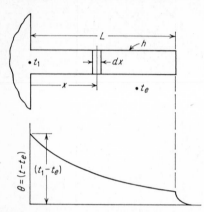

temperature t_1 by contact with an energy reservoir. This rod extends into a region which is at t_e and loses (or gains) heat on its lateral and exposed-end surfaces. If the thermal conductivity of the rod material is large compared with the surface coefficient, the temperature gradient perpendicular to the rod axis will be small, and the conduction process inside the rod may be assumed to be one-dimensional. This is the case which is analyzed here. The arrangement is shown in Fig. 11-5, and a temperature distribution is shown for a typical case wherein $t_1 > t_e$.

FIG. 11-5. Rod extending from a reservoir, with lateral and end losses.

The differential relation between t and x may be derived by writing an energy balance for the element dx having a face area, normal to the rod axis, of A and a lateral surface for convection, on its perimeter, of $P \, dx$. The rate of heat conduction at x is $-k(dt/dx) \, A$, and the difference across the two faces of element dx is

$$-\frac{d}{dx}\left[-k\left(\frac{dt}{dx}\right)A\right]dx = k\left(\frac{d^2t}{dx^2}\right)A \, dx$$

where heat in is positive. This energy gain is set equal to the rate of loss on the lateral surface, of extent $P \, dx$:

$$k\left(\frac{d^2t}{dx^2}\right)A \, dx = hP \, dx \, (t - t_e)$$

This reduces to the following equation when the temperature excess, $\theta = (t - t_e)$, is introduced. Note that $dt = d\theta$.

$$\frac{d^2\theta}{dx^2} - \frac{hP}{kA}\theta = 0 \tag{11-14}$$

One boundary condition applies at each end:

at $x = 0$ $\qquad\qquad\qquad\qquad$ $\theta = \theta_1 = t_1 - t_e$

At $x = L$, the exposed end face, the heat lost by convection, $hA(t - t_e) = hA\theta$, must be equal to the heat arriving by conduction from the inside of the rod, $-kA(d\theta/dx)$. Therefore,

at $x = L$ $\qquad$ $-kA\dfrac{d\theta}{dx} = hA\theta$ $\qquad$ or $\qquad$ $\dfrac{d\theta}{dx} = -\dfrac{h}{k}\theta$

Equation (11-14), with the two boundary conditions, may be solved for an expression for temperature excess in terms of x. However, the solution may be made more useful by first changing the variables θ and x to new ones, $\phi = \theta/\theta_1$ and $X = x/L$, where θ_1 is the temperature excess at $x = 0$, that is, $(t_1 - t_e)$. These new variables have the considerable advantages of being dimensionless and of varying only in the restricted range 0 to 1.0. The differential equation, written in terms of the new variables, becomes

$$\frac{d^2\phi}{dX^2} - \frac{hPL^2}{kA}\phi = 0 \qquad\qquad (11\text{-}15)$$

For simplicity, the square root of the constant coefficient of ϕ in Eq. (11-15) will be set equal to a new constant n. That is,

$$n = \sqrt{\frac{hPL^2}{kA}} \qquad\qquad (11\text{-}16)$$

With these changes, the differential equation and boundary conditions become

$$\frac{d^2\phi}{dX^2} - n^2\phi = 0 \qquad\qquad (11\text{-}17)$$

at $X = 0$ $\qquad\qquad\qquad\qquad$ $\phi = 1.0$

at $X = 1.0$ $\qquad\qquad\qquad\qquad$ $\dfrac{d\phi}{dX} = -\dfrac{hL}{k}\phi$

The general solution of the equation is

$$\phi = C_1 e^{nX} + C_2 e^{-nX} \qquad\qquad (11\text{-}18)$$

The boundary conditions are applied to determine the constants:

at $X = 0$ $\qquad\qquad$ $\phi = 1.0 = C_1 + C_2$

at $X = 1.0$ $\qquad$ $\dfrac{d\phi}{dX} = C_1 n e^{nX} - C_2 n e^{-nX} = -\dfrac{hL}{k}\phi$

and, therefore,

$$C_1 n e^n - C_2 n e^{-n} = -\frac{hL}{k}(C_1 e^n + C_2 e^{-n})$$

The two equations for C_1 and C_2 may be combined to give

$$C_2 = \cfrac{1}{1 + \cfrac{1 - hL/nk}{1 + hL/nk} e^{-2n}} \qquad \text{and} \qquad C_1 = 1 - C_2$$

For simplicity, the constant hL/nk is denoted as m:

$$\frac{hL}{nk} = \sqrt{\frac{hA}{kP}} = m \tag{11-19}$$

With this change, Eq. (11-18), with the values of the constants introduced, becomes

$$\phi = \frac{\theta}{\theta_1} = \frac{e^{-nX} + [(1 - m)/(1 + m)]e^{-2n}e^{nX}}{1 + [(1 - m)/(1 + m)]e^{-2n}} \tag{11-20}$$

This relation is the generalized temperature distribution, for $X = 0$ to 1.0, as a function of m and n. The definitions of m and n are to be found in Eqs. (11-19) and (11-16). Solutions of Eq. (11-20) for various values of m and n in the range of practical interest are plotted in Fig. 11-6.

Example 11-4. Find the temperature at the free end and at the middle of a horizontal brass rod 4 in. long and $\frac{1}{4}$ in. in diameter. The other end of the rod is maintained at 100°F, and the rod is surrounded by air at 60°F. Assume that the surface coefficient is constant over the whole exposed surface.

The surface coefficient is first found for free convection on a horizontal cylinder from Fig. 8-8:

$$N_{Ra} \approx 250 \qquad N_{Nu} = 2.5 \qquad h_c = \frac{2.5 \times 0.0154}{\frac{1}{48}} = 1.85 \text{ Btu/hr ft}^2 \text{ °F}$$

The radiation coefficient is estimated for a surface at 80°F by Eq. (11-10):

$$h_r = 4\sigma \left[\frac{(460 + 60) + (460 + 80)}{2}\right]^3 = 4\sigma \times 530^3 = 1.02 \text{ Btu/hr ft}^2 \text{ °F}$$

Therefore, $h = 1.85 + 1.02 = 2.87 \text{ Btu/hr ft}^2 \text{ °F}$

The values of m and n are found:

$$n = \sqrt{\frac{hPL^2}{kA}} = \sqrt{\frac{2\pi r L^2 h}{k \pi r^2}} = \sqrt{\frac{2L^2 h}{kr}} = \sqrt{\frac{2 \times 8 \times 12 \times 2.87}{9 \times 60}} = 1.010$$

$$m = \frac{hL}{nk} = \frac{2.87}{1.010 \times 60 \times 3} = 0.0158$$

The values of X at the middle and free end are 0.5 and 1.0. The generalized temperatures may be found from Fig. 11-6 as 0.73 and 0.64. It may be seen that the end convection effect is almost negligible for this case.

At $X = 0.5$ $$\frac{t - 60}{100 - 60} = 0.73 \qquad t = 60 + 29.2 = 89.2°F$$

At $X = 1.0$ $$\frac{t - 60}{100 - 60} = 0.64 \qquad t = 85.6°F$$

An inspection of the curves in Fig. 11-6 indicates that the slope of the temperature curve at the free end of the rod, that is, at $X = 1.0$, is close to zero for most values of m and n. A slope of nearly zero means that the rate of heat flow at the end is near zero and that the convection from the end face may be neglected. If this approximation is made at the outset,

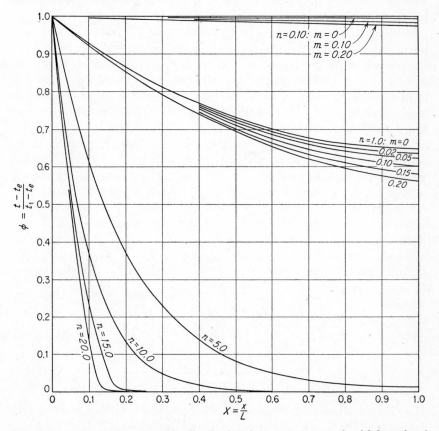

FIG. 11-6. Generalized temperature distributions in constant-area rods with lateral and end losses. (*Calculated by A. S. Shull.*)

in writing the boundary conditions for Eq. (11-17), a much simpler solution is obtained. The general solution, Eq. (11-18), is the same as before, but the boundary conditions are changed to the following:

at $X = 0$ $\qquad\qquad\qquad\qquad \phi = 1.0$

at $X = 1.0$ $\qquad\qquad\qquad\qquad \dfrac{d\phi}{dX} = 0$

These conditions give the following solution:

$$\phi = \frac{e^{-nX} + e^{-2n}e^{nX}}{1 + e^{-2n}} \tag{11-21}$$

This is, in effect, Eq. (11-20), with $m = 0$. Several $m = 0$ curves are seen in Fig. 11-6.

It should be noted here that the conditions for an adiabatic-end-face rod are exactly met by a rod which extends a distance L between two energy reservoirs of equal temperature. The temperature distribution in the rod is symmetric about its center point, and all the heat coming from either one of the reservoirs is lost on the surface of the rod before the center point is reached. Therefore, this problem is merely an adiabatic-end-face rod of length $L/2$ and is covered by Eq. (11-21).

Thermometer Error. The foregoing developments have importance in the consideration of errors to be expected in the reading of any rodlike thermometric device used in a passage through which a fluid flows. If the stem is in good contact with the passage wall and if the fluid and wall are at different temperatures, t_f and t_w, the device will indicate a temperature t_t different from t_f. The preceding analysis applies to this case. In particular, if the temperature-sensitive part of the device is at the end of the rod, the difference between t_t and t_f, that is, θ_E, is $\phi_E\theta_1 = \phi_E(t_w - t_f)$. This quantity may be found from Eq. (11-20) by taking $X = 1.0$. This error, $(t_t - t_f)$, found as a ratio to $\theta_1 = (t_w - t_f)$, is

$$\frac{t_t - t_f}{t_w - t_f} = \phi_E = \frac{e^{-n} + [(1 - m)/(1 + m)]e^{-n}}{1 + [(1 - m)/(1 + m)]e^{-2n}}$$

$$= \frac{1 + (1 - m)/(1 + m)}{e^{n} + [(1 - m)/(1 + m)]e^{-n}} \tag{11-22}$$

If end convection may be ignored, this equation is further simplified by taking $m = 0$.

In the special case of a thermometric rod, as discussed in the preceding paragraph, a peculiar circumstance arises. In the derivation of the general equation a surface coefficient h was introduced. This coefficient is meant to include all the individual agencies by which energy interchanges occur between the surface of the rod and its surroundings. These agencies are convection and radiation, and h is the sum of the two surface coefficients. In the thermometer case a difficulty arises because the convection and radiation exchanges are usually in different directions. If a warm fluid flows through a cool-walled passage, the rod gains energy by convection and loses energy by radiation. For a cool fluid and a warm-walled passage, the two flows are reversed in direction. Under either condition the differential equation (11-14) and the accompanying boundary conditions are still correct if h is correctly interpreted. h is the sum of the convection and radiation coefficients, and h_r is negative for both cases; that is, the radiation transfer is to the rod when $t_t > t_f$ and away from the rod when $t_t < t_f$. That this radiation surface coefficient is negative may be seen from Eq. (5-38). This procedure is sufficiently accurate for small temperature differences, for which h_r may be considered constant over the surface of the rod.

The complication concerning the radiation coefficient does not arise if the radiant energy interchange with the wall passage is negligible or absent. The radiation effect may sometimes be ignored when h_c is large, because of high fluid velocity or thermal conductivity. In addition, the radiation effect will be a simple parallel process if the fluid is a good absorber of radiation.

An appreciation of the magnitude of the "thermometer error," as $(t_t - t_f)$ may be called, may be obtained from Fig. 11-7. The error, divided by the temperature difference between the passage wall and the fluid $(t_w - t_f)$, is plotted from Eq. (11-22) vs. the Reynolds number for air flowing through a circular passage of diameter D. The thermometric device is assumed to be a hollow brass tube, having an OD of $0.05D$ and an ID of $0.03D$, which extends from the wall to the center line of the passage. The inside end of the tube is closed by a thin disk to which a thermocouple junction is attached. Radiation was neglected for simplicity, the properties of air at 60°F were used, and a thermal conductivity of 65 Btu/hr ft °F was used for brass. The inside surface of the brass tube was assumed adiabatic. The surface coefficient for the outside surface of the tube in the range of flow rates considered is given by Hilpert's correlation as

$$\frac{hd}{k_a} = 0.174 \left(\frac{dV\rho_a}{\mu_a}\right)^{0.618} \tag{11-23}$$

The subscript a means air, and d refers to the rod diameter, that is, $0.05D$.

In order to compute m and n, the value of P/A is found:

$$\frac{P}{A} = \frac{0.05\pi D}{(\pi D^2/4)[(0.05)^2 - (0.03)^2]} = \frac{125}{D}$$

Noting that $L = D/2$, the values of m and n are found:

$$m = \frac{1}{25}\sqrt{\frac{5hD}{k}} = 0.0010 N_{\text{Re}}{}^{0.309}$$

$$n = \frac{5}{2}\sqrt{\frac{5hD}{k}} = 0.0624 N_{\text{Re}}{}^{0.309}$$

Equation (11-22) is then solved for a Reynolds number range from 8000 to 800,000, based upon the passage diameter. The results are plotted in Fig. 11-7. The error is seen to be very high at low Reynolds numbers and to decrease to less than 5 per cent above 5×10^5.

Temperature Response. The other idealized combined-mode problem to be considered briefly in this section is the one corresponding to the temperature response of a thermometric probe in a fluid of changing temperature t_f. For simplicity, the assumption is made that the temperature-sensitive part of the probe, of mass M and volume V, is at the same temperature t throughout at any instant of time. Further, the temperature-sensitive mass is assumed to exchange energy only with the fluid, by convection. Radiation

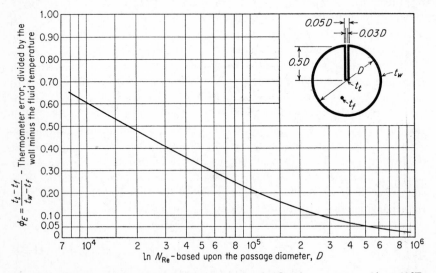

FIG. 11-7. Thermometer error vs. Reynolds number for flow in a passage. Air at 60°F; radiation interchange neglected.

exchanges and conduction processes to supports are assumed negligible. The governing differential equation is obtained by equating the rate of gain of stored energy, $Mc\,dt/d\tau$, and the rate of convection gain, $hA\,(t_f - t)$, where A is the surface area of mass M. In general, the fluid temperature t_f is a function of time τ. Transposing and rearranging, we find

$$\frac{dt}{d\tau} + p(t - t_f) = 0 \qquad (11\text{-}24)$$

where
$$p = \frac{hA}{Mc} = \frac{hA}{\rho c V} \qquad (11\text{-}25)$$

There are many circumstances of fluid temperature variation wherein a knowledge of the response characteristics of a thermometric device is important. Practical circumstances are idealized in order to make possible a mathematical solution of the problem. Two examples are considered here. In the first case the fluid temperature suddenly changes to a different, and thereafter constant, value, and in the second case the fluid temperature varies sinusoidally with time.

In the first example, assume that the fluid and thermometer mass were at the same temperature t_1 at zero time and that at the next instant of time the fluid temperature changed abruptly to t_o. We are interested in the thermometer lag $(t - t_o)$ as a function of time. The differential equation and initial condition are

$$\frac{dt}{d\tau} + p(t - t_o) = 0$$

and
$$t = t_1 \qquad \text{at } \tau = 0$$

The equation is integrated to

$$\ln (t - t_o) = -p\tau + C$$

At $\tau = 0$ $$t = t_1$$

Therefore, $$\ln (t_1 - t_o) = C$$

By combining these results and simplifying, we find

$$\frac{t - t_o}{t_1 - t_o} = e^{-p\tau} \qquad (11\text{-}26)$$

Thus the solution indicates an exponential decay of the thermometer error $(t - t_o)$. This is merely the limiting case of zero Biot number for the transient cases considered in Sec. 3-2.

For a sinusoidal variation of fluid temperature the solution is somewhat more complicated, and for brevity the details are omitted. Only the statement of the problem and the solution are given. The condition of a sinusoidal fluid temperature t_f is

$$t_f - t_o = (\Delta t)_o \sin 2\pi f \tau \tag{11-27}$$

where t_o is the average value of t_f. $(\Delta t)_o$ and f are the amplitude and frequency of the variation. The solution is written in terms of the instantaneous thermometer temperature t minus the average fluid temperature t_o. It will be noted that the thermometer temperature oscillates around the same average value t_o.

$$t - t_o = \left[\frac{(\Delta t)_o}{\sqrt{1 + (2\pi f/p)^2}} \right] \sin (2\pi f \tau - \phi_L) \tag{11-28}$$

where
$$\phi_L = \arctan \frac{2\pi f}{p}$$

The amplitude of the thermometer variation is the term in brackets and is less than $(\Delta t)_o$. The peaks of the thermometer temperature lag the peaks of the fluid temperature by the angle ϕ_L or by the time interval given below:

$$\frac{\arctan (2\pi f/p)}{2\pi f}$$

A relation for the thermometer error $(t - t_f)$ is obtained by subtracting Eq. (11-27) from Eq. (11-28). The result, after some simplification, is

$$t - t_f = - \frac{(\Delta t)_o (2\pi f/p)}{1 + (2\pi f/p)^2} \left[\cos 2\pi f \tau + \left(\frac{2\pi f}{p} \right) \sin 2\pi f \tau \right] \tag{11-29}$$

The two types of response problems considered in the preceding paragraphs are typical of those which are encountered. In many circumstances the consideration of only convection transfer is justified. In the event that other effects must be considered, more complicated equations result. Further, it must be emphasized that the foregoing analysis applies only to circumstances wherein the temperature equalization within the thermometer mass is very rapid, as for high-thermal-conductivity materials or low-frequency fluid temperature changes.

Example 11-5. As a demonstration of temperature response characteristics, consider a glass thermometer, $\frac{1}{4}$ in. in diameter, immersed for L ft of its length in a stream of air moving at the constant velocity necessary to produce a surface coefficient of 10.0 Btu/hr ft^2 °F. Conduction effects inside the body of the thermometer will be ignored. Consider the thermometer error in the following circumstance. The temperature of the air stream varies sinusoidally around a value of 60°F with an amplitude of 10°F and a frequency of $\frac{1}{4}$ cycle per minute; that is, the temperature varies sinusoidally between 50 and 70°F. We are interested in the maximum error and in the average value of the error. Clearly the algebraic average value is zero, because the thermometer lags and exceeds the air temperature. Therefore, the average of the absolute value of the error is found. Equation (11-29) applies.

The relevant properties of common glass are

$$\rho = 160 \text{ lb/ft}^3 \qquad \text{and} \qquad c = 0.20 \text{ Btu/lb °F}$$

The various constants in Eq. (11-29) are found:

$$p = \frac{hA}{Mc} = \frac{hd\pi L}{(\pi/4)d^2 L\rho c} = \frac{4h}{d\rho c} = \frac{4 \times 10.0}{[1/(4 \times 12)] \times 160 \times 0.2} = 60 \text{ hr}^{-1} = 1 \text{ min}^{-1}$$

$$2\pi f = 1.571 \text{ min}^{-1}$$

$$\frac{2\pi f}{p} = \frac{1.571}{1} = 1.571$$

The condition for the error to be a maximum is found by differentiating Eq. (11-29) and setting the result equal to zero. The condition is

$$\sin 2\pi f\tau = \frac{2\pi f}{p} \cos 2\pi f\tau$$

The maximum error is

$$\frac{(\Delta t)_o (2\pi f/p)}{\sqrt{1 + (2\pi f/p)^2}} = \frac{10 \times 1.571}{\sqrt{1 + (1.571)^2}} = 8.4°F$$

The average of the absolute value of the error may be obtained by integrating the absolute value of $(t - t_f)$ over 1 cycle, that is, from τ to $\tau + 1/f$.

$$|t - t_f|_{av} = \int_{\tau}^{\tau+1/f} |t - t_f| \, d\tau$$

This operation may be carried out through the use of the relation for $(t - t_f)$. This lengthy calculation may be avoided by noting that the error is sinusoidal and that the average height of one loop of a sinusoidal curve is $2/\pi$ of the maximum. Therefore, the average error is

$$|t - t_f|_{av} = \frac{2}{\pi} (t - t_f)_{max} = 5.4°F$$

11-6. EXTENDED SURFACE

Circumstances often arise in the design of heat-transfer equipment wherein very special arrangements of heat-transfer surface will permit a considerable reduction of cost or size. One such general arrangement, extended surface, will be discussed here.

Extended surface is the term applied to an exchange surface when one or both sides of the heat-exchange surface are augmented by adding fins, pins, or other extensions. There are many instances of the use of this technique. The cylinders and heads of air-cooled engines are finned, in air-conditioning systems the outside surfaces of the cooling and dehumidifying coils are supplied with fins, and the condenser tubes of most domestic refrigerators are attached to extra metal which extends the surface. The reason for extended surface is the same in all these cases. The fluid and flow condition on one side of the solid barrier (e.g., a tube wall) results in a higher surface coefficient than pertains for the fluid and flow condition on the other side of the wall. For example, in the refrigerator condenser tube, the condensation process on the inside surface is characterized by a much higher surface coefficient than that which pertains to the natural-convection process in air on the outside surface. The heat transfer may be substantially increased by extending the surface on the side having the high heat-transfer resistance.

As an indication of the effect of extended surface, consider the specific case of heat being transferred from water flowing through a thin-walled 1-in.-ID tube to air surrounding the tube. Inside and outside surface coefficients of 100 and 2.0 Btu/hr ft^2 °F will be assumed. If the difference between inside and outside diameters and the tube wall resistance is ignored, the conductance per unit tube length is found from Eq. (11-6) as 0.513. Now, if disk fins are applied to the outside surface in the number and size necessary to make the outside area 5.0 times the inside area and if the tube wall and fin resistance to heat flow are again neglected, a much higher conductance per unit length, equal to 2.38, is found. This is 4.6 times that for the bare tube, indicating that, for a given amount of heat to be transferred, the extended-surface exchanger will require only one fourth the length of tubing. This result is optimistic, however; the resistance of the metal reduces the true conductance considerably. Further, the presence of fins may result in an outside coefficient of less than 2.0 because of fin interference with the flow.

There are two general techniques of treating the transfer characteristics of extended surface. The analytical approach begins with certain sometimes questionable assumptions about the process and then mathematically analyzes the conduction process in the solid base and extended-surface material. In the other technique the mathematical approach is supplanted by the direct measurement of the transfer rates for the particular kind of extended surface of interest. This transfer information is then fitted by equations, which, in turn, may be used in design.

As a simplified example of the analytical treatment, consider two fluids at different temperatures, t_1 and t_2, separated by a large flat plate of thermal conductivity k. The two surface coefficients are taken as h_1 and h_2. If h_2 is substantially smaller than h_1, the fins would be applied on the side of fluid 2. For fins of rectangular cross section, as shown in Fig. 11-8, let us find the heat-flow rate q_o into the root of the fin at O.

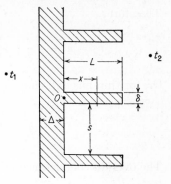

The assumptions are made that the flow of heat in the fin is one-dimensional and that the surface coefficient h_2 is constant over the whole exposed surface of the fin. The fin base temperature is taken as t_o, and temperature excess, $\theta = (t - t_2)$, is employed. This combined-mode circumstance

FIG. 11-8. Flat plate with rectangular fins.

reduces to that of a rod with convection on the lateral and end faces. This case is considered in the previous section. Equation (11-20) is the derived temperature distribution. The heat flow at O per foot length of fin, perpendicular to the plane of the figure, is obtained as follows:

$$q_o = -k\delta \left(\frac{dt}{dx}\right)_{x=0} = -\frac{k\delta}{L}\left(\frac{d\theta}{dX}\right)_{X=0} = -\frac{k\delta(t_o - t_2)}{L}\left(\frac{d\phi}{dX}\right)_{X=0} \qquad (11\text{-}30)$$

From Eq. (11-20),

$$\left(\frac{d\phi}{dX}\right)_0 = -\frac{n\{1 - [(1 - m)/(1 + m)]e^{-2n}\}}{1 + [(1 - m)/(1 + m)]e^{-2n}}$$

where n and m are defined in Eqs. (11-16) and (11-19). The P/A ratio for this fin is approximately $2/\delta$.

$$q_o = \sqrt{2kh_2\delta}(t_o - t_2)\frac{1 - [(1 - m)/(1 + m)]e^{-2n}}{1 + [(1 - m)/(1 + m)]e^{-2n}} \qquad (11\text{-}31)$$

An estimate of the increase in over-all conductance due to the fins may be made if the plate is very thin or if its thermal conductivity is very high. In this circumstance one may assume that the temperatures of the bare surface and of the base of the fin are both t_o. The over-all conductance per unit area of flat surface will be found in terms of the size and spacing of the fins. The heat dissipation for a typical sector of the outside surface consisting of one space and one fin is written in terms of an equivalent outside conductance h_2':

$$q = h_2'(s + \delta)(t_o - t_2) = h_2 s(t_o - t_2) + q_o$$

$$= h_2 s(t_o - t_2) + \sqrt{2kh_2\delta}(t_o - t_2)\frac{1 - [(1 - m)/(1 + m)]e^{-2n}}{1 + [(1 - m)/(1 + m)]e^{-2n}} \qquad (11\text{-}32)$$

Therefore,

$$h_2' = h_2 \frac{s}{s + \delta} + \frac{\sqrt{2kh_2\delta}}{s + \delta} \frac{1 - [(1 - m)/(1 + m)]e^{-2n}}{1 + [(1 - m)/(1 + m)]e^{-2n}} \quad (11\text{-}33)$$

Or, for thin fins and end convection neglected,

$$h_2' = h_2 + \frac{\sqrt{2kh_2\delta}}{s} \frac{1 - e^{-2n}}{1 + e^{-2n}} \quad (11\text{-}34)$$

The over-all conductance in terms of h_2' is

$$U_o = \frac{1}{1/h_2 + \Delta/k + 1/h_2'} \quad (11\text{-}35)$$

The conductance is higher than that for a bare wall because h_2' is larger than h_2.

The effectiveness of extended surface, defined as the heat-dissipation rate q_o divided by the dissipation rate of the bare surface at t_o covered by the fins, is, for the rectangular fin,

$$e = \frac{q_o}{q_o'} = \frac{q_o}{h_2\delta(t_o - t_2)} = \sqrt{\frac{2k}{h_2\delta}} \frac{1 - [(1 - m)/(1 + m)]e^{-2n}}{1 + [(1 - m)/(1 + m)]e^{-2n}} \quad (11\text{-}36)$$

The efficiency of the fin, defined as the ratio of q_o to the rate of heat dissipation that would result if the whole fin surface were at t_o, is also found for this case:

$$\eta = \frac{q_o}{h_2(2L + \delta)(t_o - t_2)} = \frac{\sqrt{2kh_2\delta}}{h_2(2L + \delta)} \frac{1 - [(1 - m)/(1 + m)]e^{-2n}}{1 + [(1 - m)/(1 + m)]e^{-2n}} \quad (11\text{-}37)$$

If δ is small compared with L and if end convection is neglected, that is, $m = 0$, we have

$$\eta = \sqrt{\frac{\delta}{2L}} \sqrt{\frac{k}{hL}} \frac{1 - e^{-2n}}{1 + e^{-2n}} = \frac{1}{n}\left(\frac{1 - e^{-2n}}{1 + e^{-2n}}\right) \quad (11\text{-}38)$$

The latter quantity, efficiency, is a very valuable criterion and is used to assess the relative merits of various arrangements of extended surface—for example, of the rectangular fin as considered above vs. a fin of triangular section. Many cross-sectional shapes have been analyzed both for straight fins on a plate and for circular fins on the outside of tubes. Information is available concerning optimum profiles. Some types of fins have been analyzed without the assumption of one-dimensional flow, and the effects of this simplification have been studied. Various of the other common assumptions have been questioned in a similar way. A summary of the subject is to be found in Jakob (1949) and in Schneider (1955).

The mathematical analysis does not readily yield design information for the diverse types of extended surface encountered in practice. Many types of surface have been tested, and many results have been presented. For example, Katz and coworkers have measured the performance of tubes which were rolled to produce spiral fins of various heights and spacings on the outside surface. Tests were carried out with various fluid combinations for single and banked tubes [see Katz, Beatty, and Foust (1945)]. Williams and Katz (1952) reported results for banked tubes in shell-and-tube exchangers.

11-7. NUMERICAL METHODS IN COMBINED-MODE PROCESSES

In Secs. 2-6 and 3-5 numerical methods are applied to the solution of steady-state and transient conduction processes. The finite-difference approximation of the general conduction differential equation is developed and applied under conditions in which the boundary conditions amount to the specification of temperature conditions on surfaces. The present section considers combined-mode processes, wherein the boundary conditions are more complicated and are expressed, perhaps, in terms of surface convection and radiation processes.

In order to treat processes with more complicated surface conditions, these boundary conditions must be expressed in finite-difference form. These relations, for network points on the surface, are called "surface-point equations." Such equations are used in conjunction with the finite-difference relation which applies in the conduction region in order to obtain a numerical solution. The surface-point equations are developed below for one- and two-dimensional conduction processes.

Consider a one-dimensional conduction region subdivided into a network, as shown in Fig. 11-9. Since the conduction process is one-dimensional, the exposed sur-

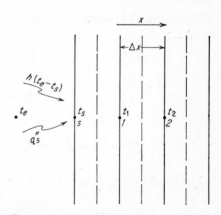

FIG. 11-9. Surface conditions for a one-dimensional conduction process.

face will be isothermal. The exposed surface is in contact with a fluid at t_e. A surface coefficient h characterizes the energy-transfer process between the fluid and the surface. In order to include all types of surface processes, we shall assume that the surface is subject to an additional heat flux q_s'', due, perhaps, to radiation or to energy generation at the surface. q_s'' is taken as positive if it is a gain at the surface.

The surface-point equation for this one-dimensional case is determined by writing an energy balance for the mass of material associated with point s, the surface point. Since the masses between the dashed lines in Fig. 11-9 are associated with planes 1 and 2, respectively, the slab of thickness $\Delta x/2$ is associated with the surface plane s. The energy balance for this mass equates the energy gains due to the conduction from plane 1, the convection from the fluid at t_e, and the additional surface flux q_s'' to the rate of increase of stored energy in the mass associated with point s. No distributed source is assumed present. The rate of energy gain, per unit area normal to x, is

$$\frac{k}{\Delta x}(t_1 - t_s) + h(t_e - t_s) + q_s''$$

The rate of change of stored energy is

$$\rho c\, \frac{\Delta x}{2}\, \frac{t_{s,\Delta\tau} - t_s}{\Delta\tau}$$

where $t_{s,\Delta\tau}$ is the temperature at s after a time interval $\Delta\tau$. The surface-point equation is, therefore,

$$(t_1 - t_s) + \frac{h\,\Delta x}{k}(t_e - t_s) + \frac{q_s''\,\Delta x}{k} = \frac{\Delta x^2}{2\alpha\,\Delta\tau}(t_{s,\Delta\tau} - t) \quad (11\text{-}39a)$$

This relation is rewritten in terms of M, defined in Sec. 3-5, and N, a Biot number:

$$M = \frac{\Delta x^2}{\alpha\,\Delta\tau} \qquad\qquad (11\text{-}40)$$

$$N = \frac{h\,\Delta x}{k} \qquad\qquad (11\text{-}41)$$

$$(t_1 - t_s) + N(t_e - t_s) + \frac{q_s''\,\Delta x}{k} = \frac{M}{2}(t_{s,\Delta\tau} - t_s) \quad (11\text{-}39b)$$

For steady state, $t_{s,\Delta\tau} = t_s$ and Eq. (11-39b) becomes

$$Nt_e + t_1 + \frac{q_s''\,\Delta x}{2k} - (N + 1)t_s = 0 \qquad (11\text{-}42)$$

This is in the form of a residual equation [see Eq. (2-45)]. For unsteady state, Eq. (11-39b) is written in the following form:

$$t_{s,\Delta\tau} = \frac{2N}{M} t_e + \frac{2}{M} t_1 + \frac{2q_s'' \, \Delta x}{kM}$$

$$+ \left(1 - \frac{2N+2}{M} \right) t_s \quad (11\text{-}43)$$

This relation is in a form similar to that of the calculation equations for unsteady-state conduction processes, Eqs. (3-31) to (3-33).

Consider the two-dimensional conduction region subdivided by a square network, as shown in Fig. 11-10. In general, the exposed surface is not

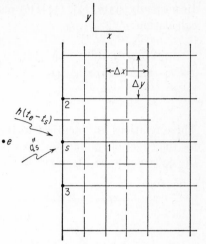

FIG. 11-10. Surface conditions for a two-dimensional conduction region.

isothermal, and t_s represents the average temperature only of the surface between the dashed lines. The mass associated with point s is $\rho \Delta x^2/2$ per unit depth. The mass associated with point s receives energy by conduction from the vicinity of points 1, 2, and 3. Convection and surface flux are also assumed present.

The sum of energy-gain rates is set equal to the time rate of change of stored energy:

$$\frac{k \, \Delta x}{\Delta x} (t_1 - t_s) + \frac{k \, \Delta x}{2 \, \Delta x} (t_2 - t_s) + \frac{k \, \Delta x}{2 \, \Delta x} (t_3 - t_s) + h \, \Delta x \, (t_e - t_s) + q_s'' \, \Delta x$$

$$= \frac{\rho c \, \Delta x^2}{2} \frac{t_{s,\Delta\tau} - t_s}{\Delta \tau} \quad (11\text{-}44a)$$

This relation is rewritten in terms of M and N, defined in Eqs. (11-40) and (11-41), as

$$(t_1 - t_s) + \frac{t_2 - t_s}{2} + \frac{t_3 - t_s}{2} + N(t_e - t_s) + \frac{q_s'' \, \Delta x}{k} = \frac{M}{2} (t_{s,\Delta\tau} - t)$$

$$(11\text{-}44b)$$

For steady state, $t_{s,\Delta\tau} = t_s$, and Eq. (11-44b) is written in the form of a residual equation:

$$Nt_e + t_1 + \frac{t_2 + t_3}{2} + \frac{q_s'' \, \Delta x}{k} - (N+2)t_s = 0 \quad (11\text{-}45)$$

In unsteady state, Eq. (11-44b) may be written in the form for repetitive calculation:

$$t_{s,\Delta\tau} = \frac{2N}{M} t_e + \frac{2}{M} t_1 + \frac{1}{M} (t_2 + t_3) + \frac{2q_s'' \, \Delta x}{kM} + \left(1 - \frac{2N+4}{M}\right) t_s$$

$$(11\text{-}46)$$

These relations are identical to those for the one-dimensional case except for the effect of conduction from points 2 and 3. If point s is at a corner, the equations must be modified for the different conduction effects.

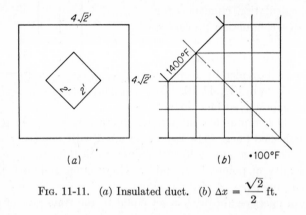

$4\sqrt{2}'$

$4\sqrt{2}'$

1400°F

$\quad (a) \qquad\qquad\qquad (b) \qquad$ •100°F

FIG. 11-11.   (a) Insulated duct.   (b) $\Delta x = \dfrac{\sqrt{2}}{2}$ ft.

We recall that in Sec. 3-5 lower limits were established for the value of the network parameter M. These limits resulted from the condition that the temperature level at a point may not have a negative effect upon the subsequent temperatures at that point. For one- and two-dimensional processes the lower limits on M were 2 and 4, respectively. The one- and two-dimensional surface-point equations (11-43) and (11-46) place an even more stringent restriction upon M. If the coefficients of t_s are to be zero or positive, then

$$M \geq 2N + 2 \qquad \text{for one-dimensional cases}$$

$$M \geq 2N + 4 \qquad \text{for two-dimensional cases}$$

We note from Eq. (11-41) that N is always positive.

The remainder of this section is devoted to the numerical solution of two problems in which combined-mode heat transfer appears. The first case considered is two-dimensional steady state, and the second is one-dimensional unsteady state.

Steady-state Numerical Solution. The two-dimensional case will be the insulated metal duct shown in Fig. 11-11. Convection and radiation processes occur at the outer surface. This is the same geometry as considered in Sec. 2-6 with isothermal surface conditions. An outside surface convection coefficient of 2.0 Btu/hr ft² °F is taken in this solution. The duct is in a large enclosure in which the air and surface temperatures are 100°F. The emissivity of the outside surface of the insulation is taken as 0.6. The fluid flowing inside the duct has a temperature of 1400°F, and the surface coefficient and metal-duct conductance are assumed sufficiently large so that the inside surface of the refractory insulation may be assumed to be at 1400°F. The thermal conductivity of the insulation is taken as 1.41 Btu/hr ft °F. The temperature distribution and heat loss are found employing a $\sqrt{2}/2$-ft grid.

The residual equation for an interior point is

$$t_1 + t_2 + t_3 + t_4 - 4t_o = R_o$$

For surface points not at the corner, Eq. (11-45) applies:

$$N = \frac{h \, \Delta x}{k} = \frac{2 \times \sqrt{2}}{2 \times 1.41} = 1$$

$$t_e + t_1 + \frac{t_2 + t_3}{2} + \frac{q_s'' \, \Delta x}{k} - 3t_s = R_s$$

For the point at the corner,

$$t_e + \frac{t_2 + t_3}{2} + \frac{q_s'' \, \Delta x}{k} - 2t_s = R_s$$

The radiation term $q_s'' \, \Delta x / k$ depends upon t_s and varies over the surface. In addition, it must be changed in computing the residual at a surface point when the temperature at that point is changed. Calculations are considerably simplified by preparing a table of $q_s'' \, \Delta x / k$ versus t_s.

$$\frac{q_s'' \, \Delta x}{k} = \frac{\Delta x}{k} \left[\frac{\sigma(T_e{}^4 - T_s{}^4)}{1/\epsilon_1 + (A_1/A_2)(1/\epsilon_2 - 1)} \right]$$

$$= -\frac{\Delta x \, \epsilon_1 \sigma(T_s{}^4 - 560^4)}{k} = -0.052 \left[\left(\frac{T_s}{100} \right)^4 - 985 \right]$$

The value is negative since q_s'' was taken positive for an energy gain.

RADIATION TERM

t_s, °F	$(q_s'' \, \Delta x)/k$, °F
100	0
200	-47
250	-80
300	-122
350	-173
400	-233

Temperatures are assumed where unknown in the network, and residuals are calculated from the three residual equations. These residuals are then reduced toward zero. The resulting distribution is shown in Fig. 11-12. The outside surface is seen to have a considerable temperature variation.

The heat-transfer rate per unit duct length may be calculated from conduction rods in the insulation, shown in Fig. 11-12, or by summing the rates of convection and radiation loss from the surface. Both calculations

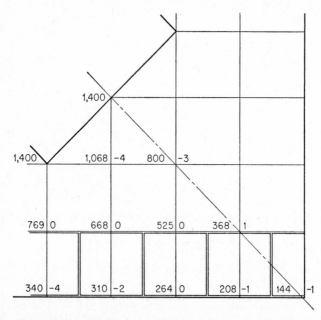

FIG. 11-12.   Temperature distribution with convection and radiation at the outside surface.

are carried out below. By conduction,

$$\frac{q}{L} = 8k \left[\frac{769-340}{2} + (668-310) + (525-264) + (368-208) + \frac{208-144}{2} \right]$$

$$= 11{,}600 \text{ Btu/hr ft}$$

By convection and radiation,

$$\frac{q}{L} = 8h\,\Delta x \left[\frac{340-100}{2} + (310-100) + (264-100) + (208-100) \right.$$

$$\left. + \frac{144-100}{2} \right] + 8k \left(\frac{162}{2} + 131 + 90 + 53 + \frac{16}{2} \right) = 7060 + 4100$$

$$= 11{,}160 \text{ Btu/hr ft}^2$$

These two estimates agree within 4 per cent. A smaller grid would presumably result in closer agreement.

Transient Numerical Solution. As an example of a numerical solution of a transient process, consider heating small, thin billets of steel, 1 in. in diameter and $\frac{3}{16}$ in. thick, by placing them at the focus of a concentrating solar collector. The solar collector produces a flux of 2×10^6 Btu/hr ft^2 at the focus, and the absorptivity of the surface of the billet for solar radiation is assumed to be 0.50. Reflected energy is assumed lost. The unexposed side of the billet is adiabatic. The total surface coefficient for the exposed surface is taken as 3 Btu/hr ft^2 °F, and the temperature of the surroundings is 60°F. The properties of the steel are

$$c = 0.15 \text{ Btu/lb °F} \qquad \rho = 468 \text{ lb/ft}^3 \qquad k = 42 \text{ Btu/hr ft °F}$$

We shall find the time necessary to raise the minimum temperature in the billet to 250°F if its initial temperature is uniformly 100°F.

The network system is shown in Fig. 11-13. A grid size of $\frac{1}{16}$ in. is taken. The adiabatic-surface condition is met by doubling the thickness of the billet and subjecting both sides to the same transfer process. The general calculation equations for the interior and surface points are

$$t_{o,\Delta\tau} = \frac{1}{M}(t_1 + t_2) + \left(1 - \frac{2}{M}\right) t_o \qquad (3\text{-}33)$$

$$t_{s,\Delta\tau} = \frac{2N}{M} t_e + \frac{2}{M} t_1 + \frac{2q_s'' \, \Delta x}{kM} + \left(1 - \frac{2N+2}{M}\right) t_s \quad (11\text{-}43)$$

The value of N is

$$N = \frac{h \, \Delta x}{k} = \frac{3}{16 \times 12 \times 42} = 0.00037$$

Clearly the effect of N is negligible in Eq. (11-43). That is, the effect of convection is negligible. Therefore, an M of 2 is permissible, and the specific equations and time interval are

$$t_{o,\Delta \tau} = \frac{t_1 + t_2}{2} \tag{3-34}$$

$$t_{s,\Delta \tau} = t_1 + \frac{q_s'' \, \Delta x}{k} = t_1 + 124 \tag{11-47}$$

since

$$\frac{q_s'' \, \Delta x}{k} = \frac{0.5(q_s'')_i \, \Delta x}{k} = 124$$

and

$$\Delta \tau = \frac{\Delta x^2}{M \alpha} = 0.0813 \text{ sec}$$

The problem is solved in Table 11-1 by the repeated application of Eqs. (3-34) and (11-47). Temperature excess, $\theta = (t - t_i)$, is employed to simplify the numerical operations.

The minimum temperature excess is at point c. A value of 150°F is reached after 10 iterations. Therefore, the necessary exposure time is approximately 0.813 sec.

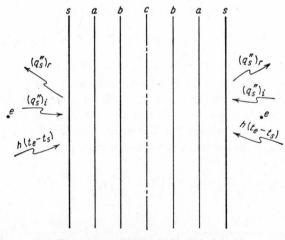

FIG. 11-13.   Radiantly heated plate.

TABLE 11-1. CALCULATION FOR PLATE OF FIG. 11-13

n	θ_s	θ_a	θ_b	θ_c	θ_b
0	0	0	0	0	0
1	124	0	0	0	0
2	124	62	0	0	0
3	186	62	31	0	31
4	186	109	31	31	31
5	233	109	70	31	70
6	233	152	70	70	70
7	276	152	111	70	111
8	...	194	111	111	111
9	...	...	153	111	153
10	...	...	...	153	

NOTATION

c	specific heat
C	conductance
e	fin effectiveness
h	surface coefficient
h_c	convection coefficient
h_r	radiation surface coefficient
k	thermal conductivity
M	the reciprocal of the grid Fourier number
N	the grid Biot number
N_{Nu}	Nusselt number
N_{Ra}	Rayleigh number
N_{Re}	Reynolds number
q''	heat flux
R_j	resistance of the jth layer
R_o	over-all resistance
t	temperature, °F or °C
T	absolute temperature
U_o	over-all coefficient of heat transmission
α	thermal diffusivity
ϵ	total hemispherical emissivity
η	fin efficiency
θ	temperature excess
μ	absolute viscosity
ρ	density of mass
σ	universal constant for black-body radiation
τ	time
ϕ	ratio of temperature excesses

REFERENCES

Jakob, M.: "Heat Transfer," vol. 1, John Wiley & Sons, Inc., New York, 1949.
Katz, D. L., K. O. Beatty, Jr., and A. S. Foust: *Trans. ASME*, vol. 60, p. 665, 1945.
Rowley, F. B., and A. B. Algren: *Univ. Minn. Eng. Exp. Sta. Bull.* 12, 1937.
Schneider, P. J.: "Conduction Heat Transfer," Addison-Wesley Publishing Company, Reading, Mass., 1955.
Williams, R. B., and D. L. Katz: *Trans. ASME*, vol. 74, p. 1307, 1952.

PROBLEMS

1. The front wall of a building is to be 8-in.-thick poured gravel concrete faced with a 4-in.-thick layer of brick and finished on the inside surface with a 1-in.-thick layer of gypsum plaster. Both surfacing materials are to be applied directly to the concrete, with no air spaces being provided. The outside and inside surface coefficients may be taken as 2.0 Btu/hr ft^2 °F. For inside and outside temperatures of 70 and 20°F, estimate the heat loss per square foot of wall and the inside surface temperature.

2. For the circumstance described in Prob. 1, find the heat loss and inside surface temperature if the plaster is applied to metal lath which is suspended 2 in. from the inside face of the concrete wall. The space between the lath and the concrete is to be filled with rock-wool insulation. What is the lowest temperature encountered in the insulation?

3. A 2-in. nominal steel pipe contains water at 250°F flowing at an average velocity of 4 fps. The air and enclosure walls surrounding the pipe are at 70°F. On the basis of outside surface free-convection and radiation coefficients computed for a bare pipe, compute and compare the heat losses per unit length for the bare pipe and for the pipe covered with a 1-in.-thick layer of 85 per cent magnesia insulation.

4. Superheated steam at 300 psia and 460°F flows at a velocity of 100 fps through a 4-in. nominal steel pipe. The pipe is covered with a 1½-in. layer of 85 per cent magnesia insulation. The surfacing material on the outside of the insulation has an emissivity of 0.90. The pipe runs horizontally through a space wherein the air and surface temperatures are 70°F. Find the heat loss per foot of pipe length and the maximum temperature in the insulation.

5. For the circumstance given in Prob. 1, plot the heat flux through the wall vs. outside wind velocity for the range 0 to 20 mph.

6. Water at 180°F flows through horizontal ½-in., type L copper tubing at a velocity of 20 fps. Saturated steam at 15 psia condenses in a filmwise manner on the outside surface. Assuming that the surfaces of the tube are isothermal, find the heat-transfer and condensation rates per foot of tube length.

7. Consider a cylindrical pressure vessel with hemispherical ends. The inside radius of the cylindrical section and hemispherical end caps is 18 in. The length of the cylindrical section is 10 ft. The steel thickness is uniformly 6 in., and the outside surface is insulated with 5 in. of 85 per cent magnesia. The vessel is to contain steam at 3500 psia and 800°F, and the estimated inside surface coefficient is 40.0 Btu/hr ft^2 °F. The surroundings are at 100°F, and a total outside surface coefficient of 3.0 Btu/hr ft^2 °F is expected.

a. Compute the rate of heat loss from the vessel.

b. Estimate the outside surface temperature on the cylindrical part. Would the computed surface temperature on the spherical part differ?   Explain.   Would it be higher or lower?

c. Compute the rate of heat loss from the vessel, assuming that all surfaces are flat and using the inside surface area throughout.   Explain the difference between the results of parts *c* and *a*.

8. A $\frac{3}{4}$-in. copper tube, $\frac{3}{4}$ in. OD and $\frac{11}{16}$ in. ID, carries water at 300°F at a high velocity.   Consider insulating this tube with a material which has a thermal conductivity of 0.10 Btu/hr ft °F.   The expected outside surface coefficient is 2.5 Btu/hr ft² °F. The inside surface and tube wall resistances may be assumed small compared with the resistance of the insulation and outside surface when insulation is present.   The surroundings are at 70°F.   Find the bare-tube heat loss, the maximum heat loss and the insulation thickness which would produce it, and the heat loss for an insulation thickness double that which would produce the maximum loss.

9. For the circumstance presented in Prob. 3, with a given outside surface coefficient of 1.5 Btu/hr ft² °F, find whether or not a maximum heat loss occurs as the insulation thickness is decreased to zero.

10. A 1-in. nominal standard-weight pipe is insulated with a 1-in.-thick layer of 85 per cent magnesia.   The outside surface of the insulation cover is painted with a 10 per cent aluminum paint.   The outside surface temperature of the insulation is 100°F, and ambient-air and surrounding temperatures are 60°F.   Find the total surface coefficient and heat loss per foot of length.

11. Consider a 2-in.-thick air space whose enclosing surfaces have emissivities of 0.70 and are at temperatures of 60 and 30°F.   Calculate the total conductance and heat-transfer rate if the air space is vertical.   Repeat the calculation if the air space is horizontal, with the 60°F below the 30°F surface.

12. A wall is to be constructed with an air space between the outside wall and the inside finish.   Assume that the surfaces enclosing the space are to be relatively smooth and that they will have emissivities of 0.9.   Two widths of air space are considered, $\frac{1}{2}$ and 2 in.   Contrast the kinds of transfer processes which will occur in these two cases. Compute the two conductances for enclosing surface temperatures of 40 and 20°F, and estimate the ratio of heat losses per unit area for the two circumstances if the sum of the resistances for the remaining elements of the wall is 3.0, in typical units.

13. For a 4-in. air space in the wall discussed in Prob. 12, consider the effect of installing reflective surfaces.   Calculate the total air-space conductances when the enclosing surfaces both have emissivities of 0.9 and 0.10 and, for the 0.10 case, when a sheet of aluminum foil of 0.10 emissivity is placed in the center of the air space, dividing it into two 2-in.-thick spaces.   Compute the percentage reductions in heat loss through the wall due to breaking up the air space if the sum of the resistances of the remaining elements of the wall is still taken as 3.0.

14. Given a 3-in.-thick vertical air space whose surface temperatures are to be taken as 40 and 0°F in all cases.   We wish to consider the effect on total conductance of breaking up the space by putting in parallel thin sheets of reflective material.   Assume that all surfaces have an emissivity of 0.08 and calculate the total air-space conductance for no sheets, one sheet, and two sheets if the sheets are placed to divide the space into layers of equal thickness.

15. A building wall is constructed as follows.   The outside surface is 3-in. brick laid against a $\frac{3}{4}$-in.-thick layer of pine sheathing.   The sheathing is attached to studs on 16-in. centers whose depth is $3\frac{5}{8}$ in.   Rock lath is attached to the studs and is covered on the inside surface with a $\frac{1}{2}$-in.-thick layer of gypsum plaster.   The rock lath and sheathing may be assumed to have emissivities of 0.9.   Compute the over-all coefficient and the heat-transfer rate per unit area if the inside temperature is 70°F and the outside temperature and wind velocity are 0°F and 15 mph. An inside surface total conductance of 1.5 may be used. The conductance of the rock lath is 0.30.

16. Well-mixed combustion gases at 14.7 psia and 1500°F are to flow from a large combustion chamber into a 6-in.-ID pipe whose wall temperature is not to exceed 500°F. Just inside the entrance to the pipe a solid-steel strut of $\frac{1}{2}$ in. diameter is to be placed across the passage, perpendicular to the direction of flow. The strut is expected to be in good thermal contact with the pipe wall at both ends where it contacts the pipe. The average velocity of the gases in the passage is to be 150 fps. Determine the maximum temperature to which the metal of the strut will be subjected. For the properties of the combustion gases use those of air at the same temperature.

17. For the circumstance of Prob. 16, the suggestion is made that a very small hole be drilled for the length of the strut and that a thermocouple junction be placed at the center to measure the gas temperature. Estimate the thermometer error for the gas conditions given in Prob. 16 if the strut is $\frac{1}{4}$-in.-diameter steel. How may the design be further modified to reduce this error?

18. A glass thermometer is to be suspended normal to a stream of air moving at a velocity of 100 fps. The air stream, initially at a temperature of 60°F, is to change abruptly to 100°F. Estimate the thermometer reading at times of 30 and 80 sec after the temperature change occurs for a $\frac{1}{4}$-in.-diameter thermometer. What effect does thermometer diameter have upon the error at a given time? Find the errors at 30 and 80 sec for a $\frac{1}{8}$-in.-diameter thermometer.

19. Develop an expression for the over-all conductance, per unit length, of a tube having extended surface on the outside. The inside and outside surface areas of the tube per unit length may be taken as A_i and A_o. Neglect the thermal resistance of the metal.

20. A $\frac{1}{16}$-in.-thick aluminum plate is provided on one side with $\frac{1}{16}$- by $\frac{1}{2}$-in. rectangular aluminum fins spaced at $\frac{1}{2}$ in. on centers. The finned side is in contact with CO_2 at 60°F, and the surface coefficient is to be 3.0 Btu/hr ft² °F. The fluid on the plain side is water at 100°F, and the surface coefficient will be 20.0 Btu/hr ft² °F. Find the effectiveness and efficiency of the fins.

21. For the circumstance described in Prob. 20, compute the rate of heat transfer per square foot of area for the bare plate and for the finned plate, assuming that the bare surface and fin base have the same temperature.

22. Plot the variations of effectiveness and efficiency vs. length for $\frac{1}{8}$-in.-thick copper fins for a surface coefficient of 4.0 Btu/hr ft² °F. Also include the curve for efficiency, if end convection is ignored.

23. For a thermometric device installed in a fluid stream whose temperature varies sinusoidally, derive the expression for the maximum thermometer error and find the "phase angle" between the stream and thermometer temperature variations.

24a. For three-dimensional conduction, develop the surface-point equations for steady- and unsteady-state processes. Include the effects of conduction, convection, surface flux, and an internal distributed source.

b. Determine the steady-state equations for surface points on outside edges and corners.

25a. For the wall in Prob. 28 of Chap. 2, assume that the side of the plate supplied with stiffeners is in contact with a fluid at 50°F and that the convection coefficient is 6 Btu/hr ft² °F. The flat surface is at 450°F. Neglecting radiation, find the heat-transfer rate per square foot of flat wall area, using a 1- by 1-in. grid.

b. Compare the over-all conductance with that of a flat wall.

c. What is the upper limit of the conductance ratio as the outside surface resistance increases?

26. For the chimney in Prob. 29 of Chap. 2, find the heat loss per foot of chimney height for a combustion-product temperature of 400°F and a surroundings temperature of 50°F. A convection coefficient of 2.0 Btu/hr ft^2 °F applies for the inside surface, and a combined convection and radiation coefficient of 4.0 Btu/hr ft^2 °F applies for the outside surface. Compute the average temperature of the outside surface of the chimney.

27. In a metallurgical process, large 2-in.-thick steel plates are to be preheated to a minimum metal temperature of 170°F by suspending them in a special salt bath maintained at 550°F. The plates are initially at 100°F throughout. The properties of steel ($k = 41.7$ and $\alpha = 0.6$) are assumed independent of temperature. A surface coefficient of 300 Btu/hr ft^2 °F is expected.

  a. Find the minimum M permissible if a grid size of $\frac{1}{2}$ in. is to be used.

  b. Using $M = 3$, find the necessary immersion time. Compare this result with that obtained from the Heisler charts.

  c. What is the average plate temperature when the minimum is 170°F?

28. An extensive stone concrete wall, 6 in. thick, is exposed to air on one side. The other side, in contact with dry insulation, may be considered adiabatic. The wall is at 60°F throughout when the air temperature begins changing at a constant rate of 10°/hr to 30°F and remains at that level thereafter. The surface coefficient is 2. Using a grid size of 2 in., find the time necessary for the minimum temperature at the wall to drop to 45°F. Where is this minimum located?

$$k = 1.0 \qquad \rho = 144 \qquad c = 0.2$$

29. The fuel elements of a nuclear reactor are $\frac{1}{2}$-in.-thick, 1- by 1-ft plates spaced 1 in. apart. The plates are cooled by pumping high-pressure water at 500°F at high velocity through the spaces. The resulting surface coefficient is high enough so that the element surface temperature is essentially equal to the water temperature. The design energy-generation rate is 2×10^7 Btu/hr ft^3 of fuel-element material, and the generation is assumed to be uniformly distributed in the element material. The properties of the fuel-element material are

$$k = 16 \text{ Btu/hr ft °F} \qquad \rho = 1170 \text{ lb/ft}^3 \qquad c = 0.028 \text{ Btu/lb °F}$$

An important design consideration is the rate of element-material temperature increase which would result from a coolant-pump failure. Assume that in such a circumstance the reactor would remain filled and pressurized and that a natural-convection coefficient of 200 Btu/hr ft^2 °F would apply between the element and the water.

  a. For normal operation, find the maximum temperature in the element material.

  b. Find the time interval, after pump failure, for the maximum element temperature to increase 100°F. Use approximate numerical methods with $\Delta x = \frac{1}{8}$ in. and assume the bulk water temperature constant during this interval.

30. Thin metal plates, $\frac{3}{8}$ in. thick, initially at 60°F, are to be heated by high-frequency electrical induction. Heating occurs in surroundings at 60°F, and a surface coefficient of 3 Btu/hr ft^2 °F applies. The heating rate is 10^6 Btu/hr ft^2 of plate surface and may be assumed generated right at the surface (on the two sides of the plate). The thermal diffusivity of the metal is 0.60 ft^2/hr. Using a $\frac{1}{16}$-in. grid, find the time necessary for the minimum metal temperature to reach 425°F.

$$k = 41.7 \text{ Btu/hr ft °F}$$

31. Heat is transferred from water at 120°F to air at 60°F through a $\frac{3}{32}$-in.-thick aluminum plate fitted with plate fins $\frac{1}{16}$ in. thick and $\frac{3}{4}$ in. high on the air side. The fin spacing is $\frac{3}{16}$ in., center to center. The water- and air-side surface coefficients may be taken as 100 and 5 Btu/hr ft^2 °F, respectively.

a. In the absence of fins, find the heat-transfer rate per square foot of plate area and the inside and outside plate surface temperatures.

b. Find the heat-transfer rate per square foot of plate area with fins, employing the results of the analysis in Sec. 11-6.

c. Repeat part b, using a numerical method and a grid size of $\frac{1}{32}$ in.

d. For the heat-transfer rates calculated in parts b and c, compute and contrast the fin efficiencies and effectivenesses.

CHAPTER 12

Design Considerations

12-1. ASPECTS OF EXCHANGER DESIGN

The principles and information summarized in preceding chapters are widely applied in the design of heat exchangers, whose primary function is to transfer heat, and in the design of devices in which heat transfer occurs in conjunction with other effects. The present chapter presents in some detail the special considerations, definitions, and information employed in design.

Many types of exchangers have been developed to meet the widely varying applications for such equipment. Shell-and-tube arrangements, often used where heat-transfer effectiveness and reliability are important, are discussed in Sec. 12-3. Exchangers of more compact design, employed where weight, space, and cost limitations are severe, are considered in Sec. 12-4. An indication of the effect of fouling of transfer surface in use is discussed in Sec. 12-5, and considerations important in obtaining optimum design sizes are presented in Sec. 12-6.

12-2. AVERAGE EXCHANGER TEMPERATURE DIFFERENCES

An exchanger provides the surface area necessary to transfer energy from one fluid stream to another. The temperatures of both fluids may change while flowing through the exchanger. Consider, for example, the simple exchanger shown in Fig. 12-1. The energy transferred between the streams results in a change in the temperature of each fluid stream if neither fluid is undergoing a phase change. As a result of the gradual change in the temperature levels in an exchanger, the temperature difference across the heat-transfer barrier, the separating surface and accompanying resistances, varies over the length of the exchanger. The over-all coefficient U_o may also vary, because of velocity, property, and other changes.

In general, the rate of heat transfer per unit area at any location in the exchanger may be written as the product of the local over-all coefficient U_o and the local over-all temperature difference between the two streams Δt_o. The values of U_o and Δt_o may vary over the exchanger. However, at this point we shall consider only the variation of Δt_o; U_o is considered constant.

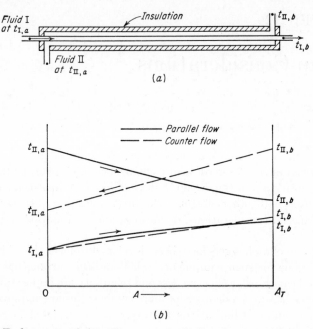

FIG. 12-1. Exchanger consisting of two concentric flow passages. (a) Single-tube exchanger. (b) Temperature distributions.

It is general practice to set the total heat-transfer rate of an exchanger equal to the product of U_o, the total exchange area A_T, and a mean temperature difference $(\Delta t_o)_m$, as in Eq. (12-1). Clearly, $(\Delta t_o)_m$ is a function of the geometry of the particular exchanger and of the way in which the fluid temperatures change through the exchanger. Therefore, Eq. (12-1) serves as the definition of $(\Delta t_o)_m$:

$$q_T = U_o A_T (\Delta t_o)_m \qquad (12\text{-}1)$$

The relation between the exchanger mean temperature difference, $(\Delta t_o)_m$, and the fluid temperature distributions is considered for several important arrangements. The simplest possible case would be an exchanger of the design shown in Fig. 12-1a with each fluid exchanging heat at a constant temperature level, as would be the case, for example, if each fluid was a pure substance changing phase at constant pressure. Then

$$t_{I,a} = t_{I,b} \qquad t_{II,a} = t_{II,b} \qquad \text{and} \qquad (\Delta t_o)_m = (t_{I,a} - t_{II,a}) = (t_{I,b} - t_{II,b})$$

A more complicated relation of considerable interest occurs when the heat-transfer process between fluids I and II in the arrangement of Fig. 12-1a causes a temperature change in both streams. There are two cases: the fluids may flow in the same direction, parallel flow; or in opposite directions, counterflow. Figure 12-1b shows the types of temperature distributions which result. Counterflow results in a higher value of $(\Delta t_o)_m$ for given initial fluid temperatures and is, therefore, the most effective arrangement.

The relation between $(\Delta t_o)_m$ and the four extreme fluid temperatures may be derived using the mass rates of flow and the specific heats of the two fluids, that is, m_I, m_{II}, c_I, and c_{II}. Fluid I is assumed flowing to the right, and fluid II flows to the right for parallel flow and to the left for counterflow. The temperatures are designated as in Fig. 12-1, regardless of the flow direction of fluid II. For any small element of exchange area dA, the heat-flow rate dq may be written as

$$dq = U_o \, \Delta t_o \, dA = m_I c_I \, dt_I = m_{II} c_{II} (\mp dt_{II})$$

where $-dt_{II}$ and $+dt_{II}$ apply to parallel and counterflow, respectively. Because of changes in t_I and t_{II}, the value of Δt_o changes as follows:

$$d(\Delta t_o) = d(t_{II} - t_I) = dt_{II} - dt_I = \mp \frac{dq}{m_{II} c_{II}} - \frac{dq}{m_I c_I}$$

$$= dq \left(\mp \frac{1}{m_{II} c_{II}} - \frac{1}{m_I c_I} \right) = U_o \, \Delta t_o \, dA \left(\mp \frac{1}{m_{II} c_{II}} - \frac{1}{m_I c_I} \right)$$

This differential relation for Δt_o may be rearranged and integrated over the area of the exchanger surface from $A = 0$, at the left end, to $A = A_T$, at the right end:

$$\int_{(\Delta t_o)_a}^{(\Delta t_o)_b} \frac{d(\Delta t_o)}{\Delta t_o} = \int_0^{A_T} \left[\mp \frac{1}{m_{II} c_{II}} - \frac{1}{m_I c_I} \right] U_o \, dA \qquad (12\text{-}2)$$

If U_o, c_I, and c_{II} are constant, the two sides are integrated and rearranged, using Eq. (12-1), to give

$$\ln \frac{(\Delta t_o)_b}{(\Delta t_o)_a} = U_o A_T \left(\mp \frac{1}{m_{II} c_{II}} - \frac{1}{m_I c_I} \right) = \frac{1}{(\Delta t_o)_m} \left(\mp \frac{q_T}{m_{II} c_{II}} - \frac{q_T}{m_I c_I} \right)$$

But since

$$q_T = m_I c_I (t_{I,b} - t_{I,a}) = \mp m_{II} c_{II} (t_{II,b} - t_{II,a})$$

$$\ln \frac{(\Delta t_o)_b}{(\Delta t_o)_a} = \frac{1}{(\Delta t_o)_m} [(t_{II,b} - t_{II,a}) - (t_{I,b} - t_{I,a})]$$

$$= \frac{1}{(\Delta t_o)_m} [(\Delta t_o)_b - (\Delta t_o)_a]$$

and

$$(\Delta t_o)_m = \frac{(\Delta t_o)_b - (\Delta t_o)_a}{\ln [(\Delta t_o)_b / (\Delta t_o)_a]} = \frac{(\Delta t_o)_a - (\Delta t_o)_b}{\ln [(\Delta t_o)_a / (\Delta t_o)_b]} = (\Delta t_o)_L \qquad (12\text{-}3)$$

The above relation for $(\Delta t_o)_m$, applicable to a single-tube exchanger with parallel or counterflow, is called the logarithmic mean temperature difference $(\Delta t_o)_L$ and is the basis upon which the mean temperature differences for many other types of exchangers are presented. This logarithmic mean temperature difference is always formed as shown in Eq. (12-3), from the differences in the fluid temperatures at the two ends of the exchanger, regardless of the relative directions of flow.

In many cases the value of U_o varies through the heat exchanger because of changes of the fluid properties, because of variations of the geometry of the exchange surface, or because of changes in the nature of the fluid flow. In this circumstance, Eq. (12-2) may not be integrated as above. If c_I and c_{II} are constant, the analysis gives

$$\ln \frac{(\Delta t_o)_b}{(\Delta t_o)_a} = \left(\mp \frac{1}{m_{II} c_{II}} - \frac{1}{m_I c_I} \right) \int_0^{A_T} U_o \, dA$$

$$= \left(\frac{t_{II,b} - t_{II,a}}{q} - \frac{t_{I,b} - t_{I,a}}{q} \right) \int_0^{A_T} U_o \, dA$$

$$= \frac{(\Delta t_o)_b - (\Delta t_o)_a}{q} \int_0^{A_T} U_o \, dA$$

Rearranging,

$$q = \left(\frac{1}{A_T} \int_0^{A_T} U_o \, dA \right) A_T (\Delta t_o)_L = (U_o)_{av} A_T (\Delta t_o)_L \qquad (12\text{-}4)$$

The term in the large parentheses is seen to be simply the average value of U_o over the exchange area.

Example 12-1. A heat exchanger is to be designed as shown in Fig. 12-1 to heat 2460 lb/hr of kerosene, which has a density and specific heat of 50.6 lb mass/ft³ and 0.50 Btu/lb °F, from 80 to 120°F. The kerosene is to flow inside the 1-in. nominal type K copper tubing, and the expected surface coefficient is 130 Btu/hr ft² °F. The kerosene is to be heated by water supplied at 200°F and at a rate of 870 lb/hr. The heat exchanger is to be insulated, and the expected surface coefficient on the water side of the copper tube is 260 Btu/hr ft² °F. Both the parallel and the counterflow arrangements will be considered. The necessary length of heat exchanger will be computed, and the errors incurred in using the average temperature differences $(\Delta t_o)_{av}$, instead of the logarithmic mean temperature differences, will be shown. The temperatures and differences are first computed denoting kerosene as fluid I and water as fluid II. The water exit temperature is found as $200 - 56.6 = 143.4$°F.

$$q_T = (mc\ \Delta t)_I = (mc\ \Delta t)_{II} \qquad \Delta t_{II} = \frac{2460 \times 0.50 \times 40}{870 \times 1.00} = 56.6°F$$

For parallel flow,

$$t_{I,a} = 80°F \qquad t_{I,b} = 120°F \qquad t_{II,a} = 200°F \qquad t_{II,b} = 143.4°F$$

$$(\Delta t_o)_a = 120° \qquad (\Delta t_o)_b = 23.4°$$

$$(\Delta t_o)_m = \frac{120 - 23.4}{\ln(120/23.4)} = \frac{96.6}{1.64} = 59.0°$$

$$(\Delta t_o)_{av} = \frac{(\Delta t_o)_a + (\Delta t_o)_b}{2} = \frac{120 + 23.4}{2} = 71.7°$$

For counterflow,

$$t_{I,a} = 80°F \qquad t_{I,b} = 120°F \qquad t_{II,a} = 143.4°F \qquad t_{II,b} = 200°F$$

$$(\Delta t_o)_a = 63.4° \qquad (\Delta t_o)_b = 80°$$

$$(\Delta t_o)_m = \frac{80 - 63.4}{\ln(80/63.4)} = \frac{16.6}{0.233} = 71.3°$$

$$(\Delta t_o)_{av} = \frac{63.4 + 80}{2} = 71.7°$$

The error in using $(\Delta t_o)_{av}$ instead of $(\Delta t_o)_m$ is seen to be very large when the difference between $(\Delta t_o)_a$ and $(\Delta t_o)_b$ is large, as for parallel flow, and small when the difference is small, as for counterflow in this case. The over-all coefficient per foot of length is calculated from Eq. (11-6). The tube OD and ID are found from Table A-11 as 1.125 and 0.995 in. The values of the surface coefficients are assumed constant throughout the exchanger.

$$U_o = \frac{2\pi}{\dfrac{2 \times 12}{130 \times 0.995} + \dfrac{\ln(1.125/0.995)}{224} + \dfrac{2 \times 12}{260 \times 1.125}} = \frac{2\pi}{0.186 + 0.00055 + 0.082}$$

$$= 23.3 \text{ Btu/hr ft °F, or } 79.3 \text{ Btu/hr ft}^2 \text{ °F (based upon outside area)}$$

$$L = \frac{q_T}{U_o(\Delta t_o)_m} = \frac{2460 \times 0.50 \times 40}{23.3(\Delta t_o)_m} = \frac{2110}{(\Delta t_o)_m}$$

$$= 35.8 \text{ ft for parallel flow}$$

$$= 29.6 \text{ ft for counterflow}$$

12-3. SHELL-AND-TUBE EXCHANGERS

Exchangers of the type discussed in the preceding section are often designed. However, a combination of space, cost, and pressure-drop limitations usually results in a preference for the more compact shell-and-tube designs shown in Figs. 12-2 to 12-4. These exchangers consist of a

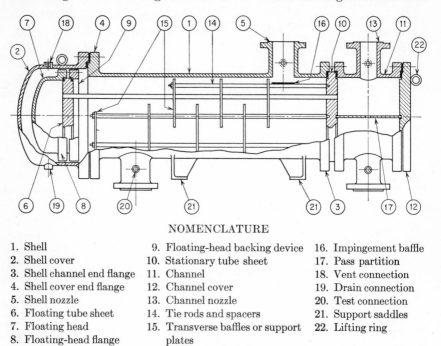

NOMENCLATURE

1. Shell	9. Floating-head backing device	16. Impingement baffle
2. Shell cover	10. Stationary tube sheet	17. Pass partition
3. Shell channel end flange	11. Channel	18. Vent connection
4. Shell cover end flange	12. Channel cover	19. Drain connection
5. Shell nozzle	13. Channel nozzle	20. Test connection
6. Floating tube sheet	14. Tie rods and spacers	21. Support saddles
7. Floating head	15. Transverse baffles or support	22. Lifting ring
8. Floating-head flange	plates	

FIG. 12-2. Typical construction and nomenclature for a floating-head type of shell-and-tube exchanger. [*From "Standards of Tubular Exchanger Manufacturers Association"* (1952).]

bundle of tubes through which one fluid passes. This bundle is enclosed by the shell which contains the other fluid. If one of the fluids is to be vaporized or condensed, it is generally introduced on the shell side. The tube-side fluid may make numerous passes of the tube bundle because of the design of the passages in the header. The tubes are generally rolled into the tube sheet which forms one of the walls of the header. The shell-side fluid may be forced to follow a devious path over the outside surfaces of the tubes by cross and longitudinal baffles inserted among the tubes.

The various designs shown have special features required for particular applications. In Fig. 12-2 typical construction and standard nomenclature are shown for a single-shell-pass, two-tube-pass exchanger. The floating head shown at the end of the exchanger, where the tube-side fluid reverses, permits free thermal expansion of the two basic parts of the exchanger. The U-tube bundle shown in Fig. 12-3c allows the same freedom if the bundle is free to move on baffles in the shell. In Fig. 12-4 arrangements are shown in which higher average temperature differences are obtained by positioning baffles to cause multiple passes of the shell-side fluid.

Mean Temperature Differences for Exchangers. The relation between the terminal fluid temperatures and the mean temperature difference defined in Eq. (12-1) is much more complicated for shell-and-tube exchangers than for the single-tube exchanger. For the single tube the logarithmic mean temperature difference resulted, Eq. (12-3). Since the temperature relations for shell-and-tube arrangements are too involved for convenient use, they are usually presented graphically. The relations for $(\Delta t_o)_m$ for shell-and-tube arrangements are written as follows:

$$(\Delta t_o)_m = F(\Delta t_o)_L \tag{12-5}$$

where $(\Delta t_o)_L$ is the logarithmic mean temperature difference for a single-pipe

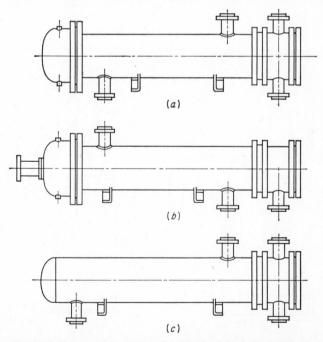

FIG. 12-3.   Single-shell-pass exchangers.   (*a*) Single-pass shell, multipass tubes.   (*b*) Single-pass shell, single-pass tubes.   (*c*) U tube; single-pass shell, multipass tubes.   [*From "Standards of Tubular Exchanger Manufacturers Association"* (1952).]

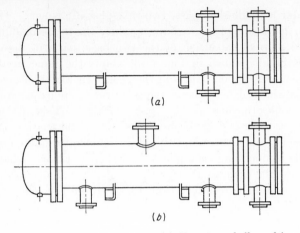

FIG. 12-4. Multiple-shell-pass exchangers. (a) Two-pass shell, multipass tubes. (b) Divided-flow shell, multipass tubes. [*From "Standards of Tubular Exchanger Manufacturers Association"* (1952).]

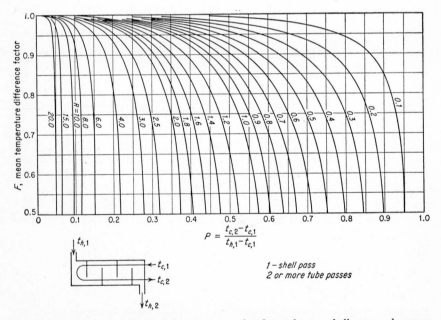

FIG. 12-5. Mean-temperature-difference correction factor for one-shell-pass exchangers. [*From "Standards of Tubular Exchanger Manufacturers Association"* (1959).]

exchanger with counterflow for the two fluid streams. F is a "correction factor" and is a function of the terminal fluid temperatures and of the exchanger arrangement. Since no arrangement can be more effective than simple counterflow, F is always 1.0 or less. Its value is an indication of the efficiency of a given arrangement for the given terminal fluid temperatures.

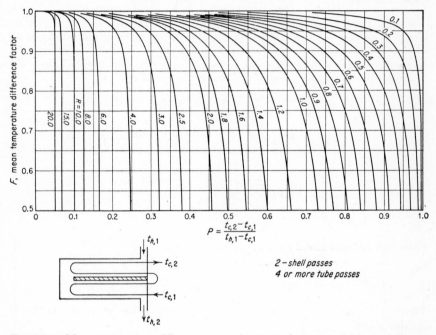

FIG. 12-6. Mean-temperature-difference correction factor for two-shell-pass exchangers. [*From "Standards of Tubular Exchanger Manufacturers Association"* (1959).]

Bowman, Mueller, and Nagle (1940) present a discussion of the method of analysis and a collection of correction-factor charts for various arrangements. Several somewhat more refined charts of the same type are presented in Figs. 12-5 and 12-6 for single- and double-shell-pass exchangers with over-all counterflow and an even number of tube passes. F is plotted against a measure of effectiveness, P, with contours of R, the heat-capacity ratio.

$$P = \frac{t_{c,2} - t_{c,1}}{t_{h,1} - t_{c,1}} \tag{12-6a}$$

$$R = \frac{t_{h,1} - t_{h,2}}{t_{c,2} - t_{c,1}} = \frac{m_c c_c}{m_h c_h} = \frac{C_c}{C_h} \tag{12-6b}$$

The subscripts h and c are for the shell- and tube-side fluids, respectively, and 1 and 2 denote temperatures in and out. C_c and C_h are called the stream-capacity rates. The derivations upon which these charts are based assume a constant over-all coefficient U_o throughout the exchanger and a shell-side fluid that is well mixed at all locations. In actual exchangers, the numerous shell-side baffles promote these conditions.

Example 12-2. In a process, 3220 lb/hr of water is to be cooled from 65 to 48°F by brine (25 per cent CaCl$_2$; $c = 0.67$). The brine flow rate is to be 12,000 lb/hr at an inlet temperature of 35°F. Considering U_o the same for all the arrangements, the necessary area of exchanger surface for exchangers having one- and two-shell passes will be compared with that for a single-tube, counterflow exchanger.

$$(\Delta t_c) = \frac{3220 \times 1.0 \times (65 - 48)}{12,000 \times 0.67} = 6.8°$$

$$(\Delta t_o)_L = \frac{(65 - 41.8) - (48 - 35)}{\ln\left[(65 - 41.8)/(48 - 35)\right]} = \frac{10.2}{\ln 1.785} = 17.6°$$

$$R = \frac{65 - 48}{41.8 - 35} = \frac{12,000 \times 0.67}{3220 \times 1.0} = 2.5$$

$$P = \frac{41.8 - 35}{65 - 35} = 0.227$$

From Figs. 12-5 and 12-6, $F_1 = 0.930$ and $F_2 = 0.981$.

$$(\Delta t_o)_{m,1} = 0.930 \times 17.6 = 16.4°$$

$$(\Delta t_o)_{m.2} = 0.981 \times 17.6 = 17.3°$$

Therefore, the ratios of the areas of the one- and two-shell-pass exchangers to that of the single-tube, counterflow exchanger are

$$\frac{17.6}{16.4} = 1.07 = \frac{1}{F_1} \quad \text{and} \quad \frac{17.6}{17.3} = 1.02 = \frac{1}{F_2}$$

Exchanger Effectiveness. The "correction-factor" method of presenting mean-temperature-difference information for exchanger arrangements has certain disadvantages. For example, F cannot be found unless the four terminal temperatures are known. Kays and London (1955) present the necessary design information for numerous exchanger arrangements in a form which is frequently more convenient. The effectiveness of an exchanger is defined as

$$\epsilon = \frac{(mc)_h(t_{h,1} - t_{h,2})}{(mc)_{\min}(t_{h,1} - t_{c,1})} = \frac{(mc)_c(t_{c,2} - t_{c,1})}{(mc)_{\min}(t_{h,1} - t_{c,1})} \tag{12-7}$$

where $(mc)_{\min}$ is the smaller of $(mc)_h$ and $(mc)_c$ and the subscripts 1 and 2 apply to the fluid streams in and out of the exchanger, respectively. The numerator of ϵ is the rate of heat transfer, and the denominator is the maximum amount that could be transferred in an ideal exchanger. Therefore, ϵ is the true effectiveness of the exchanger. Its value may be written more simply.

$$\epsilon = \frac{t_{h,1} - t_{h,2}}{t_{h,1} - t_{c,1}} \qquad \text{when } C_h \leq C_c \qquad (12\text{-}8a)$$

$$\epsilon = \frac{t_{c,2} - t_{c,1}}{t_{h,1} - t_{c,1}} \qquad \text{when } C_c \leq C_h \qquad (12\text{-}8b)$$

The effectiveness of a heat exchanger depends upon the exchanger arrangement and upon the nature of the transfer process, as indicated by the over-all transfer coefficient. To demonstrate the variables involved, let us consider counterflow in the simple exchanger shown in Fig. 12-1. Allowing for a variable U_o, we have, from the relation preceding Eq. (12-4),

$$\ln \frac{(\Delta t_o)_a}{(\Delta t_o)_b} = -\ln \frac{(\Delta t_o)_b}{(\Delta t_o)_a} = -\left(\frac{1}{m_h c_h} - \frac{1}{m_c c_c}\right) \int_0^{A_T} U_o \, dA$$

$$= -\left(\frac{1}{C_h} - \frac{1}{C_c}\right) \int_0^{A_T} U_o \, dA \qquad (12\text{-}9)$$

The terminal-temperature-difference ratio may be written as

$$\frac{(\Delta t_o)_a}{(\Delta t_o)_b} = \frac{t_{h,2} - t_{c,1}}{t_{h,1} - t_{c,2}} = \frac{(t_{h,1} - t_{c,1}) - (t_{h,1} - t_{h,2})}{(t_{h,1} - t_{c,1}) - (t_{c,2} - t_{c,1})} = \frac{1 - \dfrac{(t_{h,1} - t_{h,2})}{(t_{h,1} - t_{c,1})}}{1 - \dfrac{(t_{c,2} - t_{c,1})}{(t_{h,1} - t_{c,1})}}$$

$$= \frac{1 - \epsilon}{1 - (C_h/C_c)\epsilon} \qquad \text{for } C_h \leq C_c$$

$$= \frac{1 - (C_c/C_h)\epsilon}{1 - \epsilon} = \left[\frac{1 - \epsilon}{1 - (C_c/C_h)\epsilon}\right]^{-1} \qquad \text{for } C_c \leq C_h$$

Therefore,

$$\ln \left[\frac{1 - \epsilon}{1 - (C_h/C_c)\epsilon}\right] = -\left(1 - \frac{C_h}{C_c}\right) \frac{1}{C_h} \int_0^{A_T} U_o \, dA \qquad \text{for } C_h \leq C_c$$

$$\ln \left[\frac{1 - \epsilon}{1 - (C_c/C_h)\epsilon}\right] = -\left(1 - \frac{C_c}{C_h}\right) \frac{1}{C_c} \int_0^{A_T} U_o \, dA \qquad \text{for } C_c \leq C_h$$

The two relations are seen to involve only the ratio of the minimum and maximum thermal-capacity rates of the two streams and the integral of $U_o\, dA$ divided by the minimum of the two stream-capacity rates. The ratio of the minimum and maximum thermal-capacity rates is hereafter denoted by r. The integral divided by the minimum capacity rate is called the "number of exchanger transfer units" and is denoted by N_{TU}. That is,

$$r = \frac{C_{\min}}{C_{\max}} \quad \text{and} \quad N_{\text{TU}} = \frac{1}{C_{\min}} \int_0^{A_T} U_o\, dA$$

Both relations then reduce to

$$\ln \frac{1 - \epsilon}{1 - r\epsilon} = -(1 - r)N_{\text{TU}}$$

or

$$\epsilon = \frac{1 - e^{-(1-r)N_{\text{TU}}}}{1 - re^{-(1-r)N_{\text{TU}}}} \tag{12-10}$$

Equation (12-10) is plotted in Fig. 12-7, that is, for the single-tube exchanger of Fig. 12-1 with counterflow. The parallel-flow curve for $r = 1$ is

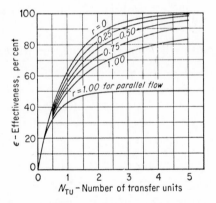

FIG. 12-7. Effectiveness vs. exchanger transfer units for the single-tube exchanger of Fig. 12-1, with counterflow. [*Adapted from Kays and London* (1955).]

included for comparison. The use of this method is demonstrated in Example 12-3.

Example 12-3. For the flow rates and temperature levels stated in Example 12-1, the necessary length of exchanger will be calculated using the ϵ, N_{TU} method for a counter-flow arrangement.

$$m_h c_h = 870 \times 1.00 = 870 \quad \text{and} \quad m_c c_c = 2460 \times 0.50 = 1230$$

Since $C_h < C_c$,

$$\epsilon = \frac{t_{h,1} - t_{h,2}}{t_{h,1} - t_{c,1}} = \frac{200 - 143.4}{200 - 80} = 0.472$$

$$r = \frac{870}{1230} = 0.707$$

With these values, we find, from Fig. 12-7,

$$N_{\mathrm{TU}} = 0.80 = \frac{1}{C_h} U_o A \qquad \text{for } U_o \text{ based upon area}$$

$$= \frac{1}{C_h} U_o L \qquad \text{for } U_o \text{ based upon length}$$

$$L = \frac{870 \times 0.80}{23.3} = 29.9 \text{ ft}$$

For the single-pipe exchanger, ϵ is seen to be a function only of r and N_{TU}. The same simple dependence is found for many more complicated arrangements, and the charts for many types of exchangers are found in

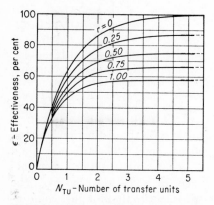

FIG. 12-8. Effectiveness of a single-shell-pass exchanger with 2, 4, 6, etc., tube passes. [*Adapted from Kays and London* (1955).]

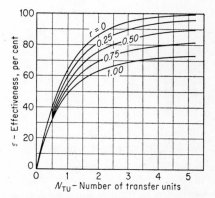

FIG. 12-9. Effectiveness of a two-shell-pass exchanger with 4, 8, 12, etc., tube passes. [*Adapted from Kays and London* (1955).]

Kays and London (1955). Figures 12-8 to 12-11 apply to common exchanger configurations for an over-all counterflow arrangement. Figures 12-8 and 12-9 are for the same arrangements as Figs. 12-5 and 12-6. Figure 12-10 is for an exchanger with three shell passes.

Figure 12-11, computed for $C_h/C_c = 1$, applies to a design commonly employed for gas-turbine regenerators. The multiple passes represent a counterflow arrangement of individual crossflow exchangers within which

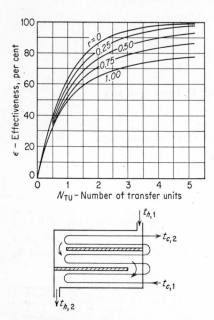

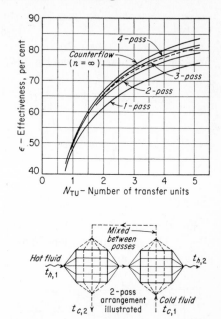

FIG. 12-10. Effectiveness of a three-shell-pass exchanger with 6, 12, 18, etc., tube passes. [*Adapted from Kays and London* (1955).]

FIG. 12-11. Effectiveness of crossflow exchangers with over-all counterflow. Crossflowing fluid is unmixed within passes. [*Adapted from Kays and London* (1955).]

the fluids are not mixed. Figure 12-12 demonstrates the distinction between mixed and unmixed streams for the shell-side fluid. The tube-side fluid is not cross-mixed because it is in tubes. For the multipass arrangements of Fig. 12-11 the shell-side fluid is assumed mixed between passes. The curve for an infinite number of passes is equivalent to that for pure counterflow and represents the limit for all such over-all counterflow exchangers.

Example 12-4. An exchanger is to be designed to cool 4800 lb/hr of Freon 12 ($c = 0.25$) from 80 to 62°F. The coolant is to be 1600 lb/hr of water at 50°F. Let us compare the necessary transfer areas for one-, two-, and three-shell-pass exchangers for an average over-all coefficient of 50 Btu/hr ft² °F.

$$m_h c_h = 4800 \times 0.25 = 1200 \qquad m_c c_c = 1600 \times 1.00 = 1600$$

$$r = \frac{1200}{1600} = 0.75 \qquad \epsilon = \frac{80 - 62}{80 - 50} = 0.60$$

From Figs. 12-8 to 12-10, we find

$$(N_{TU})_1 = 1.7 = \frac{50}{1200} A_1 \qquad A_1 = 40.8 \text{ ft}^2$$

$$(N_{TU})_2 = 1.35 = \frac{50}{1200} A_2 \qquad A_2 = 32.4 \text{ ft}^2$$

$$(N_{TU})_3 = 1.30 = \frac{50}{1200} A_3 \qquad A_3 = 31.2 \text{ ft}^2$$

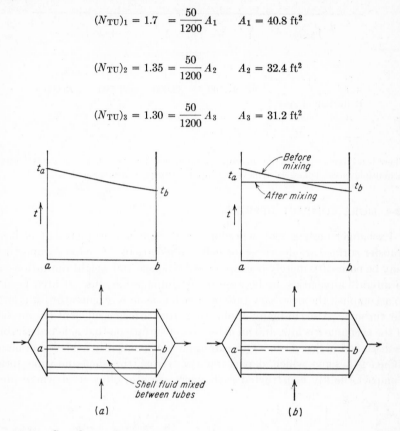

FIG. 12-12. Crossflow exchangers with unmixed and mixed shell-side fluid. (a) Both fluids unmixed. (b) Shell-side fluid mixed.

Example 12-5. A gas-turbine regenerator is to be designed to exchange heat between the turbine exhaust gases, initially at 1200°F, and the compressor delivery air, initially at 400°F. The airflow rate and specific heat are to be 100 lb/sec and 0.24 Btu/lb mass °F. The *mc* product of the two streams will be assumed the same, so that Fig. 12-11 may be used. An effectiveness of 75 per cent is desired for high-cycle thermal efficiency. The exit temperatures of both fluids and the heat-transfer area for various numbers of passes will be computed. Assume $U_o = 10.0$ Btu/hr ft² °F.

$$\epsilon = 0.75 = \frac{1200 - t_{h,2}}{1200 - 400} \qquad t_{h,2} = 600°F \qquad t_{c,2} = 1000°F$$

$$mc = 100 \times 3600 \times 0.24 = 86,400 \text{ Btu/hr } °F$$

The numbers of transfer units and areas for various arrangements are shown below:

Passes	1	2	4	∞
N_{TU}.................	4.8	3.7	3.2	3.0
A, ft^2.................	41,500	32,000	27,700	25,900
Reduction of area from 1 pass, %.....	0	23	33	38

There is a large area reduction in employing multiple passes. However, the advantage in multiple passes is largely achieved even for a two-pass arrangement.

12-4. MORE COMPACT DESIGNS

Exchanger designs which permit a very compact arrangement of heat-transfer surface are desirable for many applications. Greater compactness may be necessary merely because of severe space and weight limitations, as in aircraft auxiliaries, or because of the immense amount of area needed to accomplish the necessary rate of transfer, as in a regenerator for a large gas turbine. Also, in many applications the surface coefficient on one side of the exchanger is low, and an extension of surface on that side is desirable, as discussed in Sec. 11-6. This extension is conveniently achieved in many compact designs which depart radically from the shell-and-tube form. Compact, lightly constructed exchangers are also often used where pres-

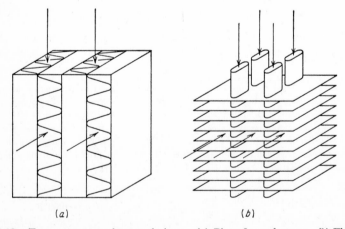

(a)   (b)

Fig. 12-13.   Two compact exchanger designs.   (a) Plate-fin exchanger.   (b) Flattened-tube–flat-fin exchanger.

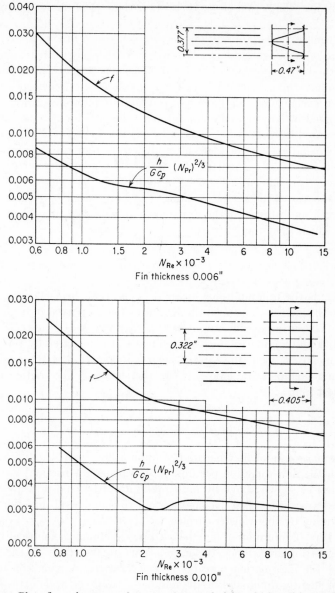

FIG. 12-14. Plate-fin exchanger performance for two designs. [*Adapted from information given by Kays and London* (1955).]

sures are low, the period of use is short, or the cost of manufacture is to be low.

The widely varied applications have given rise to many different types of compact exchanger surface. A few types are discussed here, and one of the methods of correlating data for design purposes is considered. Many workers have investigated the transfer characteristics of various types of compact exchangers. A large portion of the published information is summarized in Kays and London (1955). Results for two configurations are presented below.

The general designs of plate-fin and flattened-fin tube exchangers are shown in Fig. 12-13. Heat-transfer and friction-loss characteristics of the two designs are shown in Figs. 12-14 and 12-15. The curves apply to the extended-surface side of the exchanger and are based upon data for air. The length (or distance) in the Reynolds number is four times the hydraulic radius, which is computed from

$$4r_h = 4\frac{A_c}{A}L \tag{12-11}$$

where A_c is the minimum-flow area, A is the total heat-transfer area on the side in question, and L is the length of the flow passage from inlet to outlet. The surface coefficient is essentially equivalent to the average value computed by dividing the heat-transfer rate per unit area by the product of the mean Δt_o from the air to the prime surface and the analytically calculated "temperature efficiency" of the surface. The friction factor is computed from

$$f = \frac{\rho\tau}{G^2/2g_o} \qquad \text{where } \tau = \frac{\Delta p_f A_p}{A} \tag{12-12}$$

G is the mass rate of flow per unit minimum flow area A_c. τ is the shear stress in the flow direction per unit heat-transfer (or friction) area and is calculated as shown above by multiplying the frictional pressure drop by the total area of the flow passage normal to the general direction of flow and dividing by the transfer surface.

This type of information may be used for designing geometrically similar exchangers for air. Since the correlations are in terms of the Prandtl number, the information may be used as a first approximation for other fluids of slightly different Prandtl number. However, wide extrapolations are not reliable because there are other Prandtl number effects.

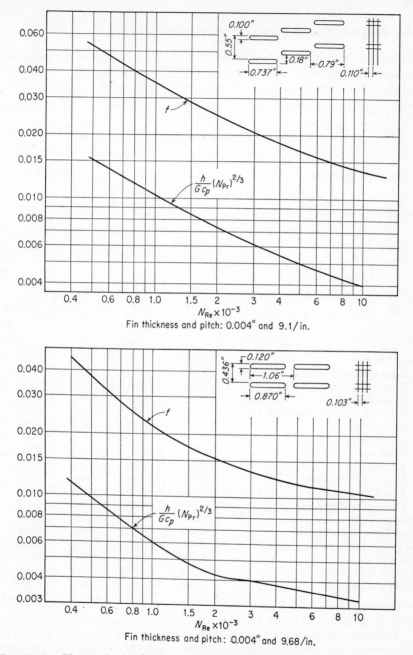

FIG. 12-15.   Flattened-tube–flat-fin exchanger performance for two arrangements. [*Adapted from information given by Kays and London* (1955).]

12-5. FOULING AND SCALING OF EXCHANGE SURFACE

In many heat-exchanger applications scaling and fouling of the exchange surface may result in a lower over-all coefficient in operation than that calculated for clean surfaces. In many applications this effect may be severe, resulting in greatly reduced exchanger effectiveness. An allowance

TABLE 12-1. FOULING FACTORS FOR WATER, HR FT^2 °F/BTU *

Temperature of heating medium........	Up to 240°F		240–400°F †	
Temperature of water.................	125°F or less		Over 125°F	
	Water velocity, fps		Water velocity, fps	
Types of water	3 ft and less	Over 3 ft	3 ft and less	Over 3 ft
Sea water...........................	0.0005	0.0005	0.001	0.001
Brackish water......................	0.002	0.001	0.003	0.002
Cooling tower and artificial spray pond:				
Treated make-up..................	0.001	0.001	0.002	0.002
Untreated.......................	0.003	0.003	0.005	0.004
City or well water (such as Great Lakes)..	0.001	0.001	0.002	0.002
Great Lakes.........................	0.001	0.001	0.002	0.002
River water:				
Minimum........................	0.002	0.001	0.003	0.002
Mississippi......................	0.003	0.002	0.004	0.003
Delaware, Schuylkill...............	0.003	0.002	0.004	0.003
East River and New York Bay.......	0.003	0.002	0.004	0.003
Chicago Sanitary Canal.............	0.008	0.006	0.010	0.008
Muddy or silty......................	0.003	0.002	0.004	0.003
Hard (over 15 grains/gal).............	0.003	0.003	0.005	0.005
Engine jacket.......................	0.001	0.001	0.001	0.001
Distilled............................	0.0005	0.0005	0.0005	0.0005
Treated boiler feedwater.............	0.001	0.0005	0.001	0.001
Boiler blowdown....................	0.002	0.002	0.002	0.002

* From "Standards of Tubular Exchanger Manufacturers Association" (1959).

† Ratings in columns 4 and 5 are based on a temperature of the heating medium of 240 to 400°F. If the heating-medium temperature is over 400°F and the cooling medium is known to scale, these ratings should be modified accordingly.

is often made for scaling and fouling in design by assigning "fouling factors" to surfaces which will become coated in use.

The fouling factor for any given scaling or fouling is equal to the equivalent thermal resistance of the scale. That is, it is the effective resistance of the scale. Therefore, the fouling factor appears as one of the terms in the relation for the over-all coefficient of heat transfer. If both sides of a surface may become fouled, two factors are included among the resistances of the barrier. For uniformity, the factors are expressed in units of hr ft^2 °F/Btu.

The magnitude of the fouling factor depends upon the nature of the scale. If the scale is uniform in composition and structure, the resistance may be calculated by dividing the scale thickness by the thermal conductivity of the scale material. However, the scale is usually of an unknown or complicated composition and structure, and the fouling factor must be known as the result of analyzing the performance of fouled exchangers.

Fouling-factor information is available for numerous applications for typical metallic-surface conditions and cleaning procedures. Table 12-1 contains such information for water from various sources and under different velocity and temperature conditions, and Table 12-2 provides information for miscellaneous fluids of engineering importance.

TABLE 12-2. Fouling Factors for Miscellaneous Fluids,
hr ft^2 °F/Btu *

Industrial gases and vapors

Manufactured gas	0.01
Engine exhaust gas	0.01
Steam (non-oil-bearing)	0.0005
Exhaust steam (oil-bearing)	0.001
Refrigerating vapors (oil-bearing)	0.002
Natural gas	0.001
Compressed air	0.002

Industrial liquids

Industrial organic heat-transfer media	0.001
Refrigerating liquids	0.001
Molten heat-transfer salts	0.0005
Hydraulic fluid	0.001

Industrial oils

Fuel oil	0.005
Engine lube oil	0.001
Transformer oil	0.001
Quench oil	0.004
Vegetable oils	0.003

* Adapted from "Standards of Tubular Exchanger Manufacturers Association" (1959).

Example 12-6. Steam at 4.0 in. Hg abs is to be extracted from the lower-pressure stages of a turbine to heat 50,000 lb/hr of sea water, prior to evaporation, from 60 to 110°F. The exchanger is to be of shell-and-tube design with two shell passes and eight tube passes. There will be 20 parallel tube circuits of 0.995-in.-ID and 1.125-in.-OD brass tubing of 61 Btu/hr ft °F thermal conductivity. Clean-steam and water surface coefficients of 600 and 300 Btu/hr ft² °F, respectively, are expected. The necessary length of tube in the exchanger is to be calculated.

The steam temperature of 125.4°F results in a required effectiveness of

$$\epsilon = \frac{t_{c,2} - t_{c,1}}{t_{h,1} - t_{c,1}} = \frac{110 - 60}{125.4 - 60} = 0.765$$

The value of N_{TU} for $r = 0$ is found from Fig. 12-9 as 1.4.

The fouling factors for water and clean steam, f_w and f_s, are found from Tables 12-1 and 12-2.

$$V_w = \frac{m}{A\rho} = \frac{50{,}000 \times 144}{3600 \times 20 \times (\pi/4)(0.995)^2 \times 59.0} = 2.18 \text{ fps}$$

$$f_w = 0.0005 \quad \text{and} \quad f_s = 0.0005$$

The over-all coefficient per unit of outside tube surface is found:

$$U_o = \frac{1}{\dfrac{1}{h_o} + f_s + \dfrac{d_o}{2k}\ln\dfrac{d_o}{d_i} + f_w\dfrac{d_o}{d_i} + \dfrac{d_o}{h_i d_i}}$$

$$= \frac{1}{\dfrac{1}{600} + 0.0005 + \dfrac{1.125}{2 \times 12 \times 61}\ln\dfrac{1.125}{0.995} + \dfrac{0.0005 \times 1.125}{0.995} + \dfrac{1.125}{300 \times 0.995}}$$

$$= \frac{1}{0.001667 + 0.0005 + 0.000094 + 0.000565 + 0.003768} = 152 \text{ Btu/hr ft}^2 \text{ °F}$$

$$N_{TU} = \frac{U_o A}{C_{\min}} = 1.4 \qquad A = \frac{1.4 \times 50{,}000 \times 0.94}{152} = 433 \text{ ft}^2$$

$$L = \frac{A}{\pi d_o} = \frac{433 \times 12}{\pi \times 1.125} = 1470 \text{ ft, or } 73.5 \text{ ft in each parallel circuit}$$

12-6. OPTIMUM DESIGN OF HEAT-TRANSFER EQUIPMENT

The preceding sections outline the special techniques and information employed in the design of exchangers of various common types. In the design of an exchanger for a particular application, that is, for a certain heat-transfer process, the designer must fix the exact arrangement, the pipe sizes and lengths, and any other design variables not specified by the nature of the application. Many choices of these remaining independent variables may result in an exchanger adequate for the task. However, it is the designer's province to make choices which will result in the best exchanger from the practical point of view. In the final analysis, the best, or optimum, exchanger is the one which accomplishes the desired end at the lowest possible total operation cost. This cost includes investment, service, pumping, and other charges.

The determination of the optimum design is difficult and complicated in many cases. However, many applications contain enough restrictions to reduce the number of independent variables to manageable proportions. The flow rates, specific heats, and terminal temperatures of the two fluids specify the task to be performed by the exchanger. There may be certain practical limitations. Extremely long exchangers are sometimes not sufficiently compact or are too difficult to install or service. A standard pipe length may be chosen for the tubes in order to reduce waste in manufacture. The choice of tubing size and material is restricted where possible to standard or readily available items. The approximate magnitude of the fluid velocities may be set at particular values to control fouling and/or corrosion. In some instances the magnitude of the fluid pressure drop in the exchanger may be unimportant. If the two fluids are to be at considerably different pressure levels, the fluid circuits are arranged to result in the lowest strength requirements. These and many other possible restraints simplify the analysis.

The large number of variables makes it impossible to set up a single, standard design procedure which will apply to all design situations. Only the most general considerations of design have wide application. In this section an analysis will be given for a particular type of design problem in which certain of the general variables, such as fluid velocity and heat-transfer rate, are assumed fixed by the application.

Consider the design of an exchanger which is to exchange a given amount of heat between a condensing vapor and a liquid. The vapor condensation temperature and the terminal liquid temperature are assumed fixed by the application. For this installation a fixed, high liquid velocity is chosen to control fouling of the transfer surface. Let us assume that a shell-and-tube exchanger of a particular flow arrangement is preferred. In this particular case the optimum design is taken to mean the exchanger which will result in the minimum owning, servicing, and operating cost per unit time. The variables which remain to be chosen to fix the design are the number, diameter, and length of the tubes. The cost will depend upon this choice.

The argument is converted to mathematical form. The fixed conditions amount to assuming as constant the total heat flow q; the mean temperature difference $(\Delta t_o)_m$; and m, ρ, and V for the liquid. The mean over-all temperature difference is fixed because the terminal temperatures, capacity rates, and general form of exchanger are fixed; that is, F and $(\Delta t_o)_L$ have particular values.

The total operating cost per unit time, C_T, is the sum of the fixed charges per unit time, C_F; the charges for servicing and cleaning per unit time, C_S; and the operating cost C_O. The operating cost is the product of the pumping loss, energy charge, and use factor. The fixed charge, due to the exchanger cost, and the service charge are fixed for a given exchanger but would certainly depend upon the heat-transfer area of the exchanger and also upon the diameter of the tubes of which the exchanger is made. Let us assume that $(C_F + C_S)$ is directly proportional to the exchange area and inversely proportional to the ID of the tubes to a small power e. That is,

$$C_F + C_S = C_1 \frac{A}{D^e} \qquad \text{cost per unit time}$$

The operating cost is given by

$$C_O = C_2 U \frac{\Delta p}{\rho} m$$

where C_2 is the total energy charge per foot-pound of energy loss due to flow friction. If, for example, a pump and drive are to be installed, C_2 is estimated by taking into account the fixed and service charges, the efficiency of the pump and drive, and the cost of the motive energy for the drive. U is the use factor, the fraction of time that the exchanger is in use. The total cost to be minimized is then written as

$$C_T = C_1 \frac{A_i}{D^e} + C_2 U \frac{\Delta p}{\rho} m \qquad (12\text{-}13)$$

The values of A_i, D, and Δp in Eq. (12-13) depend upon the tube size and upon the number of parallel circuits chosen for the exchanger. The following equations may be written among the known and unknown quantities:

$$\Delta p = f \frac{L}{D} \frac{\rho V^2}{2g_o} \qquad \text{where } f = f(N_{\text{Re}}) \qquad (12\text{-}14)$$

$$h_i = C \frac{k}{D} N_{\text{Re}}{}^a N_{\text{Pr}}{}^b = \frac{B}{D} N_{\text{Re}}{}^a \qquad (12\text{-}15)$$

$$q = \frac{A_i (\Delta t_o)_m}{R + 1/h_i} \qquad (12\text{-}16)$$

$$m = \frac{n\pi D^2 V \rho}{4} \qquad (12\text{-}17)$$

$$A_i = n\pi D L \qquad (12\text{-}18)$$

where m is the mass rate of flow of the liquid.

The first relation is the pressure loss in each parallel liquid circuit. h_i is the inside surface coefficient in the turbulent range; various fluid properties have been included in the constant B. In the heat-transfer equation, R is the sum of the resistances of the tube wall, the outside surface, and any fouling or scales on the inside and outside tube surfaces. R is assumed constant; h_i may vary. In the last two relations, n is the number of parallel tube circuits.

There are then six equations in the seven unknowns C_T, A_i, D, Δp, L, h_i, and n. Therefore, C_T may be found as a function of one of the other unknowns, D. Since N_{Re} contains D and no other unknowns, C_T will be found, for convenience, as a function of N_{Re}. n is eliminated between Eqs. (12-17) and (12-18). Then h_i from Eq. (12-15) is substituted into Eq. (12-16). Combining the two resulting relations with Eqs. (12-13) and (12-14), we have

$$
\begin{aligned}
C_T &= \left(\frac{C_1}{D^e} + \frac{C_2 U f \rho V^3}{4 \times 2g_o}\right)\left(1 + \frac{D}{RBN_{Re}{}^a}\right)\frac{qR}{(\Delta t_o)_m} \\
&= \left[\frac{C_1}{N_{Re}{}^a}\left(\frac{V\rho}{\mu}\right)^e + \frac{C_2 U f V^3}{4 \times 2g_o}\right]\left(1 + \frac{\mu N_{Re}{}^{1-a}}{\rho V R B}\right)\frac{qR}{(\Delta t_o)_m} \\
&= \left[\frac{4 \times 2g_o C_1}{C_2 U V^3}\left(\frac{\rho V}{\mu}\right)^e\frac{1}{N_{Re}{}^e} + f\right]\left(1 + \frac{\mu}{\rho V R B}N_{Re}{}^{1-a}\right)\frac{qR C_2 U V^3}{4 \times 2g_o(\Delta t_o)_m}
\end{aligned}
$$

$$(12\text{-}19)$$

The only unknown is N_{Re}, since f depends directly upon N_{Re}. The constant quantities are grouped in new constants, and the relation is rewritten.

$$
P = \frac{4 \times 2g_o C_1}{C_2 U V^3}\left(\frac{\rho V}{\mu}\right)^e \qquad Q = \frac{qR C_2 U V^3}{4 \times 2g_o(\Delta t_o)_m} \qquad S = \frac{\mu}{\rho V R B} = \frac{N_{Pr}{}^{\frac{2}{3}}}{\rho V c R C}
$$

$$
C_T = \left(\frac{P}{N_{Re}{}^e} + f\right)(1 + S N_{Re}{}^{1-a})Q \qquad (12\text{-}20)
$$

The optimum design as far as this analysis is concerned is the one corresponding to the Reynolds number which produces the minimum value of C_T.

There are practical design circumstances which result in P, S, and e values for which Eq. (12-20) does not have a minimum in the range of practical Reynolds numbers. In these cases, C_T generally decreases rapidly with increasing N_{Re} in the lower range and less rapidly thereafter. The exponent e is very effective in producing this characteristic, and for e greater than approximately 0.2, no minimum is found. In cases of no minimum value of C_T, an exchanger in the flatter portion of the curve would be called a good design.

The foregoing technique is an indication of the factors which enter into an operating-cost analysis in exchanger design. No single approach is a good general guide, however. The proper technique of analysis depends entirely upon the special and local conditions of design. Various additional aspects of optimum design are considered in McAdams (1954) and Kern (1950).

NOTATION

c	specific heat
c_p	specific heat at constant pressure, per unit mass
C_c (or C_h)	thermal capacity of a fluid stream
f	friction factor
F	arrangement "correction factor"
g_o	a conversion factor for units of force
G	mass rate of flow per unit area
h	convection coefficient
k	thermal conductivity
m	mass rate of flow
N_{Pr}	Prandtl number
N_{Re}	Reynolds number
N_{TU}	number of exchanger transfer units
p	pressure
r	ratio of fluid stream thermal capacities, arranged to be equal to or less than one
t	temperature
U_o	over-all coefficient of heat transfer
V	average fluid velocity
ϵ	heat-exchanger effectiveness
μ	absolute viscosity
ρ	density of mass

REFERENCES

Bowman, R. A., A. C. Mueller, and W. M. Nagle: *Trans. ASME*, vol. 62, p. 283, 1940.
Kays, W. M., and A. L. London: "Compact Heat Exchangers," The National Press, Palo Alto, Calif., 1955.
Kern, D. Q.: "Process Heat Transfer," McGraw-Hill Book Company, Inc., New York, 1950.
McAdams, W. H.: "Heat Transmission," 3d ed., McGraw-Hill Book Company, Inc., New York, 1954.
"Standards of Tubular Exchanger Manufacturers Association," 3d and 4th eds., 1952 and 1959.

PROBLEMS

1. Lubricating oil at 140°F is to be cooled to 100°F, by water available at 70°F, in a single-tube counterflow exchanger. The oil and water flow rates are to be 210 and 200 lb/hr, respectively. The specific heat of the oil is 0.48 Btu/lb °F. The over-all coefficient is 60 Btu/hr ft^2 °F, based upon outside surface.

a. Find the average and mean over-all temperature differences.

b. Compute the required heat-transfer area.

2. Repeat Prob. 1 for a parallel flow arrangement and compare the results.

3. Saturated steam at a pressure of 1.7 psia is to be used to heat 6 gpm of water from 60 to 110°F. A single-pipe exchanger is to be used, with the water flowing inside the tube and with the steam condensing in the annulus. Find the average and mean over-all temperature differences.

4. The tube in the exchanger of Prob. 3 is to be of 90-10 brass and to have a 1.00-in. OD and a 0.850-in. ID. Find the necessary tube length.

5. A single-tube exchanger is to be designed to be made up of 18-ft elements in series, as shown in Fig. 12-1. The exchanger is to heat 1500 lb/hr of clean water from 60 to 92°F by extracting heat from 1000 lb/hr of waste water available at 125°F. Assume that 1-in. nominal seamless steel pipe (schedule 40) is to be used and that the over-all coefficient is 80 Btu/hr ft^2 °F based upon outside surface area. For a counterflow arrangement, find (*a*) the terminal, average, and mean over-all temperature differences; (*b*) the total length of tubing required.

6. A shell-and-tube feedwater heater is to heat 100,000 lb/hr of water from 200 to 260°F. Turbine extraction steam at 40 psia is to condense on the shell side. One shell-side pass and two tube-side passes are used, and there are 60 parallel tube passages, that is, 120 tubes, of 1-in. standard seamless steel tubing. Assume an over-all coefficient of 600 Btu/hr ft^2 °F based upon inside tube surface. Find the necessary length of the tubes, without the use of charts.

7. For the conditions of Prob. 6, find the required heat-exchanger effectiveness. Compute the total area and lengths of the tubes using the "number of transfer units" method.

8. Lubricating oil for a large engine is to be cooled from 210 to 170°F at a flow rate of 3000 lb/hr, using jacket cooling water initially at 150°. A one-shell-pass, two-tube-pass exchanger made up of a total of fifty 0.398-in.-ID and 0.500-in.-OD copper tubes is to be used. An oil-side surface coefficient of 40 Btu/hr ft^2 °F is expected. The specific heat of the oil is 0.40 Btu/lb °F.

a. Neglecting exchange-surface fouling, find the necessary tube length if the cooling-water flow rate may be chosen sufficiently high to result in only a 5° temperature rise.

b. Find the percentage reduction in heat-transfer area attained by employing two- and three-shell-pass designs.

9. A refrigeration system employing F-12 as the refrigerant is to be designed to cool water from 55 to 45°F at a flow rate of 10,000 lb/hr for a manufacturing process. A submerged evaporator is to be used with two tube passes; that is, the shell of the evaporator is filled with liquid F-12 which is vaporizing. Assume that all tubes are submerged. The condenser is also to be of the one-shell-pass, two-tube-pass design with cooling water in the tubes, supplied at 65°F, with a 10° temperature increase through the exchanger. The condenser heat load is computed to be 18 × 10^4 Btu/hr, based upon the expected performance of the refrigeration system. The evaporator and condenser pressures are to be 48 and 110 psia, respectively, and superheat and subcooling may be neglected in computing temperature differences. The condenser and evaporator are to be constructed of $\frac{3}{4}$-in. nominal (schedule 40) seamless steel tubing of 8-ft length. A water velocity of 4 fps is desired in both exchangers. Find the number of tubes required in each exchanger, assuming that the heat-transfer resistance on the Freon side in both cases may be neglected.

10. Water at a flow rate of 4 gpm is to be cooled from 55 to 45°F by brine ($c = 0.70$) at 35°F available at a flow rate of 3360 lb/hr. For an over-all transfer coefficient of 200 Btu/hr ft^2 °F, compare the required transfer area for one-, two-, and three-shell-pass shell-and-tube exchangers. The brine is to pass through the tubes.

11. Fuel oil is to be heated from 55 to 110°F to facilitate pumping and delivery to a distant point where the rate of use is 12.5 gpm. Hot water is available at 124°F at a flow rate of 10 gpm. The relevant properties of oil are $c = 0.45$ and $\rho = 49$ lb/ft^3. Compare the required areas for one-, two-, and three-shell-pass shell-and-tube exchangers for an over-all coefficient of 50 Btu/hr ft^2 °F. The oil flows inside the tubes.

12. For the conditions given in Prob. 8, find the tube lengths for a single-shell-pass exchanger, allowing for the effects of fouling in use.

13. The plausibility of a crossflow regenerative heater made of $\frac{3}{4}$-in. standard steel pipe is to be investigated for a small, mobile gas-turbine system. At design conditions, the induction rate for 60°F air is 10 lb/sec. The compressor discharge, turbine inlet, and turbine exhaust temperatures are 300, 1400 and 1000°F, respectively. The compressor discharge gas at 44 psia is to flow inside the tubes at a velocity of 70 fps. The outside surface coefficient for the turbine discharge gases will be 40 Btu/hr ft^2 °F. Find the required length of the individual tubes for single-pass crossflow exchangers giving effectivenesses of 60, 65, 70, and 75 per cent.

14. If the regenerator proposed for the gas turbine discussed in Prob. 13 is to be 75 per cent effective, compare the necessary transfer area for one-, two-, and four-pass crossflow exchangers. Use the same velocity, pipe size, and outside surface coefficient as given in Prob. 13. Sketch the arrangement for each of the three exchangers and compute the individual pipe lengths.

15. Air at 420°F and 200 in. Hg abs is to be taken at a rate of 0.6 lb/sec from the jet-engine compressor discharge of a high-speed airplane and used for cabin cooling. Before being introduced into the cabin, this air is cooled by two processes. First it is passed through the tubes of a single-pass crossflow exchanger made of 48 stainless-steel tubes, of 0.200 in. ID and 0.260 in. OD, wherein the temperature is reduced to 220°F. The air is then expanded to 10 psia through a small turbine which drives a fan which supplies atmospheric air to the shell side of the exchanger for cooling. Assume that the cooling and conditioning airflow rates are the same and that the cooling air comes to the exchanger at 135°F. Assume also that the outside and inside surface coefficients are the same. The thermal conductivity of the stainless steel is 60 Btu/hr ft °F. Find the total transfer area and the length of the tubes.

16. Oil used in a heat-treating process for quenching metal parts is to be cooled with well water available at 60°F. The oil is to be cooled from 180 to 100°F at a rate of 21 gpm in a shell-and-tube exchanger, the oil being on the shell side. The tubes are to be 1-in. standard steel, and the over-all coefficient based on clean surfaces is expected to be 50 Btu/hr ft^2 °F based on inside surface. The water flow rate will be 80 lb/min, which will give a velocity under 3 fps. Properties of the oil are $c = 0.45$ Btu/lb °F, specific gravity $= 0.78$.

a. Can this exchange process be accomplished in a single-shell-pass exchanger? Explain.

b. For a two-shell-pass exchanger find the necessary transfer area for clean surfaces and the percentage increase in required transfer area when fouling is accounted for.

17. If, as in Prob. 16, 21 gpm of oil is to be cooled from 180 to 100°F by using cooling water at 60°F, we wish to consider the optimum arrangement taking into account the cost of cooling water and the fixed and service charges of transfer area. Assume that the cost per unit time for owning and servicing is C_1A and for cooling water is C_2m_c, where A is the transfer area and m_c is the water flow rate. Other costs are considered unimportant. A given number and size of tubes are to be considered, so that all the resistances are constant except the inside surface coefficient, which is assumed to vary as follows: $h_i = Bm_c{}^{0.8}$. Assuming that C_c will be greater than C_h, find an expression for the water flow rate which will result in minimum total cost.

18. A single-tube exchanger (see Fig. 12-1) is to be designed to cool 5000 lb/hr of an acid solution, used in a manufacturing process, from 200 to 90°F. Water is available in unlimited quantities at 60°F. The solution is to flow in the annulus and the water in the pipe. Available pipe of 1.30 in. OD and 1.00 in. ID is to be used, and the fixed and servicing charge per unit time may be taken as C_1A, where A is the transfer area. In order to make use of the available water supply, a pump and drive must be installed. Because of high service and power costs, the total pumping charge per unit time, $C_2(\Delta p/\rho)m_w$, is an important factor in total cost. Assume that C_h will be less than C_c and that all resistances other than the one at the inside tube surface are fixed. Develop an expression for the water velocity which will result in minimum total cost.

$$h_i = BV^{0.8} \qquad \text{and} \qquad f = C_3/V^{0.25}$$

19. Chemically dehumidified air, to be subsequently used for conditioning a space, is initially at 130°F and is to be cooled to 90°F at a flow rate of 10,000 lb/hr, using atmospheric air initially at 70°F as a coolant. A single-pass crossflow exchanger is to be used, made up of two hundred and twenty-five $\frac{3}{4}$-in. nominal standard steel pipes provided with disk fins on the outside surface. The dehumidified air is to flow across the tubes and the cooling air inside the tubes. With this flow arrangement, the inside surface coefficient will control the exchanger size, and the other resistances may be neglected by comparison. If the fixed and service charge is C_1A and the pumping cost for supplying the cooling air is $C_2(\Delta p/\rho)m$, find the air velocity and tube length which will produce the optimum design. Assume that C_h is less than C_c, $h_i = BV^{0.8}$, and $f = C_3/V^{0.2}$.

CHAPTER 13

Experimental Analogues for the Solution of Heat-transfer Problems

13-1. GENERAL

In preceding chapters we have considered two general techniques which may be employed in the solution of heat-transfer problems involving complicating features such as combined modes, several regions of differing properties, and unsteady state. These two techniques were the mathematical, leading to an "exact" solution, and the approximate, leading usually to a numerical solution. The present chapter outlines the theory and application of a third general approach, the use of analogues in the solution of heat-transfer problems.

Certain special advantages of the analogue method have resulted in its recent more widespread use. In some circumstances the analogue is superior to the mathematical and approximate numerical approach. Often problems are encountered which involve features too complicated for exact solution—for example, certain types of unsteady-state conduction in several dimensions or heat transfer by several modes in series and in parallel. In certain instances one may seek the solutions of numerous problems which, though somewhat similar, cannot be generalized in the mathematical or approximate numerical approach. In addition, circumstances often arise in which the most economical solution is the analogue one, even though other methods are applicable and practical. In these and in many other cases an analogue can often be used to advantage.

13-2. ANALOGOUS PHENOMENA

Before discussing particular kinds of analogues, it is necessary to outline the conditions which make one kind of process a possible analogue for another. Several preliminary ideas are useful. Let us consider any general phenomenon—for example, heat transfer. We characterize what happens during a process by referring to quantities or variables which are called properties, parameters, fluxes, etc. Then, in order to analyze the process mathematically, we idealize it by assuming that certain relationships, sometimes called laws, exist between various of these properties. The next step is usually the derivation of one or more differential equations from the conditions imposed by the "laws." This set of differential equations, the governing equations of the process, along with the necessary boundary and initial conditions, becomes the complete formal statement of a particular problem. An example of this kind of analysis is found in Chap. 2, where heat conduction is considered. The variables are t, x, y, z, τ, q''', k, ρ, and c. Fourier's law of conduction is used, and the result is the differential equation (2-1). The specification of the boundary conditions completes the particular problem statement.

The solution of the mathematical problem depends only upon its statement, as discussed above. Therefore, the behavior of the actual process, which is assumed to be the same as the behavior of the mathematical solution, depends only upon the formal mathematical statement. These considerations are used to discover analogous phenomena, to determine which variable in the analogue corresponds to a given one in the process of interest, and to fix the scale factors between corresponding variables.

Analogous phenomena are those which have the same forms of behavior, that is, the same form of solution. This will result if the forms of the mathematical statements, and of the differential equations in particular, are the same. Further, the way in which the variables of each of the two phenomena enter into the respective equations will indicate which are the corresponding variables. Finally, the scale factors relating each pair of corresponding variables are the ones which must be used to convert, by substitution, the differential equations of one phenomenon into the differential equations of the other. This last condition assures that the two solutions have identical form and, in fact, amounts to the reduction of the two problems to one.

From the foregoing considerations it is clear that the mere discovery of an analogous phenomenon does not yield a solution to the heat-transfer process of interest; the two formal problem statements differ only in the symbols used. The analogue is of value only if it is possible to carry out the analogous process experimentally, in a way which permits the measurement of the kind of information desired in the heat-transfer problem. The experimental analogue results can then be expressed in terms of the variables of the heat-transfer problem, by means of the previously mentioned scale factors.

The way in which the analogue is used indicates one source of inaccuracy inherent in the use of this technique. The similarity is between the mathematical statements of the two problems. However, these statements result only from idealizations of the processes. The accuracy of the method depends, therefore, upon how closely the idealizations approximate real behavior. The magnitude of this effect will depend upon the phenomena involved.

13-3. CLASSES OF ANALOGUES

There are two fundamentally different classes of analogues in general use. They are often designated by the terms "geometric" and "network." The differences between the two classes of analogues are similar in some respects to the differences between the exact mathematical and the approximate numerical techniques of solving problems. For example, the exact solution employs equations which are valid for every point in a region, whereas the approximate method uses equations which are valid only at specific points and which are derived by concentrating resistances along lines and capacitances at points. The geometric shape is crucial in the exact solution, but in the approximate solution only the sizes of the resistances and capacitances and their method of assembly into a "network" are of importance. For example, the exact solution considers the material in which conduction occurs to be spread homogeneously over space. The approximate technique in effect substitutes for small lumps of the actual material two fictitious and separate materials, one having resistance and the other capacitance. This substitution process is called "lumping."

A geometric analogue is, therefore, a homogeneous one in which the analogous phenomenon occurs uniformly in a region. The shape of the analogue is similar to the shape of the heat-transfer region. The network analogue is the analogue of the "lumped" thermal problem and appears as a network of single-purpose components. The special advantages and sphere of application of each class will become evident as various analogues are discussed.

13-4. GEOMETRIC ANALOGUES

Any phenomenon having for its differential equation an equation of the form of Eq. (2-2) would be a possible analogue for unsteady-state heat conduction with a distributed source in an isotropic material for which the thermal conductivity is independent of temperature. Similarly, if the differential equation were of the form of Eq. (2-3), the phenomenon would be a possible analogue for unsteady-state conduction in the absence of sources. However, up to the present time the geometric-analogue applications have been mainly for the solution of steady-state conduction problems. An exception is discussed by Moore (1936). The reasons for the restriction to steady state lie mainly in the difficulty of incorporating storage, that is, capacity, into a geometric analogue and in the difficulty encountered in taking data in unsteady state.

In the present brief consideration of geometric analogues, the discussion is restricted to those employed for the solution of steady-state problems, without and with distributed sources. The general differential equations in these cases are the following:

$$\nabla^2 t = 0 \tag{13-1}$$

$$\nabla^2 t + \frac{q'''}{k} = 0 \tag{13-2}$$

The first is the Laplace equation, which is the controlling differential equation for many steady-state phenomena—for example, frictionless incompressible flow and electrical conduction. The second is the Poisson equation. This equation applies to many phenomena. Each of the similar phenomena in each case is a conceivable analogue for the thermal problem, and the corresponding variables are found by comparing symbols in the equations.

The choice of analogue in a particular problem depends upon which among the conceivable ones is experimentally practical. It must be possible to simulate the boundary conditions of the heat-transfer problem and to make the necessary measurements. The best analogue in a given circumstance sometimes also depends upon what sort of information is desired. For example, in some cases the temperature distribution is sought and in others the rates of heat transfer are of primary interest. In the following discussion of the membrane and electrical analogy, the importance of these considerations is clearly seen.

13-5. MEMBRANE ANALOGUES

The behavior of a thin membrane stretched over a boundary and dilated by a pressure p follows an equation of the Poisson form if the membrane is "ideal." An ideal membrane is one which has no mass and which has a constant skin tension σ per unit length of boundary for any element of the surface. The only other requirement is that the membrane deflections be sufficiently small so that for all points on the membrane the sine of the angle of inclination of the tangent plane from the horizontal may be taken equal to the angle itself, expressed in radians. Under these conditions the differential equation relating z, the height of the membrane at (x,y) above some convenient datum, is

$$\frac{\partial^2 z}{\partial x^2} + \frac{\partial^2 z}{\partial y^2} + \frac{p}{\sigma} = 0 \tag{13-3}$$

Upon comparing this equation with Eq. (13-2), it is clear that the membrane is an analogy for two-dimensional steady-state heat conduction with a distributed source. The corresponding quantities are t and z and q'''/k and p/σ. The space coordinates correspond in the two cases. This analogue is used in practice by employing a soap film as an approximation for an ideal membrane. The boundary conditions of the heat-transfer problem, which are in the form of temperatures on boundaries, are taken into account by building up the boundary over which the soap film is to be put. The dilation pressure p is chosen to keep the deflections small. The heights z are measured at various locations. These heights are then converted into temperatures and are considered the solution of the heat-transfer problem.

The scale factors must be determined. In this case the process is carried out in considerable detail in order to demonstrate the technique. Assume the geometric scale factor, the ratio of a length in the heat-transfer problem to a corresponding length in the membrane problem, to be β. The temperature scale is redefined as $t = \gamma t'$. Converting Eq. (13-2) to the new variables, we have

$$\frac{\gamma}{\beta^2}\frac{\partial^2 t'}{\partial x^2} + \frac{\gamma}{\beta^2}\frac{\partial^2 t'}{\partial y^2} + \frac{q'''}{k} = 0 \qquad \text{or} \qquad \frac{\partial^2 t'}{\partial x^2} + \frac{\partial^2 t'}{\partial y^2} + \left(\frac{\beta^2}{\gamma}\right)\left(\frac{q'''}{k}\right) = 0$$

Comparing this with Eq. (13-3), it is clear that z and t' are identical if β and γ have been chosen so that

$$\left(\frac{\beta^2}{\gamma}\right)\left(\frac{q'''}{k}\right) = \frac{p}{\sigma}$$

from which we find

$$\beta^2\left(\frac{q'''}{k}\right)\left(\frac{\sigma}{p}\right) = \gamma = \frac{t}{t'} = \frac{t}{z}$$

or

$$t = \beta^2\left(\frac{q'''}{k}\right)\left(\frac{\sigma}{p}\right)z = \delta z \tag{13-4}$$

Thus, δ, which relates t and z, is seen to be a function of β, q'''/k, and σ/p. The first two quantities are fixed by the statement of the heat-transfer problem and by convenience considerations in analogue sizing. The value of σ/p, however, depends upon the exact nature of the soap film and the magnitude of the dilation pressure. The direct measurement of σ is impossible, and several techniques have been devised by which σ/p is inferred from an auxiliary film stretched over a circular boundary.

The steps, then, in the solution of a given heat-transfer problem are as follows. The value of β is chosen, and the similar boundaries of the analogue are cut, generally from plates, and built up or positioned to simulate the temperature boundary conditions. The soap film is formed, and the dilation pressure is applied. The values of z are then measured at various locations, usually with a probe carried on a micrometer head. From the auxiliary film information, σ/p is computed. Then δ is found, and the measured values of z are converted to temperature estimates. If heat flows are to be estimated, a technique can be used similar to that discussed in connection with approximate numerical techniques, wherein a summation of flow through "rods" along a boundary was used.

Certain practical difficulties are encountered in the use of this analogue. The soap film is very sensitive to vibration and must be studied in an enclosure. The atmosphere must be humid, to reduce evaporation. There is an aging effect; when the film is first formed, its thickness is nonuniform, and time is required for drainage of the excess soap solution. Elevations measured near boundaries are unreliable, because the film tends to overlap the boundary. These and other factors which affect accuracy will not be discussed further here. The reader is referred to Wilson and Miles (1950). Various examples of the use of this analogue are to be found in the literature [see Schneider and Çambel (1953) and Moore (1950)].

The membrane analogue finds use in another class of heat-transfer problems also. The differential equation for the membrane with a zero dilation pressure is seen from Eq. (13-3) to be

$$\frac{\partial^2 z}{\partial x^2} + \frac{\partial^2 z}{\partial y^2} = 0 \tag{13-5}$$

This is the Laplace equation and shows that this membrane is an analogue for steady-state conduction without generation. The corresponding variables are t and z, and any convenient scale factor may be employed.

13-6. GEOMETRIC ELECTRICAL ANALOGUES

The phenomenon of steady-state electrical conduction in a distributed resistance is analogous to steady-state heat conduction. The differential equation relating electrical potential e to the space coordinates is

$$\frac{\partial e^2}{\partial x^2} + \frac{\partial e^2}{\partial y^2} + \frac{\partial e^2}{\partial z^2} = 0 \tag{13-6}$$

The two-dimensional form is similar but has only two terms. These equations are again of the Laplace form. The corresponding variables are t and e, and it is clear that any scale factor may be chosen. There is a further important correspondence in this analogue, namely, that between electric current and heat flow.

The geometric electrical analogue, in contrast to the membrane analogue, is not applicable to problems involving distributed generation. However, the various types of electrical analogues have certain important advantages over membrane analogues in nongeneration problems. The inclusion of rather complicated boundary conditions, such as the presence of surface conductances on boundaries, is simply carried out in some types of electrical analogues. Further, it is generally possible to measure directly in the analogue the flux, the potential distribution, and even the total resistance, which corresponds to resistance to heat flow in the heat-transfer problem. Also, the electrical analogue may be used in three-dimensional problems. The value of these advantages depends upon the kind of problem which is to be solved.

The two general kinds of geometric electrical analogues which have been widely used are the conductive-sheet type for two-dimensional problems and the electrolytic-bath type for two- and three-dimensional problems. The conductive-sheet application, which will be discussed first, employs a sheet of material cut to the shape of the region in which thermal conduction occurs. The sheet must have appreciable electrical resistance, and paper coated with a thin conducting film is often used. Isothermal boundaries are simulated by using good conductors as boundaries. The effect of surface coefficients can be accounted for by including an extra strip of conductive sheet around the boundaries and inside the good conductors which represent the isothermal regions. Regions of differing conductivity may be obtained by punching holes in the conductive sheet.

In most applications of the conductive-sheet method, the data obtained from the analogue are in the form of the location of equipotential and flow lines. These are analogous to isothermal and adiabatic lines. The equipotential lines are located with a probe. Since equipotential and flow lines are orthogonal, the flow lines can be drawn in by eye. An alternative method of locating flow lines is to interchange equipotential and insulated boundaries and then redetermine equipotential lines. From this information the temperature distribution and heat flow can be found. Interesting and typical applications of this analogue are reported by Kayan (1945 and 1949). Several direct methods of finding heat flow are possible. They are discussed below in connection with the electrolytic-bath type of analogue.

The electrolytic-bath analogue is applicable to both two- and three-dimensional problems. The analogue consists of a tank, having a geometric form similar to that of the heat-transfer region, filled with the electrolyte. The tank sides are made of electrical insulators and conductors as required by the problem boundary conditions. Various conducting solutions have been used, and an alternating voltage is generally employed in order to prevent polarization effects. It is possible to derive several kinds of information from the analogue. One may measure voltages, from which temperatures may be found, or locate equipotential surfaces, or use the current or voltage to estimate heat flow directly. The first two techniques are relatively self-evident, and only the last is discussed in some detail.

The electrolytic analogue may be arranged to give directly the information from which heat flow can be computed. The analogue is placed in a circuit in series with an auxiliary or standard tank of cubical shape and unit volume with two opposite sides conducting. The two tanks are filled with the same electrolyte. The same current i flows through both tanks. Now the current is related to the electrical conductivity of the electrolyte, k_e, and to the Δe across the analogue by an equation of the form $i = k_e \delta_e \Delta e$, where δ_e is a function of geometry alone. The similar relation for the standard tank is $i = k_e \Delta e_s$, from which we see that $\delta_e = \Delta e_s / \Delta e$. It is clear that the heat-transfer rate for the thermal problem can be written in a similar manner as $q = k \delta_t \Delta t$, where δ_t is also a function only of geometry. The question then is, How are δ_t and δ_e related? If the two regions are the same size, they are obviously the same number. If they are geometrically similar and of different size, δ_t and δ_e will still be equal for two-dimensional problems if a unit thickness is considered in the direction of the third dimension. This is true because, with increasing size, the area across which flow occurs increases linearly, but so does the length of the flow path. For three-dimensional problems, δ_t is no longer equal to δ_e, because the area for flow increases as the square of size, whereas the length of the flow path increases only linearly. Therefore, $\delta_t = n \delta_e$, where n is the ratio of a length in the thermal region to the corresponding length in the analogue region.

Analogues of this type have been used for the solution of many types of problems in heat transfer and in other fields as well. For further information and additional methods of use, the reader is referred to Langmuir (1913) and Malavard and Miroux (1952).

13-7. NETWORK ANALOGUES FOR STEADY STATE

The network type of analogue has been previously discussed as an analogue for the lumped thermal problem. The lumping process for steady-state problems is easily carried out. The only characteristic required of the network elements is resistance. Conduction regions and surface resistances are replaced by properly sized resistances to heat flow. Distributed or point sources are both replaced by an introduction of flux at the network junctions. From these considerations we recognize many simple analogues for these steady-state lumped thermal problems. All that is required is that the analogous phenomena occur in steady state in a network of individual elements and that the flux through a given element be directly proportional to the difference in potential at the ends of the elements and inversely proportional to the resistance of the element. The laminar flow of fluid through tubes and electric current flow through resistances both satisfy these requirements. The requirement for sources can be met by the introduction of fluid in the laminar flow case and current in the electrical case at the network junctions. The electrical analogue has been widely used as a steady-state analogue and has certain inherent advantages over the laminar fluid one. Therefore, discussion will be restricted to the electrical analogue in the consideration of steady-state problems.

In order to clarify various ideas, such as lumping, a particular two-dimensional problem will be discussed. Consider a square duct of negligible wall thickness and of dimension L covered with a layer of insulation of thickness $L/2$ and thermal conductivity k. Assume that the inside and outside surface coefficients are h_i and h_o. The temperature of the fluid inside the duct is designated as t_i and the temperature of the surrounding fluid as t_o. Consider a 1-ft-long section of the duct and insulation. It is clear from symmetry considerations that only one-eighth of the section need be studied (see Fig. 13-1a). Now the lumped thermal circuit is constructed by dividing the region into square rods, in this case of cross-sectional area Δx^2, where $\Delta x = L/8$. Consider the typical square rod $abcd$. The center point e is assumed to be typical of the rod; that is, t_e is assumed equal to the average temperature over the square surface. The two-dimensional resistance characteristics of the material of the square are now replaced by resistances running in perpendicular directions. The center lines of the resistances of adjacent squares coincide to produce a network, as shown in Fig. 13-1b. The surface resistances are simulated by supplying a surface resistance for each exposed rod face. The complete lumped thermal circuit is shown in Fig. 13-1b.

The sizes of the resistances have definite values which are fixed by the statement of the heat-transfer problem. In Fig. 13-1b the resistance between h and i must be equal to the resistance between opposite faces of a rod; that is, $R' = \Delta x/(k\,\Delta x) = 1/k$. Between h and g the necessary resistance is obviously $R'/2$. On the outside surfaces R'_o must be the same resistance, as is present for a surface coefficient h_o over a surface of area Δx; therefore, $R'_o = 1/(h_o\,\Delta x)$. Similarly, $R'_i = 1/(h_i\,\Delta x)$. The thermal circuit is completed

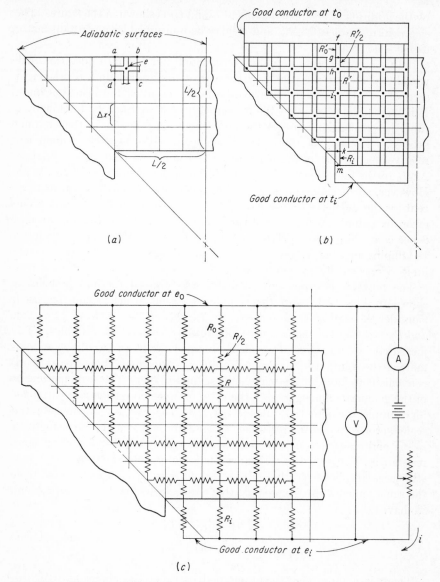

Fig. 13-1. The lumped thermal circuit and electrical analogue for two-dimensional steady state. (a) One-eighth of the duct cross section. (b) The lumped thermal circuit. (c) The electrical network analogue circuit.

by the addition of good conductors at t_c and t_i, as shown in the figure. The electrical resistances R', R'_o, and R'_i may be multiplied by a constant factor if this is convenient.

If this network were actually constructed and put into operation, one would expect that the heat flow through it, multiplied by 8 for the eight sections, would be about equal to the flow for 1 ft of the insulated duct. It is known, however, that the measured heat flow would be too low by a small percentage, because of the approximation inherent in the lumping process. The size of this error depends upon the geometry; upon the relative magnitudes of R'_o, R', and R'_i; and upon the relative size, that is, $\Delta x/L$, of the lump used. No general formulation of this error is available. However, as a rough guide one would expect an error of the order of 1 per cent for the geometry shown above for $\Delta x = L/8$ and $R'_o = R' = R'_i$. The error for a similar situation in a three-dimensional corner would be around 8 per cent, and the heat flow would be too high in the lumped circuit.* In lumping any thermal problem, it is clearly desirable to choose the relative lump size as small as possible.

The network electrical analogue for this lumped thermal problem is shown in Fig. 13-1c with the completed circuit which could be used. Consider the case in which $(e_i - e_o) = (t_i - t_o)$, $R = 1/k$, $R_i = 1/(h_i\,\Delta x)$, and $R_o = 1/(h_o\,\Delta x)$, using consistent units for each set of variables. The measured i would be equal to q in the lumped circuit and would be an estimate of the solution of the original problem. In general, however, it is not convenient to have all the scale factors equal to one. The scale factors, as in the geometric analogues, are the ratio between corresponding variables; for example, the potential scale factor is $(t_i - t_o)/(e_i - e_o)$. If the potential scale factor is r_P and the resistance scale factor is r_R, the flux scale factor is r_P/r_R, and $q = (r_P/r_R)i$. Analogues are normally constructed using large resistances. This gives a resistance scale factor different from one. It is still necessary, however, that all the various sizes of resistors required have the same value of r_R. Expressing this requirement for the above problem, we have

$$r_R = \frac{R'}{R} = \frac{R'_i}{R_i} = \frac{R'_o}{R_o} \tag{13-7}$$

There is a more convenient method of using the analogue. By this technique all the information that any analogue has to offer concerning flux can be obtained in one simple resistance measurement. For the lumped thermal circuit, $q = (t_i - t_o)/R'_T$, where R'_T, the total resistance to heat flow, is the unknown. The current i in the analogue is related to $(e_i - e_o)$

* These accuracy estimates were obtained from network electrical analogues.

and to the total analogue resistance R_T by $i = (e_i - e_o)/R_T$. It is clear that R_T, the resistance of the circuit between the two good conductors in Fig. 13-1c, depends directly upon the values of R_i, R, and R_o chosen in building the analogue. Had they been chosen twice as large, then R_T would be twice as large. Therefore, since $R_T \propto R$, $R'_T \propto R'$, and $R'/R = r_R$, we have $R'_T/R_T = r_R$. This ratio of total resistances may be expressed in several forms:

$$\frac{R'_T}{R_T} = r_R = \frac{1}{kR} = \frac{1}{h_i \, \Delta x \, R_i} = \frac{1}{h_o \, \Delta x \, R_o} \tag{13-8}$$

Solving for R'_T from each of these forms, we have

$$q = \frac{t_i - t_o}{R'_T} = \frac{kR}{R_T} (t_i - t_o) = \frac{h_i \, \Delta x \, R_i}{R_T} (t_i - t_o) = \frac{h_o \, \Delta x \, R_o}{R_T} (t_i - t_o) \tag{13-9}$$

The estimate of q is therefore obtained from lumped-thermal-problem information, the size of analogue resistors, and the total analogue resistance R_T, which may be simply and accurately measured.

The same analysis may be carried out for three-dimensional network electrical analogues. The expressions for r_R and the q estimate are

$$r_R = \frac{1}{kR \, \Delta x} = \frac{1}{h_i R_i \, \Delta x^2} = \frac{1}{h_o R_o \, \Delta x^2} \tag{13-10}$$

$$q = \frac{t_i - t_o}{R'_T} = \frac{kR \, \Delta x}{R_T} (t_i - t_o) = \frac{h_i \, \Delta x^2 \, R_i}{R_T} (t_i - t_o)$$

$$= \frac{h_o \, \Delta x^2 \, R_i}{R_T} (t_i - t_o) \tag{13-11}$$

The heat-transfer problem chosen for the demonstration and description of the lumping and analogue design technique is relatively simple. Many of the problems encountered in practice are more complicated. In many problems, for example, the area in which conduction occurs cannot be covered completely by equal-sized squares. Often the surface coefficient has different values at different locations on a surface. The bounding surfaces may not be isothermal. These and many other complications must be handled with judgment as they appear. An interesting application of the network electrical analogue for the solution of several quite complicated steady-state problems is discussed by Ellerbrock et al. (1953). Descriptions of several combinations of the network and geometric electrical-analogue techniques are described by Malavard and Miroux (1952).

13-8. NETWORK ANALOGUES FOR UNSTEADY STATE

Network analogues for unsteady-state problems are analogues for the lumped thermal circuit, which is more complicated because thermal capac-

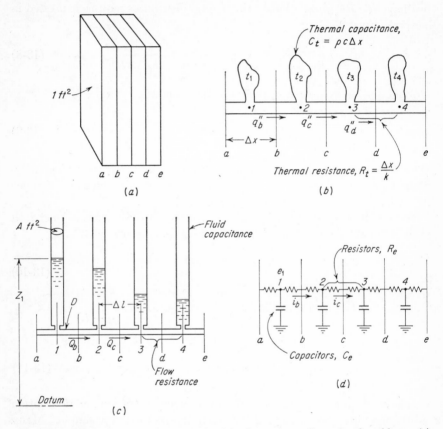

FIG. 13-2. Thermal and analogue circuits for a lumped one-dimensional problem. (a) One-dimensional region. (b) Lumped thermal circuit. (c) Laminar fluid circuit. (d) Electrical circuit.

ity must be taken into account. The methods of incorporating this characteristic into the lumped thermal and analogue circuits are similar. In each case two kinds of components are used, one having only resistance and the other only capacitance. In two dimensions the resistance elements are distributed as indicated in Fig. 13-1b and c for the steady-state problem. The point at the center of an element—for example, t_e in Fig. 13-1a—is assumed to have a temperature equal to the average for the element, and the capacitance is concentrated at such a point. The size of the capacitance is equal to the total capacity of the element it replaces. The thermal circuit then consists merely of resistance elements and reservoirs. Various circumstances and boundary conditions may be simulated in the same manner as in the steady-state lumped circuit.

There are many possible analogues of this thermal problem. In this treatment, however, we shall consider only two direct ones. The term direct is used to emphasize that the corresponding variables are physically similar and that each phenomenon is characterized by a potential, a flux, a time, etc. Other types of analogues are possible but are not now widely used. The two analogues to be considered here are the laminar fluid flow network and the resistance-capacitance electric circuit. In the laminar fluid analogue, resistors are lengths of tubing and the capacitors are reservoirs. For the electrical analogue, resistors and capacitors are used. The corresponding variables are as follows: the potentials are temperature, head, and voltage; the fluxes are rate of heat transfer, volume rate of fluid flow, and current. Time is present in each system. The arrangement of the three analogous circuits is shown in Fig. 13-2 for 1 ft^2 of cross-sectional area in a one-dimensional problem.

A few preliminary remarks concerning the potential datum are necessary. The storage of energy in the thermal system is always computed above an arbitrary datum, usually the zero of the temperature scale used. This datum does not change with time and is the same at all points. Therefore, the same conditions must be met by the datum chosen for the capacity in the analogue. The electrical capacitors must be grounded or be tied to a constant-voltage region. Similarly, the fluid-capacity tubes must be open to a constant-pressure region.

Corresponding Variables. The three phenomena are analogous because the equations relating potential, flux, and time are similar. In addition to potential, flux, and time, these equations involve only constants, that is, quantities which are independent of time. The equations are of the following form:

$$\text{Resistance} = \frac{\text{potential difference across a resistance}}{\text{flux}}$$

$$\text{Capacitance} = \frac{\text{net flux into a capacitance}}{\text{time rate of change of potential}}$$

The similarity of the forms of the equations will be shown by developing them for a typical lump of each circuit. For uniformity, the lump $b2c$ in

Fig. 13-2 will be used throughout. For the thermal system, we have

$$\text{Resistance} = \frac{R_t}{2} = \frac{\Delta x}{2k} = \frac{t_b - t_2}{q_b''} = \frac{t_2 - t_c}{q_c''} \tag{13-12}$$

$$\text{Capacitance} = C_t = \rho c \, \Delta x = - \frac{\Delta q_2''}{dt_2/d\tau} = - \frac{q_b'' - q_c''}{dt_2/d\tau} \tag{13-13}$$

For the electrical system,

$$\text{Resistance} = \frac{R_e}{2} = \frac{e_b - e_2}{i_b} = \frac{e_2 - e_c}{i_a} \tag{13-14}$$

$$\text{Capacitance} = C_e = - \frac{\Delta i_2}{de_2/d\tau} = - \frac{i_c - i_b}{de_2/d\tau} \tag{13-15}$$

For laminar flow through smooth circular tubes the relation between head loss and volume rate of flow is given by the Hagen-Poiseuille equation:

$$\Delta Z = \frac{128\mu \, \Delta L \, Q}{\pi D^4 \rho g_o}$$

or $$\text{Resistance} = \frac{R_f}{2} = \frac{Z_b - Z_2}{Q_b} = \frac{128\mu \, \Delta L}{2\pi D^4 \rho g_o} = \frac{Z_2 - Z_c}{Q_c} \tag{13-16}$$

$$\text{Capacitance} = C_f = A = - \frac{\Delta Q_2}{dZ_2/d\tau} = - \frac{Q_c - Q_b}{dZ_2/d\tau} \tag{13-17}$$

The various relations are hereby seen to be of similar form. The corresponding variables of potential and flux behave similarly in the three systems if the resistances and capacitances are all independent of potential and flux and therefore of time. This last condition is satisfied in the thermal problem if k and c are independent of temperature. It is satisfied in the fluid flow case if the flow is laminar and if the fluid properties do not change. In the electrical system it is necessary that the resistance be independent of the current flow through the resistor and that the capacitance be the same for all capacitor voltage levels. Also, in principle the capacitor must have infinite resistance, that is, allow no current leakage. The fact that these conditions are easily approximated in actual components is one of the primary reasons for the success of these analogues.

It is clear that the above requirement that k and c be independent of temperature means merely that we are referring to thermal circumstances in which k and c are constant. However, at this point we may easily see what special requirements are placed upon the analogues if k and c do depend upon the potential, temperature. In these circumstances, both R_t

and C_t depend upon potential. Therefore, for an electrical analogue, R_e and C_e must depend upon voltage in the same way. No simple resistor has the required characteristic, and variable capacitors are possible but not simple. In the fluid analogue, R_f and C_f must vary with head, Z. The variation of R_f with head is not realizable. However, variable C_f is very easily incorporated by using capacity tubes whose cross-sectional area A varies along the length. Therefore, the RC electrical analogue is not suitable for problems in which k and c vary, but the laminar fluid analogue can be used when only c varies with temperature.

A summary of the corresponding variables and their values in terms of properties of the various systems is given in Table 13-1. These values are for the one-dimensional networks. Equations (13-12) to (13-17) and the values of R_t and C_t would be somewhat different for two- and three-dimensional networks. Table 13-1 also contains the notation for a general system. The idea of a general system will be of value in the subsequent determination of scale factors.

TABLE 13-1. CORRESPONDING VARIABLES IN THE GENERAL, THERMAL, RC ELECTRICAL, AND LAMINAR FLUID FLOW SYSTEMS

Variable	General	Thermal	RC electrical	Laminar fluid
Potential........	p	t	e	Z
Flux............	I	q''	i	Q
Resistance.......	R	$R_t = \Delta x/k$	R_e	$128\mu\ \Delta L/\pi D^4 \rho g_o$
Capacitance.....	C	$C_t = \rho c\ \Delta x$	C_e	$C_f = A$
Time..........	τ	τ_t	τ_e	τ_f

Scale Factors. The determination of the scale factors will be carried out by first developing the differential equation which relates the network-point potential to resistance, capacitance, and time. This equation will be derived in terms of the behavior of a single network lump for the general system, $b2c$, shown in Fig. 13-3. The applicable equations are

$$\frac{R}{2} = \frac{p_b - p_2}{I_b} \quad \text{or} \quad I_b = \frac{2(p_b - p_2)}{R}$$

$$\frac{R}{2} = \frac{p_2 - p_c}{I_c} \quad \text{or} \quad I_c = \frac{2(p_2 - p_c)}{R}$$

$$C = -\frac{\Delta I_2}{dp_2/d\tau} = -\frac{I_c - I_b}{dp_2/d\tau} \quad \text{or} \quad I_c - I_b = -C\frac{dp_2}{d\tau}$$

Eliminating I_b and I_c from these equations, we have

$$I_c - I_b = \frac{2(p_2 - p_c)}{R} - \frac{2(p_b - p_2)}{R} = -\frac{2}{R}(p_b + p_c - 2p_2) = -C\frac{dp_2}{d\tau}$$

or
$$2(p_b + p_c - 2p_2) = RC\frac{dp_2}{d\tau} \qquad (13\text{-}18)$$

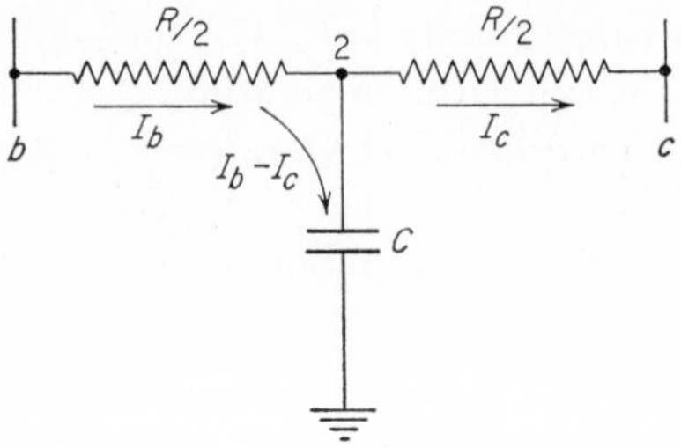

FIG. 13-3.   A general network element.

By comparison with Eq. (13-18), we may write the equations for the thermal, RC electrical, and laminar fluid flow systems as follows:

$$2(t_b + t_c - 2t_2) = R_t C_t \frac{dt_2}{d\tau_t} \qquad (13\text{-}19)$$

$$2(e_b + e_c - 2e_2) = R_e C_e \frac{de_2}{d\tau_e} \qquad (13\text{-}20)$$

$$2(Z_b + Z_c - 2Z_2) = R_f C_f \frac{dZ_2}{d\tau_f} \qquad (13\text{-}21)$$

We are interested in two sets of scale factors, one set between the thermal and electrical networks and one set between the thermal and laminar fluid networks. The two sets will be determined simultaneously. The temperature, flux, and time of the thermal problem are related to the corresponding variables of the other systems by the following linear expressions:

$$t = A_1 e + B_1 = A_2 Z + B_2$$

$$q'' = C_1 i = C_2 Q \qquad (13\text{-}22)$$

$$\tau_t = D_1 \tau_e = D_2 \tau_f$$

The restriction of the relative magnitude of these scale factors is found by determining what relation between them will reduce Eq. (13-19) to the form of Eqs. (13-20) and (13-21). This is the same procedure as that used in Sec. 13-5 in connection with the membrane analogue. Substituting the first parts of Eq. (13-22) into Eq. (13-19), we have

$$2(A_1e_b + B_1 + A_1e_c + B_1 - 2A_1e_2 - 2B_1) = R_tC_t \frac{d(A_1e_2 + B_1)}{d(D_1\tau_e)}$$

$$= R_tC_t \frac{A_1}{D_1} \frac{de_2}{d\tau_e}$$

or
$$2(e_b + e_c - 2e_2) = \frac{R_tC_t}{D_1} \frac{de_2}{d\tau_e} \qquad (13\text{-}23)$$

Similarly, substituting the second parts of Eq. (13-22) into Eq. (13-19), we find

$$2(Z_b + Z_c - 2Z_2) = \frac{R_tC_t}{D_2} \frac{dZ_2}{d\tau_f} \qquad (13\text{-}24)$$

Equations (13-23) and (13-24) are the same as (13-20) and (13-21) if

$$D_1 = \frac{R_tC_t}{R_eC_e} = \frac{\Delta\tau_t}{\Delta\tau_e} \quad \text{or} \quad \frac{R_tC_t}{\Delta\tau_t} = \frac{R_eC_e}{\Delta\tau_e} \qquad (13\text{-}25)$$

$$D_2 = \frac{R_tC_t}{R_fC_f} = \frac{\Delta\tau_t}{\Delta\tau_f} \quad \text{or} \quad \frac{R_tC_t}{\Delta\tau_t} = \frac{R_fC_f}{\Delta\tau_f} \qquad (13\text{-}26)$$

where $\Delta\tau_t$ and $\Delta\tau_e$ or $\Delta\tau_f$ mean corresponding time intervals. The result is, therefore, that the ratio of the time intervals during which a given effect occurs in the thermal and analogue networks is equal to the ratio of the products of lump resistance and capacitance. We note also that $RC/\Delta\tau$ is dimensionless and, therefore, that the system of units used in describing the various phenomena need not be the same. The scale factor relating fluxes is found by writing down typical flux relations for the three networks and then reducing the thermal one to the form of the other two:

$$q'' = \frac{2(t_b - t_2)}{R_t} \qquad i = \frac{2(e_b - e_2)}{R_e} \qquad Q = \frac{2(Z_b - Z_2)}{R_f}$$

$$q'' = C_1i = \frac{2(A_1e_b + B_1 - A_1e_2 - B_1)}{R_t} \quad \text{or} \quad i = \frac{2A_1(e_b - e_2)}{C_1R_t}$$

$$q'' = C_2Q = \frac{2(A_2Z_b + B_2 - A_2Z_2 - B_2)}{R_t} \quad \text{or} \quad Q = \frac{2A_2(Z_b - Z_2)}{C_2R_t}$$

$$\frac{A_1}{C_1R_t} = \frac{1}{R_e} \quad \text{or} \quad C_1 = \frac{A_1R_e}{R_t} \quad \text{and} \quad q'' = \frac{A_1R_e}{R_t}i \qquad (13\text{-}27)$$

$$\frac{A_2}{C_2R_f} = \frac{1}{R_f} \quad \text{or} \quad C_2 = \frac{A_2R_f}{R_t} \quad \text{and} \quad q'' = \frac{A_2R_f}{R_t}Q \qquad (13\text{-}28)$$

These flux scale factors depend only upon the relative sizes of the lump resistances and upon the potential scale factor. The potential factors A_1 and A_2 may be chosen entirely from convenience considerations; the requirement of similarity places no restriction upon these factors, because potential appears linearly in each term of the differential equation. It is also clear that there is no formal restriction upon the relative sizes of R_t, R_e, and R_f or on C_t, C_e, and C_f, except, of course, that they must be consistent throughout a network. These values may be chosen to give convenient time scale factors. There is one restriction upon the above analysis which must be recognized. These results are valid only when Eq. (13-18) applies to the capacitor. This equation does not apply when flux arrives at a capacitor junction by means other than through a resistance. Such cases arise when generation and energy storage occur simultaneously. For these and other complicated cases the scale relations will be different from those given above, but they may be determined by similar methods.

The foregoing analysis considered only "one-dimensional" networks. However, the changes necessary in Eqs. (13-19) to (13-21) to apply them to networks of more dimensions will not cause changes in any of the scale factors, and Eqs. (13-25) to (13-28) may, therefore, still be used. Changes are required, however, in the values assigned to R_t and C_t in Table 13-1, because in the lumping process different amounts of material are simulated by R_t and C_t. However, $R_t C_t = \Delta x^2 \, c\rho/k = \Delta x^2/\alpha$ is the same in one, two, and three dimensions.

The preceding scale factors are only one of the kinds of restrictions under which an analogue must operate. The actual analogue is constructed of physical components, and these components must be capable of closely approximating the ideal characteristics of the elements of the lumped thermal circuit. For example, the thermal resistances and capacitances do not leak. Small leakage, or even no leakage, is easily obtained in analogue resistors and even in the fluid-analogue capacitors. However, electrical capacitors do leak, and this factor often influences analogue design and accuracy. Changing and nonuniform analogue temperature can produce undesirable extraneous effects if the component resistances and capacitances are temperature-dependent. This fact has led to the use of constant-viscosity fluids in the fluid analogue. The accuracy of the analogue results depends upon how well the initial and boundary conditions are applied. Following these conditions closely is sometimes difficult. In solving certain types of problems, it is very difficult to measure the analogue solution without unduly affecting the behavior of the analogue. The physical quantities to be measured are flux and/or potential. Accurate instantaneous flow-rate measurement is difficult in the fluid analogue. Elaborate instrumentation is required in the electrical analogue because of the high speed of the process and because of the small currents and high resistances used. Certain other restrictions and practical difficulties are discussed below in connection with the consideration of the application of these analogues to the solution of a particular problem.

As a particular demonstration problem, the same geometry will be taken as that used in the description of the steady-state network analogue (see Fig. 13-1). The conditions will be changed to the following extent: an infinite surface coefficient on the inside surface and a constant coefficient of 2.2 Btu/hr ft^2 °F on the outside surface are assumed. The unsteady-state problem is the following. The duct, the insulation, the fluid in the duct, and the air surrounding the insulation are initially at 60°F. The temperature of the fluid flowing through the duct suddenly increases to 500°F and remains at 500°F thereafter. The air in the surroundings remains at 60°F. The insulation has the following constant properties: $k = 0.10$ Btu/hr ft °F, $\rho = 50$ lb/ft^3, and $c = 0.20$ Btu/lb °F. The duct dimensions are 16 by 16 in. We are interested in determining the instantaneous rate of heat flow from the inside fluid to the duct wall as a function of time.

The same coarseness of lump will be used as that shown in Fig. 13-1, that is, $L/8$, or $\Delta x = 2$ in. The thermal resistances and capacitances are found as follows. The resistors interior to the insulation are $R_t = 1/k = 1/0.10 = 10$, the ones adjacent to the boundaries are $R_t/2 = 5$, and those on the outside surface are $R_{t,o} = \dfrac{1}{h_o\,\Delta x} = \dfrac{1}{2.2 \times 2/12} = 2.73$. The capacitances are $C_t = \rho c\,\Delta x^2 = 2^2 \times 0.20 \times 50/12^2 = 0.278$. Therefore, the $R_t C_t$ product is 2.78 hr. Since the thermal capacity of the fluid involved in the outside convection process is small, the effect of its changing temperature is neglected.

Any level of resistance may be used in the body of the analogue. If the body resistors are R, then the ones adjacent to the boundaries must be $R/2$, and the ones simulating the outside film must be $(2.73/10)R$. The value of C may also be chosen freely. However, since the time relation results from the choice of R and C, that is, $\Delta\tau = (RC/R_t C_t)\,\Delta\tau_t$, we should arrange these choices in a way which will give the most desirable time scale. Consider first the RC electrical analogue. Unfortunately, the upper limit of the value of $R_e C_e$ results in quite short analogue time intervals. This upper limit is a result of a practical limit on the size of C_e and of the leakage tendency of capacitors. Practical values of C_e are not greater than around 100×10^{-6} farad. The limitation on R_e results from the resistance to ground through the capacitors, and this capacitor resistance is not reliable much above 10^9 ohms. Therefore, in order that the analogue circuit current be more than a thousand times as large as the leakage current through the capacitors, the maximum value of R_e should be around 10^5 ohms. These choices result in an $R_e C_e$ value of the order of 10 sec. For these values the analogue time interval corresponding to 2 hr in the thermal problem would be $\Delta\tau = (R_e C_e / R_t C_t) \Delta\tau_t = (10/2.78)2 = 7.2$ sec. This short time would require automatic recording of the current flow, which corresponds to heat flow. In addition, because of the high resistances of the analogue, the current flow would be very small, perhaps of the order of 100 microamperes. Therefore, fairly complicated instrumentation would be required to measure the voltage at a point in the analogue. This type of measurement would have to be made by an instrument which would draw not more than several microamperes from the network point.

The above time-scale difficulties do not nullify the advantages of the electrical analogue. Components can be built to perform the necessary measurements satisfactorily and to simulate complicated boundary conditions in time intervals much shorter even than those discussed above. These analogues are complicated and expensive, however, and are therefore not generally built up for simple or occasional problem solution. They are built primarily in the form of permanent analogue computers and are designed to solve many other types of problems as well. For discussions of lumping and leakage error and a description of the construction of a particular analogue, see Paschkis and Baker (1942) and Paschkis and Heisler (1944 and 1946). A basic discussion of the application of analogue computers to heat-transfer problems was given by Nolan (1954 and 1954a), and a thorough bibliography is found in Nolan (1955).

The laminar fluid flow analogue is applicable to the above problem and, in some circumstances, the construction of an analogue of this type for the solution of one or several similar problems is a very practical and convenient approach. Convenient time scales are possible. Measurements of network-point potentials, that is, head, can be easily obtained visually. Flux is estimated with comparatively simple instruments. An indication of the reasonableness of the practical time scales can be obtained by computing the length of $\frac{1}{8}$-in.-ID tubing which will result in 1 min of analogue time representing 1 hr of thermal-problem time. Tubes of $1\frac{1}{2}$ in. ID of 1.227×10^{-2} ft^2 cross-sectional area are used for capacitors, and a silicone oil having a kinematic viscosity of 0.774 ft^2/hr is used as the analogue fluid. The $R_f C_f = R_t C_t / 60$ when the same length and time units (e.g., feet and minutes) are used in both systems. Therefore, $R_f = 2.78/(60 \times 1.227 \times 10^{-2}) = 3.78$. Employing the expression for R_f found in Table 13-1, we find $\Delta L = 0.59$ ft, or just over 7 in. It is necessary to mention at this point that interpretation of analogue results is not based upon computed values of tube resistances. Calculations merely indicate the approximate length; actual resistances are obtained by calibration tests. A constant difference of head is applied across each element, and the resulting discharge rate is measured. The value of R_f is then calculated from $R_f = \Delta Z/Q$.

The time scale employed above would in certain problems be too small; in others, perhaps, too large. Analogue times may be doubled by doubling ΔL or by doubling the area of the capacity tubes. The time scale factor depends upon tube diameter to the fourth power; therefore, various tube diameters will produce considerably different factors. In addition, the choice of R_f can be adjusted to give convenient flow rates.

Several laminar fluid flow analogues have been built and used for the solution of certain complicated heat-transfer problems which occur in air-conditioning analysis. For summaries of these undertakings, the reader is referred to Leopold (1948) and Mackey and Gay (1952 and 1954).

NOTATION

C	capacitance
e	electrical potential
k	thermal conductivity
p	pressure and potential
q	heat-transfer rate
q''	heat flux
q'''	energy-generation rate per unit volume
R	resistance
t	temperature
z	elevation of membrane above a datum
σ	membrane skin tension
τ	time

REFERENCES

Ellerbrock, H. H., Jr., E. F. Schum, and A. J. Nachtigall: *NACA Tech. Note* 3060, 1953.

Kayan, C. F.: *Trans. ASME*, vol. 67, p. 713, 1945.

———: *Trans. ASME*, vol. 71, p. 9, 1949.

Langmuir, I.: *Trans. Am. Electrochem. Soc.*, vol. 24, p. 53, 1913.

Leopold, C. S.: *Trans. ASHVE*, vol. 54, p. 389, 1948.

Mackey, C. O., and N. R. Gay: *Trans. ASHVE*, vol. 58, p. 321, 1952.

——— and ———: *Trans. ASHVE*, vol. 60, p. 469, 1954.

Malavard, L., and J. Miroux: *Engrs. Dig.*, vol. 13, p. 417, 1952.

Moore, A. D.: *Ind. Eng. Chem.*, vol. 28, p. 704, 1936.

———: *J. Appl. Mech.*, vol. 72, p. 291, 1950.

Nolan, J. E.: *Computers and Automation*, November, 1954; December, 1954a; January, 1955.

Paschkis, V., and H. D. Baker: *Trans. ASME*, vol. 64, p. 105, 1942.
——— and M. P. Heisler: *Elec. Eng.*, vol. 63, p. 165, 1944.
——— and ———: *J. Appl. Phys.*, vol. 17, p. 246, 1946.
Schneider, P. J., and A. B. Çambel: *Rev. Sci. Instr.*, vol. 24, p. 513, 1953.
Wilson, L. H., and A. J. Miles: *J. Appl. Phys.*, vol. 21, p. 532, 1950.

PROBLEMS

1. Conduction heat transfer occurs in the two-dimensional region shown. The region has a thermal conductivity of 0.50 Btu/hr ft °F. The region is bounded by two isothermal surfaces at $t_1 = 120$°F and $t_2 = 60$°F and by two adiabatic surfaces. An electrolytic

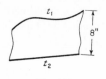

FIG. P1

analogue is built, and a unit cubical standard tank, containing the same electrolyte, is also put into the circuit. The resistances of the analogue and of the standard tank are measured to be 2.6 and 3.2 ohms. Calculate the heat-flow rate between the two isothermals.

2. A tall, square chimney with a 2- by 2-ft passage and 6-in. brick walls will contain combustion products at 700°F. The expected inside and outside surface temperatures of the chimney are 650 and 80°F. In order to determine the heat loss, a network analogue was built of one-fourth of the wall and consisted of four layers of 1600-ohm resistors. The total resistance of the analogue was found as 380 ohms.

    a. For 100 volts direct current across the analogue, find the current flow.

    b. Find the heat loss from the chimney per foot of height if k for the masonry is 0.4 Btu/hr ft °F.

3. An electrical analogue has been built to simulate a thick-walled cubical box having inside edges one-half the length of the outside edges. Because of the many symmetries of a cubical box of uniform wall thickness, the smallest representative section of the wall is one-forty-eighth of the total. The analogue of this part was built using 3300-ohm resistors, and eight layers were used for the wall. The resistance of the analogue between isothermal surfaces was 484 ohms. Compute the heat flow from the inside to the outside surface of such a box whose walls are made of concrete, with $k = 0.50$, and are 8 in. thick. Inside and outside temperatures are 400 and 100°F.

4. The analogue described in Prob. 2 is to be modified to include the effect of inside and outside surface coefficients of 5.0 and 2.0 Btu/hr ft² °F, respectively. Resistors will be applied at each circuit point on the two surfaces. For the body resistances of 1600-ohm resistors, what resistances are required on the inside and outside surfaces?

5. Aluminum rods of the T-shape cross section shown are to be used as the central electrical conductors in a large electrical distribution system. At the maximum current loading the heat-generation rate due to the dissipation of electrical energy will be 10^7 Btu/ft³ hr. The surface temperatures are to be maintained at 80°F by cooling. The question arises whether the internal temperatures will be above safe limits, and a membrane analogue of three times the actual size is to be constructed to determine the location and magnitude of the maximum temperature.

a. Specify the membrane plate design and the observations to be made.

b. If the maximum membrane deflection is to be held to $\frac{1}{2}$ in. and the estimated maximum temperature is 140°F, find the necessary value of p/σ.

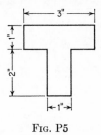

FIG. P5

6. Describe the membrane analogue which would be used to obtain the temperature distribution in the brick chimney wall discussed in Prob. 2. The analogue is to be one-quarter size. If the maximum variation in membrane elevation is to be 0.2 in., find the temperature scale factor.

7a. Sketch the network electrical analogues for Probs. 30 and 31, Chap. 2. In each case indicate the minimum fraction of the cross section which must be represented in the analogue. Use grid sizes of 3 and 2 in., respectively.

b. If the resistors in the analogue for Prob. 31 are 1600 ohms, estimate the total analogue resistance if the answer to Prob. 31 is approximately 45 Btu/hr ft.

8. Present tables similar to Table 13-1 for the two- and three-dimensional cases.

9. Draw the circuit of a network electrical analogue for the circumstance in Prob. 11, Chap. 3, for a grid of $\frac{1}{2}$ by $\frac{1}{2}$ in. Specify all resistors if the surface resistors are 1000 ohms.

10. For Prob. 26 in Chap. 3, draw the electrical and fluid network analogues for a $\frac{1}{8}$-in. network. Specify all components of an electrical analogue for a time scale ratio of 1 to 10^4 if 1 volt is to represent 1°. For the fluid analogue using oil having $\nu = 0.7$ ft²/hr and $\frac{3}{16}$-in.-ID tubes, specify approximate tube lengths and capacitor diameters for a time scale ratio of 1 to 10 if $\frac{1}{2}$ in. of head is to represent 1°. Indicate how each analogue is to be operated.

11. An electrical analogue is to be built to solve Prob. 30, Chap. 11. One resistor R and one capacitor C are to replace each $\frac{1}{16}$-in. layer of metal.

a. Sketch the complete analogue, indicating the initial conditions and the boundary conditions which will be used to match the actual problem.

b. If 10-microfarad capacitors with a resistance of 10^8 ohms are to be used and if an analogue time of 10^{-2} sec is to correspond to 1 sec in the actual problem, specify all electrical components of the analogue.

c. If 1 volt is to equal 10°, find the scale factor relating current to heat flux per unit area and specify exactly the analogue boundary condition.

Appendix

TABLE A-1. CONVERSION FACTORS

Length:
  1 ft = 12 in. = 0.3048 m = 30.48 cm
Area:
  1 ft^2 = 0.09290 m^2 = 929.0 cm^2
Volume:
  1 ft^3 = 0.02832 m^3 = 28,320 cm^3 = 28.32 liters = 7.4805 gal
Density:
  1 lb mass/ft^3 = 0.01602 g/cm = 0.1337 lb mass/gal
Specific heat:
  1 Btu/lb mass °F = 778 lb force ft/lb mass °F = 1.000654 cal/g °C = 1 I.T. cal/g °C
Thermal conductivity:
  1 Btu/hr ft °F = 12 Btu/hr ft^2 °F/in. = 4.134 × 10^{-3} cal/sec cm °C

$$= 0.01731 \text{ watt/cm °C}$$

Viscosity:
  1 lb mass/hr ft = 2.778 × 10^{-4} lb mass/sec ft = 8.634 × 10^{-6} lb force sec/ft

$$= 0.4134 \text{ centipoise}$$

TABLE A-2. THERMAL CONDUCTIVITY OF METALS AND ALLOYS *

Material	t, °F	k, Btu/hr ft °F	Material	t, °F	k, Btu/hr ft °F
Aluminum...............	32	117	Mercury................	32	4.8
	212	119		122	4.8
Antimony...............	32	10.6	Platinum	64	40.2
	212	9.7		212	41.9
Bismuth.................	64	4.7	Silver..................	32	244
	212	3.9		212	240
Cadmium................	64	53.7	Tin....................	32	36
	212	52.2		212	34
Copper..................	32	226	Zinc...................	32	65
	212	222		212	62
Gold...................	64	169	Brass:		
	212	170	90-10................	32	59
Iron....................	64	39.0		212	68
	212	36.6	70-30...............	32	56
Iron, wrought..........	64	34.9		212	60
	212	34.6	60-40................	32	61
Iron, cast..............	32	29.0		212	69
	212	28.0	Constantan (60Cu-40Ni)..	64	13.1
Steel, 1% C.............	64	26.2		212	15.5
	212	25.9	Nickel silver............	32	16.9
Lead...................	32	20.0		212	21.5
	212	19.8	Platinoid...............	64	14.5
Magnesium..............	32–212	92.0			

* From A. I. Brown and S. M. Marco, "Introduction to Heat Transfer," 3d ed., McGraw-Hill Book Company, Inc., New York, 1958.

TABLE A-3. THERMAL CONDUCTIVITY AND DENSITY OF STRUCTURAL, INSULATING, AND MISCELLANEOUS MATERIALS

Material	t, °F	k, Btu/hr ft °F	ρ, lb/ft^3	Material	t, °F	k, Btu/hr ft °F	ρ, lb/ft^3
Concrete, plasters, etc.:				Masonry materials:			
Neat cement.........	...	0.36	114	Basalt.............	...	0.7–1.6	
Concrete:				Granite.............	...	1.8–2.4	
Sand and gravel				Limestone..........	210	0.7	
aggregate.........	...	1.05 av		Marble.............	...	1.2–1.7	
Cinder aggregate....	75	0.41	97	Sandstone, dry......	60	0.75	
Cement mortar......	...	1.0	115	Shale...............	...	0.5	
Gypsum plaster......	...	0.28	70	Travertine..........	...	0.6	
Lime-cement plaster...	...	0.67	110	Building brick.......	...	0.33–0.42	
Glass:				Firebrick...........	2000	0.7–1.0	
Ordinary soda-lime-				Magnesite brick......	400	2.2	
silica..............	120	0.56	157	Woods:			
Opaque, colored.......	120	0.70		Hardwoods:			
Pyrex..............	120	0.63	139	Elm...............	...	0.083	33
Insulating materials:				Mahogany.........	...	0.075	34
Asbestos.............	80	0.090	29	White oak.........	...	0.105	42
Asbestos board,				Softwoods:			
corrugated..........	111	0.040	20	Balsa..............	...	0.03–0.05	
Asbestos paper,				Douglas fir.........	...	0.081	31
corrugated..........	150	0.037	17	Fir.................	...	0.068	25
Board, glass-fiber......	80	0.022	11	Pine...............	...	0.07–0.09	
Board, vegetable-fiber .	80	0.028	14.7	Spruce.............	...	0.06–0.07	
Board, wood-fiber.....	80	0.029	15.7	Miscellaneous materials:			
Celotex..............	90	0.028		Chalk..............	...	0.48	
Corkboard............	80	0.022	6.9	Felt, wool...........	...	0.03	
Glass wool............	75	0.023	3.0	Ice..................	...	1.26	
Gypsum board........	70	0.12	58	Leather, sole.........	...	0.09	
Hair felt.............	80	0.022	11	Paraffin.............	32	0.14	
Kapok..............	68	0.021	9.4	Rubber, hard.........	32	0.092	
85% magnesia........	150	0.035	15	Rubber, soft.........	68	0.07–0.09	
Rock wool............	150	0.023	6	Sand, dry...........	68	0.19	95
Silica aerogel........	90	0.014		Sawdust, dry........	68	0.04	13.4
Vermiculite..........	150	0.045	9	Vaseline.............	68	0.104	

TABLE A-4. PROPERTIES OF AIR AT ATMOSPHERIC PRESSURE *

t, °F	μ, lb/hr ft	k, Btu/hr ft °F	c_p, Btu/lb °F	N_{Pr}	a† $\times$ 10^{-6}, 1/ft³ °F
−100	0.0319	0.0104	0.239	0.739	10.22
−50	0.0358	0.0118	0.239	0.729	5.4
0	0.0394	0.0131	0.240	0.718	3.13
50	0.0427	0.0143	0.240	0.712	1.94
100	0.0459	0.0157	0.240	0.706	1.26
150	0.0484	0.0167	0.241	0.699	0.86
200	0.0519	0.0181	0.241	0.693	0.59
250	0.0547	0.0192	0.242	0.690	0.42
300	0.0574	0.0203	0.243	0.686	0.312
400	0.0626	0.0225	0.245	0.681	0.180
500	0.0675	0.0246	0.248	0.680	0.111
600	0.0721	0.0265	0.250	0.680	0.072
700	0.0765	0.0284	0.254	0.682	0.049
800	0.0806	0.0303	0.257	0.684	0.0346
900	0.0846	0.0320	0.260	0.687	0.0251
1000	0.0884	0.0337	0.263	0.690	0.0187

* Derived from information contained in *Natl. Bur. Standards Circ.* 564, 1955.
† $gB\rho^2/\mu k$ for standard gravity and atmospheric pressure.

TABLE A-5. PROPERTIES OF WATER *

t, °F	Saturation pressure, psia	ρ, lb/ft^3	μ, lb /hr ft	k, Btu/hr ft °F	c_p, Btu/lb °F	N_{Pr}	$a^\dagger \times 10^{-6}$, 1/ft^3 °F
40	0.122	62.43	3.74	0.326	1.0041	11.5	
50	0.178	62.41	3.16	0.334	1.0013	9.49	
60	0.256	62.36	2.72	0.341	0.9996	7.98	154
70	0.363	62.30	2.37	0.347	0.9987	6.81	238
80	0.507	62.22	2.08	0.353	0.9982	5.89	330
90	0.698	62.12	1.85	0.358	0.9980	5.15	435
100	0.949	62.00	1.65	0.363	0.9980	4.55	547
110	1.28	61.86	1.49	0.367	0.9982	4.06	670
120	1.69	61.71	1.35	0.371	0.9985	3.64	804
130	2.22	61.55	1.24	0.375	0.9989	3.29	949
140	2.89	61.38	1.13	0.378	0.9994	3.00	1100
150	3.72	61.20	1.05	0.381	1.0000	2.74	1270
160	4.74	61.00	0.968	0.384	1.0008	2.52	1450
170	5.99	60.80	0.900	0.386	1.0017	2.33	1640
180	7.51	60.58	0.839	0.388	1.0027	2.17	1840
190	9.34	60.36	0.785	0.390	1.0039	2.02	2050
200	11.53	60.12	0.738	0.392	1.0052	1.89	2270
212	14.696	59.83	0.686	0.394	1.0070	1.76	2550
220	17.19	59.63	0.655	0.394	1.0084	1.67	2750
240	24.97	59.11	0.588	0.396	1.0124	1.51	3270
260	35.43	58.86	0.534	0.397	1.0173	1.37	3830
280	49.20	57.96	0.487	0.397	1.0231	1.26	4420
300	67.01	57.32	0.449	0.396	1.0297	1.17	5040
320	89.66	56.65	0.418	0.395	1.0368	1.10	5660
340	118.01	55.94	0.393	0.393	1.0451	1.04	6300
360	153.0	55.19	0.371	0.391	1.0547	1.00	6950
380	195.8	54.38	0.351	0.388	1.0662	0.97	7610
400	247.3	53.51	0.333	0.384	1.0800	0.94	8320
420	308.8	52.61	0.316	0.379	1.0968	0.92	9070
440	381.6	51.68	0.301	0.374	1.1168	0.90	9900
460	466.9	50.70	0.285	0.368			
480	566.1	49.67	0.272	0.362			

* Adapted by Prof. W. C. Andrae from "Smithsonian Physical Tables," 9th ed., 1954; *Natl. Bur. Standards Research Paper* 1228, 1939; E. Schmidt and W. Sellschopp, *Forsch. Gebiete Ingenieurw.*, vol. 3, p. 277, 1932.

† $gB\rho^2 c_p/\mu k$ for standard gravity and low pressure.

TABLE A-6. PROPERTIES OF STEAM *

Pressure, psia	Saturated vapor	Temperature, °F						
		32	200	400	600	800	1000	1200
Viscosity, lb/hr ft								
0		0.023	0.031	0.041	0.050	0.059	0.067	0.074
500	0.054	...	...	...	0.059	0.073	0.073	0.080
1000	0.070	...	...	...	0.069	0.074	0.080	0.086
1500	0.082	...	...	...	0.082	0.082	0.087	0.092
2000	0.094	...	...	...	...	0.086	0.094	0.097
2500	0.108	...	...	...	...	0.101	0.101	0.104
3000	0.116	...	...	...	...	0.110	0.108	0.110
3500	...	...	...	...	...	0.119	0.114	0.116
Thermal conductivity, Btu/hr ft °F								
0	...	0.0092	0.0133	0.0184	0.0238	0.0292	0.0347	
250	0.0211	...	...	...	0.0247	0.0296	0.0349	
500	0.0251	...	...	...	0.0260	0.0302	0.0352	
1000	0.0316	...	...	...	0.0301	0.0314	0.0357	
1500	0.0379	...	...	...	0.0376	0.0332	0.0364	
1750	0.0408	...	...	...	...	0.0343	0.0368	
2000	0.0445	...	...	...	...	0.0355	0.0372	

* Adapted from J. Keenan and F. Keyes, "Thermodynamic Properties of Steam," 28th printing, John Wiley & Sons, Inc., New York, 1955.

TABLE A-7. PROPERTIES OF CARBON DIOXIDE, NITROGEN, AND OXYGEN AT ATMOSPHERIC PRESSURE *

t, °F	Carbon dioxide			Nitrogen			Oxygen		
	μ, lb/hr ft	k, Btu/hr ft °F	c_p, Btu/lb °F	μ, lb/hr ft	k, Btu/hr ft °F	c_p, Btu/lb °F	μ, lb/hr ft	k, Btu/hr ft °F	c_p, Btu/lb °F
−100	0.0244	0.0055	...	0.0313	0.0105	0.249	0.0359	0.0105	0.218
−10	0.0305	0.0075	0.192	0.0376	0.0129	0.249	0.0433	0.0131	0.219
80	0.0362	0.0096	0.204	0.0432	0.0151	0.249	0.0499	0.0155	0.220
170	0.0416	0.0118	0.215	0.0484	0.0172	0.249	0.0561	0.0177	0.222
260	0.0467	0.0142	0.225	0.0532	0.0193	0.250	0.0618	0.0200	0.225
350	0.0516	0.0167	0.234	0.0578	0.0212	0.251	0.0672	0.0221	0.228
440	0.0562	0.0194	0.242	0.0622	0.0230	0.252	0.0724	0.0241	0.232
530	0.0607	0.0221	0.250	0.0664	0.0248	0.254	0.0773	0.0261	0.236
620	0.0649	0.0249	0.257	0.0705	0.0265	0.257	0.0821	0.0280	0.240
710	0.0689	...	0.263	0.0742	0.0281	0.259	0.0867	...	0.243
800	0.0729	...	0.269	0.0777	0.0296	0.262	0.0911	...	0.246
890	0.0767	...	0.274	0.0811	0.0311	0.265	0.0954	...	0.249

* Derived from information contained in *Natl. Bur. Standards Circ.* 564, 1955.

TABLE A-8. PROPERTIES OF LIQUID SODIUM, POTASSIUM, AND THEIR ALLOYS *

(For alloys, % K is by weight)

Materials and properties	Temperatures, °C and °F							
	100	200	300	400	500	600	700	800
	212	392	572	752	932	1112	1292	1472
Density, g/cm³:								
Na (mp: 97.8°C)	0.927	0.905	0.882	0.858	0.834	0.809	0.783	0.757
NaK (43.4% K)	0.887	0.862	0.838	0.814	0.789	0.765	0.740	
NaK (78.6% K)	0.847	0.823	0.799	0.775	0.751	0.727	0.703	
K (mp: 63.7°C)	0.819	0.795	0.771	0.747	0.723	0.701	0.676	
Viscosity, cp:								
Na.........................	0.705	0.450	0.345	0.284	0.243	0.210	0.186	0.165
NaK (43.3% K)	0.540	0.379	0.299	0.245	0.207	0.178	0.165	
NaK (66.9% K)	0.529	0.354	0.276	0.229	0.195	0.168	0.146	
K..........................	0.436	0.299	0.227	0.194	0.169	0.153	0.140	
Thermal conductivity, watts/cm °C:								
Na...........................	...	0.815	0.757	0.712	0.668	0.627	0.590	0.547
NaK (56.5% K)...............	...	0.249	0.262	0.269	0.271			
NaK (77.7% K)...............	...	0.247	0.259	0.262	0.262	0.259	0.255	
K...........................	...	0.449	0.428	0.400	0.376	0.354		
Specific heat, cal/g °C:								
Na...........................	0.331	0.320	0.312	0.306	0.302	0.300	0.300	0.303
NaK (44.8% K)...............	0.269	0.261	0.255	0.251	0.249	0.248	0.250	
NaK (78.3% K)...............	0.225	0.217	0.212	0.210	0.209	0.209	0.211	
K...........................	0.194	0.189	0.185	0.183	0.182	0.183	0.185	0.188

* From "Liquid-metals Handbook," AEC and U.S. Dept. of the Navy, June, 1952; and "Sodium-NaK Supplement," July 1, 1955

TABLE A-9. PROPERTIES OF MISCELLANEOUS LIQUID METALS *

Element	ρ, g/cm^3	°C	c_p, cal/g °C	°C	μ, cp	°C	k, cal/ sec cm °C	°C
Aluminum (mp: 660.2°C)	2.380 2.261	660 1100	0.259	660– 1000	2.9 1.4	700 800	0.247 0.290	700 790
Bismuth (mp: 271.0°C)	10.03 9.66 9.20	300 600 962	0.0340 0.0376 0.0419	271 600 1000	1.662 0.996	304 600	0.041 0.037 0.037	300 500 700
Lead (mp: 327.4°C)	10.51 10.27 10.04 9.81	400 600 800 1000	0.039 0.037 . . .	327 500 . . .	2.116 1.700 1.185	441 551 844	0.038 0.036 0.036	400 600 700
Lithium mp: 179.0°C	0.507	200	1.0	200	0.5541	208.1	0.09	218–233
Mercury (mp: 38.87°C)	13.546 13.352 13.115	20 100 200	0.033 0.0328 0.0325	0 100 200	1.68 1.21 1.01	0 100 200	0.0196 0.0261 0.0303	0 120 220
Rubidium (mp: 30°C)	1.475	39	0.0913	39	0.6734	39	0.07	39
Tin (mp: 231.9°C)	6.83	409	0.058 0.076	250 1100	1.91 1.18	240 500	0.08 0.078	240 498
Zinc (mp: 419.5°C)	6.92 6.81 6.57	419.5 600 800	0.1199 0.1173 0.1012	419.5 600 1000	2.78 1.88	500 700	0.138 0.135	500 700
Lead-bismuth eutectic (mp: 125°C)	10.46 10.19	200 400	0.035	144–358	1.7 1.29	332 500	0.023 0.027	200 320

* From "Liquid-metals Handbook," AEC and U.S. Dept. of the Navy, June, 1952.

Table A-10. Normal Emissivities of Surfaces *†

Material	t, °F	ϵ_0	Material	t, °F	ϵ_0
	Metals and their oxides

Material	t, °F	ϵ_0	Material	t, °F	ϵ_0
Aluminum:			Iron and steel (cont.):		
Highly polished plate, 98.3% pure.	440	0.039	Iron, polished.................	800	0.14
	1070	0.057	Iron, roughly polished...........	212	0.17
Polished......................	212	0.095	Cast iron, polished..............	392	0.21
Rough polish..................	212	0.18	Wrought iron, polished..........	212	0.28
Commercial sheet...............	212	0.09	Iron plate, rusted..............	67	0.69
Heavily oxidized..............	200	0.20	Sheet steel.....................	70	0.66
	940	0.31	Cast plate.....................	73	0.81
Aluminum oxide................	530	0.63	Lead:		
	930	0.42	Pure, unoxidized...............	260	0.057
	1520	0.26		440	0.075
Aluminum surfaced roofing.......	100	0.22	Gray, oxidized.................	75	0.28
Brass:			Mercury......................	32	0.09
Highly polished (73.2 Cu, 26.7 Zn).	476	0.028		212	0.12
Highly polished (82.9 Cu, 17.0 Zn).	530	0.030	Nickel:		
Rolled plate, natural surface......	72	0.06	Electroplated, polished..........	74	0.045
Dull plate....................	120	0.22	Electroplated, not polished.......	68	0.11
Oxidized by heating.............	...	0.60	Oxide.........................	1200	0.59
Chromium, polished..............	100	0.08	Platinum, pure, polished..........	440	0.054
	2000	0.36		1160	0.104
Copper:			Silver, pure, polished.............	440	0.020
Polished......................	212	0.052	Stainless steels:		
Plate, thick oxide layer...........	77	0.78	Polished......................	212	0.074
Cuprous oxide..................	1470	0.66	Type 304, after heating..........	420	0.44
Gold, pure, highly polished.........	440	0.018	Type 310, oxidized.............	420	0.90
Iron and steel:			Tin, bright tinned iron............	76	0.04
Steel, polished.................	212	0.066			

| | Other surfaces |

Material	t, °F	ϵ_0	Material	t, °F	ϵ_0
Asbestos:			Oak, planed.....................	70	0.90
Board........................	74	0.96	Oil layer, thick on polished nickel...	...	0.82
Paper........................	100	0.93	Paints, lacquers, varnishes:		
	700	0.94	Snow-white enamel varnish on		
Brick:			rough plate.................	73	0.91
Red, rough...................	70	0.93	Black matte shellac............	...	0.91
Building......................	1832	0.45	Oil paints, all colors.	212	0.94
Fireclay......................	1832	0.75	Aluminum 10%, 22% lacquer		
Carbon:			body.......................	212	0.52
Candle soot...................	...	0.952	Paper........................	66	0.93
Lampblack, 0.003 in. or thinner...	...	0.945	Plaster, rough lime................	...	0.91
Graphite, pressed, filed surface....	...	0.98	Porcelain, glazed..................	72	0.92
Carborundum....................	1850	0.92	Roofing paper....................	69	0.91
Enamel, white, fused on iron........	66	0.90	Rubber:		
Glass:			Hard, glossy plate.............	74	0.94
Smooth......................	72	0.94	Soft, gray, rough...............	76	0.86
Pyrex, lead and soda...........	...	0.90	Water........................	32	0.95
Magnesite refractory brick.........	1832	0.38		212	0.96
Marble, light gray, polished........	72	0.93			

* Adapted from information contained in W. H. McAdams, "Heat Transmission," 3d ed., McGraw-Hill Book Company, Inc., New York, 1954.

† May be taken equal to hemispherical values except for clean, polished metal surfaces.

TABLE A-11. STANDARD DIMENSIONS OF PIPES AND TUBING

Nominal OD, in.	Actual OD, in.		Wall thickness, in.					
	Pipe	Tubing	Standard pipe and tubing	Welded and seamless steel pipe schedule			Copper tubing	
				40	80	160	Type K	Type L
$\frac{1}{8}$	0.405	...	0.068	0.068	0.095			
$\frac{1}{4}$	0.540	...	0.088	0.088	0.119			
$\frac{3}{8}$	0.675	0.500	0.091	0.091	0.126	...	0.049	0.035
$\frac{1}{2}$	0.840	0.625	0.109	0.109	0.147	0.187	0.049	0.040
$\frac{5}{8}$ *	...	0.750	...	...	...	...	0.049	0.042
$\frac{3}{4}$	1.050	0.875	0.113	0.113	0.154	0.218	0.065	0.045
1	1.315	1.125	0.133	0.133	0.179	0.250	0.065	0.050
$1\frac{1}{4}$	1.660	1.375	0.140	0.140	0.191	0.250	0.065	0.055
$1\frac{1}{2}$	1.900	1.625	0.145	0.145	0.200	0.281	0.072	0.060
2	2.375	2.125	0.154	0.154	0.218	0.343	0.083	0.070
$2\frac{1}{2}$	2.875	2.625	0.203	0.203	0.276	0.375	0.095	0.080
3	3.500	3.125	0.216	0.216	0.300	0.437	0.109	0.090
$3\frac{1}{2}$	4.000	3.625	0.226	0.226	0.318	...	0.120	0.100
4	4.500	4.125	0.237	0.237	0.337	0.531	0.134	0.110
5	5.563	5.125	0.258	0.238	0.375	0.625	0.160	0.125
6	6.625	6.125	0.280	0.280	0.432	0.718	0.192	0.140
8	8.625	8.125	0.277	0.322	0.500	0.906	0.271	0.200
10	10.75	10.125	0.307	0.365	0.593	1.125	0.338	0.250
12	12.75	12.125	0.330	0.406	0.687	1.312	0.405	0.280
14	14.0	...	...	0.437	0.750	1.406		
16	16.0	...	...	0.500	0.843	1.562		
18	18.0	...	...	0.560	0.937	1.750		
20	20.0	...	...	0.593	1.031	1.937		
24	24.0	...	...	0.687	1.218	2.312		
30	30.0							

* Tubing.

Table A-12. Diffusion Coefficients of Gases and Vapors in Air
(at 25°C and 1 Atmosphere)

Substance	D, cm²/sec	$N_{Sc} = \nu/D$
Ammonia...........	0.28	0.78
Carbon dioxide......	0.164	0.94
Hydrogen...........	0.410	0.22
Oxygen.............	0.206	0.75
Water.............	0.256	0.60
Ethyl ether.........	0.093	1.66
Methanol...........	0.159	0.97
Ethyl alcohol.......	0.119	1.30
Formic acid.........	0.159	0.97
Acetic acid.........	0.133	1.16
Aniline............	0.073	2.14
Benzene............	0.088	1.76
Toluene............	0.084	1.84
Ethyl benzene.......	0.077	2.01
Propyl benzene......	0.059	2.62

Adapted from J. H. Perry (ed.), "Chemical Engineers' Handbook," McGraw-Hill Book Company, Inc., New York, 1950.

TABLE A-13. THE ERROR FUNCTION

$\dfrac{x}{2\sqrt{\alpha\tau}}$	$f\left(\dfrac{x}{2\sqrt{\alpha\tau}}\right)$	$\dfrac{x}{2\sqrt{\alpha\tau}}$	$f\left(\dfrac{x}{2\sqrt{\alpha\tau}}\right)$	$\dfrac{x}{2\sqrt{\alpha\tau}}$	$f\left(\dfrac{x}{2\sqrt{\alpha\tau}}\right)$
0.00	0.00000	0.76	0.71754	1.52	0.96841
0.02	0.02256	0.78	0.73001	1.54	0.97059
0.04	0.04511	0.80	0.74210	1.56	0.97263
0.06	0.06762	0.82	0.75381	1.58	0.97455
0.08	0.09008	0.84	0.76514	1.60	0.97635
0.10	0.11246	0.86	0.77610	1.62	0.97804
0.12	0.13476	0.88	0.78669	1.64	0.97962
0.14	0.15695	0.90	0.79691	1.66	0.98110
0.16	0.17901	0.92	0.80677	1.68	0.98249
0.18	0.20094	0.94	0.81627	1.70	0.98379
0.20	0.22270	0.96	0.82542	1.72	0.98500
0.22	0.24430	0.98	0.83423	1.74	0.98613
0.24	0.26570	1.00	0.84270	1.76	0.98719
0.26	0.28690	1.02	0.85084	1.78	0.98817
0.28	0.30788	1.04	0.85865	1.80	0.98909
0.30	0.32863	1.06	0.86614	1.82	0.98994
0.32	0.34913	1.08	0.87333	1.84	0.99074
0.34	0.36936	1.10	0.88020	1.86	0.99147
0.36	0.38933	1.12	0.88679	1.88	0.99216
0.38	0.40901	1.14	0.89308	1.90	0.99279
0.40	0.42839	1.16	0.89910	1.92	0.99338
0.42	0.44749	1.18	0.90484	1.94	0.99392
0.44	0.46622	1.20	0.91031	1.96	0.99443
0.46	0.48466	1.22	0.91553	1.98	0.99489
0.48	0.50275	1.24	0.92050	2.00	0.995322
0.50	0.52050	1.26	0.92524	2.10	0.997020
0.52	0.53790	1.28	0.92973	2.20	0.998137
0.54	0.55494	1.30	0.93401	2.30	0.998857
0.56	0.57162	1.32	0.93806	2.40	0.999311
0.58	0.58792	1.34	0.94191	2.50	0.999593
0.60	0.60386	1.36	0.94556	2.60	0.999764
0.62	0.61941	1.38	0.94902	2.70	0.999866
0.64	0.63459	1.40	0.95228	2.80	0.999925
0.66	0.64938	1.42	0.95538	2.90	0.999959
0.68	0.66378	1.44	0.95830	3.00	0.999978
0.70	0.67780	1.46	0.96105	3.20	0.999994
0.72	0.69143	1.48	0.96365	3.40	0.999998
0.74	0.70468	1.50	0.96610	3.60	1.000000

Name Index

441

Subject Index